Also available from MJF Books:

James Herriot:
All Creatures Great and Small/All Things Bright and Beautiful

JAMES HERRIOT

All Things Wise
and Wonderful

∽

The Lord God
Made Them All

MJF BOOKS

NEW YORK

Published by MJF Books
Fine Communications
322 Eighth Avenue
New York, NY 10001

James Herriot: All Things Wise and Wonderful / The Lord God Made Them All
Copyright © 1976, 1977, 1981, 1999

ISBN-13: 978-1-56731-346-8
ISBN-10: 1-56731-346-9
Library of Congress Card Catalog # 99-75814

MJF Books and the MJF colophon are trademarks of
Fine Creative Media, Inc.

10   9   8   7   6   5   4

Contents

All Things Wise and Wonderful   Pages 1-432

The Lord God Made Them All   Pages 1-373

All things bright and beautiful,
    All creatures great and small,
All things wise and wonderful,
    The Lord God made them all.
Cecil Frances Alexander 1818-1895

All Things
Wise and Wonderful

To my dogs,
Hector and Dan
Faithful companions of the daily round.

CHAPTER

1

'Move!' bawled the drill corporal. 'Come on, speed it up!' He sprinted effortlessly to the rear of the gasping, panting column of men and urged us on from there.

I was somewhere in the middle, jog-trotting laboriously with the rest and wondering how much longer I could keep going. And as my ribs heaved agonisingly and my leg muscles protested I tried to work out just how many miles we had run.

I had suspected nothing when we lined up outside our billets. We weren't clad in PT kit but in woollen pullovers and regulation slacks and it seemed unlikely that anything violent was imminent. The corporal, too, a cheerful little cockney, appeared to regard us as his brothers. He had a kind face.

'Awright, lads,' he had cried, smiling over the fifty new airmen. 'We're just going to trot round to the park, so follow me. Le-eft turn! At the double, qui-ick march! 'eft-ight, 'eft-ight, 'eft-ight!'

That had been a long, long time ago and we were still reeling through the London streets with never a sign of a park anywhere. The thought hammered in my brain that I had been under the impression that I was fit. A country vet, especially in the Yorkshire Dales, never had the chance to get out of condition; he was always on the move, wrestling with the big animals, walking for miles between the fell-side barns; he was hard and tough. That's what I thought.

But now other reflections began to creep in. My few months of married life with Helen had been so much lotus eating. She was too good a cook and I was too faithful a disciple of her art. Just lounging by our bed-sitter's fireside was the sweetest of all occupations. I had tried to ignore the disappearance of my abdominal muscles, the sagging of my pectorals, but it was all coming home to me now.

'It's not far now, lads,' the corporal chirped from the rear, but he struck no responsive chords in the toiling group. He had said it several times before and we had stopped believing him.

But this time it seemed he really meant it, because as we turned into yet another street I could see iron railings and trees at the far end. The relief was inexpressible. I would just about have the strength to make it through the gates—to the rest and smoke which I badly needed because my legs were beginning to seize up.

We passed under an arch of branches which still bore a few autumn leaves and stopped as one man, but the corporal was waving us on.

'Come on, lads, round the track!' he shouted and pointed to a broad earthen path which circled the park.

We stared at him. He couldn't be serious! A storm of protest broke out.

'Aw no, corp . . . !' 'Have a heart, corp . . . !'

The smile vanished from the little man's face. 'Get movin', I said! Faster, faster . . . one-two, one-two.'

As I stumbled forward over the black earth, between borders of sooty rhododendrons and tired grass, I just couldn't believe it. It was all too sudden. Three days ago I was in Darrowby and half of me was still back there, back with Helen. And another part was still looking out of the rear window of the taxi at the green hills receding behind the tiled roofs into the morning sunshine; still standing in the corridor of the train as the flat terrain of southern England slid past and a great weight built up steadily in my chest.

My first introduction to the RAF was at Lord's cricket ground. Masses of forms to fill, medicals, then the issue of an enormous pile of kit. I was billeted in a block of flats in St John's Wood—luxurious before the lush fittings had been removed. But they couldn't take away the heavy bathroom ware and one of our blessings was the unlimited hot water gushing at our touch into the expensive surroundings.

After that first crowded day I retired to one of those green-tiled sanctuaries and lathered myself with a new bar of a famous toilet soap which Helen had put in my bag. I have never been able to use that soap since. Scents are too evocative and the merest whiff jerks me back to that first night away from my wife, and to the feeling I had then. It was a dull, empty ache which never really went away.

On the second day we marched endlessly; lectures, meals, inoculations. I was used to syringes but the very sight of them was too much for many of my friends. Especially when the doctor took the blood samples; one look at the dark fluid flowing from their veins and the young men toppled quietly from their chairs, often four or five in a row while the orderlies, grinning cheerfully, bore them away.

We ate in the London Zoo and our meals were made interesting by the chatter of monkeys and the roar of lions in the background. But in between it was march, march, march, with our new boots giving us hell.

And on this third day the whole thing was still a blur. We had been wakened as on my first morning by the hideous 6 a.m. clattering of dustbin lids; I hadn't really expected the silvery tones of a bugle but I found this totally unromantic din intolerable. However, at the moment my only concern was that we had completed the circuit of the park. The gates were only a few yards ahead and I staggered up to them and halted among my groaning comrades.

'Round again, lads!' the corporal yelled, and as we stared at him aghast he smiled affectionately. 'You think this is tough? Wait till they get hold of you at ITW. I'm just kinda breakin' you in gently. You'll thank me for this later. Right, at the double! One-two, one two!'

Bitter thoughts assailed me as I lurched forward once more. Another round of the park would kill me—there was not a shadow of a doubt about that. You left a loving wife and a happy home to serve king and country and this was how they treated you. It wasn't fair.

The night before I had dreamed of Darrowby. I was back in old Mr Dakin's cow byre. The farmer's patient eyes in the long, drooping-moustached face looked down at me from his stooping height.

'It looks as though it's over wi' awd Blossom, then,' he said, and rested his hand briefly on the old cow's back. It was an enormous, work-swollen hand. Mr Dakin's gaunt frame carried little flesh but the grossly thickened fingers bore testimony to a life of toil.

I dried off the needle and dropped it into the metal box where I carried my suture materials, scalpels and blades. 'Well, it's up to you of course, Mr Dakin, but this is the third time I've had to stitch her teats and I'm afraid it's going to keep on happening.'

'Aye, it's just the shape she is.' The farmer bent and examined the row of knots along the four-inch scar. 'By gaw, you wouldn't believe it could mek such a mess—just another cow standin' on it.'

'A cow's hoof is sharp,' I said. 'It's nearly like a knife coming down.'

That was the worst of very old cows. Their udders dropped and their teats became larger and more pendulous so that when they lay down in their stalls the vital milk-producing organ was pushed away to one side into the path of the neighbouring animals. If it wasn't Mabel on the right standing on it, it was Buttercup on the other side.

There were only six cows in the little cobbled byre with its low roof and wooden partitions and they all had names. You don't find cows with names any more and there aren't any farmers like Mr Dakin, who somehow scratched a living from a herd of six milkers plus a few calves, pigs and hens.

"Aye, well," he said. 'Ah reckon t'awd lass doesn't owe me anythin'. Ah remember the night she was born, twelve years ago. She was out of awd Daisy and ah carried her out of this very byre on a sack and the snow was comin' down hard. Sin' then ah wouldn't like to count how many thousand gallons o' milk she's turned out—she's still givin' four a day. Naw, she doesn't owe me a thing.'

As if she knew she was the topic of conversation Blossom turned her head and looked at him. She was the classical picture of an ancient bovine; as fleshless as her owner, with jutting pelvic bones, splayed, overgrown feet and horns with a multitude of rings along their curving length. Beneath her, the udder, once high and tight, drooped forlornly almost to the floor.

She resembled her owner, too, in her quiet, patient demeanour. I had infiltrated her teat with a local anaesthetic before stitching but I don't think she would have moved if I hadn't used any. Stitching teats puts a vet in the ideal position to be kicked, with his head low down in front of the hind feet, but there was no danger with Blossom. She had never kicked anybody in her life.

Mr Dakin blew out his cheeks. 'Well, there's nowt else for it. She'll have to go. I'll tell Jack Dodson to pick 'er up for the fatstock market on Thursday. She'll be a bit tough for eatin' but ah reckon she'll make a few steak pies.'

He was trying to joke but he was unable to smile as he looked at the old cow. Behind him, beyond the open door, the green hillside ran down to the river and the spring sunshine touched the broad sweep of the shallows with a million dancing lights. A beach of bleached stones gleamed bone-white against the long stretch of grassy bank which rolled up to the pastures lining the valley floor.

I had often felt that this smallholding would be an ideal place to live; only a mile outside Darrowby, but secluded, and with this heart-lifting vista of river and fell. I remarked on this once to Mr Dakin and the old man turned to me with a wry smile.

'Aye, but the view's not very sustainin',' he said.

It happened that I was called back to the farm on the following Thursday to 'cleanse' a cow and was in the byre when Dodson the drover called to pick up Blossom. He had collected a group of fat bullocks and cows from other farms and they stood, watched by one of his men, on the road high above.

'Nah then, Mr Dakin,' he cried as he bustled in. 'It's easy to see which one you want me to tek. It's that awd screw over there.'

He pointed at Blossom, and in truth the unkind description seemed to fit the bony creature standing between her sleek neighbours.

The farmer did not reply for a moment, then he went up between the cows and gently rubbed Blossom's forehead. 'Aye, this is the one, Jack.' He hesitated, then undid the chain round her neck. 'Off ye go, awd lass,' he murmured, and the old animal turned and made her way placidly from the stall.

'Aye, come on with ye!' shouted the dealer, poking his stick against the cow's rump.

'Doan't hit 'er!' barked Mr Dakin.

Dodson looked at him in surprise. 'Ah never 'it 'em, you know that. Just send 'em on, like.'

'Ah knaw, ah knaw, Jack, but you won't need your stick for this 'un. She'll go wherever ye want—allus has done.'

Blossom confirmed his words as she ambled through the door and, at a gesture from the farmer, turned along the track.

The old man and I stood watching as the cow made her way unhurriedly up the hill, Jack Dodson in his long khaki smock sauntering behind her. As the path wound behind a clump of sparse trees man and beast disappeared but Mr Dakin still gazed after them, listening to the clip-clop of the hooves on the hard ground.

When the sound died away he turned to me quickly. 'Right, Mr Herriot, we'll get on wi' our job, then. I'll bring your hot watter.'

The farmer was silent as I soaped my arm and inserted it into the cow. If there is one thing more disagreeable than removing the bovine afterbirth it is watching somebody else doing it, and I always try to maintain a conversation as I grope around inside. But this time it was hard work. Mr. Dakin responded to my sallies on the weather, cricket and the price of milk with a series of grunts.

Holding the cow's tail he leaned on the hairy back and, empty-eyed, blew smoke from the pipe which like most farmers at a cleansing he had prudently lit at the outset. And of course, since the going was heavy, it just would happen that the job took much longer than usual. Sometimes a placenta simply lifted out but I had to peel this one away from the cotyledons one by one, returning every few minutes to the hot water and antiseptic to re-soap my aching arms.

But at last it was finished. I pushed in a couple of pessaries, untied the sack from my middle and pulled my shirt over my head. The conversation had died and the silence was almost oppressive as we opened the byre door.

Mr Dakin paused, his hand on the latch. 'What's that?' he said softly.

From somewhere on the hillside I could hear the clip-clop of a cow's feet. There were two ways to the farm and the sound came from a narrow track which joined the main road half a mile beyond the other entrance. As we listened a cow rounded a rocky outcrop and came towards us.

It was Blossom, moving at a brisk trot, great udder swinging, eyes fixed purposefully on the open door behind us.

'What the hangment . . . ?' Mr Dakin burst out, but the old cow brushed past us and marched without hesitation into the stall which she had occupied for all those years. She sniffed enquiringly at the empty hay rack and looked round at her owner.

Mr Dakin stared back at her. The eyes in the weathered face were expressionless but the smoke rose from his pipe in a series of rapid puffs.

Heavy boots clattered suddenly outside and Jack Dodson panted his way through the odor.

'Oh, you're there, ye awd beggar!' he gasped. 'Ah thought I'd lost ye!'

He turned to the farmer. 'By gaw, I'm sorry, Mr Dakin. She must 'ave turned off at t'top of your other path. Ah never saw her go.'

The farmer shrugged. 'It's awright, Jack. It's not your fault, ah should've told ye.'

'That's soon mended anyway.' The drover grinned and moved towards Blossom. 'Come on, lass, let's have ye out o' there again.'

But he halted as Mr Dakin held an arm in front of him.

There was a long silence as Dodson and I looked in surprise at the farmer who continued to gaze fixedly at the cow. There was a pathetic dignity about the old animal as she stood there against the mouldering timber of the partition, her eyes patient and undemanding. It was a dignity which triumphed over the unsightliness of the long upturned hooves, the fleshless ribs, the broken-down udder almost brushing the cobbles.

Then, still without speaking, Mr Dakin moved unhurriedly between the cows and a faint chink of metal sounded as he fastened the chain around Blossom's neck. Then he strolled to the end of the byre and returned with a forkful of hay which he tossed expertly into the rack.

This was what Blossom was waiting for. She jerked a mouthful from between the spars and began to chew with quiet satisfaction.

'What's to do, Mr Dakin?' the drover cried in bewilderment. 'They're waiting for me at t'mart!'

The farmer tapped out his pipe on the half door and began to fill it with black shag from a battered tin. 'Ah'm sorry to waste your time, Jack, but you'll have to go without 'er.'

'Without 'er . . . ? But . . . ?'

'Aye, ye'll think I'm daft, but that's how it is. T'awd lass has come 'ome and she's stoppin' 'ome.' He directed a look of flat finality at the drover.

Dodson nodded a couple of times then shuffled from the byre. Mr Dakin followed and called after him,

'Ah'll pay ye for your time, Jack. Put it down on ma bill.'

He returned, applied a match to his pipe and drew deeply.

'Mr Herriot,' he said as the smoke rose around his ears, 'do you ever feel when summat happens that it was meant to happen and that it was for t'best?'

'Yes, I do, Mr Dakin. I often feel that.'

'Aye well, that's how I felt when Blossom came down that hill.' He reached out and scratched the root of the cow's tail. 'She's allus been a favourite and by gaw I'm glad she's back.'

'But how about those teats? I'm willing to keep stitching them up, but. . . .'

'Nay, lad, ah've had an idea. Just came to me when you were tekkin' away that cleansin' and I thowt I was ower late.'

'An idea?'

'Aye.' The old man nodded and tamped down the tobacco with his thumb. 'I can put two or three calves on to 'er instead of milkin' 'er. The old stable is empty —she can live in there where there's nobody to stand on 'er awd tits.'

I laughed. 'You're right, Mr Dakin. She'd be safe in the stable and she'd suckle three calves easily. She could pay her way.'

'Well, as ah said, it's matterless. After all them years she doesn't owe me a thing.' A gentle smile spread over the seamed face. 'Main thing is, she's come 'ome.'

My eyes were shut most of the time now as I blundered round the park and when I opened them a red mist swirled. But it is incredible what the human frame will stand and I blinked in disbelief as the iron gates appeared once more under their arch of sooty branches.

I had survived the second lap but an ordinary rest would be inadequate now. This time I would have to lie down. I felt sick.

'Good lads!' the corporal called out, cheerful as ever. 'You're doin' fine. Now we're just going to 'ave a little hoppin' on the spot.'

Incredulous wails rose from our demoralised band but the corporal was unabashed.

'Feet together now. Up! Up! Up! That's no good, come on, get some height into it! Up! Up!'

This was the final absurdity. My chest was a flaming cavern of agony. These people were supposed to be making us fit and instead they were doing irreparable damage to my heart and lungs.

'You'll thank me for this later, lads. Take my word for it. GET YOURSELVES OFF THE GROUND. UP! UP!'

Through my pain I could see the corporal's laughing face. The man was clearly a sadist. It was no good appealing to him.

And as, with the last of my strength, I launched myself into the air it came to me suddenly why I had dreamed about Blossom last night.

I wanted to go home, too.

The fog swirled over the heads of the marching men; a London fog, thick, yellow, metallic on the tongue. I couldn't see the head of the column, only the swinging lantern carried by the leader.

This 6.30 a.m. walk to breakfast was just about the worst part of the day, when my morale was low and thoughts of home rose painfully.

We used to have fogs in Darrowby, but they were country fogs, different from this. One morning I drove out on my rounds with the headlights blazing against the grey curtain ahead, seeing nothing from my tight-shut box. But I was heading up the Dale, climbing steadily with the engine pulling against the rising ground, then quite suddenly the fog thinned to a shimmering silvery mist and was gone.

And there, above the pall, the sun was dazzling and the long green line of the fells rose before me, thrusting exultantly into a sky of summer blue.

Spellbound, I drove upwards into the bright splendour, staring through the windscreen as though I had never seen it all before; the bronze of the dead bracken spilling down the grassy flanks of the hills, the dark smudges of trees, the grey farmhouses and the endless pattern of walls creeping to the heather above.

I was in a rush as usual but I had to stop. I pulled up in a gateway, Sam jumped out and we went through into a field; and as the beagle scampered over the glittering turf I stood in the warm sunshine amid the melting frost and looked back at the dark damp blanket which blotted out the low country but left this jewelled world above it.

And, gulping the sweet air, I gazed about me gratefully at the clean green land where I worked and made my living.

I could have stayed there, wandering round, watching Sam exploring with waving tail, nosing into the shady corners where the sun had not reached and the ground was iron hard and the rime thick and crisp on the grass. But I had an appointment to keep, and no ordinary one—it was with a peer of the realm. Reluctantly I got back into the car.

I was due to start Lord Hulton's tuberculin test at 9.30 a.m. and as I drove round the back of the Elizabethan mansion to the farm buildings nearby I felt a pang of misgiving; there were no animals in sight. There was only a man in tattered blue dungarees hammering busily at a makeshift crush at the exit to the fold yard.

He turned round when he saw me and waved his hammer. As I approached I looked wonderingly at the slight figure with the soft fairish hair falling over his brow, at the holed cardigan and muck-encrusted wellingtons. You would have expected him to say, 'Nah, then, Mr Herriot, how ista this mornin'?'

But he didn't, he said, 'Herriot, my dear chap, I'm most frightfully sorry, but I'm very much afraid we're not quite ready for you.' And he began to fumble with his tobacco pouch.

William George Henry Augustus, Eleventh Marquis of Hulton, always had a pipe in his mouth and he was invariably either filling it, cleaning it out with a metal reaming tool or trying to light it. I had never seen him actually smoking it. And at times of stress he attempted to do everything at once. He was obviously embarrassed at his lack of preparedness and when he saw me glance involuntarily at my watch he grew more agitated, pulling his pipe from his mouth and putting it back in again, tucking the hammer under his arm, rummaging in a large box of matches.

I gazed across to the rising ground beyond the farm buildings. Far off on the horizon I could make out tiny figures: galloping beasts, scurrying men; and faint sounds came down to me of barking dogs, irritated bellowings and shrill cries of 'Haow, haow!' 'Gerraway by!' 'Siddown, dog!'

I sighed. It was the old story. Even the Yorkshire aristocracy seemed to share this carefree attitude to time.

His lordship clearly sensed my feelings because his discomfort increased.

'It's too bad for me, old chap,' he said, spraying a few matchsticks around and dropping flakes of tobacco on the stone flags.

'I did promise to be ready for nine thirty but those blasted animals just won't cooperate.'

I managed a smile. 'Oh never mind, Lord Hulton, they seem to be getting them down the hill now and I'm not in such a panic this morning, anyway.'

'Oh splendid, splendid!' He attempted to ignite a towering mound of dark flake which spluttered feebly then toppled over the edge of his pipe. 'And come and see this! I've been rigging up a crush. We'll drive them in here and we'll really have 'em. Remember we had a spot of bother last time, what?'

I nodded. I did remember. Lord Hulton had only about thirty suckling cows but it had taken a three-hour rodeo to test them. I looked doubtfully at the rickety structure of planks and corrugated iron. It would be interesting to see how it coped with the moorland cattle.

I didn't mean to rub it in, but again I glanced unthinkingly at my watch and the little man winced as though he had received a blow.

'Dammit!' he burst out. 'What are they doing over there? Tell you what, I'll go and give them a hand!' Distractedly, he began to change hammer, pouch, pipe and matches from hand to hand, dropping them and picking them up, before finally deciding to put the hammer down and stuff the rest into his pockets. He went off at a steady trot and I thought as I had done so often that there couldn't be many noblemen in England like him.

If I had been a marquis, I felt, I would still have been in bed or perhaps just parting the curtains and peering out to see what kind of day it was. But Lord Hulton worked all the time, just about as hard as any of his men. One morning I arrived to find him at the supremely mundane task of 'plugging muck', standing on a manure heap, hurling steaming forkfuls on to a cart. And he always dressed in rags. I suppose he must have had more orthodox items in his wardrobe but I never saw them. Even his tobacco was the great smoke of the ordinary farmer—Redbreast Flake.

My musings were interrupted by the thunder of hooves and wild cries; the Hulton herd was approaching. Within minutes the fold yard was filled with milling creatures, steam rising in rolling clouds from their bodies.

The marquis appeared round the corner of the building at a gallop.

'Right, Charlie!' he yelled. 'Let the first one into the crush!'

Panting with anticipation he stood by the nailed boards as the men inside opened the yard gate. He didn't have to wait long. A shaggy red monster catapulted from the interior, appeared briefly in the narrow passage then emerged at about fifty miles an hour from the other end with portions of his lordship's creation dangling from its horns and neck. The rest of the herd pounded close behind.

'Stop them! Stop them!' screamed the little peer, but it was of no avail. A hairy torrent flooded through the opening and in no time at all the herd was legging it back to the high land in a wild stampede. The men followed them and within a few moments Lord Hulton and I were standing there just as before watching the tiny figures on the skyline, listening to the distant 'Haow, haow!' 'Gerraway by!'

'I say,' he murmured despondently. 'It didn't work terribly well, did it?'

But he was made of stern stuff. Seizing his hammer he began to bang away with undiminished enthusiasm and by the time the beasts returned the crush was rebuilt and a stout iron bar pushed across the front to prevent further break-outs.

It seemed to solve the problem because the first cow, confronted by the bar, stood quietly and I was able to clip the hair on her neck through an opening between the planks. Lord Hulton, in high good humour, settled down on an upturned oil drum with my testing book on his knee.

'I'll do the writing for you,' he cried. 'Fire away, old chap!'

I poised my calipers. 'Eight, eight.' He wrote it down and the next cow came in.

'Eight, eight,' I said, and he bowed his head again.

The third cow arrived: 'Eight, eight.' And the fourth, 'Eight, eight.'

His lordship looked up from the book and passed a weary hand across his forehead.

'Herriot, dear boy, can't you vary it a bit? I'm beginning to lose interest.'

All went well until we saw the cow which had originally smashed the crush. She had sustained a slight scratch on her neck.

'I say, look at that!' cried the peer. 'Will it be all right?'

'Oh yes, it's nothing. Superficial.'

'Ah, good, but don't you think we should have something to put on it? Some of that. . . .'

I waited for it. Lord Hulton was a devotee of May and Baker's Propamidine Cream and used it for all minor cuts and grazes in his cattle. He loved the stuff. But unfortunately he couldn't say 'Propamidine'. In fact nobody on the entire establishment could say it except Charlie the farm foreman and he only thought he could say it. He called it 'Propopamide' but his lordship had the utmost faith in him.

'Charlie!' he bawled. 'Are you there, Charlie?'

The foreman appeared from the pack in the yard and touched his cap, 'Yes, m'lord.'

'Charlie, that wonderful stuff we get from Mr Herriot—you know, for cut teats and things, Pro . . . Pero . . . what the hell do you call it again?'

Charlie paused. It was one of his big moments. 'Propopamide, m'lord.'

The marquis, intensely gratified, slapped the knee of his dungarees. 'That's it, Propopamide! Damned if I can get my tongue round it. Well done, Charlie!'

Charlie inclined his head modestly.

The whole test was a vast improvement on last time and we were finished within an hour and a half. There was just one tragedy. About half way through, one of the cows dropped down dead with an attack of hypomagnesaemia, a condition which often plagues sucklers. It was a sudden, painless collapse and I had no chance to do anything.

Lord Hulton looked down at the animal which had just stopped breathing. 'Do you think we could salvage her for meat if we bled her?'

'Well, it's typical hypomag. Nothing to harm anybody . . . you could try. It would depend on what the meat inspector says.'

The cow was bled, pulled into a van and the peer drove off to the abattoir. He came back just as we were finishing the test.

'How did you get on?' I asked him. 'Did they accept her?'

He hesitated. 'No . . . no, old chap,' he said sadly. 'I'm afraid they didn't.'

'Why? Did the meat inspector condemn the carcass?'

'Well . . . I never got as far as the meat inspector, actually . . . just saw one of the slaughtermen.'

'And what did he say?'

'Just two words, Herriot.'

'Two words . . . ?'

'Yes . . . "Bugger off!" '

I nodded. 'I see.' It was easy to imagine the scene. The tough slaughterman viewing the small, unimpressive figure and deciding that he wasn't going to be put out of his routine by some ragged farm man.

'Well, never mind, sir,' I said. 'You can only try.'

'True . . . true, old chap.' He dropped a few matches as he fumbled disconsolately with his smoking equipment.

As I was getting into the car I remembered about the Propamidine. 'Don't forget to call down for that cream, will you?'

'By Jove, yes! I'll come down for it after lunch. I have great faith in that Prom . . . Pram . . . Charlie! Damn and blast, what is it?'

Charlie drew himself up proudly. 'Propopamide, m'lord.'

'Ah yes, Propopamide!' The little man laughed, his good humour quite restored. 'Good lad, Charlie, you're a marvel!'

'Thank you, m'lord.' The foreman wore the smug expression of the expert as he drove the cattle back into the field.

It's a funny thing, but when you see a client about something you very often see him soon again about something else. It was only a week later, with the district still in the iron grip of winter, than my bedside 'phone jangled me from slumber.

After that first palpitation of the heart which I feel does vets no good at all I reached a sleepy hand from under the sheets.

'Yes?' I grunted.

'Herriot . . . I say, Herriot . . . is that you, Herriot?' The voice was laden with tension.

'Yes, it is, Lord Hulton.'

'Oh good . . . good . . . dash it, I do apologise. Frightfully bad show, waking you up like this . . . but I've got something damn peculiar here.' A soft pattering followed which I took to be matches falling around the receiver.

'Really?' I yawned and my eyes closed involuntarily. 'In what way, exactly?'

'Well, I've been sitting up with one of my best sows. Been farrowing and produced twelve nice piglets, but there's something very odd.'

'How do you mean?'

'Difficult to describe, old chap . . . but you know the . . . er . . . bottom aperture . . . there's a bloody great long red thing hanging from it.'

My eyes snapped open and my mouth gaped in a soundless scream. Prolapsed uterus! Hard labour in cows, a pleasant exercise in ewes, impossible in sows.

'Long red . . . ! When . . . ? How . . . ?' I was stammering pointlessly. I didn't have to ask.

'Just popped it out, dear boy. I was waiting for another piglet and whoops, there it was. Gave me a nasty turn.'

My toes curled tightly beneath the blankets. It was no good telling him that I had seen five prolapsed uteri in pigs in my limited experience and had failed in every case. I had come to the conclusion that there was no way of putting them back.

But I had to try. 'I'll be right out,' I muttered.

I looked at the alarm clock. It was five thirty. A horrible time, truncating the night's slumber yet eliminating any chance of a soothing return to bed for an hour before the day's work. And I hated turning out even more since my marriage. Helen was lovely to come back to, but by the same token it was a bigger wrench to leave her soft warm presence and venture into the inhospitable world outside.

And the journey to the Hulton farm was not enlivened by my memories of those five other sows. I had tried everything; full anaesthesia, lifting them upside down with pulleys, directing a jet from a hose on the everted organ, and all the time pushing, straining, sweating over the great mass of flesh which refused to go back through that absurdly small hole. The result in each case had been the conversion of my patient into pork pies and a drastic plummeting of my self-esteem.

There was no moon and the soft glow from the piggery door made the only light among the black outlines of the buildings. Lord Hulton was waiting at the entrance and I thought I had better warn him.

'I have to tell you, sir, that this is a very serious condition. It's only fair that you should know that the sow very often has to be slaughtered.'

The little man's eyes widened and the corners of his mouth drooped.

'Oh, I say! That's rather a bore . . . one of my best animals. I . . . I'm rather attached to that pig.' He was wearing a polo-necked sweater of such advanced dilapidation that the hem hung in long woollen fronds almost to his knees, and as he tremblingly attempted to light his pipe he looked very vulnerable.

'But I'll do my very best,' I added hastily. 'There's always a chance.'

'Oh, good man!' In his relief, he dropped his pouch and as he stooped the open box of matches spilled around his feet. It was some time before we retrieved them and went into the piggery.

The reality was as bad as my imaginings. Under the single weak electric bulb of the pen an unbelievable length of very solid-looking red tissue stretched from the rear end of a massive white sow lying immobile on her side. The twelve pink piglets fought and worried along the row of teats; they didn't seem to be getting much.

As I stripped off and dipped my arms into the steaming bucket I wished with all my heart that the porcine uterus was a little short thing and not this horrible awkward shape. And it was a disquieting thought that tonight I had no artificial aids. People used all sorts of tricks and various types of equipment but here in this silent building there was just the pig, Lord Hulton and me. His lordship, I knew, was willing and eager, but he had helped me at jobs before and his usefulness was impaired by the fact that his hands were always filled with his smoking items and he kept dropping things.

I got down on my knees behind the animal with the feeling that I was on my own. And as soon as I cradled the mass in my arms the conviction flooded through me that this was going to be the same as all the others. The very idea of this lot going back whence it came was ridiculous and the impression was reinforced as I began to push. Nothing happened.

I had sedated the sow heavily and she wasn't straining much against me; it was just that the thing was so huge. By a supreme effort I managed to feed a few inches back into vaginal opening but as soon as I relaxed it popped quietly out again. My strongest instinct was to call the whole thing off without delay; the end result would be the same and anyway I wasn't feeling very strong. In fact my whole being was permeated by the leaden-armed pervading weakness one feels when forced to work in the small hours.

I would try just once more. Lying flat, my naked chest against the cold concrete I fought with the thing till my eyes popped and my breath gave out, but it had not the slightest effect and it made my mind up; I had to tell him.

Rolling over on my back I looked up at him, panting, waiting till I had the wind to speak. I would say, 'Lord Hulton, we are really wasting our time here. This is an impossible case. I am going back home now and I'll ring the slaughterhouse first thing in the morning.' The prospect of escape was beguiling; I might even be able to crawl in beside Helen for an hour. But as my mouth framed the words the little man looked down at me appealingly as though he knew what I was going to say. He tried to smile but darted anxious glances at me, at the pig and back again. From the other end of the animal a soft uncomplaining grunt reminded me that I wasn't the only one involved.

I didn't say anything. I turned back on to my chest, braced my feet against the wall of the pen and began again. I don't know how long I lay there, pushing, relaxing, pushing again as I gasped and groaned and the sweat ran steadily down my back. The peer was silent but I knew he was following my progress intently because every now and then I had to brush matches from the surface of the uterus.

Then for no particular reason the heap of flesh in my arms felt suddenly smaller. I glared desperately at the thing. There was no doubt about it, it was only half the size. I had to take a breather and a hoarse croak escaped me.

'God! I think it's going back!'

I must have startled Lord Hulton in mid fill because I heard a stifled 'What . . . what . . . oh I say, how absolutely splendid!' and a fragrant shower of tobacco cascaded from above.

This was it, then. Summoning the last of my energy for one big effort I blew half an ounce or so of Redbreast Flake from the uterine mucosa and heaved forward. And, miraculously, there was little resistance and I stared in disbelief as the great organ disappeared gloriously and wonderfully from sight. I was right behind it with my arm, probing frantically away up to the shoulder as I rotated my wrist again and again till both uterine cornua were fully involuted. When I was certain beyond doubt that everything was back in place I lay there for a few moments, my arm still deep inside the sow, my forehead resting on the floor. Dimly, through the mist of exhaustion I heard Lord Hulton's cries.

'Stout fella! Dash it, how marvellous! Oh stout fella!' He was almost dancing with joy.

One last terror assailed me. What if it came out again? Quickly I seized needle and thread and began to insert a few sutures in the vulva.

'Here, hold this!' I barked, giving him the scissors.

Sitching with the help of Lord Hulton wasn't easy. I kept pushing needle or scissors into his hands then demanding them back peremptorily, and it caused a certain amount of panic. Twice he passed me his pipe to cut the ends of my suture and on one occasion I found myself trying in the dim light to thread the silk through his reaming tool. His lordship suffered too, in his turn, because I heard the occasional stifled oath as he impaled a finger on the needle.

But at last it was done. I rose wearily to my feet and leaned against the wall, my mouth hanging open, sweat trickling into my eyes. The little man's eyes were full of concern as they roved over my limply hanging arms and the caked blood and filth on my chest.

'Herriot, my dear old chap, you're all in! And you'll catch pneumonia or something if you stand around half naked. You need a hot drink. Tell you what—get yourself cleaned up and dressed and I'll run down to the house for something.' He scurried swiftly away.

My aching muscles were slow to obey as I soaped and towelled myself and pulled on my shirt. Fastening my watch round my wrist I saw that it was after seven and I could hear the farm men clattering in the yard outside as they began their morning tasks.

I was buttoning my jacket when the little peer returned. He bore a tray with a pint mug of steaming coffee and two thick slices of bread and honey. He placed it on a bale of straw and pulled up an upturned bucket as a chair before hopping on to a meal bin where he sat like a pixie on a toadstool with his arms around his knees, regarding me with keen anticipation.

'The servants are still abed, old chap,' he said. 'So I made this little bite for you myself.'

I sank on to the bucket and took a long pull at the coffee. It was black and scalding with a kick like a Galloway bullock and it spread like fire through my tired frame. Then I bit into the first slice of bread; home made, plastered thickly with farm butter and topped by a lavish layer of heather honey from the long row of hives I had often seen on the edge of the moor above. I closed my eyes in reverence as I chewed, then as I reached for the pint pot again I looked up at the small figure on the bin.

'May I say, sir, that this isn't a bite, it's a feast. It is all absolutely delicious.'

His face lit up with impish glee. 'Well, dash it . . . do you really think so? I'm so pleased. And you've done nobly, dear boy. Can't tell you how grateful I am.'

As I continued to eat ecstatically, feeling the strength ebbing back, he glanced uneasily into the pen.

'Herriot . . . those stitches. Don't like the look of them much. . . .'

'Oh yes,' I said. 'They're just a precaution. You can nick them out in a couple of days.'

'Splendid! But won't they leave a wound? We'd better put something on there.'

I paused in mid chew. Here it was again. He only needed his Propamidine to complete his happiness.

'Yes, old chap, we must apply some of that Prip . . . Prom . . . oh hell and blast, it's no good!' He threw back his head and bellowed, 'Charlie!'

The foreman appeared in the entrance, touching his cap. 'Morning, m'lord.'

'Morning, Charlie. See that this sow gets some of that wonderful cream on her. What the blazes d'you call it again?'

Charlie swallowed and squared his shoulders. 'Propopamide, m'lord.'

The little man threw his arms high in delight. 'Of course, of course! Propopamide! I wonder if I'll ever be able to get that word out?' He looked admiringly at his foreman. 'Charlie, you never fail—I don't know how you do it.'

Charlie bowed gravely in acknowledgement.

Lord Hulton turned to me. 'You'll let us have some more Propopamide, won't you, Herriot?'

'Certainly,' I replied. 'I think I have some in the car.'

Sitting there on the bucket amid the mixed aromas of pig and barley meal and coffee I could almost feel the waves of pleasure beating on me. His lordship was clearly enchanted by the whole business, Charlie was wearing the superior smile which always accompanied his demonstrations of lingual dexterity, and as for myself I was experiencing a mounting euphoria.

I could see into the pen and the sight was rewarding. The little pigs who had been sheltered in a large box during the operation were back with their mother, side by side in a long pink row as their tiny mouths enclosed the teats. The sow seemed to be letting her milk down, too, because there was no frantic scramble for position, just a rapt concentration.

She was a fine pedigree pig and instead of lying on the butcher's slab today she would be starting to bring up her family. As though reading my thoughts she gave a series of contented grunts and the old feeling began to bubble in me, the deep sense of fulfillment and satisfaction that comes from even the smallest triumph and makes our lives worth while.

And there was something else. A new thought stealing into my consciousness with a delicious fresh tingle about it. At this moment, who else in the length and breadth of Britain was eating a breakfast personally prepared and served by a marquis?

3

I am afraid of dentists.

I am particularly afraid of strange dentists, so before I went into the RAF I made sure my teeth were in order. Everybody told me they were very strict about the aircrews' teeth and I didn't want some unknown prodding around in my mouth. There had to be no holes anywhere or they would start to ache away up there in the sky, so they said.

So before my call-up I went to old Mr Grover in Darrowby and he painstakingly did all that was necessary. He was good at his job and was always gentle and careful and didn't strike the same terror into me as other dentists. All I felt when I went to his surgery was a dryness of the throat and a quivering at the knees, and providing I kept my eyes tightly shut all the time I managed to get through the visit fairly easily.

My fear of dentists dates back to my earliest experiences in the twenties. As a child I was taken to the dread Hector McDarroch in Glasgow and he did my dental work right up to my teens. Friends of my youth tell me that he inspired a similar lasting fear in them, too, and in fact there must be a whole generation of Glaswegians who feel the same.

Of course you couldn't blame Hector entirely. The equipment in those days was primitive and a visit to any dental practitioner was an ordeal. But Hector, with his booming laugh, was so large and overpowering that he made it worse. Actually he was a very nice man, cheerful and good-natured, but the other side of him blotted it all out.

The electric drill had not yet been invented or if it had, it hadn't reached Scotland, and Hector bored holes in teeth with a fearsome foot-operated machine. There was a great wheel driven by a leather belt and this powered the drill, and as you lay in the chair two things dominated the outlook; the wheel whirring by your ear and Hector's huge knee pistoning almost into your face as he pedalled furiously.

He came from the far north and at the Highland games he used to array himself in kilt and sporran and throw cabers around like matchsticks. He was so big and strong that I always felt hopelessly trapped in that chair with his bulk over me and the wheel grinding and the pedal thumping. He didn't exactly put his foot on my chest but he had me all right.

And it didn't worry him when he got into the sensitive parts with his drill; my strangled cries were of no avail and he carried on remorselessly to the end. I had the impression that Hector thought it was cissy to feel pain, or maybe he was of the opinion that suffering was good for the soul.

Anyway, since those days I've had a marked preference for small frail soft-spoken dentists like Mr Grover. I like to feel that if it came to a stand-up fight I would have a good chance of victory and escape. Also, Mr Grover understood that people were afraid, and that helped. I remember him chuckling when he told me about the big farm men who came to have their teeth extracted. Many a time, he said, he had gone across the room for his instruments and turned back to find the chair empty.

I still don't enjoy going to the dentist but I have to admit that the modern men are wonderful. I hardly see mine when I go. Just a brief glimpse of a white coat then all is done from behind. Fingers come round, things go in and out of my mouth but even when I venture to open my eyes I see nothing.

Hector McDarroch, on the other hand, seemed to take a pleasure in showing off his grisly implements, filling the long-needled syringe right in front of my eyes and squirting the cocaine ceilingwards a few times before he started on me. And worse, before an extraction he used to clank about in a tin box, producing a series of hideous forceps and examining them, whistling softly, till he found the right one.

So with all this in mind, as I sat in a long queue of airmen for the preliminary examination, I was thankful I had been to Mr Grover for a complete check-up. A dentist stood by a chair at the end of the long room and he examined the young men in blue one by one before calling out his findings to an orderly at a desk.

I derived considerable entertainment from watching the expressions on the lads' faces when the call went out. 'Three fillings, two extractions!' 'Eight fillings!' Most of them looked stunned, some thunderstruck, others almost tearful. Now and again one would try to expostulate with the man in white but it was no good; nobody was listening. At times I could have laughed out loud. Mind you, I felt a bit mean at being amused, but after all they had only themselves to blame. If only they had shown my foresight they would have had nothing to worry about.

When my name was called I strolled across, humming a little tune, and dropped nonchalantly into the chair. It didn't take the man long. He poked his way swiftly along my teeth then rapped out, 'Five fillings and one extraction!'

I sat bolt upright and stared at him in amazement.

'But . . . but . . .' I began to yammer, 'I had a check up by my own . . .'

'Next, please,' murmured the dentist.

'But Mr Grover said . . .'

'Next man! Move along!' bawled the orderly, and as I shuffled away I gazed appealingly at the white-coated figure. But he was reciting a list of my premolars and incisors and showed no interest.

I was still trembling when I was handed the details of my fate.

'Report at Regent Lodge tomorrow morning for the extraction,' the WAAF girl said.

Tomorrow morning! By God, they didn't mess about! And what the heck did it all mean, anyway? My teeth were perfectly sound. There was only that one with the bit of enamel chipped off. Mr Grover had pointed it out and said it wouldn't give any trouble. It was the tooth that held my pipe—surely it couldn't be that one.

But there came the disquieting thought that my opinion didn't matter. When my feeble protests were ignored back there it hit me for the first time that I wasn't a civilian any more.

Next morning the din from the dustbin lids had hardly subsided when the grim realisation drove into my brain. I was going to have a tooth out today! And very soon, too. I passed the intervening hours in growing apprehension; morning parade, the march through the darkness to breakfast. The dried egg and fried bread were less attractive than ever and the grey day had hardly got under way before I was approaching the forbidding façade of Regent Lodge.

As I climbed the steps my palms began to sweat. I didn't like having my teeth drilled but extractions were infinitely worse. Something in me recoiled from the idea of having a part of myself torn away by force, even if it didn't hurt. But of course, I told myself as I walked along an echoing corridor, it never did hurt nowadays. Just a little prick, then nothing.

I was nurturing this comforting thought when I turned into a large assembly room with numbered doors leading from it. About thirty airmen sat around wearing a variety of expressions from sickly smiles to tough bravado. A chilling smell of antiseptic hung on the air. I chose a chair and settled down to wait. I had been in the armed forces long enough to know that you waited a long time for everything and I saw no reason why a dental appointment should be any different.

As I sat down the man on my left gave me a brief nod. He was fat, and greasy black hair fell over his pimpled brow. Though engrossed in picking his teeth with a match he gave me a long appraising stare before addressing me in rich cockney.

'What room you goin' in, mate?'

I looked at my card. 'Room four.'

'Blimey, mate, you've 'ad it!' He removed his matchstick and grinned wolfishly.

'Had it . . . ? What do you mean?'

'Well, haven't you 'eard? That's The Butcher in there.'

'The . . . The . . . Butcher?' I quavered.

'Yeh, that's what they call the dental officer in there.' He gave an expansive smile. 'He's a right killer, that bloke, I'll tell yer.'

I swallowed. 'Butcher . . . ? Killer . . . ? Oh come on. They'll all be the same, I'm sure.'

'Don't you believe it, mate. There's good an' there's bad, and that bloke's pure murder. It shouldn't be allowed.'

'How do you know, anyway?'

He waved an airy hand. 'Oh I've been 'ere a few times and I've heard some bleedin' awful screams comin' out of that room. Spoken to some of the chaps afterwards, too. They all call 'im The Butcher.'

I rubbed my hands on the rough blue of my trousers. 'Oh you hear these tales. I'm sure they're exaggerated.'

'Well, you'll find out, mate.' He resumed his tooth picking. 'But don't say I didn't tell you.'

He went on about various things but I only half heard him. His name, it seemed, was Simkin, and he was not an aircrew cadet like the rest of us but a regular and a member of the groundstaff; he worked in the kitchens. He spoke scornfully of us raw recruits and pointed out that we would have to 'get some service in' before we were fit to associate with the real members of the Royal Air Force. I noticed, however, that despite his own years of allegiance he was still an AC2 like myself.

Almost an hour passed with my heart thumping every time the door of number four opened. I had to admit that the young men leaving that room all looked a bit shattered and one almost reeled out, holding his mouth with both hands.

'Cor! Look at that poor bugger!' Simkin drawled with ill-concealed satisfaction. 'Strike me! He's been through it, poor bleeder. I'm glad I'm not in your shoes, mate.'

I could feel the tension mounting in me. 'What room are you going into, anyway?' I asked.

He did a bit of deep exploration with his match. 'Room two, mate. I've been in there before. He's a grand bloke, one of the best. Never 'urts you.'

'Well you're lucky, aren't you?'

'Not lucky, mate.' He paused and stabbed his match at me. 'I know my way around, that's all. There's ways and means.' He allowed one eyelid to drop briefly.

The conversation was abruptly terminated as the dread door opened and a WAAF came out.

'AC2 Herriot!' she called.

I got up on shaking limbs and took a deep breath. As I set off I had a fleeting glimpse of the leer of pure delight on Simkin's face. He was really enjoying himself.

As I passed the portals my feeling of doom increased. The Butcher was another Hector McDarroch; about six feet two with rugby forward shoulders bulging his white coat. My flesh crept as he unleashed a hearty laugh and motioned me towards the chair.

As I sat down I decided to have one last try.

'Is this the tooth?' I asked, tapping the only possible suspect.

'It is indeed!' boomed The Butcher. 'That's the one.'

'Ah well,' I said with a light laugh. 'I'm sure I can explain. There's been some mistake. . . .'

'Yes . . . yes. . . .' he murmured, filling the syringe before my eyes and sending a few playful spurts into the air.

'There's just a bit of enamel off it, and Mr Grover said . . .'

The WAAF suddenly wound the chair back and I found myself in the semi-prone position with the white bulk looming over me.

'You see,' I gasped desperately. 'I need that tooth. It's the one that holds my . . .'

A strong finger was on my gum and I felt the needle going in. I resigned myself to my fate.

When he had inserted the local the big man put the syringe down. 'We'll just give that a minute or two,' he said, and left the room.

As soon as the door closed behind him the WAAF tiptoed over to me.

'This feller's loopy!' she whispered.

Half lying, I stared at her.

'Loopy . . . ? What d'you mean?'

'Crackers! Round the bend! No idea how to pull teeth!'

'But . . . but . . . he's a dentist isn't he . . . ?'

She pulled a wry face. 'Thinks he is! But he hasn't a clue!'

I had no time to explore this cheering information further because the door opened and the big man returned.

He seized a horrible pair of forceps and I closed my eyes as he started flexing his muscles.

I must admit I felt nothing. I knew he was twisting and tugging away up there but the local had mercifully done its job. I was telling myself that it would soon be over when I heard a sharp crack.

I opened my eyes. The Butcher was gazing disappointedly at my broken-off tooth in his forceps. The root was still in my gum.

Behind him the WAAF gave me a long 'I told you so' nod. She was a pretty little thing, but I fear the libido of the young men she encountered in here would be at a low ebb.

'Oh!' The Butcher grunted and began to rummage in a metal box. It took me right back to the McDarroch days as he fished out one forceps after another, opened and shut them a few times then tried them on me.

But it was of no avail, and as the time passed I was the unwilling witness of the gradual transition from heartiness to silence, then to something like panic. The man was clearly whacked. He had no idea how to shift that root.

He must have been gouging for half an hour when an idea seemed to strike him. Pushing all the forceps to one side he almost ran from the room and reappeared shortly with a tray on which reposed a long chisel and a metal mallet.

At a sign from him the WAAF wound the chair back till I was completely horizontal. Seemingly familiar with the routine, she cradled my head in her arms in a practised manner and stood waiting.

This couldn't be true, I thought, as the man inserted the chisel into my mouth and poised the mallet; but all doubts were erased as the metal rod thudded against the remnants of my tooth and my head in turn shot back into the little WAAF's bosom. And that was how it went on. I lost count of time as The Butcher banged away and the girl hung on grimly to my jerking skull.

The thought uppermost in my mind was that I had always wondered how young horses felt when I knocked wolf teeth out of them. Now I knew.

When it finally stopped I opened my eyes, and though by this time I was prepared for anything I still felt slightly surprised to see The Butcher threading a needle with a length of suture silk. He was sweating and looking just a little desperate as he bent over me yet again.

'Just a couple of stitches,' he muttered hoarsely, and I closed my eyes again.

When I left the chair I felt very strange indeed. The assault on my cranium had made me dizzy and the sensation of the long ends of the stitches tickling my tongue was distinctly odd. I'm sure that when I came out of the room I was staggering, and instinctively I pawed at my mouth.

The first man I saw was Simkin. He was where I had left him but he looked different as he beckoned excitedly to me. I went over and he caught at my tunic with one hand.

'What d'yer think, mate?' he gasped. 'They've changed me round and I've got to go into room four.' He gulped. 'You looked bloody awful comin' out there. What was it like?'

I looked at him. Maybe there was going to be a gleam of

light this morning. I sank into the chair next to him and groaned.

'By God, you weren't kidding! I've never met anybody like that—he's half killed me. They don't call him The Butcher for nothing!'

'Why . . . what . . . what did 'e do?'

'Nothing much. Just knocked my tooth out with a hammer and chisel, that's all.'

'Garn! You're 'avin' me on!' Simkin made a ghastly attempt to smile.

'Word of honour,' I said. 'Anyway, there's the tray coming out now. Look for yourself.'

He stared at the WAAF carrying the dreadful implements and turned very pale.

'Oh blimey! What . . . what else did 'e do?'

I held my jaw for a moment. 'Well he did something I've never seen before. He made such a great hole in my gum that he had to stitch me up afterwards.'

Simkin shook his head violently. 'Naow, I'm not 'avin' that! I don't believe yer!'

'All right,' I said. 'What do you think of this?'

I leaned forward, put my thumb under my lip and jerked it up to give him a close-up view of the long gash and the trailing blood-stained ends of the stitches.

He shrank away from me, lips trembling, eyes wide.

'Gawd!' he moaned. 'Oh Gawd . . . !'

It was unfortunate that the WAAF chose that particular moment to call out 'AC2 Simkin' piercingly from the doorway, because the poor fellow leaped as though a powerful electric current had passed through him. Then, head down, he trailed across the room. At the door he turned and gave me a last despairing look and I saw him no more.

This experience deepened my dread of the five fillings which awaited me. But I needn't have worried; they were trivial things and were efficiently and painlessly dealt with by RAF dentists very different from The Butcher.

And yet, many years after the war had ended, the man from room four stretched out a long arm from the past and touched me on the shoulder. I began to feel something sharp coming through the roof of my mouth and went to Mr Grover, who X-rayed me and showed me a pretty picture of that fateful root still there despite the hammer and chisel. He extracted it and the saga was ended.

The Butcher remained a vivid memory because, apart from my ordeal, I was constantly reminded of him by the dangerous wobbling of my pipe at the edge of that needless gap in my mouth.

But I did have a small solace. I finished my visit to room four with a parting shaft which gave me a little comfort. As I tottered away I paused and addressed the big man's back as he prepared for his next victim.

'By the way,' I said. 'I've knocked out a lot of teeth just like you did there.'

He turned and stared at me. 'Really? Are you a dentist?'

'No,' I replied over my shoulder as I left. 'I'm a vet!'

I like women better than men.

Mind you, I have nothing against men—after all, I am one myself—but in the RAF there were too many of them. Literally thousands, jostling, shouting, swearing; you couldn't get away from them. Some of them became my friends and have remained so until the present day, but the sheer earthy mass of them made me realise how my few months of married life had changed me.

Women are gentler, softer, cleaner, altogether nicer things and I, who always considered myself one of the boys, had come to the surprising conclusion that the companion I wanted most was a woman.

My impression that I had been hurled into a coarser world was heightened at the beginning of each day, particularly one morning when I was on fire picket duty and had the sadistic pleasure of rattling the dustbin lids and shouting 'Wakey-wakey!' along the corridors. It wasn't the cursing and the obscene remarks which struck deepest, it was the extraordinary abdominal noises issuing from the dark rooms. They reminded me of my patient, Cedric, and in an instant I was back in Darrowby answering the telephone.

The voice at the other end was oddly hesitant.

'Mr Herriot . . . I should be grateful if you would come and see my dog.' It was a woman, obviously upper class.

'Certainly. What's the trouble?'

'Well . . . he . . . er . . . he seems to suffer from . . . a certain amount of flatus.'

'I beg your pardon?'

There was a long pause. 'He has . . . excessive flatus.'

'In what way, exactly?'

'Well . . . I suppose you'd describe it as . . . windiness.' The voice had begun to tremble.

I thought I could see a gleam of light. 'You mean his stomach . . . ?'

'No, not his stomach. He passes . . . er . . . a considerable quantity of . . . wind from his . . . his . . .' A note of desperation had crept in.

'Ah, yes!' All became suddenly clear. 'I quite understand. But that doesn't sound very serious. Is he ill?'

'No, he's very fit in other ways.'

'Well then, do you think it's necessary for me to see him?'

'Oh yes, indeed, Mr Herriot. I wish you would come as soon as possible. It has become quite . . . quite a problem.'

'All right,' I said. 'I'll look in this morning. Can I have your name and address, please?'

'It's Mrs Rumney, The Laurels.'

The Laurels was a very nice house on the edge of the town standing back from the road in a large garden. Mrs Rumney herself let me in and I felt a shock of surprise at my first sight of her. It wasn't just that she was strikingly beautiful; there was an unworldly air about her. She would be around forty but had the appearance of a heroine in a Victorian novel—tall, willowy, ethereal. And I could understand immediately her hesitation on the 'phone. Everything about her suggested fastidiousness and delicacy.

'Cedric is in the kitchen,' she said. 'I'll take you through.'

I had another surprise when I saw Cedric. An enormous Boxer hurled himself on me in delight, clawing at my chest with the biggest, horniest feet I had seen for a long time. I tried to fight him off but he kept at me, panting ecstatically into my face and wagging his entire rear end.

'Sit down, boy!' the lady said sharply, then, as Cedric took absolutely no notice, she turned to me nervously. "He's so friendly.'

'Yes,' I said breathlessly, 'I can see that.' I finally managed to push the huge animal away and backed into a corner for safety. 'How often does this . . . excessive flatus occur?'

As if in reply an almost palpable sulphurous wave arose from the dog and eddied around me. It appeared that the excitement of seeing me had activated Cedric's weakness. I was up against the wall and unable to obey my first instinct to run for cover, so I held my hand over my face for a few moments before speaking.

'Is that what you meant?'

Mrs Rumney waved a lace handkerchief under her nose and the faintest flush crept into the pallor of her cheeks.

'Yes,' she replied almost inaudibly. 'Yes . . . that is it.'

'Oh well,' I said briskly. 'There's nothing to worry about. Let's go into the other room and we'll have a word about his diet and a few other things.'

It turned out that Cedric was getting rather a lot of meat and I drew up a little chart cutting down the protein and adding extra carbohydrates. I prescribed a kaolin antacid mixture to be given night and morning and left the house in a confident frame of mind.

It was one of those trivial things and I had entirely forgotten it when Mrs Rumney 'phoned again.

'I'm afraid Cedric is no better, Mr Herriot.'

'Oh I'm sorry to hear that. He's still . . . er . . . still . . . yes . . . yes . . .' I spent a few moments in thought. 'I tell you what—I don't think I can do any more by seeing him at the moment, but I think you should cut out his meat completely for a week or two. Keep him on biscuits and brown bread rusked in the oven. Try him with that and vegetables and I'll give you some powder to mix in his food. Perhaps you'd call round for it.'

The powder was a pretty strong absorbent mixture and I felt sure it would do the trick, but a week later Mrs Rumney was on the 'phone again.

'There's absolutely no improvement, Mr Herriot.' The tremble was back in her voice. 'I . . . I do wish you'd come and see him again.'

I couldn't see much point in viewing this perfectly healthy animal again but I promised to call. I had a busy day and it was after six o'clock before I got round to The Laurels. There were several cars in the drive and when I went into the house I saw that Mrs Rumney had a few people in for drinks; people like herself—upper class and of obvious refinement. In fact I felt rather a lout in my working clothes among the elegant gathering.

Mrs Rumney was about to lead me through to the kitchen when the door burst open and Cedric bounded delightedly into the midst of the company. Within seconds an aesthetic-looking gentleman was frantically beating off the attack as the great feet ripped down his waistcoat. He got away at the cost of a couple of buttons and the Boxer turned his attention to one of the ladies. She was in imminent danger of losing her dress when I pulled the dog off her.

Pandemonium broke out in the graceful room. The hostess's plaintive appeals rang out above the cries of alarm as the big dog charged around, but very soon I realised that a more insidious element had crept into the situation. The atmosphere in the room became rapidly charged with an unmistakable effluvium and it was clear that Cedric's unfortunate malady had reasserted itself.

I did my best to shepherd the animal out of the room but he didn't seem to know the meaning of obedience and I chased him in vain. And as the embarrassing minutes ticked away I began to realise for the first time the enormity of the problem which confronted Mrs Rumney. Most dogs break wind occasionally but Cedric was different; he did it all the time. And while his silent emanations were perhaps more treacherous there was no doubt that the audible ones were painfully distressing in a company like this.

Cedric made it worse, because at each rasping expulsion he would look round enquiringly at his back end then gambol about the room as though the fugitive zephyr was clearly visible to him and he was determined to corner it.

It seemed a year before I got him out of there. Mrs Rumney held the door wide as I finally managed to steer him towards it but the big dog wasn't finished yet. On his way out he cocked a leg swiftly and directed a powerful jet against an immaculate trouser leg.

After that night I threw myself into the struggle on Mrs Rumney's behalf. I felt she desperately needed my help, and I made frequent visits and tried innumerable remedies. I consulted my colleague Siegfried on the problem and he suggested a diet of charcoal biscuits. Cedric ate them in vast quantities and with evident enjoyment but they, like everything else, made not the slightest difference to his condition.

And all the time I pondered upon the enigma of Mrs Rumney. She had lived in Darrowby for several years but the townsfolk knew little about her. It was a matter of debate whether she was a widow or separated from her husband. But I was not interested in such things; the biggest mystery to me was how she ever got involved with a dog like Cedric.

It was difficult to think of any animal less suited to her personality. Apart from his regrettable affliction he was in every way the opposite to herself; a great thick-headed rumbustious extrovert totally out of place in her gracious menage. I never did find out how they came together but on my visits I found that Cedric had one admirer at least.

He was Con Fenton, a retired farm worker who did a bit of jobbing gardening and spent an average of three days a week at The Laurels. The Boxer romped down the drive after me as I was leaving and the old man looked at him with undisguised admiration.

'By gaw,' he said. 'He's a fine dog, is that!'

'Yes, he is, Con. he's a good chap, really.' And I meant it. You couldn't help liking Cedric when you got to know him. He was utterly amiable and without vice and he gave off a constant aura not merely of noxious vapours but of bonhomie. When he tore off people's buttons or sprinkled their trousers he did it in a spirit of the purest amity.

'Just look at them limbs!' breathed Con, staring rapturously at the dog's muscular thighs. 'By heck, 'e can jump ower that gate as if it weren't there. He's what ah call a dog!'

As he spoke it struck me that Cedric would be likely to appeal to him because he was very like the Boxer himself; not over-burdened with brains, built like an ox with powerful shoulders and a big constantly-grinning face—they were two of a kind.

'Aye, ah allus likes it when t'missus lets him out in t'garden,' Con went on. He always spoke in a peculiar snuffling manner. 'He's grand company.'

I looked at him narrowly. No, he wouldn't be likely to notice Cedric's complaint since he always saw him out of doors.

On my way back to the surgery I brooded on the fact that I was achieving absolutely nothing with my treatment. And though it seemed ridiculous to worry about a case like this, there was no doubt the thing had begun to prey on my mind. In fact I began to transmit my anxieties to Siegfried. As I got out of the car he was coming down the steps of Skeldale House and he put a hand on my arm.

'You've been to The Laurels, James? Tell me,' he queried solicitously, 'how is your farting Boxer today?'

'Still at it, I'm afraid,' I replied, and my colleague shook his head in commiseration.

We were both defeated. Maybe if chlorophyll tablets had been available in those days they might have helped but as it was I had tried everything. It seemed certain that nothing would alter the situation. And it wouldn't have been so bad if the owner had been anybody else but Mrs Rumney; I found that even discussing the thing with her had become almost unbearable.

Siegfried's student brother Tristan didn't help, either. When seeing practice he was very selective in the cases he wished to observe, but he was immediately attracted to Cedric's symptoms and insisted on coming with me on one occasion. I never took him again because as we went in the big dog bounded from his mistress' side and produced a particularly sonorous blast as if in greeting.

Tristan immediately threw out a hand in a dramatic gesture and declaimed: 'Speak on, sweet lips that never told a lie!' That was his only visit. I had enough trouble without that.

I didn't know it at the time but a greater blow awaited me. A few days later Mrs Rumney was on the 'phone again.

'Mr Herriot, a friend of mine has such a sweet little Boxer bitch. She wants to bring her along to be mated with Cedric.'

'Eh?'

'She wants to mate her bitch with my dog.'

'With Cedric . . . ?' I clutched at the edge of the desk. It couldn't be true! 'And . . . and are you agreeable?'

'Yes, of course.'

I shook my head to dispel the feeling of unreality. I found it incomprehensible that anyone should want to reproduce Cedric, and as I gaped into the receiver a frightening vision floated before me of eight little Cedrics all with his complaint. But of course such a thing wasn't hereditary. I took a grip of myself and cleared my throat.

'Very well, then, Mrs Rumney, you'd better go ahead.'

There was a pause. 'But Mr Herriot, I want you to supervise the mating.'

'Oh really, I don't think that's necessary.' I dug my nails into my palms. 'I think you'll be all right without me.'

'Oh but I would be much happier if you were there. Please come,' she said appealingly.

Instead of emitting a long-drawn groan I took a deep breath. 'Right,' I said. 'I'll be along in the morning.'

All that evening I was obsessed by a feeling of dread. Another acutely embarrassing session was in store with this exquisite woman. Why was it I always had to share things like this with her? And I really feared the worst. Even the daftest dog, when confronted with a bitch in heat, knows instinctively how to proceed, but with a really ivory-skulled animal like Cedric I wondered. . . .

And next morning all my fears were realised. The bitch, Trudy, was a trim little creature and showed every sign of willingness to cooperate. Cedric, on the other hand, though obviously delighted to meet her, gave no hint of doing his part. After sniffing her over, he danced around her a few times, goofy-faced, tongue lolling. Then he had a roll on the lawn before charging at her and coming to a full stop, big feet outsplayed, head down, ready to play. I sighed. It was as I thought. The big chump didn't know what to do.

This pantomime went on for some time and, inevitably, the emotional strain brought on a resurgence of his symptoms. Frequently he paused to inspect his tail as though he had never heard noises like that before.

He varied his dancing routine with occasional headlong gallops round the lawn and it was after he had done about ten successive laps that he seemed to decide he ought to do something about the bitch. I held my breath as he approached her but unfortunately he chose the wrong end to commence operations. Trudy had put up with his nonsense with great patience but when she found him busily working away in the region of her left ear it was too much. With a shrill yelp she nipped him in the hind leg and he shot away in alarm.

After that whenever he came near she warned him off with bared teeth. Clearly she was disenchanted with her bridegroom and I couldn't blame her.

'I think she's had enough, Mrs Rumney,' I said.

I certainly had had enough and so had the poor lady, judging by her slight breathlessness, flushed cheeks and waving handkerchief.

'Yes . . . yes . . . I suppose you're right,' she replied.

So Trudy was taken home and that was the end of Cedric's career as a stud dog.

This last episode decided me. I had to have a talk with Mrs Rumney and a few days later I called in at The Laurels.

'Maybe you'll think it's none of my business,' I said. 'But I honestly don't think Cedric is the dog for you. In fact he's so wrong for you that he is upsetting your life.'

Mrs Rumney's eyes widened. 'Well . . . he is a problem in some ways . . . but what do you suggest?'

'I think you should get another dog in his place. Maybe a poodle or a corgi—something smaller, something you could control.'

'But Mr Herriot, I couldn't possibly have Cedric put down.' Her eyes filled quickly with tears. 'I really am fond of him despite his . . . despite everything.'

'No, no, of course not!' I said. 'I like him too. He has no malice in him. But I think I have a good idea. Why not let Con Fenton have him?'

'Con . . . ?'

'Yes, he admires Cedric tremendously and the big fellow would have a good life with the old man. He has a couple of fields behind his cottage and keeps a few beasts. Cedric could run to his heart's content out there and Con would be able to bring him along when he does the garden. You'd still see him three times a week.'

Mrs Rumney looked at me in silence for a few moments and I saw in her face the dawning of relief and hope.

'You know, Mr Herriot, I think that could work very well. But are you sure Con would take him?'

'I'd like to bet on it. An old bachelor like him must be lonely. There's only one thing worries me. Normally they only meet outside and I wonder how it would be when they were indoors and Cedric started to . . . when the old trouble . . .'

'Oh, I think that would be all right,' Mrs Rumney broke in quickly. 'When I go on holiday Con always takes him for a week or two and he has never mentioned any . . . anything unusual . . . in that way.'

I got up to go. 'Well, that's fine. I should put it to the old man right away.'

Mrs Rumney rang within a few days. Con had jumped at the chance of taking on Cedric and the pair had apparently settled in happily together. She had also taken my advice and acquired a poodle puppy.

I didn't see the new dog till it was nearly six months old and its mistress asked me to call to treat it for a slight attack of eczema. As I sat in the graceful room looking at Mrs Rumney, cool, poised, tranquil, with the little white creature resting on her knee I couldn't help feeling how right and fitting the whole scene was. The lush carpet, the trailing velvet curtains, the fragile tables with their load of expensive china and framed miniatures. It was no place for Cedric.

Con Fenton's cottage was less than half a mile away and on my way back to the surgery, on an impulse I pulled up at the door. The old man answered my knock and his big face split into a delighted grin when he saw me.

'Come in, young man!' he cried in his strange snuffly voice. 'I'm right glad to see tha!'

I had hardly stepped into the tiny living room when a hairy form hurled itself upon me. Cedric hadn't changed a bit and I had to battle my way to the broken armchair by the fireside. Con settled down opposite and when the Boxer leaped to lick his face he clumped him companionably on the head with his fist.

'Siddown, ye great daft bugger,' he murmured with affection. Cedric sank happily on to the tattered hearthrug at his feet and gazed up adoringly at his new master.

'Well, Mr Herriot,' Con went on as he cut up some villainous-looking plug tobacco and began to stuff it into his pipe. 'I'm right grateful to ye for gettin' me this grand dog. By gaw, he's a topper and ah wouldn't sell 'im for any money. No man could ask for a better friend.'

'Well that's great, Con,' I said. 'And I can see that the big chap is really happy here.'

The old man ignited his pipe and a cloud of acrid smoke rose to the low, blackened beams. 'Aye, he's 'ardly ever inside. A gurt strong dog like 'im wants to work 'is energy off, like.'

But just at that moment Cedric was obviously working something else off because the familiar pungency rose from him even above the billowings from the pipe. Con seemed oblivious of it but in the enclosed space I found it overpowering.

'Ah well,' I gasped. 'I just looked in for a moment to see how you were getting on together. I must be on my way.' I rose hurriedly and stumbled towards the door but the redolence followed me in a wave. As I passed the table with the remains of the old man's meal I saw what seemed to be the only form of ornament in the cottage, a cracked vase holding a magnificent bouquet of carnations. It was a way of escape and I buried my nose in their fragrance.

Con watched me approvingly. 'Aye, they're lovely flowers, aren't they? T'missus at Laurels lets me bring 'ome what I want and I reckon them carnations is me favourite.'

'Yes, they're a credit to you.' I still kept my nose among the blooms.

'There's only one thing,' the old man said pensively. 'Ah don't get t'full benefit of 'em.'

'How's that, Con?'

He pulled at his pipe a couple of times. 'Well, you can hear ah speak a bit funny, like?'

'No . . . no . . . not really.'

'Oh aye, ye know ah do. I've been like it since I were a lad. I 'ad a operation for adenoids and summat went wrong.'

'Oh, I'm sorry to hear that,' I said.

'Well, it's nowt serious, but it's left me lackin' in one way.'

'You mean . . . ?' A light was beginning to dawn in my mind, an elucidation of how man and dog had found each other, of why their relationship was so perfect, of the certainty of their happy future together. It seemed like fate.

'Aye,' the old man went on sadly. 'I 'ave no sense of smell.'

CHAPTER

5

I think it was when I saw the London policeman wagging a finger at a scowling urchin that I thought of Wesley Binks and the time he put the firework through the surgery letter box.

It was what they used to call a 'banger' and it exploded at my feet as I hurried along the dark passage in answer to the door bell's ring, making me leap into the air in terror.

I threw open the front door and looked into the street. It was empty, but at the corner where the lamplight was reflected in Robson's shop window I had a brief impression of a fleeing form and a faint echo of laughter. I couldn't do anything about it but I knew Wes was out there somewhere.

Wearily I trailed back into the house. Why did this lad persecute me? What could a ten-year-old boy possibly have against me? I had never done him any harm, yet I seemed to be the object of a deliberate campaign.

Or maybe it wasn't personal. It could be that he felt I represented authority or the establishment in some way, or perhaps I was just convenient.

I was certainly the ideal subject for his little tricks of ringing the door bell and running away, because I dared not ignore the summons in case it might be a client, and also the consulting and operating rooms were such a long way from the front of the house. Sometimes I was dragged down from our bed-sitter under the tiles. Every trip to the door was an expedition and it was acutely exasperating to arrive there and see only a little figure in the distance dancing about and grimacing at me.

He varied this routine by pushing rubbish through the letter box, pulling the flowers from the tiny strip of garden we tried to cultivate between the flagstones and chalking rude messages on my car.

I knew I wasn't the only victim because I had heard complaints from others; the fruiterer who saw his apples disappear from the box in front of the shop, the grocer who unwillingly supplied him with free biscuits.

He was the town naughty boy all right, and it was incongruous that he should have been named Wesley. There was not the slightest sign in his behaviour of any strict methodist upbringing. In fact I knew nothing of his family life—only that he came from the poorest part of the town, a row of 'yards' containing tumbledown cottages, some of them evacuated because of their condition.

I often saw him wandering about in the fields and lanes or fishing in quiet reaches of the river when he should have been in school. When he spotted me on these occasions he invariably called out some mocking remark and if he happened to be with some of his cronies they all joined in the laughter at my expense. It was annoying but I used to tell myself that there was nothing personal in it. I was an adult and that was enough to make me a target.

Wes's greatest triumph was undoubtedly the time he removed the grating from the coal cellar outside Skeldale House. It was on the left of the front steps and underneath it was a steep ramp down which the coalmen tipped their bags.

I don't know whether it was inspired intuition but he pinched the grating on the day of the Darrowby Gala. The festivities started with a parade through the town led by the Houlton Silver Band and as I looked down from the windows of our bed-sitter I could see them all gathering in the street below.

'Look, Helen,' I said. 'They must be starting the march from Trengate. Everybody I know seems to be down there.'

Helen leaned over my shoulder and gazed at the long lines of boy scouts, girl guides, ex-servicemen, with half the population of the town packed on the pavements, watching. 'Yes, it's quite a sight, isn't it? Let's go down and see them move off.'

We trotted down the long flights of stairs and I followed her out through the front door. And as I appeared in the entrance I was suddenly conscious that I was the centre of attention. The citizens on the pavements, waiting patiently for the parade to start, had something else to look at now. The little brownies and wolf cubs waved at me from their ranks and there were nods and smiles from the people across the road and on all sides.

I could divine their thoughts. 'There's t'young vitnery coming out of his house. Not long married, too. That's his missus next to him.'

A feeling of wellbeing rose in me. I don't know whether other newly married men feel the same, but in those early days I was aware of a calm satisfaction and fulfilment. And I was proud to be the 'vitnery' and part of the life of the town. There was my plate on the wall beside me, a symbol of my solid importance. I was a man of substance now. I had arrived.

Looking around me, I acknowledged the greeting with a few dignified little smiles, raising a gracious hand now and then rather like a royal personage on view. Then I noticed that Helen hadn't much room by my side, so I stepped to the left to where the grating should have been and slid gracefully down into the cellar.

It would be a dramatic touch to say I disappeared from view; in fact I wish I had, because I would have stayed down there and avoided further embarrassment. But as it was I travelled only so far down the ramp and stuck there with my head and shoulders protruding into the street.

My little exhibition caused a sensation among the spectators. Nothing in the Gala parade could compete with this. One or two of the surrounding faces expressed alarm but loud laughter was the general response. The adults were almost holding each other up but the little brownies and wolf cubs made my most appreciative audience, breaking their ranks and staggering about helplessly in the roadway while their leaders tried to restore order.

I caused chaos, too, in the Houlton Silver Band, who were hoisting their instruments prior to marching off. If they had any ideas about bursting into tune they had to abandon them temporarily because I don't think any of them had breath to blow.

It was, in fact, two of the bandsmen who extricated me by linking their hands under my armpits. My wife was of no service at all in the crisis and I could only look up at her reproachfully as she leaned against the doorpost dabbing at her eyes.

It all became clear to me when I reached street level. I was flicking the coal dust from my trousers and trying to look unconcerned when I saw Wesley Binks doubled up with mirth, pointing triumphantly at me and at the hole over the cellar. He was quite near, jostling among the spectators, and I had my first close look at the wild-eyed little goblin who had plagued me. I may have made an unconscious movement towards him because he gave me a last malevolent grin and disappeared into the crowd.

Later I asked Helen about him. She could only tell me that Wesley's father had left home when he was about six years old, that his mother had remarried and the boy now lived with her and his stepfather.

Strangely, I had another opportunity to study him quite soon afterwards. It was about a week later and my feathers were still a little ruffled after the grating incident when I saw him sitting all alone in the waiting room. Alone, that is, except for a skinny black dog in his lap.

I could hardly believe it. I had often rehearsed the choice phrases which I would use on this very occasion but the sight of the animal restrained me; if he had come to consult me professionally I could hardly start pitching into him right away. Maybe later.

I pulled on a white coat and went in.

'Well, what can I do for you?' I asked coldly.

The boy stood up and his expression of mixed defiance and desperation showed that it had cost him something to enter this house.

'Summat matter wi' me dog,' he muttered.

'Right, bring him through.' I led the way along the passage to the consulting room.

'Put him on the table please,' I said, and as he lifted the little animal I decided that I couldn't let this opportunity pass. While I was carrying out my examination I would quite casually discuss recent events. Nothing nasty, no clever phrases, just a quiet probe into the situation. I was just about to say something like 'What's the idea of all those tricks you play on me?' when I took my first look at the dog and everything else fled from my mind.

He wasn't much more than a big puppy and an out-and-out mongrel. His shiny black coat could have come from a labrador and there was a suggestion of terrier in the pointed nose and pricked ears, but the long string-like tail and the knock-kneed fore limbs baffled me. For all that he was an attractive little creature with a sweetly expressive face.

But the things that seized my whole attention were the yellow blobs of pus in the corners of the eyes, the muco-purulent discharge from the nostrils and the photophobia which made the dog blink painfully at the light from the surgery window.

Classical canine distemper is so easy to diagnose but there is never any satisfaction in doing so.

'I didn't know you had a dog,' I said. 'How long have you had him?'

'A month. Feller got 'im from t'dog and cat home at Hartington and sold 'im to me.'

'I see.' I took the temperature and was not surprised to find it was 104°F.

'How old is he?'

'Nine months.'

I nodded. Just about the worst age.

I went ahead and asked all the usual questions but I knew the answers already.

Yes, the dog had been slightly off colour for a week or two. No, he wasn't really ill, but listless and coughing occasionally. And of course it was not until the eyes and nose began to discharge that the boy became worried and brought him to see me. That was when we usually saw these cases—when it was too late.

Wesley imparted the information defensively, looking at me under lowered brows as though he expected me to clip his ear at any moment. But as I studied him any aggressive feelings I may have harboured evaporated quickly. The imp of hell appeared on closer examination to be a neglected child. His elbows stuck out through holes in a filthy jersey, his shorts were similarly ragged, but what appalled me most was the sour smell of his unwashed litle body. I hadn't thought there were children like this in Darrowby.

When he had answered my questions he made an effort and blurted out one of his own.

'What's matter with 'im?'

I hesitated a moment. 'He's got distemper, Wes.'

'What's that?'

'Well, it's a nasty infectious disease. He must have got it from another sick dog.'

'Will 'e get better?'

'I hope so. I'll do the best I can for him.' I couldn't bring myself to tell a small boy of his age that his pet was probably going to die.

I filled a syringe with a 'mixed macterin' which we used at that time against the secondary invaders of distemper. It never did much good and even now with all our antibiotics we cannot greatly influence the final outcome. If you can catch a case in the early viral phase then a shot of hyperimmune serum is curative, but people rarely bring their dogs in until that phase is over.

As I gave the injection the dog whimpered a little and the boy stretched out a hand and patted him.

'It's awright, Duke,' he said.

'That's what you call him, is it—Duke?'

'Aye.' He fondled the ears and the dog turned, whipped his strange long tail about and licked the hand quickly. Wes smiled and looked up at me and for a moment the tough mask dropped from the grubby features and in the dark wild eyes I read sheer delight. I swore under my breath. This made it worse.

I tipped some boracic crystals into a box and handed it over. 'Use this dissolved in water to keep his eyes and nose clean. See how his nostrils are all caked and blocked up—you can make him a lot more comfortable.'

He took the box without speaking and almost with the same movement dropped three and sixpence on the table. It was about our average charge and resolved my doubts on that score.

'When'll ah bring 'im back?' he asked.

I looked at him doubtfully for a moment. All I could do was repeat the injections, but was it going to make the slightest difference?

The boy misread my hesitation.

'Ah can pay!' he burst out. 'Ah can get t'money!'

'Oh I didn't mean that, Wes. I was just wondering when it would be suitable. How about bringing him in on Thursday?'

He nodded eagerly and left with his dog.

As I swabbed the table with disinfectant I had the old feeling of helplessness. The modern veterinary surgeon does not see nearly as many cases of distemper as we used to, simply because most people immunise their puppies at the earliest possible moment. But back in the thirties it was only the few fortunate dogs who were inoculated. The disease is so easy to prevent but almost impossible to cure.

The next three weeks saw an incredible change in Wesley Binks's character. He had built up a reputation as an idle scamp but now he was transformed into a model of industry, delivering papers in the mornings, digging people's gardens, helping to drive the beasts at the auction mart. I was perhaps the only one who knew he was doing it for Duke.

He brought the dog in every two or three days and paid on the nail. I naturally charged him as little as possible but the money he earned went on other things—fresh meat from the butcher, extra milk and biscuits.

'Duke's looking very smart today,' I said on one of the visits. 'I see you've been getting him a new collar and lead.'

The boy nodded shyly then looked up at me, dark eyes intent. 'Is 'e any better?'

'Well, he's about the same, Wes. That's how it goes—dragging on without much change.'

'When . . . will ye know?'

I thought for a moment. Maybe he would worry less if he understood the situation. 'The thing is this. Duke will get better if he can avoid the nervous complications of distemper.'

'Wot's them?'

'Fits, paralysis and a thing called chorea which makes the muscles twitch.'

'Wot if he gets them?'

'It's a bad lookout in that case. But not all dogs develop them.' I tried to smile reassuringly. 'And there's one thing in Duke's favour—he's not a pure bred. Cross bred dogs have a thing called hybrid vigour which helps them to fight disease. After all, he's eating fairly well and he's quite lively, isn't he?'

'Aye, not bad.'

'Well then, we'll carry on. I'll give him another shot now.'

The boy was back in three days and I knew by his face he had momentous news.

'Duke's a lot better—'is eyes and nose 'ave dried up and he's eatin' like a 'oss!' He was panting with excitement.

I lifted the dog on to the table. There was no doubt he was

enormously improved and I did my best to join in the rejoicing.

'That's great, Wes,' I said, but a warning bell was tinkling in my mind. If nervous symptoms were going to supervene, this was the time—just when the dog was apparently recovering.

I forced myself to be optimistic. 'Well now, there's no need to come back any more but watch him carefully and if you see anything unusual bring him in.'

The ragged little figure was overjoyed. He almost pranced along the passage with his pet and I hoped fervently that I would not see them in there again.

That was on the Friday evening and by Monday I had put the whole thing out of my head and into the category of satisfying memories when the boy came in with Duke on the lead.

I looked up from the desk where I was writing in the day book. 'What is it, Wes?'

'He's dotherin'.'

I didn't bother going through to the consulting room but hastened from behind the desk and crouched on the floor, studying the dog intently. At first I saw nothing, then as I watched I could just discern a faint nodding of the head. I placed my hand on the top of the skull and waited. And it was there; the slight but regular twitching of the temporal muscles which I had dreaded.

'I'm afraid he's got chorea, Wes.' I said.

'What's that?'

'It's one of the things I was telling you about. Sometimes they call it St Vitus' Dance. I was hoping it wouldn't happen.'

The boy looked suddenly small and forlorn and he stood there silent, twisting the new leather lead between his fingers. It was such an effort for him to speak that he almost closed his eyes.

'Will 'e die?'

'Some dogs do get over it, Wes.' I didn't tell him that I had seen it happen only once. 'I've got some tablets which might help him. I'll get you some.'

I gave him a few of the arsenical tablets I had used in my only cure. I didn't even know if they had been responsible but I had nothing more to offer.

Duke's chorea pursued a text book course over the next two weeks. All the things which I had feared turned up in a relentless progression. The twitching spread from his head to his limbs, then his hindquarters began to sway as he walked.

His young master brought him in repeatedly and I went through the motions, trying at the same time to make it clear that it was all hopeless. The boy persisted doggedly, rushing about meanwhile with his paper deliveries and other jobs, insisting on paying though I didn't want his money. Then one afternoon he called in.

'Ah couldn't bring Duke,' he muttered. 'Can't walk now. Will you come and see 'im?'

We got into my car. It was a Sunday, about three o'clock and the streets were quiet. He led me up the cobbled yard and opened the door of one of the houses.

The stink of the place hit me as I went in. Country vets aren't easily sickened but I felt my stomach turning. Mrs Binks was very fat and a filthy dress hung shapelessly on her as she slumped, cigarette in mouth, over the kitchen table. She was absorbed in a magazine which lay in a clearing among mounds of dirty dishes and her curlers nodded as she looked up briefly at us.

On a couch under the window her husband sprawled asleep, open-mouthed, snoring out the reek of beer. The sink, which held a further supply of greasy dishes, was covered in a revolting green scum. Clothes, newspapers and nameless rubbish littered the floor and over everything a radio blasted away at full strength.

The only clean new thing was the dog basket in the corner. I went across and bent over the little animal. Duke was now prostrate and helpless, his body emaciated and jerking uncontrollably. The sunken eyes had filled up again with pus and gazed apathetically ahead.

'Wes,' I said. 'You've got to let me put him to sleep.'

He didn't answer, and as I tried to explain, the blaring radio drowned my words. I looked over at his mother.

'Do you mind turning the radio down?' I asked.

She jerked her head at the boy and he went over and turned the knob. In the ensuing silence I spoke to him again.

'It's the only thing, believe me. You can't let him die by inches like this.'

He didn't look at me. All his attention was fixed desperately on his dog. Then he raised a hand and I heard his whisper.

'Awright.'

I hurried out to the car for the Nembutal.

'I promise you he'll feel no pain,' I said as I filled the syringe. And indeed the little creature merely sighed before lying motionless, the fateful twitching stilled at last.

I put the syringe in my pocket. 'Do you want me to take him away, Wes?'

He looked at me bewilderedly and his mother broke in.

'Aye, get 'im out. Ah never wanted t'bloody thing 'ere in t'first place.' She resumed her reading.

I quickly lifted the little body and went out. Wes followed me and watched as I opened the boot and laid Duke gently on top of my black working coat.

As I closed the lid he screwed his knuckles into his eyes and his body shook. I put my arm across his shoulders, and as he leaned against me for a moment and sobbed I wondered if he had ever been able to cry like this—like a little boy with somebody to comfort him.

But soon he stood back and smeared the tears across the dirt on his cheeks.

'Are you going back into the house, Wes?' I asked.

He blinked and looked at me with a return of his tough expression.

'Naw!' he said and turned and walked away. He didn't look back and I watched him cross the road, climb a wall and trail away across the fields towards the river.

And it has always seemed to me that at that moment Wes walked back into his old life. From then on there were no more odd jobs or useful activities. He never played any more tricks on me but in other ways he progressed into more serious misdemeanorus. He set barns on fire, was up before the magistrates for theft and by the time he was thirteen he was stealing cars.

Finally he was sent to an approved school and then he disappeared from the district. Nobody knew where he went and most people forgot him. One person who didn't was the police sergeant.

'That young Wesley Binks,' he said to me ruminatively. 'He

was a wrong 'un if ever I saw one. You know, I don't think he ever cared a damn for anybody or any living thing in his life.'

'I know how you feel, sergeant,' I replied, 'But you're not entirely right. There was one living thing. . . .'

6

Tristan would never have won any prizes as an exponent of the haute cuisine.

We got better food in the RAF than most people in wartime Britain but it didn't compare with the Darrowby fare. I suppose I had been spoiled; first by Mrs Hall, then by Helen. There were only brief occasions at Skeldale House when we did not eat like kings and one of those was when Tristan was installed as temporary cook.

It began one morning at breakfast in the days when I was still a bachelor and Tristan and I were taking our places at the mahogany dining table. Siegfried bustled in, muttered a greeting and began to pour his coffee. He was unusually distrait as he buttered a slice of toast and cut into one of the rashers on his plate, then after a minute's thoughtful chewing he brought down his hand on the table with a suddenness that made me jump.

'I've got it!' he exclaimed.

'Got what?' I enquired.

Siegfried put down his knife and fork and wagged a finger at me. 'Silly, really, I've been sitting here puzzling about what to do and it's suddenly clear.'

'Why, what's the trouble?'

'It's Mrs Hall,' he said. 'She's just told me her sister has been taken ill and she has to go and look after her. She thinks she'll be away for a week and I've been wondering who I could get to look after the house.'

'I see.'

'Then it struck me.' He sliced a corner from a fried egg. 'Tristan can do it.'

'Eh?' His brother looked up, startled, from his *Daily Mirror*. 'Me?'

'Yes, you! You spend a lot of time on your arse. A bit of useful activity would be good for you.'

Tristan looked at him warily. 'What do you mean—useful activity?'

'Well, keeping the place straight,' Siegfried said. 'I wouldn't expect perfection but you could tidy up each day, and of course prepare the meals.'

'Meals?'

'That's right.' Siegfried gave him a level stare. 'You can cook, can't you?'

'Well, er, yes . . . I can cook sausage and mash.'

Siegfried waved an expansive hand. 'There you are, you see, no problem. Push over those fried tomatoes, will you, James?'

I passed the dish silently. I had only half heard the conversation because part of my mind was far away. Just before breakfast I had had a phone call from Ken Billings, one of our best farmers, and his words were still echoing in my head.

'Mr Herriot, that calf you saw yesterday is dead. That's the third 'un I've lost in a week and I'm flummoxed. I want ye out here this mornin' to have another look round.'

I sipped my coffee absently. He wasn't the only one who was flummoxed. Three fine calves had shown symptoms of acute gastric pain, I had treated them and they had died. That was bad enough but what made it worse was that I hadn't the faintest idea what was wrong with them.

I wiped my lips and got up quickly. 'Siegfried, I'd like to go to Billings' first. Then I've got the rest of the round you gave me.'

'Fine, James, by all means.' My boss gave me a sweet and encouraging smile, balanced a mushroom on a piece of fried bread and conveyed it to his mouth. He wasn't a big eater but he did love his breakfast.

On the way to the farm my mind beat about helplessly. What more could I do than I had already done? In these obscure cases one was driven to the conclusion that the animal had eaten something harmful. At times I had spent hours roaming around pastures looking for poisonous plants but that was pointless with Billings's calves because they had never been out; they were mere babies of a month old.

I had carried out post mortem examinations of the dead animals but had found only a non-specific gastro-enteritis. I had sent kidneys to the laboratory for lead estimation with negative result; like their owner, I was flummoxed.

Mr Billings was waiting for me in his yard.

'Good job I rang you!' he said breathlessly. 'There's another 'un startin'.'

I rushed with him into the buildings and found what I expected and dreaded; a small calf kicking at its stomach, getting up and down, occasionally rolling on its straw bed. Typical abdominal pain. But why?

I went over it as with the others. Temperature normal, lungs clear, only rumenal atony and extreme tenderness as I palpated the abdomen.

As I was putting the thermometer back in its case the calf suddenly toppled over and went into a frothing convulsion. Hastily I injected sedatives, calcium, magnesium, but with a feeling of doom. I had done it all before.

'What the hell is it?' the farmer asked, voicing my thoughts.

I shrugged. 'It's acute gastritis, Mr Billings, but I wish I knew the cause. I could swear this calf has eaten some irritant or corrosive poison.'

'Well, dang it, they've nobbut had milk and a few nuts.' The farmer spread his hands. 'There's nothing they can get to hurt them.'

Again, wearily, I went through the old routine; ferreting around in the calf pen, trying to find some clue. An old paint tin, a burst packet of sheep dip. It was amazing, the things you came across in the clutter of a farm building.

But not at Mr Billings's place. He was meticulously tidy, particularly with his calves, and the window sills and shelves were free from rubbish. It was the same with the milk buckets, scoured to spotless cleanliness after every feed.

Mr Billings had a thing about his calves. His two teenage sons were fanatically keen on farming and he encouraged them in all the agricultural skills; but he fed the calves himself.

'Feeding them calves is t'most important job in stock rearing,' he used to say. 'Get 'em over that first month and you're halfway there.'

And he knew what he was talking about. His charges never suffered from the normal ailments of the young; no scour, no joint ill, no pneumonia. I had often marvelled at it, but it made the present disaster all the more unbearable.

'All right,' I said with false breeziness as I left. 'Maybe this one won't be so bad. Give me a ring in the morning.'

I did the rest of my round in a state of gloom and at lunch I was still so preoccupied that I wondered what had happened when Tristan served the meal. I had entirely forgotten about Mrs Hall's absence.

However, the sausage and mash wasn't at all bad and Tristan was lavish with his helpings. The three of us cleaned our plates pretty thoroughly, because morning is the busiest working time in practice and I was always famished by midday.

My mind was still on Mr Billings's problem during the afternoon calls and when we sat down to supper I was only mildly surprised to find another offering of sausage and mash.

'Same again, eh?' Siegfried grunted, but he got through his plateful and left without further comment.

The next day started badly. I came into the dining room to find the table bare and Siegfried stamping around.

'Where the hell is our breakfast?' he burst out. 'And where the hell is Tristan?'

He pounded along the passage and I heard his shouts in the kitchen 'Tristan! Tristan!'

I knew he was wasting his time. His brother often slept in and it was just more noticeable this morning.

My boss returned along the passage at a furious gallop and I steeled myself for some unpleasantness as the young man was rousted from his bed. But Tristan, as usual, was master of the situation. Siegfried had just begun to take the stairs three at a time when his brother descended from the landing, knotting his tie with perfect composure. It was uncanny. He always got more than his share of sleeping time but was rarely caught between the sheets.

'Sorry, chaps,' he murmured. 'Afraid I overslept.'

'Yes, that's all right!' shouted Siegfried. 'But how about our bloody breakfast? I gave you a job to do!'

Tristan was contrite. 'I really do apologise, but I was up late last night, peeling potatoes.'

His brother's face flushed. 'I know all about that!' he barked. 'You didn't start till after closing time at the Drovers!'

'Well, that's right.' Tristan swallowed and his face assumed the familiar expression of pained dignity. 'I did feel a bit dry last night. Think it must have been all the cleaning and dusting I did.'

Siegfried did not reply. He shot a single exasperated look at the young man then turned to me. 'We'll have to make do with bread and marmalade this morning, James. Come through to the kitchen and we'll . . .'

The jangling telephone cut off his words. I lifted the receiver and listened and it must have been the expression on my face which stopped him in the doorway.

'What's the matter, James?' he asked as I came away from the 'phone. 'You look as though you've had a kick in the belly.'

I nodded. 'That's how I feel. That calf is nearly dead at Billings's and there's another one ill. I wish you'd come out there with me, Siegfried.'

My boss stood very still as he looked over the side of the pen at the little animal. It didn't seem to know where to put itself, rising and lying down, kicking at some inward pain, writhing its hindquarters from side to side. As he watched it fell on its side and began to thrash around with all four limbs.

'James,' he said quietly. 'That calf has been poisoned.'

'That's what I thought, but how?'

Mr Billings broke in. 'It's no good talkin' like that, Mr Farnon. We've been over this place time and time again and there's nowt for them to get.'

'Well, we'll go over it again.' Siegfried stalked around the calf house as I had done and when he returned his face was expressionless.

'Where do you get the nuts from?' he grunted, crumbling one of the cubes between his fingers.

Mr Billings threw his arms wide. 'From t'local mili. Ryders' best. You can't fault them, surely.'

Siegfried said nothing. Ryders were noted for their meticulous preparation of cattle food. He went over the sick calf with stethoscope and thermometer, digging his fingers into the hairy abdominal wall, staring impassively at the calf's face to note its reaction. He did the same with my patient of yesterday whose glazing eyes and cold extremities told their grim tale. Then he gave the calves almost the same treatment as I had and we left.

He was silent for the first half mile, then he beat the wheel suddenly with one hand. 'There's an irritant poison there, James! As sure as God made little apples there is. But I'm damned if I know where it's coming from.'

Our visit had taken a long time and we returned to Skeldale House for lunch. Like myself, his mind was still wrestling with Mr Billings's problem and he hardly winced as Tristan placed a steaming plateful of sausage and mash before him. Then, as he prodded the mash with a fork, he appeared to come to the surface.

'God almighty!' he exclaimed. 'Have we got this again?'

Tristan smiled ingratiatingly. 'Yes, indeed. Mr Johnson told me they were a particularly fine batch of sausages today. Definitely superior, he said.'

'Is that so?' His brother gave him a sour glance. 'Well, they look the bloody same to me. Like supper yesterday—and like lunch.' His voice began to rise, then he subsided.

'Oh, what the hell,' he muttered, and began to toy listlessly with the food. Clearly those calves had drained him and I knew how he felt.

I got through my share without much difficulty—I've always liked sausage and mash.

But my boss is a resilient character and when we met in the late afternoon he was bursting with his old spirit.

'That call to Billings's shook me, James, I can tell you,' he said. 'But I've revisited a few of my other cases since then and they're all improving nicely. Raises the morale tremendously. Here, let me get you a drink.'

He reached into the cupboard above the mantelpiece for the gin bottle and after pouring a couple of measures he looked benignly at his brother who was tidying the sitting room.

Tristan was making a big show, running a carpet sweeper up and down, straightening cushions, flicking a duster at everything in sight. He sighed and panted with effort as he bustled around, the very picture of a harassed domestic. He needed only a mob cap and frilly apron to complete the image.

We finished our drinks and Siegfried immersed himself in the *Veterinary Record* as savoury smells began to issue from the kitchen. It was about seven o'clock when Tristan put his head round the door.

'Supper is on the table,' he said.

My boss put down the *Record,* rose and stretched expansively. 'Good, I'm ready for it, too.'

I followed him into the dining room and almost cannoned into his back as he halted abruptly. He was staring in disbelief at the tureen in the middle of the table.

'Not bloody sausage and mash again!' he bellowed.

Tristan shuffled his feet. 'Well, er, yes—it's very nice really.'

'Very nice! I'm beginning to dream about the blasted stuff. Can't you cook anything else?'

'Well, I told you.' Tristan looked wounded. 'I told you I could cook sausage and mash.'

'Yes, you did!' shouted his brother. 'But you didn't say you couldn't cook anything BUT sausage and bloody mash!'

Tristan made a non-committal gesture and his brother sank wearily down at the table.

'Go on, then,' he sighed. 'Dish it out and heaven help us.'

He took a small mouthful from his plate then gripped at his stomach and emitted a low moan. 'This stuff is killing me. I don't think I'll ever be the same after this week.'

The following day opened in dramatic fashion. I had just got out of bed and was reaching for my dressing gown when an explosion shook the house. It was a great 'WHUFF' which rushed like a mighty wind through passages and rooms, rattling the windows and leaving an ominous silence in its wake.

I dashed out to the landing and ran into Siegfried, who stared wide-eyed at me for a moment before galloping downstairs.

In the kitchen Tristan was lying on his back amid a litter of pans and dishes. Several rashers of bacon and a few smashed eggs nestled on the flags.

'What the hell's going on?' Siegfried shouted.

His brother looked up at him with mild interest. 'I really don't know. I was lighting the fire and there was a bang.'

'Lighting the fire . . . ?'

'Yes, I've had a little difficulty these last two mornings. The thing wouldn't go. I think the chimney needs sweeping. These old houses . . .'

'Yes, yes!' Siegfried burst out. 'We know, but what the hell happened?'

Tristan sat up. Even then, among the debris with smuts all over his face, he still retained his poise. 'Well, I thought I'd hurry things along a bit,' (His agile mind was forever seeking new methods of conserving energy.) 'I soaked a piece of cotton wool in ether and chucked that in.'

'Ether?'

'Well yes, it's inflammable, isn't it?'

'Inflammable!' His brother was pop-eyed. 'It's bloody well explosive! It's a wonder you didn't blow the whole place up.'

Tristan rose and dusted himself off. 'Ah well, never mind. I'll soon have breakfast ready.'

'You can forget that.' Siegfried took a long shuddering breath then went over to the bread tin, extracted a loaf and began to saw at it. 'The breakfast's on the floor, and anyway, by the time you've cleared up this mess we'll be gone. Bread and marmalade all right for you, James?'

We went out together again. My boss had arranged that Ken Billings should postpone his calf feeding till we got there so that we could witness the process.

It wasn't a happy arrival. Both the calves had died and the farmer's eyes held a look of desperation.

Siegfried's jaw clenched tight for a moment than he motioned with his hand. 'Please carry on, Mr Billings. I want to see you feed them.'

The nuts were always available for the little animals but we watched intently as the farmer poured the milk into the buckets and the calves started to drink. The poor man had obviously given up hope and I could tell by his apathetic manner that he hadn't much faith in this latest ploy.

Neither had I, but Siegfried prowled up and down like a caged panther as though willing something to happen. The calves raised white-slobbered muzzles enquiringly as he hung over them but they could offer no more explanation of the mystery than I could myself.

I looked across the long row of pens. There were still more than thirty calves left in the building and the terrible thought arose that the disease might spread through all of them. My mind was recoiling when Siegfried stabbed a finger at one of the buckets.

'What's that?' he snapped.

The farmer and I went over and gazed down at a circular

black object about half an inch across floating on the surface of the milk.

'Bit o' muck got in somehow,' Mr Billings mumbled. 'I'll 'ave it out.' He put his hand into the bucket.

'No, let me!' Siegfried carefully lifted the thing, shook the milk from his fingers and studied it with interest.

'This isn't muck,' he murmured. 'Look, it's concave—like a little cup.' He rubbed a corner between thumb and forefinger. 'I'll tell you what it is, it's a scab. Where the heck has it come from?'

He began to examine the neck and head of the calf, then became very still as he handled one of the little horn buds. 'There's a raw surface here. You can see where the scab belongs.' He placed the dark cup over the bud and it fitted perfectly.

The farmer shrugged. 'Aye, well, I can understand that. I disbudded all the calves about a fortnight sin'.'

'What did you use, Mr Billings?' My colleague's voice was soft.

'Oh, some new stuff. Feller came round sellin' it. You just paint it on—it's a lot easier than t'awd caustic stick.'

'Have you got the bottle?'

'Aye, it's in t'house. I'll get it.'

When the farmer returned Siegfried read the label and handed the bottle to me.

'Butter of Antimony, Jim. Now we know.'

'But . . . what are you on about?' asked the farmer bewilderedly.

Siegfried looked at him sympathetically. 'Antimony is a deadly poison, Mr Billings. Oh, it'll burn your horn buds off, all right, but if it gets in among the food, that's it.'

The farmer's eyes widened. 'Yes, dang it, and when they put their heads down to drink that's just when the scabs would fall off!'

'Exactly,' Siegfried said. 'Or they maybe knocked the horn buds on the sides of the bucket. Anyway, let's make sure the others are safe.'

We went round all the calves, removing the lethal crusts and scrubbing the buds clean, and when we finally drove away we knew that the brief but painful episode of the Billings calves was over.

In the car, my colleague put his elbows on the wheel and drove with his chin cupped in his hands. He often did this when in contemplative mood and it never failed to unnerve me.

'James,' he said, 'I've never seen anything like that before. It really is one for the book.'

His words were prophetic, for as I write about it now I realise that it has never been repeated in the thirty-five years that have passed since then.

At Skeldale House we parted to go our different ways. Tristan, no doubt anxious to redeem himself after the morning's explosive beginning, was plying mop and bucket and swabbing the passage with the zeal of one of Nelson's sailors.

But when Siegfried drove away, the activity stopped abruptly and as I was leaving with my pockets stuffed with the equipment for my round I glanced into the sitting room and saw the young man stretched in his favourite chair.

I went in and looked with some surprise at a pan of sausages balanced on the coals.

'What's this?' I asked.

Tristan lit a Woodbine, shook out his *Daily Mirror* and put his feet up. 'Just prepared lunch, old lad.'

'In here?'

'Yes, Jim, I've had enough of that hot stove—there's no comfort through there. And anyway, the kitchen's such a bloody long way away.'

I gazed down at the reclining form. 'No need to ask what's on the menu?'

'None at all, old son.' Tristan looked up from his paper with a seraphic smile.

I was about to leave when a thought struck me. 'Where are the potatoes?'

'In the fire.'

'In the fire!'

'Yes, I just popped them in there to roast for a while. They're delicious that way.'

'Are you sure?'

'Absolutely, Jim. I'll tell you—you'll fall in love with my cooking all over again.'

I didn't get back till nearly one o'clock. Tristan was not in the sitting room but a haze of smoke hung on the air and a reek like a garden bonfire prickled in my nostrils.

I found the young man in the kitchen. His *savoir faire* had vanished and he was prodding desperately at a pile of coal black spheres.

I stared at him. 'What are those?'

'The bloody potatoes, Jim! I fell asleep for a bit and this happened!'

He gingerly sawed through one of the objects. In the centre of the carbonaceous ball I could discern a small whitish marble which seemed to be all that remained of the original vegetable.

'Hell's bells, Triss! What are you going to do?'

He gave me a stricken glance. 'Hack out the centres and mash 'em up together. It's all I CAN do.'

This was something I couldn't bear to watch. I went upstairs, had a wash then took my place at the dining table. Siegfried was already seated and I could see that the little triumph of the morning had cheered him. He greeted me jovially.

'James, wasn't that the damndest thing at Ken Billings'? It's so satisfying to get it cleared up.'

But his smile froze as Tristan appeared and set down the tureens before him. From one peeped the inevitable sausages and the other contained an amorphous dark grey mass liberally speckled with black foreign bodies of varying size.

'What in the name of God,' he enquired with ominous quiet, 'is this?'

His brother swallowed. 'Sausage and mash,' he said lightly.

Siegfried gave him a cold look. 'I am referring to this.' He poked warily at the dark mound.

'Well, er, it's the potatoes.' Tristan cleared his throat. 'Got a little burnt, I'm afraid.'

My boss made no comment. With dangerous calm he spooned some of the material on to his plate, raised a forkful and began to chew slowly. Once or twice he winced as a particularly tough fragment of carbon cracked between his molars, then he closed his eyes and swallowed.

For a moment he was still, then he grasped his midriff with both hands, groaned and jumped to his feet.

'No, that's enough!' he cried. 'I don't mind investigating poisonings on the farms but I object to being poisoned myself in my own home!' He strode away from the table and paused at the door. 'I'm going over to the Drovers for lunch.'

As he left another spasm seized him. He clutched his stomach again and looked back.

'Now I know just how those poor bloody calves felt!'

I suppose it was a little thoughtless of me to allow my scalpel to flash and flicker quite so close to Rory O'Hagan's fly buttons.

The incident came back to me as I sat in my room in St John's Wood reading Black's *Veterinary Dictionary*. It was a bulky volume to carry around and my RAF friends used to rib me about my 'vest pocket edition', but I had resolved to keep reading it in spare moments to remind me of my real life.

I had reached the letter 'C' and as the word 'Castration' looked up at me from the page I was jerked back to Rory.

I was castrating pigs. There were several litters to do and I was in a hurry and failed to notice the Irish farm worker's mounting apprehension. His young boss was catching the little animals and handing them to Rory who held them upside down, gripped between his thighs with their legs apart, and as I quickly incised the scrotums and drew out the testicles my blade almost touched the rough material of his trouser crutch.

'For God's sake, have a care, Mr Herriot!' he gasped at last.

I looked up from my work. 'What's wrong, Rory?'

'Watch what you're doin' with that bloody knife! You're whippin' it round between me legs like a bloody Red Indian. You'll do me a mischief afore you've finished!'

'Aye, be careful, Mr Herriot,' the young farmer cried. 'Don't geld Rory instead of the pig. His missus ud never forgive ye.' He burst into a loud peal of laughter, the Irishman grinned sheepishly and I giggled.

That was my undoing because the momentary inattention sent the blade slicing across my left forefinger. The razor-sharp edge went deep and in an instant the entire neighbourhood seemed flooded with my blood. I thought I would never staunch the flow. The red ooze continued, despite a long session of self-doctoring from the car boot, and when I finally drove away my finger was swathed in the biggest, clumsiest dressing I had ever seen. I had finally been forced to apply a large pad of cotton wool held in place with an enormous length of three-inch bandage.

It was dark when I left the farm. About five o'clock on a late December day, the light gone early and the stars beginning to show in a frosty sky. I drove slowly, the enormous finger jutting upwards from the wheel, pointing the way between the headlights like a guiding beacon. I was within half a mile of Darrowby with the lights of the little town beginning to wink between the bare roadside branches when a car approached, went past, then I heard a squeal of brakes as it stopped and began to double back.

It passed me again, drew into the side and I saw a frantically waving arm. I pulled up and a young man jumped from the driving seat and ran towards me.

He pushed his head in at the window. 'Are you the vet?' His voice was breathless, panic-stricken.

'Yes, I am.'

'Oh thank God! We're passing through on the way to Manchester and we've been to your surgery . . . they said you were out this way . . . described your car. Please help us!'

'What's the trouble?'

'It's our dog . . . in the back of the car. He's got a ball stuck in his throat. I . . . I think he might be dead.'

I was out of my seat and running along the road before he had finished. It was a big white saloon and in the darkness of the back seat of a wailing chorus issued from several little heads silhouetted against the glass.

I tore open the door and the wailing took on words.

'Oh Benny, Benny, Benny . . . !'

I dimly discerned a large dog spread over the knees of four small children. 'Oh Daddy, he's dead, he's dead!'

'Let's have him out,' I gasped, and as the young man pulled on the forelegs I supported the body, which slid and toppled on to the tarmac with a horrible limpness.

I pawed at the hairy form. 'I can't see a bloody thing! Help me pull him round.'

We dragged the unresisting bulk into the headlights' glare and I could see it all. A huge, beautiful collie in his luxuriant prime, mouth gaping, tongue lolling, eyes staring lifelessly at nothing. He wasn't breathing.

The young father took one look then gripped his head with both hands. 'Oh God, oh God. . . .' From within the car I heard the quiet sobbing of his wife and the piercing cries from the back. 'Benny . . . Benny. . . .'

I grabbed the man's shoulder and shouted at him. 'What did you say about a ball?'

'It's in his throat . . . I've had my fingers in his mouth for ages but I couldn't move it.' The words came mumbling up from beneath the bent head.

I pushed my hand into the mouth and I could feel it all right. A sphere of hard solid rubber not much bigger than a golf ball and jammed like a cork in the pharynx, effectively blocking the trachea. I scrabbled feverishly at the wet smoothness but there was nothing to get hold of. It took me about three seconds to realise that no human agency would ever get the ball out that way and without thinking I withdrew my hands, braced both thumbs behind the angle of the lower jaw and pushed.

The ball shot forth, bounced on the frosty road and rolled sadly on to the grass verge. I touched the corneal surface of the eye. No reflex. I slumped to my knees, burdened by the hopeless regret that I hadn't had the chance to do this just a bit sooner. The only function I could perform now was to take the body back to Skeldale House for disposal. I couldn't allow the family to drive to Manchester with a dead dog. But I wished fervently that I had been able to do more, and as I passed my hand along the richly coloured coat over the ribs the vast bandaged finger stood out like a symbol of my helplessness.

It was when I was gazing dully at the finger, the heel of my hand resting in an intercostal space, that I felt the faintest flutter from below.

I jerked upright with a hoarse cry. 'His heart's still beating! He's not gone yet!' I began to work on the dog with all I had. And out there in the darkness of that lonely country road it wasn't much. No stimulant injections, no oxygen cylinders or intratracheal tubes. But I depressed his chest with my palms every three seconds in the old-fashioned way, willing the dog to breathe as the eyes still stared at nothing. Every now and then I blew desperately down the throat or probed between the ribs for that almost imperceptible beat.

I don't know which I noticed first, the slight twitch of an eyelid or the small lift of the ribs which pulled the icy Yorkshire air into his lungs. Maybe they both happened at once but from that moment everything was dreamlike and wonderful. I lost count of time as I sat there while the breathing became deep and regular and the animal began to be aware of his surroundings; and by the time he started to look around him and twitch his tail tentatively I realised suddenly that I was stiff-jointed and almost frozen to the spot.

With some difficulty I got up and watched in disbelief as the collie staggered to his feet. The young father ushered him round to the back where he was received with screams of delight.

The man seemed stunned. Throughout the recovery he had kept muttering, 'You just flicked that ball out . . . just flicked it out. Why didn't I think of that . . . ?' And when he turned to me before leaving he appeared to be still in a state of shock.

'I don't . . . I don't know how to thank you,' he said huskily. 'It's a miracle.' He leaned against the car for a second. 'And now what is your fee? How much do I owe you?'

I rubbed my chin. I had used no drugs. The only expenditure had been time.

'Five bob,' I said. 'And never let him play with such a little ball again.'

He handed the money over, shook my hand and drove away. His wife, who had never left her place, waved as she left, but my greatest reward was in the last shadowy glimpse of the back seat where little arms twined around the dog, hugging him ecstatically, and in the cries, thankful and joyous, fading into the night.

'Benny . . . Benny . . . Benny. . . .''

Vets often wonder after a patient's recovery just how much credit they might take. Maybe it would have got better without treatment—it happened sometimes; it was difficult to be sure.

But when you know without a shadow of a doubt that, even without doing anything clever, you have pulled an animal back from the brink of death into the living, breathing world, it is a satisfaction which lingers, flowing like balm over the discomforts and frustrations of veterinary practice, making everything right.

Yet, in the case of Benny the whole thing had an unreal quality. I never even glimpsed the faces of those happy children nor that of their mother huddled in the front seat. I had a vague impression of their father but he had spent most of the time with his head in his hands. I wouldn't have known him if I met him in the street. Even the dog, in the unnatural glare of the headlights, was a blurred memory.

It seemed the family had the same feeling because a week later I had a pleasant letter from the mother. She apologised for skulking out of the way so shamelessly, she thanked me for saving the life of their beloved dog who was now prancing around with the children as though nothing had happened, and she finished with the regret that she hadn't even asked me my name.

Yes, it had been a strange episode, and not only were those people unaware of my name but I'd like to bet they would fail to recognise me if they saw me again.

In fact, looking back at the affair, the only thing which stood out unequivocal and substantial was my great white-bound digit which had hovered constantly over the scene, almost taking on a personality and significance of its own. I am sure that is what the family remembered best about me because of the way the mother's letter began.

'Dear Vet with the bandaged finger . . .'

8

My stint in London was nearing its end. Our breaking-in weeks were nearly over and we waited for news of posting to Initial Training Wing.

The air was thick with rumours. We were going to Aberystwyth in Wales; too far away for me, I wanted the north. Then we were going to Newquay in Cornwall; worse still. I was aware that the impending birth of AC2 Herriot's child did not influence the general war strategy but I still wanted to be as near to Helen as possible at the time.

The whole London phase is blurred in my memory. Possibly because everything was so new and different that the impressions could not be fully absorbed, and also perhaps because I was tired most of the time. I think we were all tired. Few of us were used to being jerked from slumber at 6 a.m. every morning and spending the day in continual physical activity. If we weren't being drilled we were being marched to meals, to classes, to talks. I had lived in a motor car for a few years and the rediscovery of my legs was painful.

There were times, too, when I wondered what it was all about. Like all the other young men I had imagined that after a few brisk preliminaries I would be sitting in an aeroplane, learning to fly, but it turned out that this was so far in the future that it was hardly mentioned. At the ITW we would spend months learning navigation, principles of flight, morse and many other things.

I was thankful for one blessing. I had passed the mathematics exam. I have always counted on my fingers and still do and I had been so nervous about this that I went to classes with the ATC in Darrowby before my call-up, dredging from my schooldays horrific calculations about trains passing each other at different speeds and water running in and out of bath tubs. But I had managed to scrape through and felt ready to face anything.

There were some unexpected shocks in London. I didn't anticipate spending days mucking out some of the dirtiest piggeries I had ever seen. Somebody must have had the idea of converting all the RAF waste food into pork and bacon and of course there was plenty of labour at hand. I had a strong feeling of unreality as, with other aspiring pilots, I threw muck and swill around hour after hour.

My disenchantment was happily blotted from my mind the day we received news of the posting. It seemed too good to be true—I was going to Scarborough. I had been there and I knew it was a beautiful seaside resort, but that wasn't why I was so delighted. It was because it was in Yorkshire.

As we marched out of the station into the streets of Scarborough I could hardly believe I was back in my home county. But if there had been any doubt in my mind it would have been immediately resolved by my first breath of the crisp, tangy air. Even in winter there had been no 'feel' to the soft London air and I half closed my eyes as I followed the tingle all the way down to my lungs.

Mind you, it was cold. Yorkshire is a cold place and I could remember the sensation almost of shock at the start of my first winter in Darrowby.

It was after the first snow and I followed the clanging ploughs up the Dale, bumping along between high white mounds till I reached old Mr Stokill's gate. With my fingers on the handle I looked through the glass at the new world beneath me. The white blanket rolled down the hillside and lapped over the roofs of the dwelling and outbuildings of the little farm. Beyond, it smoothed out and concealed the familiar features, the stone walls bordering the fields, the stream on the valley floor, turning the whole scene into something unknown and exciting.

But the thrill I felt at the strange beauty was swept away as I got out and the wind struck me. It was an Arctic blast screaming from the east, picking up extra degrees of cold as it drove over the frozen white surface. I was wearing a heavy overcoat and woollen gloves but the gust whipped its way right into my bones. I gasped and leaned my back against the car while I buttoned the coat up under my chin, then I struggled forward to where the gate shook and rattled. I fought it open and my feet crunched as I went through.

Coming round the corner of the byre I found Mr Stokill forking muck on to a heap, making a churned brown trail across the whiteness.

'Now then,' he muttered along the side of a half-smoked cigarette. He was over seventy but still ran the smallholding single-handed. He told me once that he had worked as a farm hand for six shillings a day for thirty years, yet still managed to save enough to buy his own little place. Maybe that was why he didn't want to share it.

'How are you, Mr Stokill?' I said, but just then the wind tore through the yard, clutching icily at my face, snatching my breath away so that I turned involuntarily to one side with an explosive 'Aaahh!'

The old farmer looked at me in surprise, then glanced around as though he had just noticed the weather.

'Aye, blows a bit thin this mornin', lad.' Sparks flew from the end of his cigarette as he leaned for a moment on the fork.

He didn't seem to have much protection against the cold. A light khaki smock fluttered over a ragged navy waistcoat, clearly once part of his best suit, and his shirt bore neither collar nor stud. The white stubble on his fleshless jaw was a reproach to my twenty-four years and suddenly I felt an inadequate city-bred softie.

The old man dug his fork into the manure pile and turned towards the buildings. 'Ah've got a nice few cases for ye to see today. Fust 'un's in 'ere.' He opened a door and I staggered gratefully into a sweet bovine warmth where a few shaggy little bullocks stood hock deep in straw.

'That's the youth we want.' He pointed to a dark roan standing with one hind foot knuckled over. 'He's been on three legs for a couple o' days. Ah reckon he's got foul.'

I walked up to the little animal but he took off at a speed which made light of his infirmity.

'We'll have to run him into the passage. Mr Stokill,' I said. 'Just open the gate, will you?'

With the rough timbers pushed wide I got behind the bullock and sent him on to the opening. It seemed as though he was going straight through but at the entrance he stopped, peeped into the passage and broke away. I galloped a few times round the yard after him, then had another go. The result was the same. After half a dozen tries I wasn't cold any more. I'll back chasing young cattle against anything else for working up a sweat, and I had already forgotten the uncharitable world outside. And I could see I was going to get warmer still because the bullock was beginning to enjoy the game, kicking up his heels and frisking around after each attempt.

I put my hands on my hips, waited till I got my breath back then turned to the farmer.

'This is hopeless. He'll never go in there,' I said. 'We'd maybe better try to get a rope on him.'

'Nay, lad, there's no need for that. We'll get him through t'gate right enough.' The old man ambled to one end of the yard and returned with an armful of clean straw. He sprinkled it freely in the gate opening and beyond in the passage, then turned to me. 'Now send 'im on.'

I poked a finger into the animal's rump and he trotted forward, proceeded unhesitatingly between the posts and into the passage.

Mr Stokill must have noticed my look of bewilderment.

'Aye, 'e just didn't like t'look of them cobbles. Once they was covered over he was awright.'

'Yes . . . yes . . . I see.' I followed the bullock slowly through.

He was indeed suffering from foul of the foot, the mediaeval term given because of the stink of the necrotic tissue between the cleats, and I didn't have any antibiotics or sulphonamides to treat it. It is so nice and easy these days to give an injection, knowing that the beast will be sound in a day or two. But all I could do was wrestle with the lunging hind foot, dressing the infected cleft with a crude mixture of copper sulphate and Stockholm tar and finishing with a pad of cotton wool held by a tight bandage. When I had finished I took off my coat and hung it on a nail. I didn't need it any more.

Mr Stokill looked approvingly at the finished job. 'Capital, capital,' he murmured. 'Now there's some little pigs in this pen got a bit o' scour. I want you give 'em a jab wi' your needle.'

We had various *E coli* vaccines which sometimes did a bit of good in these cases and I entered the pen hopefully. But

I left in a hurry because the piglets' mother didn't approve of a stranger wandering among her brood and she came at me open-mouthed, barking explosively. She looked as big as a donkey and when the cavernous jaws with the great yellowed teeth brushed my thigh I knew it was time to go. I hopped rapidly into the yard and crashed the door behind me.

I peered back ruminatively into the pen. 'We'll have to get her out of there before I can do anything, Mr Stokill.'

'Aye, you're right, young man, ah'll shift 'er.' He began to shuffle away.

I held up a hand. 'No, it's all right, I'll do it.' I couldn't let this frail old man go in there and maybe get knocked down and savaged, and I looked around for a means of protection. There was a battered shovel standing against a wall and I seized it.

'Open the door, please,' I said. 'I'll soon have her out.'

Once more inside the pen I held the shovel in front of me and tried to usher the huge sow towards the door. But my efforts at poking her rear end were fruitless; she faced me all the time, wide-mouthed and growling as I circled. When she got the blade of the shovel between her teeth and began to worry it I called a halt.

As I left the pen I saw Mr Stokill dragging a large object over the cobbles.

'What's that?' I asked.

'Dustbin,' the old man grunted in reply.

'Dustbin! What on earth . . . ?'

He gave no further explanation but entered the pen. As the sow came at him he allowed her to run her head into the bin then, bent double, he began to back her towards the open door. The animal was clearly baffled. Suddenly finding herself in this strange dark place she naturally tried to retreat from it and all the farmer did was guide her.

Before she knew what was happening she was out in the yard. The old man calmly removed the bin and beckoned to me. 'Right you are, Mr Herriot, you can get on now.'

It had taken about twenty seconds.

Well, that was a relief, and anyway I knew what to do next. Lifting a sheet of corrugated iron which the farmer had ready

I rushed in among the little pigs. I would pen them in a corner and the job would be over in no time.

But their mother's irritation had been communicated to the family. It was a big litter and there were sixteen of them hurtling around like little pink racehorses. I spent a long time diving frantically after them, jamming the sheet at a bunch only to see half of them streaking out the other end, and I might have gone on indefinitely had I not felt a gentle touch on my arm.

'Haud on, young man, haud on.' The old farmer looked at me kindly. 'If you'll nobbut stop runnin' after 'em they'll settle down. Just bide a minute.'

Slightly breathless, I stood by his side and listened as he addressed the little creatures.

'Giss-giss, giss-giss,' murmured Mr Stokill without moving. 'Giss-giss, giss-giss.'

The piglets slowed their headlong gallop to a trot, then, as though controlled by telepathy, they all stopped at once and stood in a pink group in one corner.

'Giss-giss,' said Mr. Stokill approvingly, advancing almost imperceptibly with the sheet. 'Giss-giss.'

He unhurriedly placed the length of metal across the corner and jammed his foot against the bottom.

'Now then, put the toe of your wellington against t'other end and we' ave' em,' he said quietly.

After that the injection of the litter was a matter of a few minutes. Mr Stokill didn't say, 'Well, I'm teaching you a thing or two today, am I not?' There was no hint of triumph or self-congratulation in the calm old eyes. All he said was, 'I'm keepin' you busy this mornin', young man. I want you to look at a cow now. She's got a pea in her tit.'

'Peas' and other obstructions in the teats were very common in the days of hand milking. Some of them were floating milk calculi, others tiny pedunculated tumours, injuries to the teat lining, all sorts of things. It was a whole diverting little field in itself and I approached the cow with interest.

But I didn't get very near before Mr Stokill put his hand on my shoulder.

'Just a minute, Mr Herriot, don't touch 'er tit yet or she'll clout ye. She's an awd bitch. Wait a minute till ah rope 'er.'

'Oh right,' I said. 'But I'll do it.'

He hesitated. 'Ah reckon I ought to . . .'

'No, no, Mr Stokill, that's quite unnecessary, I know how to stop a cow kicking,' I said primly. 'Kindly hand me that rope.'

'But . . . she's a bugger . . . kicks like a 'oss. She's a right good milker but . . .'

'Don't worry,' I said, smiling. 'I'll stop her little games.'

I began to unwind the rope. It was good to be able to demonstrate that I did know something about handling animals even though I had been qualified for only a few months. And it made a change to be told before and not after the job that a cow was a kicker. A cow once kicked me nearly to the other end of the byre and as I picked myself up the farmer said unemotionally, 'Aye, she's allus had a habit o' that.'

Yes, it was nice to be warned, and I passed the rope round the animal's body in front of the udder and pulled it tight in a slip knot. Just like they taught us at college. She was a scrawny red shorthorn with a woolly poll and she regarded me with a contemplative eye as I bent down.

'All right, lass,' I said soothingly, reaching under her and gently grasping the teat. I squirted a few jets of milk then something blocked the end. Ah yes, there it was, quite large and unattached. I felt sure I could work it through the orifice without cutting the sphincter.

I took a firmer grip, squeezed tightly and immediately a cloven foot shot out like a whip lash and smacked me solidly on the knee. It is a particularly painful spot to be kicked and I spent some time hopping round the byre and cursing in a fervent whisper.

The farmer followed me anxiously. 'Ee, ah'm sorry, Mr Herriot, she's a right awd bugger. Better let me . . .'

I held up a hand. 'No, Mr Stokill. I already have her roped. I just didn't tie it tight enough, that's all.' I hobbled back to the animal, loosened the knot then retied it, pulling till my eyes popped. When I had finished, her abdomen was lifted high and nipped in like a wasp-waisted Victorian lady of fashion.

'That'll fix you,' I grunted, and bent to my work again. A few spurts of milk then the thing was at the teat end again, a pinkish-white object peeping through the orifice. A little extra pressure and I would be able to fish it out with the hypodermic needle I had poised ready. I took a breath and gripped hard.

This time the hoof caught me half way up the shin bone. She hadn't been able to get so much height into it but it was just as painful. I sat down on a milk stool, rolled up my trouser leg and examined the roll of skin which hung like a diploma at the end of a long graze where the sharp hoof had dragged along.

'Now then, you've 'ad enough, young man.' Mr Stokill removed my rope and gazed at me with commiseration. 'Ordinary methods don't work with this 'un. I 'ave to milk her twice a day and ah knaw.'

He fetched a soiled length of plough cord which had obviously seen much service and fastened it round the cow's hock. The other end had a hook which he fitted into a ring on the byre wall. It was just the right length to stretch taut, pulling the leg slightly back.

The old man nodded. 'Now try.'

With a feeling of fatalism I grasped the teat again. And it was as if the cow knew she was beaten. She never moved as I nipped hard and winkled out the offending obstruction—a milk calculus. She couldn't do a thing about it.

'Ah, thank ye, lad,' the farmer said. 'That's champion. Been bothering me a bit has that. Didn't know what it was.' He held up a finger. 'One last job for ye. A young heifer with a bit o' stomach trouble, ah think. Saw her last night and she was a bit blown. She's in an outside buildin'.'

I put on my coat and we went out to where the wind welcomed us with savage glee. As the knife-like blast hit me, whistling up my nose and making my eyes water, I cowered in the lee of the stable.

'Where is this heifer?' I gasped.

Mr Stokill did not reply immediately. He was lighting another cigarette, apparently oblivious of the elements. He clamped the lid on an ancient brass lighter and jerked his thumb.

'Across the road. Up there.'

I followed his gesture over the buried walls, across the narrow roadway between the ploughed-out snow dunes to where the fell rose steeply in a sweep of unbroken white to join the leaden sky. Unbroken, that is, except for a tiny barn, a grey stone speck just visible on the last airy swell hundreds of feet up where the hillside joined the moorland above.

'Sorry,' I said, still crouching against the wall. 'I can't see anything.'

The old man, lounging in the teeth of the wind, looked at me in surprise. 'You can't? Why, t'barn's good enough to see, isn't it?'

'The barn?' I pointed a shaking finger at the heights. 'You mean that building? The heifer's surely not in there!'

'Aye, she is. Ah keep a lot o' me young beasts in them spots.'

'But . . . but . . .' I was gabbling now. 'We'll never get up there! That snow's three feet deep!'

He blew smoke pleasurably from his nostrils. 'We will, don't tha worry. Just hang on a second.'

He disappeared into the stable and after a few moments I peeped inside. He was saddling a fat brown cob and I stared as he led the little animal out, climbed stiffly on to a box and mounted.

Looking down at me he waved cheerfully. 'Well, let's be goin'. Have you got your stuff?'

Bewilderedly I filled my pockets. A bottle of bloat mixture, a trochar and cannula, a packet of gentian and nux vomica. I did it in the dull knowledge that there was no way I could get up that hill.

On the other side of the road an opening had been dug and Mr Stokill rode through. I slithered in his wake, looking up hopelessly at the great smooth wilderness rearing above us.

Mr Stokill turned in the saddle. 'Get haud on t'tail,' he said.

'I beg your pardon?'

'Get a haud of 'is tail.'

As in a dream I seized the bristly hairs.

'No, both 'ands,' the farmer said patiently.

'Like this?'

'That's grand, lad. Now 'ang on.'

He clicked his tongue, the cob plodded resolutely forward and so did I.

And it was easy! The whole world fell away beneath us as we soared upwards, and leaning back and enjoying it I watched the little valley unfold along its twisting length until I could see away into the main Dale with the great hills billowing round and white into the dark clouds.

At the barn the farmer dismounted. 'All right, young man?'

'All right, Mr Stokill.' As I followed him into the little building I smiled to myself. This old man had once told me that he left school when he was twelve, whereas I had spent most of the twenty-four years of my life in study. Yet when I looked back on the last hour or so I could come to only one conclusion.

I'd had more of books, but he had more of learning.

9

I had plenty of company for Christmas that year. We were billeted in the Grand Hotel, the massive Victorian pile which dominated Scarborough in turreted splendour from its eminence above the sea, and the big dining room was packed with several hundred shouting airmen. The iron discipline was relaxed for a few hours to let the Yuletide spirit run free.

It was so different from other Christmases I had known that it ought to have remained like a beacon in my mind, but I know that my strongest memory of Christmas will always be bound up with a certain little cat.

I first saw her one autumn day when I was called to see one of Mrs Ainsworth's dogs, and I looked in some surprise at the furry black creature sitting before the fire.

'I didn't know you had a cat,' I said.

The lady smiled. 'We haven't, this is Debbie.'

'Debbie?'

'Yes, at least that's what we call her. She's a stray. Comes here two or three times a week and we give her some food. I don't know where she lives but I believe she spends a lot of her time around one of the farms along the road.'

'Do you ever get the feeling that she wants to stay with you?'

'No.' Mrs Ainsworth shook her head. 'She's a timid little thing. Just creeps in, has some food then flits away. There's something so appealing about her but she doesn't seem to want to let me or anybody into her life.'

I looked again at the little cat. 'But she isn't just having food today.'

'That's right. It's a funny thing but every now and again she slips through here into the lounge and sits by the fire for a few minutes. It's as though she was giving herself a treat.'

'Yes . . . I see what you mean.' There was no doubt there

was something unusual in the attitude of the little animal. She was sitting bolt upright on the thick rug which lay before the fireplace in which the coals glowed and flamed. She made no effort to curl up or wash herself or do anything other than gaze quietly ahead. And there was something in the dusty black of her coat, the half-wild scrawny look of her, that gave me a clue. This was a special event in her life, a rare and wonderful thing; she was lapping up a comfort undreamed of in her daily existence.

As I watched she turned, crept soundlessly from the room and was gone.

'That's always the way with Debbie,' Mrs Ainsworth laughed. 'She never stays more than ten minutes or so, then she's off.'

Mrs Ainsworth was a plumpish, pleasant-faced woman in her forties and the kind of client veterinary surgeons dream of; well off, generous, and the owner of three cosseted Basset hounds. And it only needed the habitually mournful expression of one of the dogs to deepen a little and I was round there post haste. Today one of the Bassets had raised its paw and scratched its ear a couple of times and that was enough to send its mistress scurrying to the 'phone in great alarm.

So my visits to the Ainsworth home were frequent but undemanding, and I had ample opportunity to look out for the little cat that had intrigued me. On one occasion I spotted her nibbling daintily from a saucer at the kitchen door. As I watched she turned and almost floated on light footsteps into the hall then through the lounge door.

The three Bassets were already in residence, draped snoring on the fireside rug, but they seemed to be used to Debbie because two of them sniffed her in a bored manner and the third merely cocked a sleepy eye at her before flopping back on the rich pile.

Debbie sat among them in her usual posture; upright, intent, gazing absorbedly into the glowing coals. This time I tried to make friends with her. I approached her carefully but she leaned away as I stretched out my hand. However, by patient wheedling and soft talk I managed to touch her and gently stroked her cheek with one finger. There was a moment when she responded by putting her head on one side and rubbing back against my hand but soon she was ready to leave. Once outside the house she darted quickly along the road then through a gap in a hedge and the last I saw was the little black figure flitting over the rain-swept grass of a field.

'I wonder where she goes,' I murmured half to myself.

Mrs. Ainsworth appeared at my elbow. 'That's something we've never been able to find out.'

It must have been nearly three months before I heard from Mrs. Ainsworth, and in fact I had begun to wonder at the Bassets' long symptomless run when she came on the 'phone.

It was Christmas morning and she was apologetic, 'Mr Herriot, I'm so sorry to bother you today of all days. I should think you want a rest at Christmas like anybody else.' But her natural politeness could not hide the distress in her voice.

'Please don't worry about that,' I said. 'Which one is it this time?'

'It's not one of the dogs. It's . . . Debbie.'

'Debbie? She's at your house now?'

'Yes . . . but there's something wrong. Please come quickly.'

Driving through the market place I thought again that Darrowby on Christmas Day was like Dickens come to life; the empty square with the snow thick on the cobbles and hanging from the eaves of the fretted lines of roofs; the shops closed and the coloured lights of the Christmas trees winking at the windows of the clustering houses, warmly inviting against the cold white bulk of the fells behind.

Mrs Ainsworth's home was lavishly decorated with tinsel and holly, rows of drinks stood on the sideboard and the rich aroma of turkey and sage and onion stuffing wafted from the kitchen. But her eyes were full of pain as she led me through to the lounge.

Debbie was there all right, but this time everything was different. She wasn't sitting upright in her usual position; she was stretched quite motionless on her side, and huddled close to her lay a tiny black kitten.

I looked down in bewilderment. 'What's happened here?'

'It's the strangest thing,' Mrs Ainsworth replied. 'I haven't seen her for several weeks then she came in about two hours ago —sort of staggered into the kitchen, and she was carrying the kitten in her mouth. She took it through to the lounge and laid it on the rug and at first I was amused. But I could see all was not well because she sat as she usually does, but for a long time—over an hour—then she lay down like this and she hasn't moved.'

I knelt on the rug and passed my hand over Debbie's neck and ribs. She was thinner than ever, her fur dirty and mudcaked. She did not resist as I gently opened her mouth. The tongue and mucous membranes were abnormally pale and the lips ice-cold against my fingers. When I pulled down her eyelid and saw the dead white conjunctiva a knell sounded in my mind.

I palpated the abdomen with a grim certainty as to what I would find and there was no surprise, only a dull sadness as my fingers closed around a hard lobulated mass deep among the viscera. Massive lymphosarcoma. Terminal and hopeless. I put my stethoscope on her heart and listened to the increasingly faint, rapid beat then I straightened up and sat on the rug looking sightlessly into the fireplace, feeling the warmth of the flames on my face.

Mrs Ainsworth's voice seemed to come from afar. 'Is she ill, Mr Herriot?'

I hesitated. 'Yes . . . yes, I'm afraid so. She has a malignant growth.' I stood up. 'There's absolutely nothing I can do. I'm sorry.'

'Oh!' Her hand went to her mouth and she looked at me wide-eyed. When at last she spoke her voice trembled. 'Well. you must put her to sleep immediately. It's the only thing to do. We can't let her suffer.'

'Mrs Ainsworth,' I said. 'There's no need. She's dying now—in a coma—far beyond suffering.'

She turned quickly away from me and was very still as she fought with her emotions. Then she gave up the struggle and dropped on her knees beside Debbie.

'Oh, poor little thing!' she sobbed and stroked the cat's head again and again as the tears fell unchecked on the matted fur. 'What she must have come through. I feel I ought to have done more for her.'

For a few moments I was silent, feeling her sorrow, so discordant among the bright seasonal colours of this festive room. Then I spoke gently.

'Nobody could have done more than you,' I said. 'Nobody could have been kinder.'

'But I'd have kept her here—in comfort. It must have been

terrible out there in the cold when she was so desperately ill—
I daren't think about it. And having kittens, too—I . . . I wonder how many she did have?'

I shrugged. 'I don't suppose we'll ever know. Maybe just this
one. It happens sometimes. And she brought it to you, didn't
she?'

'Yes . . . that's right . . . she did . . . she did.' Mrs
Ainsworth reached out and lifted the bedraggled black morsel.
She smoothed her finger along the muddy fur and the tiny mouth
opened in a soundless miaow. 'Isn't it strange? She was dying and
she brought her kitten here. And on Christmas Day.'

I bent and put my hand on Debbie's heart. There was no beat.

I looked up. 'I'm afraid she's gone.' I lifted the small body,
almost feather light, wrapped it in the sheet which had been
spread on the rug and took it out to the car.

When I came back Mrs Ainsworth was still stroking the kitten. The tears had dried on her cheeks and she was brighteyed
as she looked at me.

'I've never had a cat before,' she said.

I smiled. 'Well it looks as though you've got one now.'

And she certainly had. That kitten grew rapidly into a sleek
handsome cat with a boisterous nature which earned him the
name of Buster. In every way he was the opposite to his timid
little mother. Not for him the privations of the secret outdoor
life; he stalked the rich carpets of the Ainsworth home like a
king and the ornate collar he always wore added something
more to his presence.

On my visits I watched his development with delight but the
occasion which stays in my mind was the following Christmas
Day, a year from his arrival.

I was out on my rounds as usual. I can't remember when I
haven't had to work on Christmas Day because the animals
have never got round to recognising it as a holiday; but with
the passage of the years the vague resentment I used to feel has
been replaced by philosophical acceptance. After all, as I tramped
around the hillside barns in the frosty air I was working up a
better appetite for my turkey than all the millions lying in bed
or slumped by the fire; and this was aided by the innumerable
aperitifs I received from the hospitable farmers.

I was on my way home, bathed in a rosy glow. I had consumed

several whiskies—the kind the inexpert Yorkshiremen pour as though it was ginger ale—and I had finished with a glass of old Mrs Earnshaw's rhubarb wine which had seared its way straight to my toenails. I heard the cry as I was passing Mrs Ainsworth's house.

'Merry Christmas, Mr Herriot!' She was letting a visitor out of the front door and she waved at me gaily. 'Come in and have a drink to warm you up.'

I didn't need warming up but I pulled in to the kerb without hesitation. In the house there was all the festive cheer of last year and the same glorious whiff of sage and onion which set my gastric juices surging. But there was not the sorrow; there was Buster.

He was darting up to each of the dogs in turn, ears pricked, eyes blazing with devilment, dabbing a paw at them then streaking away.

Mrs Ainsworth laughed. 'You know, he plagues the life out of them. Gives them no peace.'

She was right. To the Bassets, Buster's arrival was rather like the intrusion of an irreverent outsider into an exclusive London club. For a long time they had led a life of measured grace; regular sedate walks with their mistress, superb food in ample quantities and long snoring sessions on the rugs and armchairs. Their days followed one upon another in unruffled calm. And then came Buster.

He was dancing up to the youngest dog again, sideways this time, head on one side, goading him. When he started boxing with both paws it was too much even for the Basset. He dropped his dignity and rolled over with the cat in a brief wrestling match.

'I want to show you something.' Mrs Ainsworth lifted a hard rubber ball from the sideboard and went out to the garden, followed by Buster. She threw the ball across the lawn and the cat bounded after it over the frosted grass, the muscles rippling under the black sheen of his coat. He seized the ball in his teeth, brought it back to his mistress, dropped it at her feet and waited expectantly. She threw it and he brought it back again.

I gasped incredulously. A feline retriever!

The Bassets looked on disdainfully. Nothing would ever have induced them to chase a ball, but Buster did it again and again as though he would never tire of it.

Mrs Ainsworth turned to me. 'Have you every seen anything like that?'

'No,' I replied. 'I never have. He is a most remarkable cat.'

She snatched Buster from his play and we went back into the house where she held him close to her face, laughing as the big cat purred and arched himself ecstatically against her cheek.

Looking at him, a picture of health and contentment, my mind went back to his mother. Was it too much to think that that dying little creature with the last of her strength had carried her kitten to the only haven of comfort and warmth she had ever known in the hope that it would be cared for there? Maybe it was.

But it seemed I wasn't the only one with such fancies. Mrs Ainsworth turned to me and though she was smiling her eyes were wistful.

'Debbie would be pleased," she said.

I nodded. 'Yes, she would. . . . It was just a year ago today she brought him, wasn't it?'

'That's right.' She hugged Buster to her again. 'The best Christmas present I ever had.'

10

I stared in disbelief at the dial of the weighing machine. Nine stone seven pounds! I had lost two stones since joining the RAF. I was cowering in my usual corner in Boots' Chemist's shop in Scarborough, where I had developed the habit of a weekly weigh-in to keep a morbid eye on my progressive emaciation. It was incredible and it wasn't all due to the tough training.

On our arrival in Scarborough we had a talk from our Flight Commander, Flt Lieut Barnes. He looked us over with a contemplative eye and said, 'You won't know yourselves when you leave here.' That man knew what he was talking about.

We were never at rest. It was PT and Drill, PT and Drill, over and over. Hours of bending and stretching and twisting down on the prom in singlets and shorts while the wind whipped over us from the wintry sea. Hours of marching under the bellowings of our sergeant; quick march, slow march, about turn. We even marched to our navigation classes, bustling along at the RAF quick time, arms swinging shoulder high.

They marched us regularly to the top of Castle Hill where we fired off every conceivable type of weapon; twelve bores, .22 rifles, revolvers, Browning machine guns. We even stabbed at dummies with bayonets. In between they had us swimming, playing football or rugby or running for miles along the beach and on the cliff tops towards Filey.

At first I was too busy to see any change in myself, but one morning after a few weeks our flight was coming to the end of a five-mile run. We dropped down from the Spa to a long stretch of empty beach and the sergeant shouted, 'Right, sprint to those rocks! Let's see who gets there first!'

We all took off on the last hundred yards' dash and I was mildly surprised to find that the first man past the post was myself—and I wasn't really out of breath. That was when the realisation hit me. Mr Barnes had been right. I didn't know myself.

When I left Helen I was a cosseted young husband with a little double chin and the beginnings of a spare tyre, and now I was a lithe, tireless greyhound. I was certainly fit, but there was something wrong. I shouldn't have been as thin as this. Another factor was at work.

In Yorkshire when a man goes into a decline during his wife's pregnancy they giggle behind their hands and say he is 'carrying' the baby. I never laugh at these remarks because I am convinced I 'carried' my son.

I base this conclusion on a variety of symptoms. It would be an exaggeration to say I suffered from morning sickness, but my suspicions were certainly aroused when I began to feel a little queasy in the early part of the day. This was followed by a growing uneasiness as Helen's time drew near and a sensation, despite my physical condition, of being drained and miserable. With the onset in the later stages of unmistakable labour pains in my lower abdomen all doubts were resolved and I knew I had to do something about it.

I had to see Helen. After all, she was just over that hill which I could see from the top windows of the Grand. Maybe that wasn't strictly true, but at least I was in Yorkshire and a bus would take me to her in three hours. The snag was that there was no leave from ITW. They left us in no doubt about that. They said the discipline was as tough as a Guards regiment and the restrictions just as rigid. I would get compassionate leave when the baby was born, but I couldn't wait till then. The grim knowledge that any attempt to dodge off unofficially would be like a minor desertion and would be followed by serious consequences, even prison, didn't weigh with me.

As one of my comrades put it: 'One bloke tried it and finished up in the Glasshouse. It isn't worth it, mate.'

But it was no good. I am normally a law-abiding citizen but I had not a single scruple. I had to see Helen. A surreptitious study of the timetables revealed that here was a bus at 2 p.m. which got to Darrowby at five o'clock, and another leaving Darrowby at six which arrived in Scarborough at nine. Six hours travelling to have one hour with Helen. It was worth it.

At first I couldn't see a way of getting to the bus station at two o'clock in the afternoon because we were never free at that time, but my chance came quite unexpectedly. One Friday lunchtime we learned that there were no more classes that day but we were confined to the Grand till evening. Most of my friends collapsed thankfully on to their beds, but I slunk down the long flights of stone stairs and took up a position in the foyer where I could watch the front door.

There was a glass-fronted office on one side of the entrance where the SPs sat and kept an eye on all departures. There was only one on duty today and I waited till he turned and moved to the back of the room then I walked quietly past him and out into the square.

That part had been almost too easy, but I felt naked and exposed as I crossed the deserted space between the Grand and the hotels on the opposite side. It was better once I had rounded the corner and I set off at a brisk pace for the west. All I needed was a little bit of luck and as I pressed, dry-mouthed, along the empty street it seemed I had found it. The shock when I saw the two burly SPs strolling towards me was like a blow but was immediately followed by a strange calm.

They would ask me for the pass I didn't have, then they would want to know what I was doing there. It wouldn't be much good telling them I had just popped out for a breath of air—this street led to both the bus and railway stations and it wouldn't need a genius to rumble my little game. Anyway, there was no cover here, no escape, and I wondered idly if there had ever been a veterinary surgeon in the Glasshouse. Maybe I was about to set up some kind of a record.

Then behind me I heard the rhythmic tramp of marching feet and the shrill "eft 'ight, 'eft, 'ight,' that usually went with it. I turned and saw a long blue column approaching with a corporal in charge. As they swung past me I looked again at the SPs and my heart gave a thud. They were laughing into each other's faces at some private joke; they hadn't seen me. Without thinking I tagged on to the end of the marching men and within a few seconds was past the SPs unnoticed.

With my mind working with the speed of desperation, it seemed I would be safest where I was till I could break away in the direction of the bus station. For a while I had a glorious feeling of anonymity then the corporal, still shouting, glanced back. He faced to the front again then turned back more slowly for another look. He appeared to find something interesting because he shortened his stride till he was marching opposite me.

As he looked me up and down I examined him in turn from the corner of my eye. He was a shrivelled, runtish creature with fierce little eyes glinting from a pallid, skull-like face. It was some time before he spoke.

'Who the——hell are you?' he enquired conversationally. It was the number one awkward question but I discerned the faintest gleam of hope; he had spoken in the unmistakable harsh, glottal accent of my home town.

'Herriot, corporal. Two flight, four squadron,' I replied in my broadest Glasgow.

'Two flight, four . . . ! This is one flight, three squadron. What the——hell are ye daein' here?'

Arms swinging high, staring rigidly ahead, I took a deep breath. Concealment was futile now.

'Tryin' to get tae see ma wife, corp. She's havin' a baby soon.'

I glanced quickly at him. His was not the kind of face to reveal weakness by showing surprise but his eyes widened fractionally. 'Get tae see yer wife? Are ye——daft or whit?'

'It's no' far, corp. She lives in Darrowby. Three hours in the bus. Ah wid be back tonight.'

'Back tonight! Ye want yer——heid examinin'!'

'I've got tae go!'

'Eyes front!' he screamed suddenly at the men before us. ' 'eft 'ight, 'eft 'ight!' Then he turned and studied me as though I were an unbelievable phenomenon. He was interesting to me, too, as a typical product of the bad times in Glasgow between the wars. Stunted, undernourished, but as tough and belligerent as a ferret.

'D'ye no' ken,' he said at length, 'that ye get——leave when yer wife has the wean?'

'Aye, but a canna' wait that long. Gimme a break, corp.'

'Give ye a——break! D'ye want tae get me——shot?'

'No, corp, just want tae get to the bus station.'

'Jesus! Is that a'?' He gave me a final incredulous look before quickening his steps to the head of the column. When he returned he surveyed me again.

'Whit part o' Glesca are ye frae?'

'Scotstounhill,' I replied. 'How about you?'

'Govan.'

I turned my head slightly towards him. 'Ranger supporter, eh?'

He did not change expression, but an eyebrow flickered and I knew I had him.

'Whit a team!' I murmured reverently. 'Many's the time I've stood on the terraces at Ibrox.'

He said nothing and I began to recite the names of the great Rangers team of the thirties. 'Dawson, Gray, McDonald, Meiklejohn, Simpson, Brown.' His eyes took on a dreamy expression and by the time I had intoned 'Archibald, Marshall, English, McPhail and Morton,' there was something near to a wistful smile on his lips.

Then he appeared to shake himself back to normality.

"Eft 'ight, 'eft 'ight!" he bawled. 'C'mon, c'mon, pick it up!' Then he muttered to me from the corner of his mouth. 'There's the——bus station. When we march past it run like——!'

He took off again, shouting to the head of the flight, I saw the buses and the windows of the waiting room on my left and dived across the road and through the door. I snatched off my cap and sat trembling among a group of elderly farmers and their wives. Through the glass I could see the long lines of blue moving away down the street and I could still hear the shouts of the corporal.

But he didn't turn round and I saw only his receding back, the narrow shoulders squared, the bent legs stepping it out in time with his men. I never saw him again but to this day I wish I could take him to Ibrox and watch the Rangers with him and maybe buy him a half and half pint at one of the Govan pubs. It wouldn't have mattered if he had turned out to be a Celtic supporter at that decisive moment because I had the Celtic team on my tongue all ready to trot out, starting with Kennaway, Cook, McGonigle. It is not the only time my profound knowledge of football has stood me in good stead.

Sitting on the bus, still with my cap on my lap to avoid attracting attention, it struck me that the whole world changed within a mile or two as we left the town. Back there the war was everywhere, filling people's mind and eyes and thoughts; the teeming thousands of uniformed men, the RAF and army vehicles, the almost palpable atmosphere of anticipation and suspense. And suddenly it all just stopped.

It vanished as the wide sweep of grey-blue sea fell beneath the rising ground behind the town, and as the bus trundled westward I looked out on a landscape of untroubled peace. The long moist furrows of the new-turned soil glittered under the pale February sun, contrasting with the gold stubble fields and the grassy pastures where sheep clustered around their feeding troughs. There was no wind and the smoke rose straight from the farm chimneys and the bare branches of the roadside trees were still as they stretched across the cold sky.

There were many things that pulled at me. A man in breeches and leggings carrying on his shoulder a bale of hay to some outlying cattle; a group of farm men burning hedge clippings and the fragrance of the wood smoke finding its way into the bus. The pull was stronger as the hours passed and the beginnings of my own familiar countryside began to appear beyond the windows. Maybe it was a good thing I didn't see Darrowby; Helen's home was near the bus route and I dropped off well short of the town.

She was alone in the house and she turned her head as I walked into the kitchen. The delight on her face was mixed with astonishment; in fact I know we were both astonished, she because I was so skinny and I because she was so fat. Helen, with the baby only two weeks away, was very large indeed, but not too large for me to get my arms around her, and we stood there in the middle of the flagged floor clasped together for a long time with neither of us saying much.

When I released her she looked at me, wide-eyed. 'I hardly knew you when you walked in then.'

'I felt the same way about you.'

'I'm not surprised.' She laughed and rested her hand on her bulging abdomen. 'He's kicking like mad now. I'm sure it's going to be a boy.' A fleeting concern showed in her eyes and she reached out a hand and touched my fleshless cheeks. 'Don't they feed you properly?'

'Oh, the food's very good,' I replied. 'But unfortunately they run it all off again.'

'Anyway, I'll get you a good meal now.' She gazed at me

thoughtfully. 'Pity we've finished our meat ration, but how about some egg and chips?'

'Marvellous.'

She cooked me egg and chips and sat by me while I ate. We carried on a rather halting conversation and it came to me with a bump that my mind had been forced on to different tracks since I had left her. In those few months my brain had become saturated with the things of my new life—even my mouth was full of RAF slang and jargon. In our bed-sitter we used to talk about my cases, the funny things that happened on my rounds, but now, I thought helplessly, there wasn't much point in telling her that AC2 Phillips was on jankers again, that vector triangles were the very devil, that Don McGregor though he had discovered the secret of Sergeant Hynd's phenomenally shiny boots.

But it really didn't matter. My worries melted as I looked at her. I had been wondering if she was well and there she was, bouncing with energy, shining-eyed, rosy-cheeked and beautiful. There was only one jarring note and it was a strange one. Helen was wearing a 'maternity dress' which expanded with the passage of time by means of an opening down one side. Anyway, I hated it. It was blue with a high red collar and I thought it cheap-looking and ugly. I was aware that austerity had taken over in England and that a lot of things were shoddy, but I desperately wished my wife had something better to wear. In all my life there have been very few occasions when I badly wanted more money and that was one of them, because on my wage of three shillings a day as an AC2 I was unable to drape her with expensive clothes.

The hour winged past and it seemed no time at all before I was back on the top road waiting in the gathering darkness for the Scarborough bus. The journey back was a bit dreary as the black-out vehicle bumped and rattled its way through the darkened villages and over the long stretches of anonymous countryside. It was cold, too, but I sat there happily with the memory of Helen wrapped around me like a warm quilt.

The whole day had been a triumph. I had got away by a lucky stroke and there would be no problem getting back into the Grand because one of my pals would be on sentry duty and it would be a case of 'pass friend'. Closing my eyes in the gloom I could still feel Helen in my arms and I smiled to myself at the memory of her bounding healthiness. What a tremendous relief to see her looking so wonderful, and though the simple repast of egg and chips had seemed like a banquet I realised that my greatest nourishment had been feasting my eyes on Helen.

That dress still niggled at me as it has, for some reason, right down the years, but compared with the other elements of that magic hour it was a little thing.

11

'Hey you! Where the 'ell d'you think you're goin'?'

Coming from the RAF Special Police it was a typical mode of address and the man who barked it out wore the usual truculent expression.

'Extra navigation class, corporal,' I replied.

'Lemme see your pass!'

He snatched it from my hand, read it and returned it without looking at me. I slunk out into the street feeling like a prisoner on parole.

Not all the SPs were like that but I found most of them lacking in charm. And it brought home to me with a rush something which had been slowly dawning on me ever since I joined the Air Force; that I had been spoiled for quite a long time now. Spoiled by the fact that I had always been treated with respect because I was a veterinary surgeon, a member of an honourable profession. And I had taken it entirely for granted.

Now I was an AC2, the lowest form of life in the RAF, and the 'Hey you!' was a reflection of my status. The Yorkshire farmers don't rush out and kiss you, but their careful friendliness and politeness is something which I have valued even more since my service days. Because that was when I stopped taking it for granted.

Mind you, you have to put up with a certain amount of cheek in most jobs, and veterinary practice is no exception. Even now I can recall the glowering face of Ralp Beamish the racehorse trainer, as he watched me getting out of my car.

'Where's Mr Farnon? he grunted.

My toes curled. I had heard that often enough, especially among the horse fraternity around Darrowby.

'I'm sorry, Mr Beamish, but he'll be away all day and I thought I'd better come along rather than leave it till tomorrow.'

He made no attempt to hide his disgust. He blew out his fat, purpled cheeks, dug his hands deep in his breeches pockets and looked at the sky with a martyred air.

'Well come on, then.' He turned and stumped away on his short, thick legs towards one of the boxes which bordered the yard. I sighed inwardly as I followed him. Being an unhorsey vet in Yorkshire was a penance at times, especially in a racing stable like this which was an equine shrine. Siegfried, apart altogether from his intuitive skill, was able to talk the horse language. He could discuss effortlessly and at length the breeding and points of his patients; he rode, he hunted, he even looked the part with his long aristocratic face, clipped moustache and lean frame.

The trainers loved him and some, like Beamish, took it as a mortal insult when he failed to come in person to minister to their valuable charges.

He called to one of the lads who opened a box door.

'He's in there,' he muttered. 'Came in lame from exercise this morning.'

The lad led out a bay gelding and there was no need to trot the animal to diagnose the affected leg; he nodded down on his near fore in an unmistakable way.

'I think he's lame in the shoulder,' Beamish said.

I went round the other side of the horse and picked up the off fore. I cleaned out the frog and sole with a hoof knife; there was no sign of bruising and no sensitivity when I tapped the handle of the knife against the horn.

I felt my way up over the coronet to the fetlock and after some palpation I located a spot near the distal end of the metacarpus which was painful on pressure.

I looked up from my crouching position. 'This seems to be the trouble, Mr Beamish. I think he must have struck into himself with his hind foot just there.'

'Where?' The trainer leaned over me and peered down at the leg. 'I can't see anything.'

'No, the skin isn't broken, but he flinches if you press here.'

Beamish prodded the place with a stubby forefinger.

'Well, he does,' he grunted. 'But he'd flinch anywhere if you squeeze him like you're doing.'

My hackles began to rise at his tone but I kept my voice calm. 'I'm sure that's what it is. I should apply a hot antiphlogistine poultice just above the fetlock and alternate with a cold hose on it twice a day.'

'Well, I'm just as sure you're wrong. It's not down there at all. The way that horse carries his leg he's hurt his shoulder.' He gestured to the lad. 'Harry, see that he gets some heat on that shoulder right away.'

If the man had struck me I couldn't have felt worse. I opened my mouth to argue but he was walking away.

'There's another horse I want you to look at,' he said. He led the way into a nearby box and pointed to a big brown animal with obvious signs of blistering on the tendons of a fore limb.

'Mr Farnon put a red blister on that leg six months ago. He's been resting in here ever since. He's going sound now—d'you think he's ready to go out?'

I went over and ran my fingers over the length of the flexor tendons, feeling for signs of thickening. There was none. Then I lifted the foot and as I explored further I found a tender area in the superficial flexor.

I straightened up. 'He's still a bit sore,' I said. 'I think it would be safer to keep him in for a bit longer.'

'Can't agree with you,' Beamish snapped. He turned to the lad. 'Turn him out, Harry.'

I stared at him. Was this a deliberate campaign to make me feel small? Was he trying to rub in the fact that he didn't think much of me? Anyway, he was beginning to get under my skin and I hoped my burning face wasn't too obvious.

'One thing more,' Beamish said. 'There's a horse through here been coughing. Have a look at him before you go.'

We went through a narrow passage into a smaller yard and Harry entered a box and got hold of a horse's head collar. I followed him, fishing out my thermometer.

As I approached the animal's rear end he laid back his ears, whickered and began to caper around. I hesitated, then nodded to the lad.

'Lift his fore leg while I take his temperature, will you?' I said.

The lad bent down and seized the foot but Beamish broke in. 'Don't bother, Harry, there's no need for that. He's quiet as a sheep.'

I paused for a moment. I felt I was right but my stock was

low on this establishment. I shrugged, lifted the tail and pushed the thermometer into the rectum.

The two hind feet hit me almost simultaneously but as I sailed backwards through the door I remember thinking quite clearly that the one on the chest had made contact fractionally before the one on the abdomen. But my thoughts were rapidly clouded by the fact that the lower hoof had landed full on my solar plexus.

Stretched on the concrete of the yard I gasped and groaned in a frantic search for breath. There was a moment when I was convinced I was going to die but at last a long wailing respiration came to my aid and I struggled painfully into a sitting position. Through the open door I could see Harry hanging on to the horse's head and staring at me with frightened eyes. Mr Beamish, on the other hand, showed no interest in my plight; he was anxiously examining the horse's hind feet one after the other. Obviously he was worried lest they may have sustained some damage by coming into contact with my nasty hard ribs.

Slowly I got up and drew some long breaths. I was shaken but not really hurt. And I suppose it was instinct that had made me hang on to my thermometer; the delicate tube was still in my hand.

My only emotion as I went back into the box was cold rage.

'Lift that bloody foot like I told you!' I shouted at the unfortunate Harry.

'Right, sir! Sorry, sir!' He bent, lifted the foot and held it cupped firmly in his hands.

I turned to Beamish to see if he had any observation to make, but the trainer was silent, gazing at the big animal expressionlessly.

This time I took the temperature without incident. It was 101°F. I moved to the head and opened the nostril with finger and thumb, revealing a slight muco-purulent discharge. Submaxillary and post-pharyngeal glands were normal.

'He's got a bit of cold,' I said. 'I'll give him an injection and leave you some sulphonamide—that's what Mr Farnon uses in these cases.' If my final sentence reassured him in any way he gave no sign, watching dead-faced as I injected 10 cc of Prontosil.

Before I left I took a half-pound packet of sulphonamide from the car boot. 'Give him three ounces of this immediately in a pint of water, then follow it with one and a half ounces night and morning and let us know if he isn't a lot better in two days.'

Mr Beamish received the medicine unsmilingly and as I opened the car door I felt a gush of relief that the uncomfortable visit was at an end. It seemed to have lasted a long time and there had been no glory for me in it. I was starting the engine when one of the little apprentices panted up to the trainer.

'It's Almira, sir. I think she's chokin'!'

'Choking!' Beamish stared at the boy then whipped round to me. 'Almira's the best filly I have. You'd better come!'

It wasn't over yet, then. With a feeling of doom I hurried after the squat figure back into the yard where another lad stood by the side of a beautiful chestnut filly. And as I saw her a cold hand closed around my heart. I had been dealing with trivia but this was different.

She stood immobile, staring ahead with a peculiar intensity. The rise and fall of her ribs was accompanied by a rasping, bubbling wheeze and at each intake her nostrils flared wildly. I had never seen a horse breathe like this. And there were other things; saliva drooled from her lips and every few seconds she gave a retching cough.

I turned to the apprentice. 'When did this start?'

'Not long ago, sir. I saw her an hour since and she were as right as a bobbin.'

'Are you sure?'

'Aye, I was givin' 'er some hay. There was nowt ailin' her then.'

'What the devil's wrong with he?' Beamish exclaimed.

Well, it was a good question and I didn't have a clue to the answer. As I walked bemusedly round the animal, taking in the trembling limbs and terrified eyes, a jumble of thoughts crowded my brain. I had seen 'choking' horses—the dry choke when the gullet becomes impacted with food—but they didn't look like this. I felt my way along the course of the oesophagus and it was perfectly clear. And anyway the respiration was quite different. This filly looked as though she had some obstruction in her airflow. But what . . . ? And how . . . ? Could there be a foreign body in there? Just possible, but that was something else I had never seen.

'Well, damn it, I'm asking you! What is it? What d'you make

of her?' Mr. Beamish was becoming impatient and I couldn't blame him.

I was aware that I was slightly breathless. 'Just a moment while I listen to her lungs.'

'Just a moment!' the trainer burst out. 'Good God, man, we haven't got many moments! This horse could die!'

He didn't have to tell me. I had seen that ominous trembling of the limbs before and now the filly was beginning to sway a little. Time was running out.

Dry mouthed, I ausculated the chest. I knew there was nothing wrong with her lungs—the trouble seemed to be in the throat area—but it gave me a little more time to think. Even with the stethoscope in my ears I could still hear Beamish's voice.

'It would have to be this one! Sir Eric Horrocks gave five thousand pounds for her last year. She's the most valuable animal in my stables. Why did this have to happen?'

Groping my way over the ribs, my heart thudding, I heartily agreed with him. Why in heaven's name did I have to walk into this nightmare? And with a man like Beamish who had no faith in me.

He stepped forward and clutched my arm. 'Are you sure Mr Farnon isn't available?'

'I'm sorry,' I replied huskily. 'He's over thirty miles away.'

The trainer seemed to shrivel within himself. 'That's it then. We're finished. She's dying.'

And he was right. The filly had begun to reel about, the breathing louder and more stertorous than ever, and I had difficulty in keeping the stethoscope on her chest wall. It was when I was resting my hand on her flank to steady her that I noticed the little swelling under the skin. It was a circular plaque, like a penny pushed under the tissue. I glanced sharply at it. Yes, it was clearly visible. And there was another one higher up on the back . . . and another and another. My heart gave a quick double thump . . . so that was it.

'What am I going to tell Sir Eric?' the trainer groaned. 'That his filly is dead and the vet didn't know what was wrong with her?' He glared desperately around him as though in the faint hope that Siegfried might magically appear from nowhere.

I called over my shoulder as I trotted towards the car. 'I never said I didn't know. I do know. She's got urticaria.'

He came shambling after me. 'Urti . . . what the blazes is that?'

'Nettlerash,' I replied, fumbling among my bottles for the adrenalin.

'Nettlerash!' His eyes widened. 'But that couldn't cause all this!'

I drew 5 cc of the adrenalin into the syringe and started back. 'It's nothing to do with nettles. It's an allergic condition, usually pretty harmless, but in a very few cases it causes oedema of the larynx—that's what we've got here.'

It was difficult to raise the vein as the filly staggered around, but she came to rest for a few seconds and I dug my thumb into the jugular furrow. As the big vessel came up tense and turgid I thrust in the needle and injected the adrenalin. Then I stepped back and stood by the trainer's side.

Neither of us said anything. The spectacle of the toiling animal and the harrowing sound of the breathing absorbed us utterly.

The grim knowledge that she was on the verge of suffocation appalled me and when she stumbled and almost fell the hand in my pocket gripped more tightly on the scalpel which I had taken from my car along with the adrenalin. I knew only too well that tracheotomy was indicated here but I didn't have a tube with me. If the filly did go off her legs I should have to start cutting into her windpipe, but I put the thought away from me. For the moment I had to depend on the adrenalin.

Beamish stretched out a hand in a helpless gesture. 'It's hopeless, isn't it?' he whispered.

I shrugged. 'There's a small chance. If the injection can reduce the fluid in the larynx in time . . . we'll just have to wait.'

He nodded and I could read more than one emotion in his face; not just the dread of breaking the news to the famous owner but the distress of a horse-lover as he witnessed the plight of the beautiful animal.

At first I thought it was imagination, but it seemed that the breathing was becoming less stertorous. Then as I hovered in an agony of uncertainty I noticed that the salivation was diminishing; she was able to swallow.

From that moment events moved with unbelievable rapidity. The symptoms of allergies appear with dramatic suddenness but mercifully they often disappear as quickly following treatment. Within fifteen minutes the filly looked almost normal. There was still a slight wheeze in her respirations but she was looking around her, quite free from distress.

Beamish, who had been watching like a man in a daze, pulled a handful of hay from a bale and held it out to her. She snatched it eagerly from his hand and began to eat with great relish.

'I can't believe it,' the trainer muttered almost to himself. 'I've never seen anything work as fast as that injection.'

I felt as though I was riding on a pink cloud with all the tension and misery flowing from me in a joyful torrent. Thank God there were moments like this among the traumas of veterinary work; the sudden transition from despair to triumph, from shame to pride.

I almost floated to the car and as I settled in my seat Beamish put his face to the open window.

'Mr Herriot . . .' He was not a man to whom gracious speech came easily and his cheeks, roughened and weathered by years of riding on the open moor, twitched as he sought for words. 'Mr Herriot, I've been thinking . . . you don't have to be a horsey man to cure horses, do you?'

There was something like an appeal in his eyes as we gazed at each other. I laughed suddenly and his expression relaxed. It was an indescribable satisfaction for me to hear voiced the conviction I had always held.

"I'm glad to hear somebody say that at last," I said, and drove away.

CHAPTER

12

I was on guard outside the Grand. It was after midnight, with a biting wind swirling across the empty square, and I was so cold and bored that it was a relief even to slap the butt of my rifle in salute as a solitary officer went by.

Wryly I wondered how, after my romantic ideas of training to be a pilot, I came to be defending the Grand Hotel at Scarborough against all comers. In a baleful way it seemed comic, and as I tramped frigidly round my short guard route, I kept telling myself, right, keep your sense of humour about it. On my right was a wall almost as tall as I was, and as I passed it continually, grimly trying to focus on how funny this all was, the wall reminded me of Mr Bailes' dog Shep. Now there was a creature with a sense of humour. I should think on him for a bit.

Mr Bailes' little place was situated about half way along Highburn Village and to get into the farmyard you had to walk twenty yards or so between five-foot walls. On the left was the neighbouring house, on the right the front garden of the farm. In this garden Shep lurked for most of the day.

He was a huge dog, much larger than the average collie. In fact I am convinced he was part Alsatian because though he had a luxuriant black and white coat there was something significant in the massive limbs and in the noble brown-shaded head with its upstanding ears. He was quite different from the stringy little animals I saw on my daily round.

As I walked between the walls my mind was already in the byre, just visible at the far end of the yard. Because one of the Bailes cows, Rose by name, had the kind of obscure digestive ailment which interferes with veterinary surgeons' sleep. They are so difficult to diagnose. This animal had begun to grunt and go off her milk two days ago and when I had seen her yesterday I had flitted from one possibility to the other. Could be a wire. But the fourth stomach was contracting well and there were plenty of rumenal sounds. Also she was eating a little hay in a half-hearted way.

Could it be impaction . . . . ? Or a partial torsion of the gut . . . ? There was abdominal pain without a doubt and that nagging temperature of 102.5°—that was damn like a wire. Of course I could settle the whole thing by opening the cow up, but Mr Bailes was an old-fashioned type and didn't like the idea of my diving into his animal unless I was certain of my diagnosis. And I wasn't—there was no getting away from that.

Anyway, I had built her up at the front end so that she was standing with her fore feet on a half door and had given her a strong oily purgative. 'Keep the bowels open and trust in God,' an elderly colleague had once told me. There was a lot in that.

I was half way down the alley between the walls with the hope bright before me that my patient would be improved when from nowhere an appalling explosion of sound blasted into my right ear. It was Shep again.

The wall was just the right height for the dog to make a leap and bark into the ear of the passers by. It was a favourite gambit of his and I had been caught before; but never so successfully as now. My attention had been so far away and the dog had timed his jump to a split second so that his bark came at the highest point, his teeth only inches from my face. And his voice befitted his size, a great bull bellow surging from the depths of his powerful chest and booming from his gaping jaws.

I rose several inches into the air and when I descended, heart thumping, head singing, I glared over the wall. But as usual all I saw was the hairy form bounding away out of sight round the corner of the house.

That was what puzzled me. Why did he do it? Was he a savage creautre with evil designs on me or was it his idea of a joke? I never got near enough to him to find out.

I wasn't in the best of shape to receive bad news and that was what awaited me in the byre. I had only to look at the farmer's face to know that the cow was worse.

'Ah reckon she's got a stoppage,' Mr Bailes muttered gloomily.

I gritted my teeth. The entire spectrum of abdominal disorders were lumped as 'stoppages' by the older race of farmers. 'The oil hasn't worked, then?'

'Nay, she's nobbut passin' little hard bits. It's a proper stoppage, ah tell you.'

'Right, Mr Bailes,' I said with a twisted smile. 'We'll have to try something stronger.' I brought in from my car the gastric lavage outfit I loved so well and which has so sadly disappeared from my life. The long rubber stomach tube, the wooden gag with its leather straps to buckle behind the horns. As I pumped in the two gallons of warm water rich in formalin and sodium chloride I felt like Napoleon sending in the Old Guard at Waterloo. If this didn't work nothing would.

And yet I didn't feel my usual confidence. There was something different here. But I had to try. I had to do something to start this cow's insides functioning because I did not like the look of her today. The soft grunt was still there and her eyes had begun to retreat into her head—the worst sign of all in bovines. And she had stopped eating altogether.

Next morning I was driving down the single village street when I saw Mrs Bailes coming out of the shop. I drew up and pushed my head out of the window.

'How's Rose this morning, Mrs Bailes?'

She rested her basket on the ground and looked down at me gravely. 'Oh, she's bad, Mr Herriot. Me husband thinks she's goin' down fast. If you want to find him you'll have to go across the field there. He's mendin' the door in that little barn.'

A sudden misery enveloped me as I drove over to the gate leading into the field. I left the car in the road and lifted the latch.

'Damn! Damn! Damn!' I muttered as I trailed across the green. I had a nasty feeling that a little tragedy was building up here. If this animal died it would be a sickening blow to a small farmer with ten cows and a few pigs. I should be able to do something about it and it was a depressing thought that I was getting nowhere.

And yet, despite it all, I felt peace stealing into my soul. It was a large field and I could see the barn at the far end as I walked with the tall grass brushing my knees. It was a meadow ready for cutting and suddenly I realised that it was high summer, the sun was hot and that every step brought the fragrance of clover and warm grass rising about me into the crystal freshness of the air. Somewhere nearby a field of broad beans was in full flower and as the exotic scent drifted across I found myself inhaling with half-closed eyes as though straining to discern the ingredients of the glorious melange.

And then there was the silence; it was the most soothing thing of all. That and the feeling of being alone. I looked drowsily around at the empty green miles sleeping under the sunshine. Nothing stirred, there was no sound.

Then without warning the ground at my feet erupted in an incredible blast of noise. For a dreadful moment the blue sky was obscured by an enormous hairy form and a red mouth went 'WAAAHH!' in my face. Almost screaming, I staggered back and as I glared wildly I saw Shep disappearing at top speed towards the gate. Concealed in the deep herbage right in the middle of the field he had waited till he saw the whites of my eyes before making his assault.

Whether he had been there by accident or whether he had spotted me arriving and slunk into position I shall never know, but from his point of view the result must have been eminently satisfactory because it was certainly the worst fright I have ever had. I live a life which is well larded with scares and alarms, but this great dog rising bellowing from that empty landscape was something on its own. I have heard of cases where sudden terror and stress has caused involuntary evacuation of the bowels and I know without question that this was the occasion when I came nearest to suffering that unhappy fate.

I was still trembling when I reached the barn and hardly said a word as Mr Bailes led me back across the road to the farm.

And it was like rubbing it in when I saw my patient. The flesh had melted from her and she stared at the wall apathetically from sunken eyes. The doom-laden grunt was louder.

'She must have a wire!' I muttered. 'Let her loose for a minute, will you?'

Mr Bailes undid the chain and Rose walked along the byre. At the end she turned and almost trotted back to her stall, jumping quite freely over the gutter. My Bible in those days was Udall's *Practice of Veterinary Medicine* and the great man stated therein that if a cow moved freely she was unlikely to have a foreign body in her reticulum. I pinched her withers and she didn't complain . . . it had to be something else.

'It's worst stoppage ah've seen for a bit,' said Mr Bailes. 'Ah gave her a dose of some right powerful stuff this mornin' but it's done no good.'

I passed a weary hand over my brow. 'What was that, Mr Bailes?' It was always a bad sign when the client started using his own medicine.

The farmer reached to the cluttered windowsill and handed me a bottle. 'Doctor Hornibrook's Stomach Elixir. A sovereign remedy for all diseases of cattle.' The Doctor, in top hat and frock coat, looked confidently out at me from the label as I pulled out the cork and took a sniff. I blinked and staggered back with watering eyes. It smelt like pure ammonia but I was in no position to be superior about it.

'That dang grunt!' The farmer hunched his shoulders. 'What's cause of it?'

It was no good my saying it sounded like a circumscribed area of peritonitis because I didn't know what was behind it.

I decided to have one last go with the lavage. It was still the strongest weapon in my armoury but this time I added two pounds of black treacle to the mixture. Nearly every farmer had a barrel of the stuff in his cow house in those days and I had only to go into the corner and turn the tap.

I often mourn the passing of the treacle barrel because molasses was a good medicine for cattle, but I had no great hopes this time. The clinical instinct I was beginning to develop told me that something inside this animal was fundamentally awry.

It was not till the following afternoon that I drove into Highburn. I left the car outside the farm and was about to walk between the walls when I paused and stared at a cow in the field on the other side of the road. It was a pasture next to the hayfield of yesterday and that cow was Rose. There could be no mistake—she was a fine deep red with a distinctive white mark like a football on her left flank.

I opened the gate and within seconds my cares dropped from me. She was wonderfully, miraculously improved, in fact she looked like a normal animal. I walked up to her and scratched the root of her tail. She was a docile creature and merely looked round at me as she cropped the grass; and her eyes were no longer sunken but bright and full.

She seemed to take a fancy to a green patch further into

the field and began to amble slowly towards it. I followed, entranced, as she moved along, shaking her head impatiently against the flies, eager for more of the delicious herbage. The grunt had disappeared and her udder hung heavy and turgid between her legs. The difference since yesterday was incredible.

As the wave of relief flooded through me I saw Mr Bailes climbing over the wall from the next field. He would still be mending that barn door.

As he approached I felt a pang of commiseration. I had to guard against any display of triumph. He must be feeling just a bit silly at the moment after showing his lack of faith in me yesterday with his home remedies and his general attitude. But after all the poor chap had been worried—I couldn't blame him. No, it wouldn't do to preen myself unduly.

'Ah, good morning to you, Mr Bailes,' I said expansively. 'Rose looks fine today, doesn't she?'

The farmer took off his cap and wiped his brow. 'Aye, she's a different cow, all right.'

'I don't think she needs any more treatment,' I said. I hesitated. Perhaps one little dig would do no harm. 'But it's a good thing I gave her that extra lavage yesterday.'

'Yon pumpin' job?' Mr Bailes raised his eyebrows. 'Oh that had nowt to do with it.'

'What . . . what do you mean? It cured her, surely.'

'Nay, lad, nay, Jim Oakley cured her.'

'Jim . . what on earth . . . ?'

'Aye, Jim was round 'ere last night. He often comes in of an evenin' and he took one look at the cow and told me what to do. Ah'll tell you she was like dyin'—that pumpin' job hadn't done no good at all. He told me to give her a bloody good gallop round t'field.'

'What!'

'Aye, that's what he said. He'd seen 'em like that afore and a good gallop put 'em right. So we got Rose out here and did as he said and by gaw it did the trick. She looked better right away.'

I drew myself up. 'And who,' I asked frigidly, 'is Jim Oakley?'

'He's t'postman, of course.'

'The postman!'

'Aye, but he used to keep a few beasts years ago. He's a very clever man wi' stock, is Jim.'

'No doubt, but I assure you, Mr Bailes . . .'

The farmer raised a hand. 'Say no more, lad. Jim put 'er right and there's no denyin' it. I wish you'd seen 'im chasin' 'er round. He's as awd as me, but by gaw 'e did go. He can run like 'ell, can Jim.' He chuckled reminiscently.

I had had about enough. During the farmer's eulogy I had been distractedly scratching the cow's tail and had soiled my hand in the process. Mustering the remains of my dignity I nodded to Mr Bailes.

'Well, I must be on my way. Do you mind if I go into the house to wash my hands?'

'You go right in,' he replied. 'T'missus will get you some hot water.'

Walking back down the field the cruel injustice of the thing bore down on me increasingly. I wandered as in a dream through the gate and across the road. Before entering the alley between the walls I glanced into the garden. It was empty. Shuffling beside the rough stones I sank deeper into my misery. There was no doubt I had emerged from that episode as a complete Charlie. No matter where I looked I couldn't see a gleam of light.

It seemed to take a long time to reach the end of the wall and I was about to turn right towards the door of the farm kitchen when from my left I heard the sudden rattle of a chain then a roaring creature launched itself at me, bayed once, mightily, into my face and was gone.

This time I thought my heart would stop. With my defences at their lowest I was in no state to withstand Shep. I had quite forgotten that Mrs Bailes occasionally tethered him in the kennel at the entrance to discourage unwelcome visitors, and as I half lay against the wall, the blood thundering in my ears, I looked dully at the long coil of chain on the cobbles.

I have no time for people who lose their temper with animals but something snapped in my mind then. All my frustration burst from me in a torrent of incoherent shouts and I grabbed the chain and began to pull on it frenziedly. That dog which had tortured me was there in that kennel. For once I knew where to get at him and this time I was going to have the matter out with him. The kennel would be about ten feet away and at first I saw nothing. There was only the dead weight on the end of the chain. Then as I hauled inexorably a nose appeared, then a head, then all of the big animal hanging limply by his collar. He showed no desire to get up and greet me but I was merciless and dragged him inch by inch over the cobbles till he was lying at my feet.

Beside myself with rage, I crouched, shook my fist under his nose and yelled at him from a few inches' range.

'You big bugger! If you do that to me again I'll knock your bloody head off! Do you hear me, I'll knock your bloody head clean off!'

Shep rolled frightened eyes at me and his tail flickered apologetically between his legs. When I continued to scream at him he bared his upper teeth in an ingratiating grin and finally rolled on his back where he lay inert with half-closed eyes.

So now I knew. He was a softie. All his ferocious attacks were just a game. I began to calm down but for all that I wanted him to get the message.

'Right, mate,' I said in a menacing whisper. 'Remember what I've said!' I let go the chain and gave a final shout. 'Now get back in there!'

Shep, almost on his knees, tail tucked well in, shot back into his kennel and I turned toward the farmhouse to wash my hands.

The memory of my discomfiture fermented in the back of my mind for some time. I had no doubt then that I had been unfairly judged, but I am older and wiser now and in retrospect I think I was wrong.

The symptoms displayed by Mr Bailes' cow were typical of displacement of the abomasum (when the fourth stomach slips round from the right to the left side) and it was a condition that was just not recognised in those early days.

At the present time we correct the condition by surgery—pushing the displaced organ back to the right side and tacking it there with sutures. But sometimes a similar result can be obtained by casting the cow and rolling her over, so why not by making her run . . . ? I freely admit that I have many times adopted Jim Oakley's precept of a 'bloody good gallop,' often with spectacular results. To this day I frequently learn things from farmers, but that was one time when I learned from a postman.

I was surprised when, about a month later, I received another call to one of Mr Bailes' cows. I felt that after my performance with Rose he would have called on the services of Jim Oakley for any further trouble. But no, his voice on the 'phone was as polite and friendly as ever, with not a hint that he had lost faith. It was strange. . . .

Leaving my car outside the farm I looked warily into the front garden before venturing between the walls. A faint tinkle of metal told me that Shep was lurking there in his kennel and I slowed my steps; I wasn't going to be caught again. At the end of the alley I paused, waiting, but all I saw was the end of a nose which quietly withdrew as I stood there. So my outburst had got through to the big dog—he knew I wasn't going to stand any more nonsense from him.

And yet, as I drove away after the visit I didn't feel good about it. A victory over an animal is a hollow one and I had the uncomfortable feeling that I had deprived him of his chief pleasure. After all, every creature is entitled to some form of recreation and though Shep's hobby could result in the occasional heart failure it was, after all, his thing and part of him. The thought that I had crushed something out of his life was a disquieting one. I wasn't proud.

So that when, later that summer, I was driving through Highburn I paused in anticipation outside the Bailes farm. The village street, white and dusty, slumbered under the afternoon sun. In the blanketing silence nothing moved—except for one small man strolling towards the opening between the walls. He was fat and very dark—one of the tinkers from a camp outside the village—and he carried an armful of pots and pans.

From my vantage point I could see through the railings into the front garden where Shep was slinking noiselessly into position beneath the stones. Fascinated, I watched as the man turned unhurriedly into the opening and the dog followed the course of the disembodied head along the top of the wall.

As I expected it all happened half way along. The perfectly timed leap, the momentary pause at the summit then the tremendous 'WOOF!' into the unsuspecting ear.

It had its usual effect. I had a brief view of flailing arms and flying pans followed by a prolonged metallic clatter, then the little man reappeared like a projectile, turned right and sped away from me up the street. Considering his almost round physique he showed an astonishing turn of speed, his little legs pistoning, and he did not pause till he disappeared into the shop at the far end of the village.

I don't know why he went in there because he wouldn't find any stronger restorative than ginger pop.

Shep, apparently well satisfied, wandered back over the grass and collapsed in a cool patch where an apple tree threw its shade over the grass; head on paws he waited in comfort for his next victim.

I smiled to myself as I let in the clutch and moved off. I would stop at the shop and tell the little man that he could collect his pans without the slightest fear of being torn limb from limb, but my overriding emotion was one of relief that I had not cut the sparkle out of the big dog's life.

All this passed through my mind as I stood on the frozen ground outside the Grand Hotel at two o'clock in the morning. I looked up at that venerable edifice, my eyes glittering fiendishly, half from the cold and half from the deranged spark of my recovered humour. I felt my rigid lips creak apart, and my head tilt back to aim at what I took to be Flt Lieut Barnes's window. "Woof!" I roared into the night. "Woof! Woof!"

I suppose once you embark on a life of crime it gets easier all the time. Making a start is the only hard bit.

At any rate, that is how it seemed to me as I sat in the bus, playing hookey again. There had been absolutely no trouble about dodging out of the Grand, the streets of Scarborough had been empty of SPs and nobody had given me a second look as I strolled casually into the bus station.

It was Saturday, 13 February. Helen was expecting our baby this week-end. It could happen any time and I just didn't see how I could sit here these few miles away and do nothing. I had no classes today or tomorrow so I would miss nothing and nobody would miss me. It was, I told myself, a mere technical offence, and anyway I had no option. Like the first time, I just had to see Helen.

And it wouldn't be long now, I thought, as I hurried up to the familiar doorway of her home. I went inside and gazed disappointedly at the empty kitchen—somehow I had been sure she would be standing there waiting for me with her arms wide. I shouted her name but nothing stirred in the house. I was still there, listening, when her father came through from an inner room.

'You've got a son,' he said.

I put my hand on the back of a chair. 'What . . . ?'

'You've got a son.' He was so calm.

'When . . . ?'

'Few minutes ago. Nurse Brown's just been on the 'phone. Funny you should walk in.'

As I leaned on the chair he gave me a keen look. 'Would you like a drop of whisky?'

'Whisky? No—why?'

'Well you've gone a bit white, lad, that's all. Anyway, you'd better have something to eat.'

'No, no, no thanks, I've got to get out there.'

He smiled. 'There's no hurry, lad. Anyway, they won't want anybody there too soon. Better eat something.'

'Sorry, I couldn't. Would you—would you mind if I borrowed your car?'

I was still trembling a little as I drove away. If only Mr Alderson had led up to it gradually—he might have said, 'I've got some news for you,' or something like that, but his direct approach had shattered me. When I pulled up outside Nurse Brown's it still hadn't got through to me that I was a father.

Greenside Nursing Home sounded impressive, but it was in fact Nurse Brown's dwelling house. She was State Registered and usually had two or three of the local women in at a time to have their babies.

She opened the door herself and threw up her hands. 'Mr Herriot! It hasn't taken you long! Where did you spring from?' She was a cheerfully dynamic little woman with mischievous eyes.

I smiled sheepishly. 'Well, I just happened to drop in on Mr Alderson and got the news.'

'You might have given us time to get the little fellow properly washed,' she said. 'But never mind, come up and see him. He's a fine baby—nine pounds.'

Still in a dreamlike state I followed her up the stairs of the little house into a small bedroom. Helen was there, in the bed, looking flushed.

'Hello,' she said.

I went over and kissed her.

'What was it like?' I enquired nervously.

'Awful,' Helen replied without enthusiasm. Then she nodded towards the cot beside her.

I took my first look at my son. Little Jimmy was brick red in colour and his face had a bloated, dissipated look. As I hung over him he twisted his tiny fists under his chin and appeared to be undergoing some mighty internal struggle. His face swelled and darkened as he contorted his features then from deep among the puffy flesh his eyes fixed me with a baleful glare and he stuck his tongue out of the corner of his mouth.

'My god!' I exclaimed.

The nurse looked at me, startled. 'What's the matter?'

'Well, he's a funny-looking little thing isn't he?'

'What!' She stared at me furiously. 'Mr Herriot, how can you say such a thing? He's a beautiful baby!'

I peered into the cot again. Jimmy greeted me with a lopsided leer, turned purple and blew a few bubbles.

'Are you sure he's all right?' I said.

There was a tired giggle from the bed but Nurse Brown was not amused.

'All right! What exactly do you mean?' She drew herself up stiffly.

I shuffled my feet. 'Well, er—is there anything wrong with him?'

I thought she was going to strike me. 'Anything . . . how dare you! Whatever are you talking about? I've never heard such nonsense!' She turned appealing towards the bed, but Helen, a weary smile on her face, had closed her eyes.

I drew the enraged little woman to one side. 'Look, Nurse, have you by chance got any others on the premises?'

'Any other what?' she asked icily.

'Babies—new babies. I want to compare Jimmy with another one.'

Her eyes widened. 'Compare him! Mr Herriot, I'm not going to listen to you any longer—I've lost patience with you!'

'I'm asking you, Nurse,' I repeated. 'Have you any more around?'

There was a long pause as she looked at me as though I was something new and incredible. "Well—there's Mrs Dewburn in the next room. Little Sidney was born about the same time as Jimmy.'

'Can I have a look at him?' I gazed at her appealingly.

She hesitated then a pitying smile crept over her face. 'Oh you . . . you . . . just a minute, then.'

She went into the other room and I heard a mumble of voices. She reappeared and beckoned to me.

Mrs Dewburn was the butcher's wife and I knew her well. The face on the pillow was hot and tired like Helen's.

'Eee, Mr Herriot, I didn't expect to see you. I thought you were in the army.'

'RAF, actually, Mrs Dewburn. I'm on—er—leave at the moment.'

I looked in the cot. Sidney was dark red and bloated, too, and he, also, seemed to be wrestling with himself. The inner battle showed in a series of grotesque facial contortions culminating in a toothless snarl.

I stepped back involuntarily. 'What a beautiful child,' I said.

'Yes, isn't he lovely,' said his mother fondly.

'He is indeed, gorgeous.' I took another disbelieving glance into the cot. 'Well, thank you very much, Mrs Dewburn. It was kind of you to let me see him.'

'Not at all, Mr Herriot, it's nice of you to take an interest.'

Outside the door I took a long breath and wiped my brow. The relief was tremendous. Sidney was even funnier than Jimmy.

When I returned to Helen's room Nurse Brown was sitting on the bed and the two women were clearly laughing at me. And of course, looking back, I must have appeared silly. Sidney Dewburn and my son are now two big, strong, remarkably good-looking young men, so my fears were groundless.

The little nurse looked at me quizzically. I think she had forgiven me.

'I suppose you think all your calves and foals are beautiful right from the moment they are born?'

'Well yes,' I replied. 'I have to admit it—I think they are.'

As I have said before, ideas do not come readily to me, but on the bus journey back to Scarborough a devilish scheme began to hatch in my brain.

I was due for compassionate leave, but why should I take it now? Helen would be in the Nursing Home for a fortnight and there didn't seem any sense in my mooning round Darrowby on my own. The thing to do would be to send myself a telegram a fortnight from now announcing the birth, and we would be able to spend my leave together.

It was interesting how my moral scruples dissolved in the face of this attraction, but anyway, I told myself, where was the harm? I wasn't scrounging anything extra, I was just altering the time. The RAF or the war effort in general would suffer no mortal blow. Long before the darkened vehicle had rolled into the town I had made up my mind and on the following day I wrote to a friend in Darrowby and arranged about the telegram.

But I wasn't such a hardened criminal as I thought, because as the days passed doubts began to creep in. The rules at ITW were rigidly strict. I would be in trouble if I was found out. But the prospect of a holiday with Helen blotted out all other considerations.

When the fateful day arrived my room mates and I were stretched on our beds after lunch when a great voice boomed along the corridor.

'AC2 Herriot! Come on, let's have you, Herriot!'

My stomach lurched. Somehow I hadn't reckoned on Flight Sergeant Blackett coming into this. I had thought maybe an LAC or a corporal, even one of the sergeants might have handled it, not the great man himself.

Flight Sergeant Blackett was an unsmiling martinet of immense natural presence which a gaunt six feet two inch frame, wide bony shoulders and a craggy countenance did nothing to diminish. It was usually the junior NCOs who dealt with our misdemeanours, but if Flight Sergeant Blackett ever took a hand it was a withering experience.

I heard it again. The same bull bellow which echoed over our heads on the square every morning.

'Herriot! Let's be having you, Herriot!'

I was on my way at a brisk trot out of the room and along the polished surface of the corridor. I came to a halt stiffly in front of the tall figure.

'Yes, Flight Sergeant.'

'You Herriot?'

'Yes, Flight Sergeant.'

The telegram between his fingers scuffed softly against the blue serge of his trousers as he swung his hand to and fro. My pulse rate accelerated painfully as I waited.

'Well now, lad, I'm pleased to tell you that your wife has had her baby safely.' He raised the telegram to his eyes. 'It says 'ere, "A boy, both well. Nurse Brown." Let me be the first to congratulate you.' He held out his hand and as I took it he smiled. Suddenly he looked very like Gary Cooper.

'Now you'll want to get off right away and see them both, eh?'

I nodded dumbly. He must have thought I was an unemotional character.

He put a hand on my shoulder and guided me into the orderly room.

'Come on, you lot, get movin'!' The organ tones rolled over the heads of the airmen seated at the tables. 'This is important.

Got a brand new father 'ere. Leave pass, railway warrant, pay, double quick!'

'Right, Flight. Very good, Flight.' The typewriters began to tap.

The big man went over to a railway timetable on the wall. 'You haven't far to go, anyway. Let's see—Darrowby, Darrowby . . . yes, there's a train out of here for York at three twenty.' He looked at his watch. 'You ought to make that if you get your skates on.'

A deepening sense of shame threatened to engulf me when he spoke again.

'Double back to your room and get packed. We'll have your documents ready.'

I changed into my best blue, filled my kit bag and threw it over my shoulder, then hurried back to the orderly room.

The Flight Sergeant was waiting. He handed me a long envelope. 'It's all there, son, and you've got plenty of time.' He looked me up and down, walked round me and straightened the white flash in my cap. 'Yes, very smart. We've got to have you lookin' right for your missus, haven't we?' He gave me the Gary Cooper smile again. He was a handsome, kind-eyed man and I'd never noticed it.

He strolled with me along the corridor. 'This'll be your first 'un, of course?'

'Yes, Flight.'

He nodded. 'Well, it's a great day for you. I've got three of 'em, meself. Getting big now but I miss 'em like hell with this ruddy war. I really envy you, walking in that door tonight and seeing your son for the very first time.'

Guilt drove through me in a searing flood and as we halted at the top of the stairs I was convinced my shifty eyes and furtive glances would betray me. But he wasn't really looking at me.

'You know, lad,' he said softly, gazing somewhere over my head. 'This is the best time of your life coming up.'

We weren't allowed to use the main stairways and as I clattered down the narrow stone service stairs I heard the big voice again.

'Give my regards to them both.'

I had a wonderful time with Helen, walking for miles, discovering the delights of pram pushing, with little Jimmy miraculously improved in appearance. Everything was so much better than if I had taken my leave at the official time and there is no doubt my plan was a success.

But I was unable to gloat about it. The triumph was dimmed and to this day I have reservations about the whole thing.

Looking back I know this was one of the happiest little interludes in my entire life and I suppose it was silly to allow the niceness of Flt Sgt Blackett to throw a tiny shadow over it.

14

'You must have to be a bit of an idiot to be a country vet.' The young airman was laughing as he said it, but I felt there was some truth in his words. He had been telling me about his job in civil life and when I described my own working hours and conditions he had been incredulous.

There was one time I would have agreed with him wholeheartedly. It was nine o'clock on a filthy wet night and I was still at work. I gripped the steering wheel more tightly and shifted in my seat, groaning softly as my tired muscles complained.

Why had I entered this profession? I could have gone in for something easier and gentler—like coalmining or lumberjacking. I had started feeling sorry for myself three hours ago, driving across Darrowby market place on the way to a calving. The shops were shut and even through the wintry drizzle there was a suggestion of repose, of work done, of firesides and books and drifting tobacco smoke. I had all those things, plus Helen, back there in our bed-sitter.

I think the iron really entered when I saw the carload of young people setting off from the front of the Drovers; three girls and three young fellows, all dressed up and laughing and obviously on their way to a dance or party. Everybody was set for comfort and a good time; everybody except Herriot, rattling towards the cold wet hills and the certain prospect of toil.

And the case did nothing to raise my spirits. A skinny little heifer stretched on her side in a ramshackle open-fronted shed littered with old tin cans, half bricks and other junk; it was difficult to see what I was stumbling over since the only light came from a rusty oil lamp whose flame flickered and dipped in the wind.

I was two hours in that shed, easing out the calf inch by inch.

It wasn't a malpresentation, just a tight fit, but the heifer never rose to her feet and I spent the whole time on the floor, rolling among the bricks and tins, getting up only to shiver my way to the water bucket while the rain hurled itself icily against the shrinking flesh of my chest and back.

And now here I was, driving home frozen-faced with my skin chafing under my clothes and feeling as though a group of strong men had been kicking me enthusiastically from head to foot for most of the evening. I was almost drowning in self-pity when I turned into the tiny village of Copton. In the warm days of summer it was idyllic, reminding me always of a corner of Perthshire, with its single street hugging the lower slopes of a green hillside and a dark drift of trees spreading to the heathery uplands high above.

But tonight it was a dead black place with the rain sweeping across the headlights against the tight-shut houses; except for a faint glow right in the middle where the light from the village pub fell softly on the streaming roadway. I stopped the car under the swinging sign of the Fox and Hounds and on an impulse opened the door. A beer would do me good.

A pleasant warmth met me as I went into the pub. There was no bar counter, only high-backed settles and oak tables arranged under the whitewashed walls of what was simply a converted farm kitchen. At one end a wood fire crackled in an old black cooking range and above it the tick of a wall clock sounded above the murmur of voices. It wasn't as lively as the modern places but it was peaceful.

'Now then, Mr Herriot, you've been workin',' my neighbour said as I sank into the settle.

'Yes, Ted, how did you know?'

The man glanced over my soiled mackintosh and the wellingtons which I hadn't bothered to change on the farm. 'Well, that's not your Sunday suit, there's blood on your nose end and cow shit on your ear.' Ted Dobson was a burly cowman in his thirties and his white teeth showed suddenly in a wide grin.

I smiled too and plied my handkerchief. 'It's funny how you always want to scratch your nose at times like that.'

I looked around the room. There were about a dozen men drinking from pint glasses, some of them playing dominoes. They were all farm workers, the people I saw when I was called from my bed in the darkness before dawn; hunched figures they were then, shapeless in old greatcoats, cycling out to the farms, heads down against the wind and rain, accepting the facts of their hard existence. I often thought at those times that this happened to me only occasionally, but they did it every morning.

And they did it for thirty shillings a week; just seeing them here made me feel a little ashamed.

Mr Waters, the landlord, whose name let him in for a certain amount of ribbing, filled my glass, holding his tall jug high to produce the professional froth.

'There y'are, Mr Herriot, that'll be sixpence. Cheap at 'alf the price.'

Every drop of beer was brought up in that jug from the wooden barrels in the cellar. It would have been totally impracticable in a busy establishment, but the Fox and Hounds was seldom bustling and Mr Waters would never get rich as a publican. But he had four cows in the little byre adjoining this room, fifty hens pecked around in his long back garden and he reared a few litters of pigs every year from his two sows.

'Thank you, Mr Waters.' I took a deep pull at the glass. I had lost some sweat despite the cold and my thirst welcomed the flow of rich nutty ale. I had been in here a few times before and the faces were all familiar. Especially old Albert Close, a retired shepherd who sat in the same place every night at the end of the settle hard against the fire.

He sat as always, his hands and chin resting on the tall crook which he had carried through his working days, his eyes blank. Stretched half under the seat, half under the table lay his dog, Mick, old and retired like his master. The animal was clearly in the middle of a vivid dream; his paws pedalled the air spasmodically, his lips and ears twitched and now and then he emitted a stifled bark.

Ted Dobson nudged me and laughed. 'Ah reckon awd Mick's still rounding up them sheep.'

I nodded. There was little doubt the dog was reliving the great days, crouching and darting, speeding in a wide arc round the perimeter of the field at his master's whistle. And Albert himself. What lay behind those empty eyes? I could imagine him in his youth, striding the windy uplands, covering endless miles over moor and rock and beck, digging that same crook into the turf at every step. There were no fitter men than the Dales shepherds, living in the open in all weathers, throwing a sack over their shoulders in snow and rain.

And there was Albert now, a broken, arthritic old man gazing apathetically from beneath the ragged peak of an ancient tweed cap. I noticed he had just drained his glass and I walked across the room.

'Good evening, Mr Close,' I said.

He cupped an ear with his hand and blinked up at me. 'Eh?'

I raised my voice to a shout. 'How are you, Mr Close?'

'Can't complain, young man,' he murmured. 'Can't complain.'

'Will you have a drink?'

'Aye, thank ye.' He directed a trembling finger at his glass. 'You can put a drop i' there, young man.'

I knew a drop meant a pint and beckoned to the landlord who plied his jug expertly. The old shepherd lifted the recharged glass and looked up at me.

'Good 'ealth,' he grunted.

'All the best,' I said and was about to return to my seat when the old dog sat up. My shouts at his master must have wakened him from his dream because he stretched sleepily, shook his head a couple of times and looked around him. And as he turned and faced me I felt a sudden sense of shock.

His eyes were terrible. In fact I could hardly see them as they winked painfully at me through a sodden fringe of pus-caked lashes. Rivulets of discharge showed dark and ugly against the white hair on either side of the nose.

I stretched my hand out to him and the dog wagged his tail briefly before closing his eyes and keeping them closed. It seemed he felt better that way.

I put my hand on Albert's shoulder. 'Mr Close, how long has he been like this?'

'Eh?'

I increased my volume. 'Mick's eyes. They're in a bad state.'

'Oh aye.' The old man nodded in comprehension. 'He's got a bit o' caud in 'em. He's allus been subjeck to it ever since 'e were a pup.'

'No, it's more than cold, it's his eyelids.'

'Eh?'

I took a deep breath and let go at the top of my voice.

'He's got turned-in eyelids. It's rather a serious thing.'

The old man nodded again. 'Aye, 'e lies a lot wi' his head at foot of t'door. It's draughty there.'

'No, Mr Close!' I bawled. 'It's got nothing to do with that. It's a thing called entropion and it needs an operation to put it right.'

'That's right, young man.' He took a sip at his beer. 'Just a bit o 'caud. Ever since he were a pup he's been subjeck . . .'

I turned away wearily and returned to my seat. Ted Dobson looked at me enquiringly.

'What was that about?'

'Well, it's a nasty thing, Ted. Entropion is when the eyelids are turned in and the lashes rub against the eyeball. Causes a lot of pain, sometimes ulceration or even blindness. Even a mild case is damned uncomfortable for a dog.'

'I see,' Ted said ruminatively. 'Ah've noticed awd Mick's had mucky eyes for a long time but they've got worse lately.'

'Yes, sometimes it happens like that, but often it's congenital. I should think Mick has had a touch of it all his life but for some reason it's suddenly developed to this horrible state.' I turned again towards the old dog, sitting patiently under the table, eyes still tight shut.

'He's sufferin' then?'

I shrugged my shoulders. 'Well, you know what it's like if you have a speck of dust in your eyes or even one lash turned in. I should say he feels pretty miserable.'

'Poor awd beggar. Ah never knew it was owt like that.' He drew on his cigarette. 'And could an operation cure it?'

'Yes, Ted, it's one of the most satisfying jobs a vet can do. I always feel I've done a dog a good turn when I've finished.'

'Aye, ah bet you do. It must be a nice feelin'. But it'll be a costly job, ah reckon?'

I smiled wryly. 'It depends how you look at it. It's a fiddly business and takes time. We usually charge about a pound for it.' A human surgeon would laugh at a sum like that, but it would still be too much for old Albert.

For a few moments we were both silent, looking across the room at the old man, at the threadbare coat, the long tatter of trouser bottoms falling over the broken boots. A pound was two weeks of the old age pension. It was a fortune.

Ted got up suddenly. 'Any road, somebody ought to tell 'im. Ah'll explain it to 'im.'

He crossed the room. 'Are ye ready for another, Albert?'

The old shepherd glanced at him absently then indicated his glass, empty again. 'Aye, ye can put a drop i' there, Ted.'

The cowman waved to Mr Waters then bent down. 'Did ye understand what Mr Herriot was tellin' ye, Albert?' he shouted.

'Aye . . . aye . . . Mick's got a bit o' caud in 'is eyes.'

'Nay, 'e hasn't! it's nowt of t'soart! It's a en . . . a en . . . summat different.'

'Keeps gettin' caud in 'em.' Albert mumbled, nose in glass.

Ted yelled in exasperation. 'Ye daft awd divil! Listen to what ah'm sayin'—ye've got to take care of 'im and . . .'

But the old man was far away. 'Ever sin 'e were a pup . . . allus been subjeck to it. . . .'

Though Mick took my mind off my own troubles at the time, the memory of those eyes haunted me for days. I yearned to get my hands on them. I knew an hour's work would transport the old dog into a world he perhaps had not known for years, and every instinct told me to rush back to Copton, throw him in the car and bear him back to Darrowby for surgery. I wasn't worried about the money but you just can't run a practice that way.

I regularly saw lame dogs on farms, skinny cats on the streets and it would have been lovely to descend on each and every one and minister to them out of my knowledge. In fact I had tried a bit of it and it didn't work.

It was Ted Dobson who put me out of my pain. He had come in to the town to see his sister for the evening and he stood leaning on his bicycle in the surgery doorway, his cheerful, scrubbed face gleaming as if it would light up the street.

He came straight to the point. 'Will ye do that operation on awd Mick, Mr Herriot?'

'Yes, of course, but . . . how about . . . ?'

'Oh that'll be right. T'lads at Fox and Hounds are seein' to it. We're takin' it out of the club money.'

'Club money?'

'Aye, we put in a bit every week for an outin' in t'summer. Trip to t'seaside or summat like.'

'Well, it's extremely kind of you, Ted, but are you quite sure? Won't any of them mind?'

Ted laughed. 'Nay, it's nowt, we won't miss a quid. We drink ower much on them do's anyway.' He paused. 'All t'lads want this job done—it's been gettin' on our bloody nerves watchin' t'awd dog ever since you told us about 'im.'

'Well, that's great,' I said. 'How will you get him down?'

'Me boss is lendin' me 'is van. Wednesday night be all right?'

'Fine.' I watched him ride away then turned back along the passage. It may seem to modern eyes that a lot of fuss had been made over a pound but in those days it was a very substantial sum, and some idea may be gained from the fact that four pounds a week was my commencing salary as a veterinary surgeon.

When Wednesday night arrived it was clear that Mick's operation had become something of a gala occasion. The little van was crammed with regulars from the Fox and Hounds and others rolled up on their bicycles.

The old dog slunk fearfully down the passage to the operating room, nostrils twitching at the unfamiliar odours of ether and antiseptic. Behind him trooped the noisy throng of farm men, their heavy boots clattering on the tiles.

Tristan, who was doing the anaesthesia, hoisted the dog on the table and I looked around at the unusual spectacle of rows of faces regarding me with keen anticipation. Normally I am not in favour of lay people witnessing operations but since these men were sponsoring the whole thing they would have to stay.

Under the lamp I got my first good look at Mick. He was a handsome, well-marked animal except for those dreadful eyes. As he sat there he opened them a fraction and peered at me for a painful moment before closing them against the bright light; that, I felt, was how he spent his life, squinting carefully and briefly at his surroundings. Giving him the intravenous barbiturate was like doing him a favour, ridding him of his torment for a while.

And when he was stretched unconscious on his side I was able to carry out my first examination. I parted the lids, wincing at the matted lashes, awash with tears and discharge; there was a long standing keratitis and conjunctivitis but with a gush of relief I found that the cornea was not ulcerated.

'You know,' I said. 'This is a mess, but I don't think there's any permanent damage.'

The farm men didn't exactly break into a cheer but they were enormously pleased. The carnival air was heightened as they chattered and laughed and when I poised my scalpel it struck me that I had never operated in such a noisy environment.

But I felt almost gleeful as I made the first incision; I had been looking forward so much to this moment. Starting with the left eye I cut along the full length parallel to the margin of the lid then made a semicircular sweep of the knife to include half an inch of the tissue above the eye. Seizing the skin with forceps I stripped it away, and as I drew the lips of the bleeding wound together with stitches I noticed with intense gratification how the lashes were pulled high and away from the corneal surface they had irritated, perhaps for years.

I cut away less skin from the lower lid—you never need to take so much there—then started on the right eye. I was slicing away happily when I realised that the noise had subsided; there were a few mutterings, but the chaff and laughter had died. I glanced up and saw big Ken Appleton, the horseman from Laurel Grove; it was natural that he should catch my eye, because he was six feet four and built like the Shires he cared for.

'By gaw, it's 'ot in 'ere,' he whispered, and I could see he meant it because sweat was streaming down his face.

I was engrossed in my work or I would have noticed that he wasn't only sweating but deadly pale. I was stripping the skin from the eyelid when I heard Tristan's yell.

'Catch him!'

The big man's surrounding friends supported him as he slid gently to the floor and he stayed there, sleeping peacefully, till I had inserted the last stitch. Then as Tristan and I cleaned up and put the instruments away he began to look around him and his companions helped him to his feet. Now that the cutting was over the life had returned to the party and Ken came in for some leg-pulling; but his was not the only white face.

'I think you could do with a drop of whisky, Ken,' Tristan said. He left the room and returned with a bottle which, with typical hospitality, he dispensed to all. Beakers, measuring glasses and test tubes were pressed into service and soon there was a boisterous throng around the sleeping dog. When the van finally roared off into the night the last thing I heard was the sound of singing from the packed interior.

They brought Mick back in ten days for removal of the stitches. The wounds had healed well but the keratitis had still not cleared and the old dog was still blinking painfully. I didn't see the final result of my work for another month.

It was when I was again driving home through Copton from an evening call that the lighted doorway of the Fox and Hounds recalled me to the little operation which had been almost forgotten in the rush of new work. I went in and sat down among the familiar faces.

Things were uncannily like before. Old Albert Close in his usual place, Mick stretched under the table, his twitching feet testifying to another vivid dream. I watched him closely until I could stand it no longer. As if drawn by a magnet I crossed the room and crouched by him.

'Mick!' I said. 'Hey, wake up, boy!'

The quivering limbs stilled and there was a long moment when I held my breath as the shaggy head turned towards me. Then with a kind of blissful disbelief I found myself gazing into the wide, clear, bright eyes of a young dog.

Warm wine flowed richly through my veins as he faced me, mouth open in a panting grin, tail swishing along the stone flags. There was no inflammation, no discharge, and the lashes, clean and dry, grew in a soft arc well clear of the corneal surface which they had chafed and rasped for so long. I stroked his head and as he began to look around him eagerly I felt a thrill of utter delight at the sight of the old animal exulting in his freedom, savouring the new world which had opened to him. I could see Ted Dobson and the other men smiling conspiratorially as I stood up.

'Mr Close,' I shouted. 'Will you have a drink?'

'Aye, you can put a drop i' there, young man.'

'Mick's eyes are a lot better.'

The old man raised his glass. 'Good 'ealth. Aye, it were nobbut a bit o' caud.'

'But Mr Close . . . !'

'Nasty thing, is caud in t'eyes. T'awd feller keeps lyin' in that door'ole and ah reckon he'll get it again. Ever since 'e were a pup 'e's been subjeck . . .'

CHAPTER

15

As I bent over the wash basin in the 'ablutions' and went into another violent paroxysm of coughing I had a growing and uncomfortable conviction that I was a mere pawn.

The big difference between my present existence and my old life as a vet was that I used to make up my own mind as to how I would do things, whereas in the RAF all the decisions which affected me were made by other people. I didn't much like being a pawn because the lives of us lowly airmen were ruled by a lot of notions and ideas dreamed up by individuals so exalted that we never knew them.

And so many of these ideas seemed crazy to me.

For instance, who decided that all our bedroom windows should be nailed open throughout a Yorkshire winter so that the healthy mist could swirl straight from the black ocean and settle icily on our beds as we slept? The result was an almost one hundred per cent incidence of bronchitis in our flight, and in the mornings the Grand Hotel sounded like a chest sanatorium with a harrowing chorus of barks and wheezes.

The cough seized me again, racking my body, threatening to dislodge my eyeballs. It was a temptation to report sick but I hadn't done it yet. Most of the lads stuck it out till they had roaring fevers before going sick and by now, at the end of February, nearly all of them had spent a few days in hospital. I was one of the few who hadn't. Maybe there was a bit of bravado in my stand—because most of them were eighteen- or nineteen-year-olds and I was a comparatively old man in my twenties—but there were two other reasons. Firstly, it was very often after I had got dressed and been unable to eat breakfast that I felt really ill. But by then it was too late. You had to report sick before seven o'clock or suffer till next day.

Another reason was that I didn't like the look of the sick

parade. As I went out to the corridor with my towel round my shoulders a sergeant was reading a list and inflating his lungs at the same time.

'Get on parade, the sick!' he shouted. 'C'mon, c'mon, let's be 'avin' you!'

From various doors an unhappy group of invalids began to appear, shuffling over the linoleum, each draped with his 'small kit', haversack containing pyjamas, canvas shoes, knife, fork, spoon, etc.

The sergeant unleashed another bellow. 'Get into line, there! Come on, you lot, hurry it up, look lively!'

I looked at the young men huddled there, white-faced and trembling. Most of them were coughing and spluttering and one of them clutched his abdomen as though he had a ruptured appendix.

'Parade!' bawled the sergeant. 'Parade, atten-shun! Parade stan'-at ease! Atten-shun! Le-eft turn! Qui-ick march! 'Eft-'ight, 'eft-'ight, 'eft-ight, 'eft-ight!'

The hapless band trailed wearily off. They had a march of nearly a mile through the rain to the sick quarters in another hotel above the Spa, and as I turned into my room it was with a renewed resolve to hang on as long as possible.

Another thing that frightened us all for a spell was the suggestion, drifting down from somewhere on high, that it wasn't enough to go jogging around Scarborough on our training runs; we ought to stop every now and then and do a bit of shadow boxing like fighters. This idea seemed too outrageous to be true but we had it from the sergeant himself, who came with us on our runs. Some VIP had passed it down, claiming that it would instil belligerence in us. We were thoroughly alarmed for a while, including the sergeant, who had no desire to be seen in charge of a bunch of apparent lunatics dancing around punching at the air. Mercifully, somebody had the strength to resist this one and the whole thing fell through.

But of all these brilliant schemes the one I remember best was the one that decided we had to scream at the end of our physical training session. Apart from running miles all over the place, we had long periods of PT down on the rain-swept prom with the wind cutting in from the sea on our goose-pimpled limbs. We became so good at these exercises that it was decided to put on a show for a visiting air marshal. Not only our flight but several squadrons all performing in unison in front of the Grand.

We trained for months for the big day, doing the same movements over and over again till we were perfect. At first the barrel-chested PT sergeant shouted instructions at us all the time, then as we got better all he did was call out 'Exercise three, commence'. And finally it all became so much a part of our being that he merely sounded a tiny peep on his whistle at the beginning of each exercise.

By spring we were really impressive. Hundreds of men in shorts and singlets swinging away as one out there on the square, with the PT sergeant up on the balcony above the doorway where he would stand with the air marshal on the day. The thing that made it so dramatic was the utter silence; the forest of waving limbs and swaying bodies with not a sound but the peep of the whistle.

Everything was lovely till somebody had the idea of the screaming. Up till then we had marched silently from the square at the end of the session, but that was apparently not good enough. What we had to do now was count up to five at the end of the last exercise, then leap into the air, scream at the top of our voices and run off the square at top speed.

And I had to admit that it seemed quite a brainwave. We tried it a few times, then we began to put our hearts into it, jumping high, yelling like dervishes then scuttling away into the various openings among the hotels around the square.

It must have looked marvellous from the balcony. The great mass of white-clad men going through the long routine in a cathedral hush, a few seconds of complete immobility at the end then the whole concourse erupting with a wild yell and disappearing, leaving the empty square echoing. And this last touch had another desirable aspect; it was further proof of our latent savagery. The enemy would have quaked at that chilling sound.

The sergeant had a little trouble with a lad in my flight, a tall gangling red-haired youth called Cromarty who stood in the line in front of me a few feet to my right. Cromarty seemed unable to enter into the spirit of the thing.

'Come on. lad,' the sergeant said one day. 'Put a bit of devil into it! You got to sound like a killer. You're floating up and down there like a ruddy fairy godmother.'

Cromarty did try, but the thing seemed to embarrass him. He gave a little hop, an apologetic jerk of his arms and a feeble cry.

The sergeant ran his hand through his hair. 'No, no, lad! You've got to let yourself go!' He looked around him. 'Here, Devlin, come out and show 'im how it's done.'

Devlin, a grinning Irishman, stepped forward. The scream was the high point of his day. He stood relaxed for a moment then without warning catapulted himself high in the air, legs and arms splayed, head back, while a dreadful animal cry burst from his gaping mouth.

The sergeant took an involuntary step backwards. 'Thanks, Devlin, that's fine,' he said a little shakily, then he turned to Cromarty. 'Now you see how I want it, boy, just like that. So work at it.'

Cromarty nodded. He had a long, serious face and you could see he wanted to oblige. After that I watched him each day and there was no doubt he was improving. His inhibitions were gradually being worn down.

It seemed that nature was smiling on our efforts because the great day dawned with blue skies and warm sunshine. Every man among the hundreds who marched out into the square had been individually prepared. Newly bathed, fresh haircut, spotless white shorts and singlet. We waited in our motionless lines before the newly painted door of the Grand while, on the balcony above, gold braid glinted on the air marshal's cap.

He stood among a knot of the top RAF brass of Scarborough, while in one corner I could see our sergeant, erect in long white flannels, his great chest sticking out further than ever. Beneath us the sea shimmered and the golden bay curved away to the Filey cliffs.

The sergeant raised his hand. 'Peep' went the whistle and we were off.

There was something exhilarating about being part of this smooth machine. I had a wonderful sense of oneness with the arms and legs which moved with mine all around. It was effortless. We had ten exercises to do and at the end of the first we stood rigid for ten seconds, then the whistle piped and we started again.

The time passed too quickly as I revelled in our perfection. At the end of exercise nine I came to attention, waiting for the whistle, counting under my breath. Nothing stirred, the silence was profound. Then, from the motionless ranks, as unexpected as an exploding bomb, Cromarty in front of me launched himself upwards in a tangle of flailing limbs and red hair and unleashed a long bubbling howl. He had put so much into his leap that he seemed to take a long time to come down and even after his descent the shattering sound echoed on.

Cromarty had made it at last. As fierce and warlike a scream, as high a jump as ever the sergeant could desire. The only snag was that he was too soon.

When the whistle went for the last exercise a lot of people didn't hear it because of the noise and many others were in a state of shock and came in late. Anyway, it was a shambles and the final yell and scuttle a sad anticlimax. I myself, though managing to get a few inches off the ground, was unable to make any sound at all.

Had Cromarty not been serving in the armed forces of a benign democracy he would probably have been taken quietly away and shot. As it was, there was really nothing anybody could do to him. NCOs weren't even allowed to swear at the men.

I felt for the PT sergeant. There must have been a lot he wanted to say but he was grievously restricted. I saw him with Cromarty later. He put his face close to the young man's.

'You . . . you . . .' His features worked as he fought for words. 'You THING you!'

He turned and walked away with bowed shoulders. At that moment I'm sure he felt like a pawn too.

CHAPTER

16

There is no doubt that when I looked back at my life in Darrowby I was inclined to bathe the whole thing in a rosy glow, but occasionally the unhappy things came to mind.

That man, distraught and gasping on the surgery steps. 'I's no good, I can't bring him in. He's stiff as a board!'

My stomach lurched. It was another one. 'Jasper, you mean?'

'Yes, he's in the back of my car, right here.'

I ran across the pavement and opened the car door. It was as I feared; a handsome Dalmatian stretched in a dreadful tetanic spasm, spine arched, head craning desperately backward, legs like four wooden rods groping at nothing.

I didn't wait to talk but dashed back into the house for syringe and drugs.

I leaned into the car, tucked some papers under the dog's head, injected the apomorphine and waited.

The man looked at me with anxious eyes. 'What is it?'

'Strychnine poisoning, Mr. Bartle. I've just given an emetic to make him vomit.' As I spoke the animal brought up the contents of his stomach on to the paper.

'Will that put him right?'

'It depends on how much of the poison has been absorbed.' I didn't feel like telling him that it was almost invariably fatal, that in fact I had treated six dogs in the last week with the same condition and they had all died. 'We'll just have to hope.'

He watched me as I filled another syringe with barbiturate. 'What are you doing now?'

'Anaesthetising him.' I slipped the needle into the radial vein and as I slowly trickled the fluid into the dog's bloodstream the taut muscles relaxed and he sank into a deep slumber.

'He looks better already,' Mr. Bartle said.

'Yes, but the trouble is when the injection wears off he may go back into a spasm. As I say, it all depends on how much of the strychnine has got into his system. Keep him in a quiet place with as little noise as possible. Any sound can bring on a spasm. When he shows signs of coming out of it give me a ring.'

I went back into the house. Seven cases in a week! It was tragic and scarcely believable, but there was no doubt left in my mind now. This was malicious. Some psychopath in our little town was deliberately putting down poison to kill dogs. Strychnine poisoning was something that cropped up occasionally. Gameskeepers and other people used the deadly drug to kill vermin, but usually it was handled with great care and placed out of reach of domestic pets. Trouble started when a burrowing dog came across the poison by accident. But this was different.

I had to warn pet owners somehow. I lifted the 'phone and spoke to one of the reporters on the *Darrowby and Houlton Times*. He promised to put the story in the next edition, along with advice to keep dogs on their leads and otherwise supervise pets more carefully.

Then I rang the police. The sergeant listened to my account. 'Right, Mr. Herriot, I agree with you that there's some crackpot going around and we'll certainly investigate this matter. If you'll just give me the names of the dog owners involved . . . thank you . . . thank you. We'll see these people and check round the local chemists to see if anybody has been buying strychnine lately. And of course we'll keep our eyes open for anybody acting suspiciously.'

I came away from the 'phone feeling that I might have done something to halt the depressing series of events, but I couldn't rid myself of a gloomy apprehension that more trouble was round the corner. But my mood lightened when I saw Johnny Clifford in the waiting room.

Johnny always made me feel better because he was invariably optimistic and wore a cheerful grin which never altered, even though he was blind. He was about my own age and he sat there in his habitual pose, one hand on the head of his guide dog, Fergus.

'Is it inspection time again already, Johnny?' I asked.

'Aye, it is that, Mr Herriot, it's come round again. It's been a quick six months.' He laughed and held out his card.

I squatted and looked into the face of the big Alsatian sitting motionless and dignified by his master's side. 'Well, and how's Fergus these days?'

'Oh he's in grand fettle. Eatin' well and full of life.' The hand on the head moved round to the ears and at the other end the tail did a bit of sweeping along the waiting-room floor.

As I looked at the young man, his face alight with pride and affection, I realised afresh what this dog meant to him. He had told me that when his failing sight progressed to total blindness in his early twenties he was filled with a despair which did not lessen until he was sent to train with a guide dog and met Fergus; because he found something more than another living creature to act as his eyes, he found a friend and companion to share every moment of his days.

'Well, we'd better get started,' I said. 'Stand up a minute, old lad, while I take your temperature.' That was normal and I went over the big animal's chest with a stethoscope, listening to the reassuringly steady thud of the heart. As I parted the hair along the neck and back to examine the skin I laughed.

'I'm wasting my time here, Johnny. You've got his coat in perfect condition.'

'Aye, never a day goes by but he gets a good groomin'.'

I had seen him at it, brushing and combing tirelessly to bring extra lustre to the sleek swathes of hair. The nicest thing anybody could say to Johnny was, 'That's a beautiful dog you've got.' His pride in that beauty was boundless even though he had never seen it himself.

Treating guide dogs for the blind has always seemed to me to be one of a veterinary surgeon's most rewarding tasks. To be in a position to help and care for these magnificent animals is a privilege, not just because they are highly trained and valuable but because they represent in the ultimate way something which has always lain near the core and centre of my life: the mutually depending, trusting and loving association between man and animal.

Meeting these blind people was a humbling experience which sent me about my work with a new appreciation of my blessings.

I opened the dog's mouth and peered at the huge gleaming teeth. It was dicing with danger to do this with some Alsatians, but with Fergus you could haul the great jaws apart and nearly put your head in and he would only lick your ear. In fact he was at it now. My cheek was nicely within range and he gave it a quick wipe with his large wet tongue.

'Hey, just a minute, Fergus!' I withdrew and plied my handkerchief. 'I've had a wash this morning. And anyway, only little dogs lick—not big tough Alsatians.'

Johnny threw back his head and gave a great peal of laughter. 'There's nowt tough about him, he's the softest dog you could ever meet.'

'Well, that's the way I like them,' I said. I reached for a tooth scaler. 'There's just a bit of tartar on one of his back teeth. I'll scrape it off right now.'

When I had finished I looked in the ears with an auroscope. There was no canker but I cleaned out a little wax.

Then I went round the feet, examining paws and claws. They always fascinated me, these feet; wide, enormous, with great spreading toes. They had to be that size to support the big body and the massive bones of the limbs.

'All correct except that one funny claw, Johnny.'

'Aye, you allus have to trim that 'un don't you? I could feel it was growin' long again.'

'Yes, that toe seems to be slightly crooked or it would wear down like the others with all the walking he does. You have a great time going walks all day, don't you, Fergus?'

I dodged another attempted lick and closed my clippers around the claw. I had to squeeze till my eyes popped before the overgrown piece shot away with a loud crack.

'By gosh, we'd go through some clippers if all dogs had claws like that,' I gasped. 'It just about does them in every time he calls.'

Johnny laughed again and dropped his hand on the great head with that gesture which said so much.

I took the card and entered my report on the dog's health along with the things I had done. Then I dated it and handed it back. 'That's it for this time, Johnny. He's in excellent order and there's nothing more I need do to him.'

'Thank you, Mr Herriot. See you next time round, then.' The young man took hold of the harness and I followed the two of them along the passage and out of the front door. I watched as Fergus halted by the kerb and waited till a car had passed before crossing the road.

They hadn't gone very far along the road when a woman with a shopping bag stopped them. She began to chatter animatedly, looking down repeatedly at the big dog. She was talking about Fergus and Johnny rested his hand on the noble head and nodded and smiled. Fergus was his favourite topic.

Shortly after midday Mr Bartle rang to say Jasper showed signs of returning spasms and before sitting down to lunch I rushed round to his house and repeated the barbiturate injection. Mr Bartle owned one of the local mills, producing cattle food for the district. He was a very bright man indeed.

"Mr Herriot,' he said. 'Please don't misunderstand me. I have every faith in you, but isn't there anything else you can do? I am so very fond of this dog.'

I shrugged helplessly. 'I'm sorry, but I can't do any more.'

'But is there no antidote to this poison?'

'No, I'm afraid there isn't.'

'Well. . . .' He looked down with drawn face at the unconscious animal. 'What's going on? What's happening to Jasper when he goes stiff like he did? I'm only a layman but I like to understand things.'

'I'll try to explain it,' I said. 'Strychnine is absorbed into the nervous system and it increases the conductivity of the spinal cord.'

'What does that mean?'

'It means that the muscles become more sensitive to outside stimuli so that the slightest touch or sound throws them into violent contractions.'

'But why does a dog stretch out like that?'

'Because the extensor muscles are stronger than the flexors, causing the back to be arched and the legs extended.'

He nodded. 'I see, but . . . I believe it is usually fatal. What is it that . . . kills them?'

'They die of asphyxia due to paralysis of the respiratory centre or contraction of the diaphragm.'

Maybe he wanted to ask more, but it was painful for him and he stayed silent.

'There's one thing I'd like you to know, Mr Bartle,' I said. 'It is almost certainly not a painful condition.'

'Thank you.' He bent and briefly stroked the sleeping dog. 'So nothing more can be done?'

I shook my head. 'The barbiturate keeps the spasms in abeyance and we'll go on hoping he hasn't absorbed too much strychnine. I'll call back later, or you can ring me if he gets worse. I can be here in a few minutes.'

Driving away, I pondered on the irony that made Darrowby a paradise for dog killers as well as dog lovers. There were grassy tracks everywhere; wandering by the river's edge, climbing the fell-sides and coiling green and tempting among the heather on the high tops. I often felt sympathy for pet owners in the big cities, trying to find places to walk their dogs. Here in Darrowby we could take our pick. But so could the poisoner. He could drop his deadly bait unobserved in a hundred different places.

I was finishing the afternoon surgery when the 'phone rang. It was Mr Bartle.

'Has he started the spasms again?' I asked.

There was a pause. 'No, I'm afraid Jasper is dead. He never regained consciousness.'

'Oh . . . I'm very sorry.' I felt a dull despair. That was the seventh death in a week.

'Well, thank you for your treatment, Mr Herriot. I'm sure nothing could have saved him.'

I hung up the 'phone wearily. He was right. Nothing or nobody could have done any good in this case, but it didn't help. If you finish up with a dead animal there is always the feeling of defeat.

Next day I was walking on to a farm when the farmer's wife called to me. 'I have a message for you to ring back to the surgery.'

I heard Helen's voice at the other end. 'Jack Brimham has just come in with his dog. I think it's another strychnine case.'

I excused myself and drove back to Darrowby at top speed. Jack Brimham was a builder. He ran a one-man business and whatever job he was on—repairing roofs or walls or chimneys— his little white rough-haired terrier went with him, and you could usually see the little animal nosing among the piles of bricks, exploring in the surrounding fields.

Jack was a friend, too. I often had a beer with him at the Drovers' Arms and I recognised his van outside the surgery. I trotted along the passage and found him leaning over the table in the consulting room. His dog was stretched there in that attitude which I dreaded.

'He's gone, Jim,' he muttered.

I looked at the shaggy little body. There was no movement, the eyes stared silently. The legs, even in death, strained across the smooth surface of the table. It was pointless, but I slipped my hand inside the thigh and felt for the femoral artery. There was no pulse.

'I'm sorry, Jack,' I said.

He didn't answer for a moment. 'I've been readin' about this in the paper, Jim, but I never thought it would happen to me. It's a bugger, isn't it?'

I nodded. He was a craggy-faced man, a tough Yorkshireman with a humour and integrity which I liked and a soft place inside which his dog had occupied. I did not know what to say to him.

'Who's doin' this?' he said, half to himself.

'I don't know, Jack. Nobody knows.'

'Well I wish I could have five minutes with him, that's all.' He gathered the rigid little form into his arms and went out.

My troubles were not over for that day. It was about 11 p.m. and I had just got into bed when Helen nudged me.

'I think there's somebody knocking at the front door, Jim.'

I opened the window and looked out. Old Boardman, the lame veteran of the first war who did odd jobs for us, was standing on the steps.

'Mr Herriot,' he called up to me. 'I'm sorry to bother you at this hour, but Patch is ill.'

I leaned further out. 'What's he doing?'

'He's like a bit o' wood—stiff like, and laid on 'is side.'

I didn't bother to dress, just pulled my working corduroys over my pyjamas and went down the stairs two at a time. I grabbed what I needed from the dispensary and opened the front door. The old man, in shirt sleeves, caught at my arm.

'Come quickly, Mr Herriot!' He limped ahead of me to his little house about twenty yards away in the lane round the corner.

Patch was like all the others. The fat spaniel I had seen so often waddling round the top yard with his master was in that nightmare position on the kitchen floor, but he had vomited, which gave me hope. I administered the intravenous injection but as I withdrew the needle the breathing stopped.

Mrs Boardman, in nightgown and slippers, dropped on her knees and stretched a trembling hand towards the motionless animal.

'Patch. . . .' She turned and stared at me, wide-eyed. 'He's dead!'

I put my hand on the old woman's shoulder and said some sympathetic words. I thought grimly that I was getting good at it. As I left I looked back at the two old people. Boardman was kneeling now by his wife and even after I had closed the door I could hear their voices: 'Patch . . . oh Patch.'

I almost reeled over the few steps to Skeldale House and before going in I stood in the empty street breathing the cool air and trying to calm my racing thoughts. With Patch gone, this thing was getting very near home. I saw that dog every day. In fact all the dogs that had died were old friends—in a little town like Darrowby you came to know your patients personally. Where was it going to end?

I didn't sleep much that night and over the next few days I was obsessed with apprehension. I expected another poisoning with every 'phone call and took care never to let my own dog, Sam, out of the car in the region of the town. Thanks to my job I was able to exercise him miles away on the summits of the fells, but even there I kept him close to me.

By the fourth day I was beginning to feel more relaxed. Maybe the nightmare was over. I was driving home in the late afternoon past the row of grey cottages at the end of the Houlton Road when a woman ran waving into the road.

'Oh, Mr Herriot,' she cried when I stopped. 'I was just goin' to t'phone box when I saw you.'

I pulled up by the kerb. 'It's Mrs Clifford, isn't it?'

'Yes, Johnny's just come in and Fergus 'as gone queer. Collapsed and laid on t'floor.'

'Oh no!' An icy chill drove through me and for a moment I stared at her, unable to move. Then I threw open the car door and hurried after Johnny's mother into the end cottage. I halted abruptly in the little room and stared down in horror. The very sight of the splendid dignified animal scrabbling helplessly on the linoleum was a desecration, but strychnine is no respecter of such things.

'Oh God!' I breathed. 'Has he vomited, Johnny?'

'Aye, me mum said he was sick in t'back garden when we came in.' The young man was sitting very upright in a chair by the side of his dog. Even now there was a half smile on his face, but he looked strained as he put out his hand in the old gesture and failed to find the head that should have been there.

The bottle of barbiturate wobbled in my shaking hand as I filled the syringe. I tried to put away the thought that I was doing what I had done to all the others—all the dead ones. At my feet Fergus panted desperately, then as I bent over him he suddenly became still and went into the horrible distinctive spasm, the great limbs I knew so well straining frantically into space, the head pulled back grotesquely over the spine.

This was when they died, when the muscles were at full contraction. As the barbiturate flowed into the vein I waited for signs of relaxation but saw none. Fergus was about twice as heavy as any of the other victims I had treated and the plunger went to the end of the syringe without result.

Quickly I drew in another dose and began to inject it, my tension building as I saw how much I was administering. The recommended dose was 1 cc per 5 lb. body weight and beyond that you could kill the animal. I watched the gradations on the glass barrel of the syringe and my mouth went dry when the dose crept far beyond the safety limit. But I knew I had to relieve this spasm and continued to depress the plunger relentlessly.

I did it in the grim knowledge that if he died now I would never know whether to blame the strychnine or myself for his death.

The big dog had received more than a lethal amount before peace began to return to the taut body and even then I sat back on my heels, almost afraid to look in case I had brought about his end. There was a long agonising moment when he lay still and apparently lifeless then the rib cage began to move almost imperceptibly as the breathing recommenced.

Even then I was in suspense. The anaesthesia was so deep that he was only just alive, yet I knew that the only hope was to keep him that way. I sent Mrs Clifford out to phone Siegfried that I would be tied up here for a while, then I pulled up a chair and settled down to wait.

The hours passed as Johnny and I sat there, the dog strteched between us. The young man discussed the case calmly and without self-pity. There was no suggestion that this was anything more than a pet animal lying at his feet—except for the tell-tale reaching for the head that was no longer there.

Several times Fergus showed signs of going into another spasm and each time I sent him back into his deep, deep insensibility, pushing him repeatedly to the brink with a fateful certainty that it was the only way.

It was well after midnight when I came sleepily out into the darkness. I felt drained. Watching the life of the friendly, clever, face-licking animal flicker as he lay inert and unheeding had been a tremendous strain, but I had left him sleeping—still anaesthetised but breathing deeply and regularly. Would he wake up and start the dread sequence again? I didn't know and I couldn't stay any longer. There was a practice with other animals to attend to.

But my anxiety jerked me into early wakefulness next morning. I tossed around till seven thirty telling myself this wasn't the way to be a veterinary surgeon, that you couldn't live like this. But my worry was stronger than the voice of reason and I slipped out before breakfast to the roadside cottage.

My nerves were like a bowstring as I knocked on the door. Mrs Clifford answered and I was about to blurt out my enquiries when Fergus trotted from the inner room.

He was still a little groggy from the vast dosage of barbiturate but he was relaxed and happy, the symptoms had gone, he was himself again. With a gush of pure joy I knelt and took the great head between my hands. He slobbered at me playfully with his wet tongue and I had to fight him off.

He followed me into the living room where Johnny was seated at the table, drinking tea. He took up his usual position, sitting upright and proud by his master's side.

"You'll have a cup, Mr Herriot?' Mrs Clifford asked, poising the teapot.

'Thanks, I'd love one, Mrs Clifford,' I replied.

No tea ever tased better and as I sipped I watched the young man's smiling face.

'What a relief, Mr Herriot! I sat up with him all night, listenin' to the chimes of the church clock. It was just after four when I knew we'd won because I heard 'im get to his feet and sort o' stagger about. I stopped worryin' then, just listened to 'is feet patterin' on the linoleum. It was lovely!'

He turned his head to me and I looked at the slightly upturned eyes in the cheerful face.

'I'd have been lost without Fergus,' he said softly. 'I don't know how to thank you.'

But as he unthinkingly rested his hand on the head of the big dog who was his pride and delight I felt that the gesture alone was all the thanks I wanted.

That was the end of the strychnine poisoning outbreak in Darrowby. The older people still talk about it, but nobody ever had the slightest clue to the identity of the killer and it is a mystery to this day.

I feel that the vigilance of the police and the publicity in the press frightened this twisted person off, but anyway it just stopped and the only cases since then have been accidental ones.

To me it is a sad memory of failure and frustration. Fergus was my only cure and I'm not sure why he recovered. Maybe the fact that I pushed the injection to dangerous levels because I was desperate had something to do with it, or maybe he just didn't pick up as much poison as the others. I'll never know.

But over the years when I saw the big dog striding majestically in his harness, leading his master unerringly around the streets of Darrowby, I always had the same feeling.

If there had to be just one saved, I'm glad it was him.

CHAPTER
17

A tender nerve twinged as the old lady passed me the cup of tea. She looked just like Mrs Beck.

One of the local churches was having a social evening to entertain us lonely airmen and as I accepted the cup and sat down I could hardly withdraw my eyes from the lady's face.

Mrs Beck! I could see her now standing by the surgery window.

'Oooh, I never thought you were such a 'eartless man, Mr Herriot.' Her chin trembled and she looked up at me reproachfully.

'But Mrs Beck,' I said. 'I assure you I am not being in the least heartless. I just cannot carry out a major operation on your cat for ten shillings.'

'Well, I thought you would've done it for a poor widder woman like me.'

I regarded her thoughtfully, taking in the small compact figure, the healthy cheeks, the neat helmet of grey hair pulled tightly into a bun. Was she really a poor widow? There was cause for doubt. Her next-door neighbor in Rayton village was a confirmed sceptic.

'It's all a tale, Mr Herriot,' he had said. 'She tries it on wi' everybody, but I'll tell you this—she's got a long stockin'. Owns property all over t'place.'

I took a deep breath. 'Mrs Beck. We often do work at reduced rates for people who can't afford to pay, but this is what we call a luxury operation.'

'Luxury!' The lady was aghast. 'Eee, ah've been tellin' you how Georgina keeps havin' them kittens. She's at it all the time and it's gettin' me down. Ah can't sleep for worryin' when t'next lot's comin'.' She dabbed her eyes.

'I understand and I'm sorry. I can only tell you again that the only way to prevent this trouble is to spay your cat and the charge is one pound.'

'Nay, I can't afford that much!'

I spread my hands. 'But you are asking me to do it for half the price. That's ridiculous. This operation involves the removal of the uterus and ovaries under a general anaesthetic. You just can't do a job like that for ten shillings.'

'Oh, you are cruel!' She turned and looked out of the window and her shoulders began to shake. 'You won't even take pity on a poor widder.'

This had been going on for ten minutes and it began to dawn on me that I was in the presence of a stronger character than myself. I glanced at my watch—I should have been on my round by now and it was becoming increasingly obvious that I wasn't going to win this argument.

I sighed. Maybe she really was a poor widow. 'All right, Mrs Beck, I'll do it for ten shillings, just this once. Will Tuesday afternoon be all right for you?'

She swung round from the window, her face crinkling magically into a smile. 'That'll suit me grand! Eee, that's right kind of you.' She tripped past me and I followed her along the passage.

'Just one thing,' I said as I held the front door open for her. 'Don't give Georgina any food from midday on Monday. She must have an empty stomach when you bring her in.'

'Bring 'er in?' She was a picture of bewilderment. 'But I 'aven't got no car. I thought you'd be collectin' her.'

'Collecting! But Rayton's five miles away!'

'Yes, and bring 'er back afterwards, too. I 'ave no transport.'

'Collect . . . operate on her . . . take her back! All for ten shillings!'

She was still smiling but a touch of steel glinted in her eyes. 'Well, that's what you agreed to charge—ten shillings.'

'But . . . but . . .'

'Oh now you're startin' again.' The smile faded and she put her head on one side. 'And I'm only a poor . . .'

'Okay, okay,' I said hastily. 'I'll call on Tuesday.'

And when Tuesday afternoon came round I cursed my softness. If that cat had been brought in I could have operated on her at two o'clock and been out on the road doing my farm calls by two thirty. I didn't mind working at a loss for half an hour, but how long was this business going to take?

On my way out I glanced through the open door of the sitting room. Tristan was supposed to be studying but was sleeping soundly in his favourite chair. I went in and looked down at him, marvelling at the utter relaxation, seen only in a dedicated sleeper. His face was as smooth and untroubled as a baby's, the *Daily Mirror,* open at the comic strips, had fallen across his chest and a burnt-out Woodbine hung from one dangling hand.

I shook him gently. 'Like to come with me, Triss? I've got to pick up a cat.'

He came round slowly, stretching and grimacing, but his fundamental good nature soon reasserted itself.

'Certainly, Jim,' he said with a final yawn. 'It will be a pleasure.'

Mrs Beck lived half way down the left side of Rayton village. I read 'Jasmine Cottage' on the brightly painted gate, and as we went up the garden path the door opened and the little woman waved gaily.

'Good afternoon, gentlemen, I'm right glad to see you both.' She ushered us into the living-room among good, solid-looking furniture which showed no sign of poverty. The open cupboard of a mahogany sideboard gave me a glimpse of glasses and bottles. I managed to identify Scotch, cherry brandy and sherry before she nudged the door shut with her knee.

I pointed to a cardboard box loosely tied with string. 'Ah, good, you've got her in there, have you?'

'Nay, bless you, she's in t'garden. She allus has a bit of play out there of an afternoon.'

'In the garden, eh?' I said nervously. 'Well, please get her in, we're in rather a hurry.'

We went through a tiled kitchen to the back door. Most of these cottages had a surprising amount of land behind them and Mrs Beck's patch was in very nice order. Flower beds bordered a smooth stretch of lawn and the sunshine drew glittering colours from the apples and pears among the branches of the trees.

'Georgina,' carolled Mrs Beck. 'Where are you, my pet?'

No cat appeared and she turned to me with a roguish smile. 'I think the little imp's playin' a game with us. She does that, you know.'

'Really?' I said without enthusiasm. 'Well, I wish she'd show herself. I really don't have much . . .'

At that moment a very fat tabby darted from a patch of chrysanthemums and flitted across the grass into a clump of rhododendrons with Tristan in close pursuit. The young man dived among the greenery and the cat emerged from the other end at top speed, did a couple of laps of the lawn then shot up a gnarled tree.

Tristan, eyes gleaming in anticipation, lifted a couple of windfall apples from the turf. 'I'll soon shift the bugger from there, Jim,' he whispered and took aim.

I grabbed his arm. 'For heaven's sake, Triss!' I hissed. 'You can't do that. Put those things down.'

'Oh . . . all right.' He dropped the apples and made for the tree. 'I'll get hold of her for you, anyway.'

'Wait a minute.' I seized his coat as he passed. 'I'll do it. You stay down here and try to catch her if she jumps.'

Tristan looked disappointed but I gave him a warning look. The way the cat had moved, it struck me that it only needed a bit of my colleague's ebullience to send the animal winging into the next county. I began to climb the tree.

I like cats, I've always liked them, and since I feel that animals recognise this in a person I have usually been able to approach and handle the most difficult types. It is not too much to say that I prided myself on my cat technique; I didn't foresee any trouble here.

Puffing slightly, I reached the top branch and extended a hand to the crouching animal.

'Pooss-pooss,' I cooed, using my irresistible cat tone.

Georgina eyed me coldly and gave no answering sign other than a higher arching of the back.

I leaned further along the branch. 'Pooss-pooss, pooss-pooss.' My voice was like molten honey, my finger near her face. I would rub her cheek ever so gently and she would be mine. It never failed.

'Pah!' replied Georgina warningly but I took no heed and touched the fur under her chin.

'Pah-pah!' Georgina spat and followed with a lightning left hook which opened a bloody track across the back of my hand.

Muttering fervently, I retreated and nursed my wounds. From below Mrs Beck gave a tinkling laugh.

'Oh, isn't she a little monkey! She's that playful, bless her.'

I snorted and began to ease my way along the branch again. This time, I thought grimly, I would dispense with finesse. The quick grab was indicated here.

As though reading my thoughts the little creature tripped to the end of the branch and as it bent low under her weight she dropped lightly to the grass.

Tristan was on her in a flash, throwing himself full length and seizing her by the hind leg. Georgina whipped round and unhesitatingly sank her teeth into his thumb but Tristan's core of resilience showed. After a single howl of agony he changed his grip at lightning speed to the scruff of the neck.

A moment later he was standing upright holding a dangling fighting fury high in the air.

'Right, Jim,' he called happily. 'I have her.'

'Good lad! Hang on!' I said breathlessly and slithered down the tree as quickly as I could. Too quickly, in fact, as an ominous ripping sound announced the removal of a triangular piece of my jacket elbow.

But I couldn't bother with trifles. Ushering Tristan at a gallop into the house I opened the cardboard box. There were no sophisticated cat containers in those days and it was a tricky job to enclose Georgina, who was lashing out in all directions and complaining bitterly in a bad-tempered wail.

It took a panting ten minutes to imprison the cat but even with several yards of rough twine round the floppy cardboard I still didn't feel very secure as I bore it to the car.

Mrs Beck raised a finger as we were about to drive away. I carefully explored my lacerated hand and Tristan sucked his thumb as we waited for her to speak.

'Mr. Herriot, I 'ope you'll be gentle with 'er,' she said anxiously. 'She's very timid, you know.'

We had covered barely half a mile before sounds of strife arose from the back.

'Get back! Get in there. Get back, you bugger!'

I glanced behind me. Tristan was having trouble. Georgina clearly didn't care for the motion of the car and from the slits in the box clawed feet issued repeatedly; on one occasion an enraged spitting face got free as far as the neck. Tristan kept pushing everything back with great resolution but I could tell from the rising desperation of his cries that he was fighting a losing battle.

I heard the final shout with a feeling of inevitability.

'She's out, Jim! The bugger's out!'

Well this was great. Anybody who has driven a car with a hysterical cat hurtling around the interior will appreciate my situation. I crouched low over the wheel as the furry creature streaked round the sides or leaped clawing at the roof or windscreen with Tristan lunging vainly after her.

But cruel fate had not finished with us yet. My colleague's gasps and grunts from the rear ceased for a moment to be replaced by a horrified shriek.

'The bloody thing's shitting, Jim! She's shitting everywhere!'

The cat was obviously using every weapon at her disposal and he didn't have to tell me. My nose was way ahead of him, and I frantically wound down the window. But I closed it just as quickly at the rising image of Georgina escaping and disappearing into the unknown.

I don't like to think of the rest of that journey. I tried to breathe through my mouth and Tristan puffed out dense clouds of Woodbine smoke but it was still pretty terrible. Just outside Darrowby I stopped the car and we made a concerted onslaught on the animal; at the cost of a few more wounds, including a particularly painful scratch on my nose, we cornered her and fastened her once more in the box.

Even on the operating table Georgina had a few tricks left. We were using ether and oxygen as anaesthetic and she was particularly adept at holding her breath while the mask was on her face then returning suddenly to violent life when we thought she was asleep. We were both sweating when she finally went under.

I suppose it was inevitable, too, that she should be a difficult case. Ovaro-hysterectomy in the cat is a fairly straightforward procedure and nowadays we do innumerable cases uneventfully, but in the thirties, particularly in country practice, it was infrequently done and consequently a much larger undertaking.

I personally had my own preferences and aversions in this field. For instance, I found thin cats easy to do and fat cats difficult. Georgina was extremely fat.

When I opened her abdomen an ocean of fat welled up at me,

obscuring everything, and I spent a long nerve-racking period lifting out portions of bowel or omentum with my forceps, surveying them gloomily and stuffing them back in again. A great weariness had begun to creep over me by the time I at last managed to grip the pink ovary between the metallic jaws and drew forth the slender string of uterus. After that it was routine, but I still felt a strange sense of exhaustion as I inserted the last stitch.

I put the sleeping cat into the box and beckoned to Tristan. 'Come on, let's get her home before she comes round.' I was starting along the passage when he put his hand on my arm.

'Jim,' he said gravely. 'You know I'm your friend.'

'Yes, Triss, of course.'

'I'd do anything for you, Jim.'

'I'm sure you would.'

He took a deep breath. 'Except one thing. I'm not going back in that bloody car.'

I nodded dully. I really couldn't blame him.

'That's all right,' I said. 'I'll be off then.'

Before leaving I sprinkled the interior with pine-smelling disinfectant but it didn't make much difference. In any case my main emotion was the hope that Georgina wouldn't wake up before I got to Rayton, and that was shattered before I had crossed Darrowby market place. The hair prickled on the back of my neck as an ominous droning issued from the box on the rear seat. It was like the sound of a distant swarm of bees but I knew what it meant; the anaesthetic was wearing off.

Once clear of the town I put my foot on the boards. This was something I rarely did because whenever I pushed my vehicle above forty miles an hour there was such a clamour of protest from engine and body that I always feared the thing would disintegrate around me. But at this moment I didn't care. Teeth clenched, eyes staring, I hurtled forward, but I didn't see the lonely strip of tarmac or the stone walls flitting past; all my attention was focused behind me, where the swarm of bees was getting nearer and the tone angrier.

When it developed into a bad-tempered yowling and was accompanied by the sound of strong claws tearing at cardboard I began to tremble. As I thundered into Rayton village I glanced behind me. Georgina was half out of the box. I reached back and grasped her scruff and when I stopped at the gate of Jasmine Cottage I pulled on the brake with one hand and lifted her on to my lap with the other.

I sagged in the seat, my breath escaping in a great explosion of relief; and my stiff features almost bent into a smile as I saw Mrs Beck pottering in her garden.

She took Georgina from me with a cry of joy but gasped in horror when she saw the shaven area and the two stitches on the cat's flank.

'Oooh, my darlin'! What 'ave those nasty men been doin' to you?' She hugged the animal to her and glared at me.

'She's all right, Mrs Beck, she's fine,' I said. 'You can give her a little milk tonight and some solid food tomorrow. There's nothing to worry about.'

She pouted. 'Oh, very well. And now . . .' She gave me a sidelong glance. 'I suppose you'll want your money?'

'Well, er . . .'

'Wait there, then. I'll get it.' She turned and went into the house.

Standing there, leaning against the reeking car, feeling the sting of the scratches on my hands and nose and examining the long tear on my jacket elbow I felt physically and emotionally spent. All I had done this afternoon was spay a cat but I had nothing more to offer.

Apathetically I watched the lady coming down the path. She was carrying a purse. At the gate she stopped and faced me.

'Ten shillin's, wasnt' it?'

'That's right.'

She rummaged in the purse for some time before pulling out a ten-shilling note which was regarded sadly.

'Oh Georgina, Georgina, you *are* an expensive pussy,' she soliloquised.

Tentatively I began to extend my hand but she pulled the note away. 'Just a minute, I'm forgettin'. You 'ave to take the stitches out, don't you?'

'Yes, in ten days.'

She set her lips firmly. 'Well there's plenty of time to pay ye then—ye'll be here again.'

'Here again . . . ? But you can't expect . . .'

'I allus think it's unlucky to pay afore a job's finished,' she said. 'Summat terrible might happen to Georgina.'

'But . . . but . . .'

'Nay, ah've made up me mind,' she said. She replaced the money and snapped the purse shut with an air of finality before turning towards the house. Halfway up the path she looked over her shoulder and smiled.

'Aye, that'll be the best way. Ye can collect your full fee on your final visit.'

CHAPTER

18

We were ready to march away from Scarborough. And it was ironical that we were leaving just when the place was beginning to smile on us.

In the May sunshine we stood on parade outside the Grand at 7 a.m. as we had done throughout the Yorkshire winter, mostly in darkness, often with the icy rain blowing in our faces. But now I felt a pang of regret as I looked over the heads at the wide beautiful bay stretching beneath its cliffs to the far head-land, the sand clean-washed and inviting, the great blue expanse of sea shimmering and glittering and over everything the deli-cious sea-smell of salt and seaweed, raising memories of holidays and happy things lost in the war.

'Atten-shun!' Flight Sergeant Blackett's bellow rolled over us as we stiffened in our ranks, every man carrying full kit, our packs braced with sheets of cardboard to give the sharp, rec-tangular look, hair cut short, boots gleaming, buttons shining like gold. Without our knowing, No. ten ITW had moulded us into a smart, disciplined unit, very different from the shambling, half-baked crew of six months ago. We had all passed our exams and were no longer AC2s but Leading Aircraftsmen, and as LAC Herriot my wage had rocketed from three shillings to a dizzying seven and threepence a day.

'Right turn!' Again the roar. 'By the left qui-ick march!'

Arms high, moving as one, we swung past the front of the Grand for the last time. I shot a parting glance at the great build-ing—like a dignified Victorian lady stripped of her finery—and I made a resolve. I would come back some day, when the war was over, and see the Grand Hotel as it should be.

And I did, too. Years later, Helen and I sat in deep armchairs in the lounge where the SPs had barked. Waiters padded over the thick carpets with tea and muffins while a string orchestra played selections from *Rose Marie*.

And in the evening we dined in the elegant room with its long unbroken line of window looking down on the sea. This room had been the cold open terrace where I learned to read the Aldis lamp flickering from the lighthouse, but now we sat in luxurious warmth eating grilled sole and watching the lights of the harbour and town beginning to wink in the gathering dusk.

But that was very much in the future as the tramping feet echoed along Huntriss Row on the way to the station and the long lines of blue left the emptying square. We didn't know where we were going, everything was uncertain.

Black's *Veterinary Dictionary* dug into my back through the layer of cardboard. It was an unwieldy article but it reminded me of good days and gave me hope of more to come.

'It's the same the whole world over, it's the poor wot gets the blame. It's the rich wot gets the pleasure . . .'

We were on a 'toughening course', living under canvas in the depths of Shropshire, and this was one of the occasions when we were all gathered together—hundreds of sunburned men—in a huge marquee waiting to be addressed by a visiting air commodore.

Before the great man arrived the platform was occupied by a lascivious sergeant who was whittling away the time by leading us in a succession of bawdy ditties accompanied by gestures. 'It's the rich wot gets the . . .', but instead of 'pleasure' he made a series of violent pumping movements with his forearm.

I was intrigued by the reaction of the airman on my right. He was a slim, pink-faced lad of about nineteen and his lank fair hair fell over his face as he jumped up and down. He was really throwing himself into it, bawling out the indelicate words, duplicating the sergeant's gesticulations with maniacal glee. He was, I had recently learned, the son of a bishop.

We had been joined on this course by the Oxford University Air Squadron. They were a group of superior and delicately nurtured young men and since I had spent three full days peeling potatoes with them I had come to know most of them very well. 'Spud bashing' is an unequalled method of becoming familiar with one's fellow men and as, hour after hour, we filled countless bins with our produce, the barriers crumbled steadily until at the end of three days we didn't have many secrets from each other.

The bishop's son had found something hilarious in the idea of a qualified veterinary surgeon leaving his practice to succour his country by removing the skins from thousands of tubers. And I, on the other hand, derived some reward from watching his antics. He was a charming and likeable lad but he seized avidly on anything with the faintest salacious slant. They say parsons' sons are a bit wild when let off the leash, and I suppose an escapee from a bishop's palace is even more susceptible to the blandishments of the big world.

I looked at him again. All around him men were yelling their heads off, but his voice, mouthing the four-letter words with relish, rang above the rest and he followed the actions of the conducting sergeant like a devoted acolyte.

It was all so different from Darrowby. My early days in the RAF with all the swearing and uninhibited conversation made me realise, perhaps for the first time, what kind of community I had left behind me. Because I often think that one of the least permissive societies in the history of mankind was the agricultural community of rural Yorkshire in the thirties. Among the farmers anything to do with sex or the natural functions was unmentionable.

It made my work more difficult because if the animal's ailment had the slightest sexual connotation its owner would refuse to go into details if Helen or our secretary Miss Harbottle answered the 'phone. 'I want the vet to come and see a cow,' was as far as they would go.

Today's case was typical and I looked at Mr Hopps with some irritation.

'Why didn't you say your cow wasn't coming into season? There's a new injection for that now but I haven't got it with me. I can't carry everything in my car, you know.'

The farmer studied his feet. 'Well, it was a lady on t'phone and I didn't like to tell 'er that Snowdrop wasn't bullin'.' He looked up at me sheepishly. 'Can't you do owt about it, then?'

I sighed. 'Maybe I can. Bring me a bucket of hot water and some soap.'

As I lathered my arm I felt a twinge of disappointment. I'd have liked to try that new Prolan injection. But on the other hand there was a certain interest in these rectal examinations.

'Hold her tail, please,' I said, and began to work my hand carefully past the anal ring.

We were doing a lot of this lately. The profession had awakened quite suddenly to the fact that bovine infertility was no longer an impenetrable mystery. We were carrying out more and more of these examinations, and as I say, they had a strange fascination.

Siegfried put it with his usual succinctness one morning.

'James,' he said. 'There is more to be learned up a cow's arse than in many an encyclopedia.'

And, groping my way into this animal, I could see what he meant. Through the rectal wall I gripped the uterine cervix, then I worked along the right horn. It felt perfectly normal, as did the fallopian tube when I reached it. In another moment the ovary rested between my fingers like a walnut; but it was a walnut with a significant bulge and I smiled to myself. That swelling was the corpus luteum, the 'yellow body' which was exerting its influence on the ovary and preventing the initiation of the normal oestral cycle.

I squeezed gently on the base of the bulge and felt it part from the ovary and swim off into space. That was lovely—just what was required—and I looked happily along the cow's back at the farmer.

'I think I've put things right, Mr Hopps. She should come on within the next day or two and you can get her served right away.'

I withdrew my arm, smeared with filth almost to the shoulder, and began to swill it with the warm water. This was the moment when young people with dewy-eyed ambitions to be veterinary surgeons usually decided to be lawyers or nurses instead. A lot of teenagers came round with me to see practice and it seemed to me that the sooner they witnessed the realities of the job the better it would be for them. A morning's pregnancy diagnoses or something similar had a salutary effect in sorting out the sheep from the goats.

As I left the farm I had the satisfied feeling that I had really done something, and a sensation of relief that Mr Hopps' delicacy hadn't resulted in an abortive visit.

And when little Mr Gilby crashed moaning on the cobbles of his byre floor, my first thought was that it was unfair that it should happen to him of all people.

Because the natural delicacy and reticence of the times were embodied in him to an extreme degree. Even his physical make-up had something ethereal about it; nine stones of tiny bones, taut skin with no fat and a gentle, innocent face, almost child-like despite his fifty years. Nobody had ever heard Mr Gilby swear or use a vulgar expression; in fact he was the only farmer I have ever known who talked about cow's 'manure'.

Besides, as a strict methodist he didn't drink or indulge in worldly pleasures and had never been known to tell a lie. Altogether he was so good that I would have regarded him with deep suspicion if he had been anybody else. But I had come to know Mr. Gilby. He was a nice little man, he was as honest as the day. I would have trusted him with my life.

That was why I was so sad to see him lying there. It had happened so quickly. We had only just come into the byre and he had pointed to a black Angus Cross cow almost opposite the door.

'That's er. Got a touch o'cold, I think.' He knew I would want to take the temperature and grasped the tail before putting one foot across the channel so that he could slide between the cow and her neighbour. That was when it happened; when his legs were wide apart in the worst possible position.

In a way I wasn't surprised because that tail had been swishing bad-temperedly as we came in, and I am always a bit wary of black cows anyway. She didn't seem to like our sudden entry and lashed out with her right hind foot with the speed of light, catching him with her flinty hoof full in the crutch as his legs were splayed. He was wearing only frayed, much-washed overall trousers and the protection was nil.

I winced as the foot went home with an appalling thud, but Mr Gilby showed no emotion at all. He dropped as though on the receiving end of a firing squad and lay motionless on the hard stones, his hands clutched between his legs. It was only after several seconds that he began to moan softly.

As I hurried to his aid I felt it was wrong that I should be witnessing this disintegration of his modest façade. The little farmer, I was sure, would rather have died than be caught in this inelegant position, grovelling on the floor gripping frantically at an unmentionable area. I kneeled on the cobbles and patted his shoulder while he fought his inner battle with his agony.

After a while he felt well enough to sit up and I put my arm around him and supported him while perspiration bedewed the greenish pallor of his face. That was when the embarrassment began to creep in, because though he had removed his hands from their compromising position he was clearly deeply ashamed at being caught in a coarse attitude.

I felt strangely helpless. The little man couldn't relieve his feelings in the usual way by cursing the animal and fate in general, nor could I help him to laugh the thing off with a few earthy remarks. This sort of thing happens now and then in the present day and usually gives rise to a certain amount of ripe comment, often embracing the possible effect on the victim's future sex life. It all helps.

But here in Mr Gilby's byre there was only an uncomfortable silence. After a time the colour began to return to his cheeks and the little man struggled slowly to his feet. He took a couple of deep breaths then looked at me unhappily. Obviously he thought he owed me some explanation, even apology, for his tasteless behaviour.

As the minutes passed the tension rose. Mr Gilby's mouth twitched once or twice as though he were about to speak but he seemed unable to find the words. At length he appeared to come to a decision. He cleared his throat, looked around him carefully then put his lips close to my ear. He clarified the whole situation by one hoarsely whispered, deeply confidential sentence.

'Right in the privates, Mr. Herriot.'

CHAPTER

20

Little pictures kept floating up into my mind. Memories from the very early days at Skeldale House. Before the RAF, before Helen. . . .

Siegfried and I were at breakfast in the big dining-room. My colleague looked up from a letter he was reading.

'James, do you remember Stewie Brannan?'

I smiled. 'I could hardly forget. That was quite a day at Brawton races.' I would always carry a vivid recollection of Siegfried's amiable college chum with me.

'Yes . . . yes, it was.' Siegfried nodded briefly. 'Well I've got a letter from him here. He's got six kids now, and though he doesn't complain, I don't think life is exactly a picnic working in a dump like Hensfield. Especially when he knocks a bare living out of it.' He pulled thoughtfully at the lobe of his ear. 'You know, James, it would be rather nice if he could have a break. Would you be willing to go through there and run his practice for a couple of weeks so that he could take his family on holiday?'

'Certainly. Glad to. But you'll be a bit pushed here on your own, won't you?'

Siegfried waved a hand. 'It'll do me good. Anyway it's the quiet time for us. I'll write back today.'

Stewie grasped the opportunity eagerly and within a few days I was on the road to Hensfield. Yorkshire is the biggest county in England and it must be the most varied. I could hardly believe it when, less than two hours after leaving the clean grassy fells and crystal air of Darrowby, I saw the forest of factory chimneys sprouting from the brown pall of grime.

This was the industrial West Riding and I drove past mills as dark and satanic as any I had dreamed of, past long rows of dreary featureless houses where the workers lived. Everything was black; houses, mills, walls, trees, even the surrounding hill-sides, smeared and soiled from the smoke which drifted across the town from a hundred belching stacks.

Stewie's surgery was right in the heart of it, a gloomy edifice in a terrace of sooty stone. As I rang the bell I read the painted board: 'Stewart Brannan MRCVS, Veterinary Surgeon and Canine Specialist.' I was wondering what the Royal College would think about the last part when the door opened and my colleague stood before me.

He seemed to fill the entrance. If anything he was fatter than before, but that was the only difference. Since it was August I couldn't expect him to be wearing his navy nap overcoat, but otherwise he was as I remembered him in Darrowby; the big, meaty, good-natured face, the greasy black hair slicked across the brow which always seemed to carry a gentle dew of per-spiration.

He reached out, grabbed my hand and pulled me delightedly through the doorway.

'Jim! Great to see you!' He put an arm round my shoulders as we crossed a dark hallway. 'It's a good of you to help me out like this. The family are thrilled—they're all in the town shop-ping for the holiday. We've got fixed up in a flat at Blackpool.' His permanent smile widened.

We went into a room at the back where a rickety kitchen-type table stood on brown linoleum. I saw a sink in one corner, a few shelves with bottles and a white-painted cupboard. The atmosphere held a faint redolence of carbolic and cat's urine.

'This is where I see the animals,' Stewie said contentedly. He looked at his watch. 'Twenty past five—I have a surgery at five thirty. I'll show you round till then.'

It didn't take long because there wasn't much to see. I knew there was a more fashionable veterinary firm in Hensfield and that Stewie made his living from the poor people of the town; the whole set-up was an illustration of practice on a shoestring. There didn't seem to be more than one of anything—one straight suture needle, one curved needle, one pair of scissors, one syringe. There was a sparse selection of drugs and an extraor-dinary array of dispensing bottles and jars. These bottles were of many strange shapes—weird things which I had never seen in a dispensary before.

Stewie seemed to read my thoughts. 'It's nothing great, Jim.

I haven't a smart practice and I don't make a lot, but we manage to clear the housekeeping and that's the main thing.'

The phrase was familiar. 'Clear the housekeeping'—that was how he had put it when I first met him at Brawton races. It seemed to be the lodestar of his life.

The end of the room was cut off by a curtain which my colleague drew to one side.

'This is what you might call the waiting room.' He smiled as I looked in some surprise at half a dozen wooden chairs arranged round the three walls. 'No high-powered stuff, Jim, no queues into the streets, but we get by.'

Some of Stewie's clients were already filing in; two little girls with a black dog, a cloth-capped old man with a terrier on a string, a teenage boy carrying a rabbit in a basket.

'Right,' the big man said. 'We'll get started.' He pulled on a white coat, opened the curtain and said, 'First please.'

The little girls put their dog on the table. He was a long-tailed mixture of breeds and he stood trembling with fear, rolling his eyes apprehensively at the white coat.

"All right, lad,' Stewie murmured. 'I'm not going to hurt you.' He stroked and patted the quivering head before turning to the girls. 'What's the trouble, then?'

'It's 'is leg, 'e's lame,' one of them replied.

As if in confirmation the little dog raised a fore leg and held it up with a pitiful expression. Stewie engulfed the limb with his great hand and palpated it with the utmost care. And it struck me immediately—the gentleness of this shambling bear of a man.

'There's nothing broken,' he said. 'He's just sprained his shoulder. Try to rest it for a few days and rub this in night and morning.'

He poured some whitish liniment from a winchester bottle into one of the odd-shaped bottles and handed it over.

One of the little girls held out her hand and unclasped her fingers to reveal a shilling in her palm.

'Thanks,' said Stewie without surprise. 'Goodbye.'

He saw several other cases, then as he was on his way to the curtain two grubby urchins appeared through the door at the other end of the room. They carried a clothes basket containing a widely varied assortment of glassware.

Stewie bent over the basket, lifting out HP sauce bottles,

pickle jars, ketchup containers and examining them with the air of a connoisseur. At length he appeared to come to a decision.

'Threepence,' he said.

'Sixpence,' said the urchins in unison.

'Fourpence,' grunted Stewie.

'Sixpence,' chorused the urchins.

'Fivepence,' my colleague muttered doggedly.

'Sixpence!' There was a hint of triumph in the cry.

Stewie sighed. 'Go on then.' He passed over the coin and began to stack the bottles under the sink.

'I just scrape off the labels and give them a good boil up, Jim.'

'I see.'

'It's a big saving.'

'Yes, of course.' The mystery of the strangely shaped dispensing bottles was suddenly resolved.

It was six thirty when the last client came through the curtain. I had watched Stewie examining each animal carefully, taking his time and treating their conditions ably within the confines of his limited resources. His charges were all around a shilling or two shillings and it was easy to see why he only just cleared the housekeeping.

One other thing I noticed; the people all seemed to like him. He had no 'front' but he was kind and concerned. I felt there was a lesson there.

The last arrival was a stout lady with a prim manner and a very correct manner of speech.

'My dog was bit last week,' she announced, 'and I'm afraid the wound is goin' antiseptic.'

'Ah yes.' Stewie nodded gravely. The banana fingers explored the tumefied area on the animal's neck with a gossamer touch. 'It's quite nasty, really. He could have an abscess there if we're not careful.'

He took a long time over clipping the hair away, swabbing out the deep puncture with peroxide of hydrogen. Then he puffed in some dusting powder, applied a pad of cotton wool and secured it with a bandage. He followed with an anti-staphylococcal injection and finally handed over a sauce bottle filled to the rim with acriflavine solution.

'Use as directed on the label,' he said, then stood back as the lady opened her purse expectantly.

A long inward struggle showed in the occasional twitches of his cheeks and flickerings of his eyelids but finally he squared his shoulders.

'That,' he said resolutely, 'will be three and sixpence.'

It was a vast fee by Stewie's standards, but probably the minimum in other veterinary establishments, and I couldn't see how he could make any profit from the transaction.

As the lady left, a sudden uproar broke out within the house. Stewie gave me a seraphic smile.

'That'll be Meg and the kids. Come and meet them.'

We went out to the hall and into an incredible hubbub. Children shouted, screamed and laughed, spades and pails clattered, a large ball thumped from wall to wall and above it all a baby bawled relentlessly.

Stewie moved into the mob and extracted a small woman.

'This,' he murmured with quiet pride, 'is my wife.' He gazed at her like a small boy admiring a film star.

'How do you do,' I said.

Meg Brannan took my hand and smiled. Any glamour about her existed only in her husband's eye. A ravaged prettiness still remained but her face bore the traces of some tough years. I could image her life of mother, housewife, cook, secretary, receptionist and animal nurse.

'Oh, Mr Herriot, it is good of you and Mr Farnon to help us out like this. We're so looking forward to going away.' Her eyes held a faintly desperate gleam but they were kind.

I shrugged. 'Oh it's a pleasure, Mrs Brannan. I'm sure I'll enjoy it and I hope you all have a marvellous holiday.' I really meant it—she looked as though she needed one.

I was introduced to the children but I never really got them sorted out. Apart from the baby, who yelled indefatigably from leather lungs, I think there were three little boys and two little girls, but I couldn't be sure—they moved around too quickly.

The only time they were silent was for a brief period at supper when Meg fed them and us from a kind of cauldron in which floated chunks of mutton, potatoes and carrots. It was very good, too, and was followed by a vast blancmange with jam on top.

The tumult broke out again very soon as the youngsters raced through their meal and began to play in the room. One thing I found disconcerting was that the two biggest boys kept throwing a large, new, painted ball from one to the other across the table as we ate. The parents said nothing about it—Meg, I felt, because she had stopped caring, and Stewie because he never had cared.

Only once when the ball whizzed past my nose and almost carried away a poised spoonful of blancmange did their father remonstrate.

'Now then, now then,' he murmured absently, and the throwing was re-sited more towards the middle of the table.

Next morning I saw the family off. Stewie had changed his dilapidated Austin Seven for a large rust-encrusted Ford V Eight. Seated at the wheel he waved and beamed through the cracked side windows with serene contentment. Meg, by his side, managed a harassed smile and at the other windows an assortment of dogs and children fought for a vantage point. As the car moved away a pram, several suitcases and a cot swayed perilously on the roof, the children yelled, the dogs barked, the baby bawled, then they were gone.

As I re-entered the house the unaccustomed silence settled around me, and with the silence came a faint unease. I had to look after this practice for two weeks and the memory of the thinly furnished surgery was not reassuring. I just didn't have the tools to tackle any major problem.

But it was easy to comfort myself. From what I had seen this wasn't the sort of place where dramatic things happened. Stewie had once said he made most of his living by castrating tom cats and I supposed if you threw in a few ear cankers and minor ailments that would be about it.

The morning surgery seemed to confirm this impression; a few humble folk led in nondescript pets with mild conditions and I happily dispensed a series of Bovril bottles and meat paste jars containing Stewie's limited drug store.

I had only one difficulty and that was with the table, which kept collapsing when I lifted the animals on to it. For some obscure reason it had folding legs held by metal struts underneath and these were apt to disengage at crucial moments, causing the patient to slide abruptly to the floor. After a while I got the hang of the thing and kept one leg jammed against the struts throughout the examination.

It was about 10.30 a.m. when I finally parted the curtains and found the waiting room empty and only the distinctive cat-dog smell lingering on the air. As I locked the door it struck me that I had very little to do till the afternoon surgery. At Darrowby I would have been dashing out to start the long day's driving round the countryside, but here almost all the work was done at the practice house.

I was wondering how I would put the time in after the single outside visit on the book when the door bell rang. Then it rang again followed by a frantic pounding on the wood. I hurried through the curtain and turned the handle. A well dressed young couple stood on the step. The man held a Golden Labrador in his arms and behind them a caravan drawn by a large gleaming car stood by the kerb.

'Are you the vet?' the girl gasped. She was in her twenties, auburn haired, extremely attractive, but her eyes were terrified.

I nodded. 'Yes—yes, I am. What's the trouble?'

'It's our dog.' The young man's voice was hoarse, his face deathly pale. 'A car hit him.'

I glanced over the motionless yellow form. 'Is he badly hurt?'

There were a few moments of silence then the girl spoke almost in a whisper. 'Look at his hind leg.'

I stepped forward and as I peered into the crook of the man's arm a freezing wave drove through me. The limb was hanging off at the hock. Not fractured but snapped through the joint and dangling from what looked like a mere shred of skin. In the bright morning sunshine the white ends of naked bones glittered with a sickening lustre.

It seemed a long time before I came out of my first shock and found myself staring stupidly at the animal. And when I spoke the voice didn't sound like my own.

'Bring him in,' I muttered, and as I led the way back through the odorous waiting room the realisation burst on me that I had been wrong when I thought that nothing ever happened here.

21

I held the curtains apart as the young man staggered in and placed his burden on the table.

Now I could see the whole thing; the typical signs of a road accident; the dirt driven savagely into the glossy gold of the coat, the mutiple abrasions. But that mangled leg wasn't typical. I had never seen anything like it before.

I dragged my eyes round to the girl. 'How did it happen?'

'Oh, just in a flash.' The tears welled in her eyes. 'We are on a caravanning holiday. We had no intention of staying in Hensfield'—(I could understand that)—'but we stopped for a newspaper, Kim jumped out of the car and that was it.'

I looked at the big dog stretched motionless on the table. I reached out a hand and gently ran my fingers over the noble outlines of the head.

'Poor old lad,' I murmured and for an instant the beautiful hazel eyes turned to me and the tail thumped briefly against the wood.

'Where have you come from?' I asked.

'Surrey,' the young man replied. He looked rather like the prosperous young stockbroker that the name conjured up.

I rubbed my chin. 'I see. . . .' A way of escape shone for a moment in the tunnel. 'Perhaps if I patch him up you could get him back to your own vet there.'

He looked at his wife for a moment then back at me. 'And what would they do there? Amputate his leg?'

I was silent. If an animal in this condition arrived in one of those high-powered southern practices with plenty of skilled assistance and full surgical equipment that's what they probably would do. It would be the only sensible thing.

The girl broke in on my thoughts. 'Anyway, if it's at all possible to save his leg something has to be done right now. Isn't that so?' She gazed at me appealingly.

'Yes,' I said huskily. 'That's right.' I began to examine the dog. The abrasions on the skin were trivial. He was shocked but his mucous membranes were pink enough to suggest that there was no internal haemorrhage. He had escaped serious injury except for that terrible leg.

I stared at it intently, appalled by the smooth glistening articular surfaces of the tibio-tarsal joint. There was something obscene in its exposure in a living animal. It was as though the hock had been broken open by brutal inquisitive hands.

I began a feverish search of the premises, pulling open drawers, cupboards, opening tins and boxes. My heart leaped at each little find; a jar of catgut in spirit, a packet of lint, a sprinkler tin of iodoform, and—treasure trove indeed—a bottle of barbiturate anaesthetic.

Most of all I needed antibiotics, but it was pointless looking for those because they hadn't been discovered yet. But I did hope fervently for just an ounce or two of sulphanilamide, and there I was disappointed, because Stewie's menage didn't stretch to that. It was when I came upon the box of plaster of paris bandages that something seemed to click.

At that time in the late thirties the Spanish civil war was vivid in people's minds. In the chaos of the later stages there had been no proper medicaments to treat the terrible wounds. They had often been encased in plaster and left, in the grim phrase, to 'stew in their own juice'. Sometimes the results were surprisingly good.

I grabbed the bandages. I knew what I was going to do. Gripped by a fierce determination I inserted the needle into the radial vein and slowly injected the anaesthetic. Kim blinked, yawned lazily and went to sleep. I quickly laid out my meagre armoury then began to shift the dog into a better position. But I had forgotten about the table and as I lifted the hind quarters the whole thing gave way and the dog slithered helplessly towards the floor.

'Catch him!' At my frantic shout the man grabbed the inert form, then I reinserted the slots in their holes and got the wooden surface back on the level.

'Put your leg under there,' I gasped, then turned to the girl. 'And would you please do the same at the other end. This table mustn't fall over once I get started.'

Silently they complied and as I looked at them, each with a

leg jammed against the underside, I felt a deep sense of shame. What sort of place did they think this was?

But for a long time after I forgot everything. First I put the joint back in place, slipping the ridges of the tibial-tarsal trochlea into the grooves at the distal end of the tibia as I had done so often in the anatomy lab at college. And I noticed with a flicker of hope that some of the ligaments were still intact and, most important, that a few good blood vessels still ran down to the lower part of the limb.

I never said a word as I cleaned and disinfected the area, puffed iodoform into every crevice and began to stitch. I stitched interminably, pulling together shattered tendons, torn joint capsule and fascia. It was a warm morning and as the sun beat on the surgery window the sweat broke out on my forehead. By the time I had sutured the skin a little river was flowing down my nose and dripping from the tip. Next, more iodoform, then the lint and finally two of the plaster bandages, making a firm cast above the hock down over the foot.

I straightened up and faced the young couple. They had never moved from their uncomfortable postures as they held the table upright but I gazed at them as though seeing them for the first time.

I mopped my brow and drew a long breath. 'Well, that's it. I'd be inclined to leave it as it is for a week, then wherever you are let a vet have a look at it.'

They were silent for a moment then the girl spoke. 'I would rather you saw it yourself.' Her husband nodded agreement.

'Really?' I was amazed. I had thought they would never want to see me, my smelly waiting room or my collapsible table again.

'Yes, of course we would,' the man said. 'You have taken such pains over him. Whatever happens we are deeply grateful to you, Mr Brannan.'

'Oh, I'm not Mr Brannan, he's on holiday. I'm his locum, my name is Herriot.'

He held out his hand. 'Well thank you again, Mr Herriot. I am Peter Gillard and this is my wife. Marjorie.'

We shook hands and he took the dog in his arms and went out to the car.

For the next few days I couldn't keep Kim's leg out of my mind. At times I felt I was crazy trying to salvage a limb that was joined to the dog only by a strip of skin. I had never met anything remotely like it before and in unoccupied moments the hock joint with all its imponderables would float across my vision.

There were plenty of these moments because Stewie's was a restful practice. Apart from the three daily surgeries there was little activity, and in particular the uncomfortable pre-breakfast call so common in Darrowby was unknown here.

The Brannans had left the house and me in the care of Mrs Holroyd, an elderly widow of raddled appearance who slouched around in a flowered overall down which ash cascaded from a permanently dangling cigarette. She wasn't a good riser but she soon had me trained, because after a few mornings when I couldn't find her I began to prepare my own breakfast and that was how it stayed.

However, at other times she looked after me very well. She was what you might call a good rough cook and pushed large tasty meals at me regularly with a 'There y'are, luv,' watching me impassively till I started to eat. The only thing that disturbed me was the long trembling finger of ash which always hung over my food from the cigarette that was part of her.

Mrs Holroyd also took telephone messages when I wasn't around. There weren't many outside visits but two have stuck in my memory.

The first was when I looked on the pad and read, 'Go to Mr Pimmarov to see bulldog,' in Mrs Holroyd's careful backsloped script.

'Pimmarov?' I asked her. 'Was he a Russian gentleman?'

'Dunno, luv, never asked 'im.'

'Well—did he sound foreign? I mean did he speak broken English?'

'Nay, luv, Yorkshire as me, 'e were.'

'Ah well, never mind, Mrs Holroyd. What's his address?'

She gave me a surprised look. 'How should ah know? He never said.'

'But . . . but Mrs Holroyd. How can I visit him when I don't know where he lives?'

'Well you'll know best about that, luv.'

I was baffled. 'But he must have told you.'

'Now then, young man, Pimmarov was all 'e told me. Said you would know.' She stuck out her chin, her cigarette quivered and she regarded me stonily. Maybe she had had similar sessions

◄ 171 ►

with Stewie, but she left me in no doubt that the interview was over.

During the day I tried not to think about it but the knowledge that somewhere in the nighbourhood there was an ailing bulldog that I could not succour was worrying. I just hoped it was nothing fatal.

A phone call at 7 p.m. resolved my fears.

'Is that t'vet?' The voice was gruff and grumpy.

'Yes . . . speaking.'

'Well, ah've been waitin' all day for tha. When are you comin' to see ma flippin' bulldog?'

A light glimmered. But still . . . that accent . . . no suggestion of the Kremlin . . . not a hint of the Steppes.

'Oh, I'm terribly sorry,' I gabbled. 'I'm afraid there's been a little misunderstanding. I'm doing Mr Brannan's work and I don't know the district. I do hope your dog isn't seriously ill.'

'Nay, nay, nobbut a bit o' cough, but ah want 'im seein' to.'

'Certainly, certainly, I'll be right out, Mr . . . er . . .'

'Pym's ma name and ah live next to t'post office in Roff village.'

'Roff?'

'Aye, two miles outside Hensfield.'

I sighed with relief. 'Very good, Mr Pym, I'm on my way.'

'Thank ye.' The voice sounded mollified. 'Well, tha knows me now, don't tha—Pym o' Roff.'

The light was blinding. 'Pym o' Roff!' Such a simple explanation.

A lot of Mrs Holroyd's messages were eccentric but I could usually interpret them after some thought. However one bizarre entry jolted me later in the week. It read simply: 'Johnson, 12, Back Lane, Smiling Harry Syphilis.'

I wrestled with this for a long time before making a diffident approach to Mrs Holroyd.

She was kneading dough for scones and didn't look up as I entered the kitchen.

'Ah, Mrs Holroyd.' I rubbed my hands nervously. 'I see you have written down that I have to go to Mr Johnson's.'

'That's right, luv.'

'Well, er . . . fine, but I don't quite understand the other part—the Smiling Harry Syphilis.'

She shot a sidelong glance at me. 'Well that's 'ow you spell the word, isn't it? Ah looked it up once in a doctor's book in our 'ouse,' she said defensively.

'Oh yes, of course, yes, you've spelled it correctly. It's just the Smiling . . . and the Harry.'

Her eyes glinted dangerously and she blew a puff of smoke at me. 'Well, that's what t'feller said. Repeated it three times. Couldn't make no mistake.'

'I see. But did he mention any particular animal?'

'Naw, 'e didn't. That was what 'e said. That and no more.' A grey spicule of ash toppled into the basin and was immediately incorporated in the scones. 'Ah do ma best, tha knows!'

'Of course you do, Mrs Holroyd,' I said hastily. 'I'll just pop round to Back Lane now.'

And Mr Johnson put everything right within seconds as he led me to a shed on his allotment.

'It's me pig, guvnor. Covered wi' big red spots. Reckon it's Swine Erysipelas."

Only he pronounced it arrysipelas and he did have a slurring mode of speech. I really couldn't blame Mrs Holroyd.

Little things like that enlivened the week but the tension still mounted as I awaited the return of Kim. And even when the seventh day came round I was still in suspense because the Gillards did not appear at the morning surgery. When they failed to show up at the afternoon session I began to conclude that they had had the good sense to return south to a more sophisticated establishment. But at five thirty they were there.

I knew it even before I pulled the curtains apart. The smell of doom was everywhere, filling the premises, and when I went through the curtains it hit me; the sickening stink of putrefaction.

Gangrene. It was the fear which had haunted me all week and now it was realised.

There were about half a dozen other people in the waiting room, all keeping as far away as possible from the young couple who looked up at me with strained smiles. Kim tried to rise when he saw me but I had eyes only for the dangling useless hind limb where my once stone-hard plaster hung in sodden folds.

Of course it had to happen that the Gillards were last in and I was forced to see all the other animals first. I examined them and prescribed treatment in a stupor of misery and shame. What had I done to that beautiful dog out there? I had been crazy to try that experiment. A gangrenous leg meant that even amputation might be too late to save his life. Death from septicaemia was likely now and what the hell could I do for him in this ramshackle surgery?

When at last it was their turn the Gillards came in with Kim limping between them, and it was an extra stab to realise afresh what a handsome animal he was. I bent over the great golden head and for a moment the friendly eyes looked into mine and the tail waved.

'Right,' I said to Peter Gillard, putting my arms under the chest. 'You take the back end and we'll lift him up.'

As we hoisted the heavy dog on to the table the flimsy structure disintegrated immediately, but this time the young people were ready for it and thrust their legs under the struts like a well-trained team till the surface was level again.

With Kim stretched on his side I fingered the bandage. It usually took time and patience with a special saw to remove a plaster but this was just a stinking pulp. My hands shook as I cut the bandage lengthways with scissors and removed it.

I had steeled myself against the sight of the cold dead limb with its green flesh but though there was pus and serous fluid everywhere the exposed flesh was a surprising, healthy pink. I took the foot in my hand and my heart gave a great bound. It was warm and so was the leg, right up to the hock. There was no gangrene.

Feeling suddenly weak I leaned against the table. 'I'm sorry about the terrible smell. All the pus and discharge have been decomposing under the bandage for a week but despite the mess it's not as bad as I feared.'

'Do you . . . do you think you can save his leg?' Marjorie Gillard's voice trembled.

'I don't know. I honestly don't know. So much has to happen. But I'd say it was a case of so far so good.'

I cleaned the area thoroughly with spirit, gave a dusting of iodoform and applied fresh lint and two more plaster bandages.

'You'll feel a lot more comfortable now, Kim,' I said, and the big dog flapped his tail against the wood at the sound of his name.

I turned to his owners. 'I want him to have another week in plaster, so what would you like to do?'

'Oh, we'll stay around Hensfield,' Peter Gillard replied. 'We've found a place for our caravan by the river—it's not too bad.'

'Very well, till next Saturday, then.' I watched Kim hobble out, holding his new white cast high, and as I went back into the house relief flowed over me in a warm wave.

But at the back of my mind the voice of caution sounded. There was still a long way to go. . . .

CHAPTER
22

The second week went by without incident. I had a mildly indecent postcard from Stewie and a view of Blackpool Tower from his wife. The weather was scorching and they were having the best holiday of their lives. I tried to picture them enjoying themselves but I had to wait a few weeks for the evidence—a snap taken by a beach photographer. The whole family were standing in the sea, grinning delightedly into the camera as the wavelets lapped round their ankles. The children brandished buckets and spades, the baby dangled bandy legs towards the water, but it was Stewie who fascinated me. A smile of blissful contentment beamed from beneath a knotted handkerchief, sturdy braces supported baggy flannel trousers rolled decorously calf high. He was the archetype of the British father on holiday.

The last event of my stay in Hensfield was a visit to the local greyhound track. Stewie had an appointment there every other Friday to inspect the dogs.

The Hensfield stadium was not prepossessing from the outside. It had been built in a natural hollow in the sooty hills and was surrounded by ramshackle hoardings.

It was a cool night and as I drove down to the entrance I could hear the tinny blaring from the loudspeakers. It was George Formby singing 'When I'm Cleaning Windows' and strumming on his famous ukelele.

There are all kinds of greyhound tracks. My own experience had been as a student, accompanying vets who officiated under the auspices of the National Greyhound Racing Club, but this was an unlicensed or 'flapping' track, and vastly different. I know there are many highly reputable flapping tracks but this one had a seedy air. It was, I thought wryly, just the sort of place that would be under the care of Stewie.

First I had to go to the manager's office. Mr Coker was a

hard-eyed man in a shiny pin-striped suit and he nodded briefly before giving me a calculating stare.

'Your duties here are just a formality,' he said, twisting his features into a smile. 'There'll be nothing to trouble you.'

I had the impression that he was assessing me with quiet satisfaction, looking me up and down, taking in my rumpled jacket and slacks, savouring my obvious youth and inexperience. He kept the smile going as he stubbed out his cigar. 'Well, I hope you'll have a pleasant evening.'

'Thank you,' I replied, and left.

I met the judge, timekeeper and other officials then went down to a long glass-fronted bar overlooking the track. Quite suddenly I felt I was in an alien environment. The place was rapidly filling up and the faces around me were out of a different mould from the wholesome rural countenances of Darrowby. There seemed to be a large proportion of fat men in camel coats with brassy blondes in tow. Shifty-looking characters studied race cards and glared intently at the flickering numbers on the tote board.

I looked at my watch. It was time to inspect the dogs for the first race. 'When I'm cleanin' winders!' bawled George Formby as I made my way round the edge of the track to the paddock, a paved enclosure with a wire-netting surround. Five dogs were being led round the perimeter and I stood in the centre and watched them for a minute or two. Then I halted them and went from one to the other, looking at their eyes, examining their mouths for salivation and finally palpating their abdomens.

They all appeared bright and normal except number four which seemed rather full in the stomach region. A greyhound should only have a light meal on the morning of a race and nothing thereafter and I turned to the man who was holding the animal.

'Has this dog been fed within the last hour or two?' I asked.

'No,' he replied. 'He's had nothing since breakfast.'

As I passed my fingers over the abdomen again I had the feeling that several of the onlookers were watching me with unusual intentness. But I dismissed it as imagination and passed on to the next animal.

Number four was second favourite but from the moment it left its trap it was flagging. It finished last and from the darkness on the far side of the track a storm of booing broke out. I was able to make out some of the remarks which came across on the night air. 'Open your bloody eyes, vet!' was one of them. And here, in the long, brightly lit bar I could see people nudging each other and looking at me.

I felt a thrill of anger. Maybe some of those gentlemen down there thought they could cash in on Stewie's absence. I probably looked a soft touch to them.

My next visit to the paddock was greeted with friendly nods and grins from all sides. In fact there was a strong atmosphere of joviality. When I went round the dogs all was well until I came to number five and this time I couldn't be mistaken. Under my probing fingers the stomach bulged tensely and the animal gave a soft grunt as I squeezed.

'You'll have to take this dog out of the race,' I said. 'He's got a full stomach.'

The owner was standing by the kennel lad.

'Can't 'ave!' he burst out. 'He's had nowt!'

I straightened up and looked him full in the face but his eyes were reluctant to meet mine. I knew some of the tricks; a couple of pounds of steak before the race; a bowlful of bread crumbs and two pints of milk—the crumbs swelled beautifully within a short time.

'Would you like me to vomit him?' I began to move away. 'I've got some washing soda in my car—we'll soon find out.'

The man held up a hand. 'Naw, naw, I don't want you messin' about with me dog.' He gave me a malevolent glare and trailed sulkily away.

I had only just got back to the bar when I heard the announcement over the loudspeakers. 'Will the vet please report to the manager's office.'

Mr Coker looked up from his desk and glared at me through a haze of cigar smoke. 'You've taken a dog out of the race!'

'That's right. I'm sorry, but his stomach was full.'

'But damn it . . . !' He stabbed a finger at me then sbusided and forced a tortured smile across his face. 'Now, Mr Herriot, we have to be reasonable in these matters. I've no doubt you know your job, but don't you think there's just a chance you could be wrong?' He waved his cigar expansively. 'After all, anybody can make a mistake, so perhaps you would be kind enough to reconsider.' He stretched his smile wider.

'No, I'm sorry, Mr Coker, but that would be impossible.'

There was a long pause. 'That's your last word, then?'

'It is.'

The smile vanished and he gave me a threatening stare.

'Now look,' he said. 'You've mucked up that race and it's a serious matter. I don't want any repetition, do you understand?' He ground his cigar out savagely and his jaw jutted. 'So I hope we won't have any more trouble like this.'

'I hope so, too, Mr Coker,' I said as I went out.

It seemed a long way down to the paddock on my next visit. It was very dark now and I was conscious of the hum of the crowd, the shouts of the bookies and George and his ukelele still going full blast. 'Oh, don't the wind blow cold!' he roared.

This time it was dog number two. I could feel the tension as I examined him and found the same turgid belly.

'This one's out,' I said, and apart from a few black looks there was no argument.

They say bad news travels fast and I had hardly started my return journey when George was switched off and the loud-speaker asked me to report to the manager's office.

Mr Coker was no longer at his desk. He was pacing up and down agitatedly and when he saw me he did another length of the room before coming to a halt. His expression was venomous and it was clear he had decided that the tough approach was best.

'What the bloody hell do you thing you're playing at?' he barked. 'Are you trying to ruin this meeting?'

'No,' I replied. 'I've just taken out another dog which was unfit to run. That's my job. That's what I'm here for.'

His face flushed deep red. 'I don't think you know what you're here for. Mr Brannan goes off on holiday and leaves us at the mercy of a young clever clogs like you, throwing your weight about and spoiling people's pleasure. Wait till I see him!'

'Mr Brannan would have done just the same as I have. Any veterinary surgeon would.'

'Rubbish! Don't tell me what it's all about—you're still wet behind the ears.' He advanced slowly towards me. 'But I'll tell you this, I've had enough! So get it straight, once and for all —no more of this nonsense. Cut it out!'

I felt my heart thudding as I went down to see the dogs for

the next race. As I examined the five animals the owners and kennel lads fixed me with a hypnotic stare as though I were some strange freak. My pulse began to slow down when I found there were no full stomachs this time and I glanced back in relief along the line. I was about to walk away when I noticed that number one looked a little unusual. I went back and bent over him, trying to decide what it was about him that had caught my attention. Then I realised what it was—he looked sleepy. The head was hanging slightly and he had an air of apathy.

I lifted his chin and looked into his eyes. The pupils were dilated and every now and then there was a faint twitch of nystagmus. There was absolutely no doubt about it—he had received some kind of sedative. He had been doped.

The men in the paddock were very still as I stood upright. For a few moments I gazed through the wire netting at the brightly lit green oval, feeling the night air cold on my cheeks. George was still at it on the loudspeakers.

'Oh Mr Wu,' he trilled. 'What can I do?'

Well I knew what I had to do, anyway. I tapped the dog on the back.

'This one's out,' I said.

I didn't wait for the announcement and was half way up the steps to the manager's office before I heard the request for my presence blared across the stadium.

When I opened the door I half expected Mr Coker to rush at me and attack me and I was surprised when I found him sitting at his desk, his head buried in his hands. I stood there on the carpet for some time before he raised a ghastly countenance to me.

'Is it true?' he whispered despairingly. 'Have you done it again?'

I nodded. 'Afraid so.'

His lips trembled but he didn't say anything, and after a brief, disbelieving scrutiny he sank his head in his hands again.

I waited for a minute or two but when he stayed like that, quite motionless, I realised that the audience was at an end and took my leave.

I found no fault with the dogs for the next race and as I left the paddock an unaccustomed peace settled around me. I couldn't understand it when I heard the loudspeaker again—

'Will the vet please report . . .' But this time it was to the paddock and I wondered if a dog had been injured. Anyway, it
would be a relief to do a bit of real vetting for a change.

But when I arrived there were no animals to be seen; only
two men cradling a fat companion in their arms.

'What's this?' I asked one of them.

'Ambrose 'ere fell down the steps in the stand and skinned
'is knee.'

I stared at him. 'But I'm a vet, not a doctor.'

'Ain't no doctor on the track,' the man mumbled. 'We reckoned you could patch 'im up.'

Ah well, it was a funny night. 'Put him over on that bench,'
I said.

I rolled up the trouser to reveal a rather revolting fat dimpled
knee. Ambrose emitted a hollow groan as I touched a very
minor abrasion on the patella.

'It's nothing much,' I said. 'You've just knocked a bit of
skin off.'

Ambrose looked at me tremblingly. 'Aye, but it could go
t'wrong way, couldn't it? I don't want no blood poisonin'.'

'All right, I'll put something on it.' I looked inside Stewie's
medical bag. The selection was limited but I found some tincture
of iodine and I poured a little on a pad of cotton wool and
dabbed the wound.

Ambrose gave a shrill yelp. 'Bloody 'ell, that 'urts! What are
you doin' to me?' His foot jerked up and rapped me sharply
on the elbow.

Even my human patients kicked me, it seemed. I smiled
reassuringly. 'Don't worry, it won't sting for long. I'll put a
bandage on now.'

I bound up the knee, rolled down the trouser and patted
the fat man's shoulder. 'There you are—good as new.'

He got off the bench, nodded, then grimacing painfully,
prepared to leave. But an afterthought appeared to strike him
and he pulled a handful of change from his pocket. He rummaged among it with a forefinger before selecting a coin which
he pressed into my palm.

'There y'are,' he said.

I looked at the coin. It was a sixpence, the fee for my only
piece of doctoring of my own species. I stared stupidly at it
for a long time and when I finally looked up with the half-

formed idea of throwing Ambrose's honorarium back at his head the man was limping into the crowd and was soon lost to sight.

Back in the bar I was gazing apathetically through the glass at the dogs parading round the track when I felt a hand on my arm. I turned and recognised a man I had spotted earlier in the evening. He was one of a group of three men and three women, the men dark, tight-suited, the women loud and over-dressed. There was something sinister about them and I remembered thinking that in different clothes the men could have passed without question as a group of bandits.

The man put his face close to mine and I had a brief impression of black, darting eyes and a predatory smile.

'Is number three fit?' he whispered.

I couldn't understand the question. He seemed to know I was the vet and surely it was obvious that if I had passed the dog I considered him fit.

'Yes,' I replied. 'Yes, he is.'

The man nodded vigorously and gave me a knowing glance from hooded eyes. He returned and held a short, intimate conversation with his friends, then they all turned and looked over at me approvingly.

I was bewildered, then it struck me that they may have thought I was giving them an inside tip. To this day I am not really sure but I think that was it because when number three finished nowhere in the race their attitude changed dramatically and they flashed me some black glares which made them look more like bandits than ever.

Anyway I had no more trouble down at the paddock for the rest of the evening. No more dogs to take out, which was just as well, because I had made enough enemies for one night.

After the last race I looked around the long bar. Most of the tables were occupied by people having a final drink, but I noticed an empty one and sank wearily into a chair. Stewie had asked me to stay for half an hour after the finish to make sure all the dogs got away safely and I would stick to my bargain even though what I wanted most in the world was to get away from here and never come back.

George was still in splendid voice on the loudspeakers. 'I always get to bed by half past nine,' he warbled, and I felt strongly that he had a point there.

Along the bar counter were assembled most of the people with whom I had clashed; Mr Coker and other officials and dog owners. There was a lot of nudging and whispering and I didn't have to be told the subject of their discussion. The bandits, too, were doing their bit with fierce side glances and I could almost feel the waves of antagonism beating against me.

My gloomy thoughts were interrupted by the arrival of a bookie and his clerk. The bookie dropped into a chair opposite me and tipped out a huge leather bag on to the table. I had never seen so much money in my life. I peered at the man over a mountain of fivers and pounds and ten-shilling notes while little streams and tributaries of coins ran down its flanks.

The two of them began a methodical stacking and counting of the loot while I watched hypnotically. They had eroded the mountain to about half its height when the bookie caught my eye. Maybe he thought I looked envious or poverty-stricken or just miserable because he put his finger behind a stray half crown and flicked it expertly across the smooth surface in my direction.

'Get yourself a drink, son,' he said.

It was the second time I had been offered money during the last hour and I was almost as much taken aback as the first time. The bookie looked at me expressionlessly for a moment then he grinned. He had an attractively ugly, good-natured face that I liked instinctively and suddenly I felt grateful to him, not for the money but for the sight of a friendly face. It was the only one I had seen all evening.

I smiled back. 'Thanks,' I said. I lifted the half crown and went over to the bar.

I awoke next morning with the knowledge that it was my last day at Hensfield. Stewie was due back at lunch time.

When I parted the now familiar curtains at the morning surgery I still felt a vague depression, a hangover from my unhappy night at the dog track.

But when I looked into the waiting room my mood lightened immediately. There was only one animal among the odd assortment of chairs but that animal was Kim, massive, golden and beautiful, sitting between his owners, and when he saw me he sprang up with swishing tail and laughing mouth.

There was none of the smell which had horrified me before

but as I looked at the dog I could sniff something else—the sweet, sweet scent of success. Because he was touching the ground with that leg; not putting any weight on it but definitely dotting it down as he capered around me.

In an instant I was back in my world again and Mr Coker and the events of last night were but the dissolving mists of a bad dream.

I could hardly wait to get started.

'Get him on the table,' I cried, then began to laugh as the Gillards automatically pushed their legs against the collapsible struts. They knew the drill now.

I had to restrain myself from doing a dance of joy when I got the plaster off. There was a bit of discharge but when I cleaned it away I found healthy granulation tissue everywhere. Pink new flesh binding the shattered joint together, smoothing over and hiding the original mutilation.

'Is his leg safe now?' Marjorie Gillard asked softly.

I looked at her and smiled. 'Yes, it is. There's no doubt about it now.' I rubbed my hand under the big dog's chin and the tail beat ecstatically on the wood. 'He'll probably have a stiff joint but that won't matter, will it?'

I applied the last of Stewie's bandages then we hoisted Kim off the table.

'Well, that's it,' I said. 'Take him to your own vet in another fortnight. After that I don't think he'll need a bandage at all.'

The Gillards left on their journey back to the south and a couple of hours later Stewie and his family returned. The children were very brown; even the baby, still bawling resolutely, had a fine tan. The skin had peeled off Meg's nose but she looked wonderfully relaxed. Stewie, in open necked shirt and with a face like a boiled lobster, seemed to have put on weight.

'That holiday saved our lives, Jim,' he said. 'I can't thank you enough, and please tell Siegfried how grateful we are.' He looked fondly at his turbulent brood flooding through the house, then as an afterthought he turned to me.

'Is everything all right in the practice?'

'Yes, Stewie, it is. I had my ups and downs of course.'

He laughed. 'Don't we all.'

'We certainly do, but everything's fine now.'

And everything did seem fine as I drove away from the smoke. I watched the houses thin and fall away behind me till the whole world opened out clean and free and I saw the green line of the fells rising over Darrowby.

I suppose we all tend to remember the good things but as it turned out I had no option. The following Christmas I had a letter from the Gillards with a packet of snapshots showing a big golden dog clearing a gate, leaping high for a ball, strutting proudly with a stick in his mouth. There was hardly any stiffness in the leg, they said; he was perfectly sound.

So even now when I think of Hensfield the thing I remember best is Kim.

23

There was a lot of shouting in the RAF. The NCOs always seemed to be shouting at me or at somebody else and a lot of them had impressively powerful voices. But for sheer volume I don't think any of them could beat Len Hampson.

I was on the way to Len's farm and on an impulse I pulled up the car and leaned for a moment on the wheel. It was a hot still day in late summer and this was one of the softer corners of the Dales, sheltered by the enclosing fells from the harsh winds which shrivelled all but the heather and the tough moorland grass.

Here, great trees, oak, elm and sycamore in full rich leaf, stood in gentle majesty in the green dips and hollows, their branches quite still in the windless air.

In all the grassy miles around me I could see no movement, nor could I hear anything except the fleeting hum of a bee and the distant bleating of a sheep.

Through the open window drifted the scents of summer; warm grass, clover and the sweetness of hidden flowers. But in the car they had to compete with the all-pervading smell of cow. I had spent the last hour injecting fifty wild cattle and I sat there in soiled breeches and sweat-soaked shirt looking out sleepily at the tranquil landscape.

I opened the door and Sam jumped out and trotted into a nearby wood. I followed him into the cool shade, into the damp secret fragrance of pine needles and fallen leaves which came from the dark heart of the crowding boles. From somewhere in the branches high above I could hear that most soothing of sounds, the cooing of a woodpigeon.

Then, although the farm was two fields away, I heard Len Hampson's voice. He wasn't calling the cattle home or anything like that. He was just conversing with his family as he always did in a long tireless shout.

I drove on to the farm and he opened the gate to let me into the yard.

'Good morning, Mr Hampson,' I said.

'NOW THEN, MR HERRIOT, he bawled. 'IT'S A GRAND MORNIN'.'

The blast of sound drove me back a step but his three sons smiled contentedly. No doubt they were used to it.

I stayed at a safe distance. 'You want me to see a pig.'

'AYE, A GOOD BACON PIG. GONE RIGHT OFF. IT HASN'T ATE NOWT FOT TWO DAYS.'

We went into the pig pen and it was easy to pick out my patient. Most of the big white occupants careered around at the sight of a stranger, but one of them stood quietly in a corner.

It isn't often a pig will stand unresisting as you take its temperature but this one never stirred as I slipped the thermometer into its rectum. There was only a slight fever but the animal had the look of doom about it; back slightly arched, unwilling to move, eyes withdrawn and anxious.

I looked up at Len Hampson's red-faced bulk leaning over the wall of the pen.

'Did this start suddenly or gradually?' I asked.

'RIGHT SUDDEN!' In the confined space the full throated yell was deafening. 'HE WERE AS RIGHT AS NINEPENCE ON MONDAY NIGHT AND LIKE THIS ON TUESDAY MORNIN'.'

I felt my way over the pig's abdomen. The musculature was tense and boardlike and the abdominal contents were difficult to palpate because of this, but the whole area was tender to the touch.

'I've seen them like this before,' I said. 'This pig has a ruptured bowel. They do it when they are fighting or jostling each other, especially when they are full after a meal.'

'WHAT'S GOIN' TO 'APPEN THEN?'

'Well, the food material has leaked into the abdomen, causing peritonitis. I've opened up pigs like this and they are a mass of adhesions—the abdominal organs all growing together. I'm afraid the chances of recovery are very small.'

He took off his cap, scratched his bald head and replaced the tattered headgear. 'THAT'S A BUGGER. GOOD PIG AN' ALL. IS IT 'OPELESS?' He still gave tongue at the top of his voice despite his disappointment.

'Yes, I'm afraid it's pretty hopeless. They usually eat very little and just waste away. It would really be best to slaughter him.'

'NAY, AH DON'T LIKE THAT MUCH! AH ALLUS LIKE TO 'AVE A GO. ISN'T THERE SUMMAT WE CAN DO? WHERE THERE'S LIFE THERE'S 'OPE, THA KNAWS.'

I smiled. 'I suppose there's always some hope, Mr Hampson.'

'WELL THEN, LET'S GET ON. LET'S TRY!'

'All right.' I shrugged. 'He's not really in acute pain—more discomfort—so I suppose there's no harm in treating him. I'll leave you a course of powders.'

As I pushed my way from the pen I couldn't help noticing the superb sleek condition of the other pigs.

'My word,' I said. 'These pigs are in grand fettle. I've never seen a better lot. You must feed them well.'

It was a mistake. Enthusiasm added many decibels to his volume.

'*Aye!*' he bellowed. 'YOU'VE GOT TO GIVE STOCK A BIT O' GOOD STUFF TO MEK 'EM DO RIGHT!'

My head was still ringing when I reached the car and opened the boot. I handed over a packet of my faithful sulphonamide powders. They had done great things for me but I didn't expect much here.

It was strange that I should go straight from the chief shouter of the practice to the chief whisperer. Elijah Wentworth made all his communications *sotto voce*.

I found Mr Wentworth hosing down his cow byre and he turned and looked at me with his habitual serious expression. He was a tall thin man, very precise in his speech and ways, and though he was a hard-working farmer he didn't look like one. This impression was heightened by his clothes which were more suited to office work than his rough trade.

A fairly new trilby hat sat straight on his head as he came over to me. I was able to examine it thoroughly because he came so close that we were almost touching noses.

He took a quick look around him. 'Mr Herriot,' he whispered, 'I've got a real bad case.' He spoke always as though every pronouncement was of the utmost gravity and secrecy.

'Oh I'm sorry to hear that. What's the trouble?'

'Fine big bullock, Mr Herriot. Goin' down fast.' He moved

in closer till he could murmur directly into my ear. 'I suspect TB.' He backed away, face drawn.

'That doesn't sound so good,' I said. 'Where is he?'

The farmer crooked a finger and I followed him into a loose box. The bullock was a Hereford Cross and should have weighed about ten hundredweight, but was gaunt and emaciated. I could understand Mr Wentworth's fears, but I was beginning to develop a clinical sense and it didn't look like TB to me.

'Is he coughing?' I asked.

'No, never coughs, but he's a bit skittered.'

I went over the animal carefully and there were a few things —the submaxillary oedema, the pot-bellied appearance, the pallor of the mucous membranes—which made diagnosis straightforward.

'I think he's got liver fluke, Mr Wentworth. I'll take a dung sample and have it examined for fluke eggs but I want to treat him right away.'

'Liver fluke? Where would he pick that up?'

'Usually from a wet pasture. Where has he been running lately?'

The farmer pointed through the door. 'Over yonder. I'll show you.'

I walked with him a few hundred yards and through a couple of gates into a wide flat field lying at the base of the fell. The squelchy feel of the turf and the scattered tufts of bog grass told the whole story.

'This is just the place for it,' I said. 'As you know, it's a parasite which infests the liver, but during its life cycle it has to pass through a snail and that snail can only live where there is water.'

He nodded slowly and solemnly several times then began to look around him and I knew he was going to say something. Again he came very close then scanned the horizon anxiously. In all directions the grassland stretched empty and bare for miles but he still seemed worried he might be overheard.

We were almost cheek to cheek as he breathed the words into my ear. 'Ah know who's to blame for this.'

'Really? Who is that?'

He made another swift check to ensure that nobody had sprung up through the ground then I felt his hot breath again. 'It's me landlord.'

'How do you mean?'

'Won't do anything for me.' He brought his face round and looked at me wide-eyed before taking up his old position by my ear. 'Been goin' to drain this field for years but done nowt.'

I moved back. 'Ah well, I can't help that, Mr Wentworth. In any case there's other things you can do. You can kill the snails with copper sulphate—I'll tell you about that later—but in the meantime I want to dose your bullock.'

I had some hexachlorethane with me in the car and I mixed it in a bottle of water and administered it to the animal. Despite his bulk he offered no resistance as I held his lower jaw and poured the medicine down his throat.

'He's very weak, isn't he?' I said.

The farmer gave me a haggard look. 'He is that. I doubt he's a goner.'

'Oh don't give up hope, Mr Wentworth. I know he looks terrible but if it is fluke then the treatment will do a lot for him. Let me know how he goes on.'

It was about a month later, on a market day, and I was strolling among the stalls which packed the cobbles. In front of the entrance to the Drovers' Arms the usual press of farmers stood chatting among themselves, talking business with cattle dealers and corn merchants, while the shouts of the stallholders sounded over everything.

I was particularly fascinated by the man in charge of the sweet stall. He held up a paper bag and stuffed into it handfuls of assorted sweetmeats while he kept up a nonstop brazen-voiced commentary.

'Lovely peppermint drops! Delicious liquorice allsorts! How about some sugar candies! A couple o' bars o' chocolate! Let's 'ave some butterscotch an' all! Chuck in a beautiful slab o' Turkish Delight!' Then holding the bulging bag aloft in triumph "ere! 'ere! Who'll give me a tanner for the lot?'

Amazing, I thought as I moved on. How did he do it? I was passing the door of the Drovers when a familiar voice hailed me.

'HEY! MR HERRIOT!' There was no mistaking Len Hampson. He hove in front of me, red-faced and cheerful. 'REMEMBER THAT PIG YE DOCTORED FOR ME?' He had clearly consumed a few market-day beers and his voice was louder than ever.

The packed mass of farmers pricked up their ears. There is nothing so intriguing as the ailments of another farmer's livestock.

'Yes, of course, Mr Hampson,' I replied.

'WELL 'E NEVER DID NO GOOD!' bawled Len.

I could see the farmers' faces lighting up. It is more interesting still when things go wrong.

'Really? Well I'm sorry.'

'NAW 'E DIDN'T. AH'VE NEVER SEEN A PIG GO DOWN AS FAST!'

'Is that so?'

'AYE, FLESH JUST MELTED OFF 'IM!'

'Oh, what a pity. But if you recall I rather expected . . .'

'WENT DOWN TO SKIN AND BONE 'E DID!' The great bellow rolled over the market place, drowning the puny cries of the stallholders. In fact the man with the sweets had suspended operations and was listening with as much interest as the others.

I looked around me uneasily. 'Well, Mr Hampson, I did warn you at the time . . .'

'LIKE A WALKIN' SKELETON 'E WERE! NEVER SEEN SUCH A OBJECK!'

I realised Len wasn't in the least complaining. He was just telling me, but for all that I wished he would stop.

'Well, thank you for letting me know,' I said. 'Now I really must be off . . .'

'AH DON'T KNOW WHAT THEM POWDERS WERE YOU GAVE 'IM.'

I cleared my throat. 'Actually they were . . .'

'THEY DID 'IM NO BLOODY GOOD ANY ROAD!'

'I see. Well as I say, I have to run . . .'

'AH GOT MALLOCK TO KNOCK 'IM ON T'HEAD LAST WEEK.'

'Oh dear . . .'

'FINISHED UP AS DOG MEAT, POOR BUGGER!'

'Quite . . . quite . . .'

'WELL, GOOD DAY TO YE, MR HERRIOT.' He turned and walked away, leaving a quivering silence behind him.

With an uncomfortable feeling that I was the centre of attention I was about to retreat hastily when I felt a gentle hand on my arm. I turned and saw Elijah Wentworth.

'Mr Herriot,' he whispered. 'About that bullock.'

I stared at him, struck by the coincidence. The farmers stared, too, but expectantly.

'Yes, Mr Wentworth?'

"Well now, I'll tell you.' He came very near and breathed into my ear. 'It was like a miracle. He began to pick up straight away after you treated him.'

I stepped back. 'Oh marvellous! But speak up, will you, I can't quite hear you.' I looked around hopefully.

He came after me again and put his chin on my shoulder. 'Yes, I don't know what you gave 'im but it was wonderful stuff. I could hardly believe it. Every day I looked at 'im he had put on a bit more.'

'Great! But do speak a little louder,' I said eagerly.

'He's as fat as butter now.' The almost inaudible murmur wafted on my cheek. 'Ah'm sure he'll get top grade at the auction mart.'

I backed away again. 'Yes . . . yes . . . what was that you said?'

'I was sure he was dyin', Mr Herriot, but you saved him by your skill,' he said, but every word was pianissimo, sighed against my face.

The farmers had heard nothing and, their interest evaporating, they began to talk among themselves. Then as the man with the sweets started to fill his bags and shout again Mr Wentworth moved in and confided softly and secretly into my private ear.

'That was the most brilliant and marvellous cure I 'ave ever seen.'

24

It must be unusual to feel senile in one's twenties, but it was happening to me. There were a few men of my own age among my RAF friends but for the most part I was surrounded by eighteen- and nineteen-year-olds.

It seemed that the selection boards thought this the optimum age for training pilots, navigators and air gunners and I often wondered how we elderly gentlemen had managed to creep in.

These boys used to pull my leg. The fact that I was not merely married but a father put me in the dotage class, and the saddest part was that I really did feel old in their company. They were all having the most marvellous time; chasing the local girls, drinking, going to dances and parties, carried along on the frothy insouciance which a war engenders. And I often thought that if it had all happened a few years earlier I would have been doing the same.

But it was no good now. Most of me was still back in Darrowby. During the day there was enough pressure to keep my mind occupied in the evenings when I was off the leash all I wanted to do were the simple things I had done with Helen; the long games of bezique by the fireside in our bedsitter, tense battles on the push-ha'penny board; we even used to throw rings at hooks on a board on the wall. Kids' games after a hard slog round the practice, but even now as I look down the years I know I have never found a better way of living.

It was when we were lying in bed one night that Helen brought up the subject of Granville Bennett.

'Jim,' she murmured sleepily. 'Mr Bennett 'phoned again today. And his wife rang last week. They keep asking us to have a meal with them.'

'Yes . . . yes . . .' I didn't want to talk about anything at that moment. This was always a good time. The dying flames sent lights and shadows dancing across the ceiling. Oscar Rabin's band was playing *Deep Purple* on the bedside radio Ewan Ross gave us for a wedding present and I had just pulled off an unexpected victory at push-ha'penny. Helen was a dab hand at that game, urging the coins expertly up the board with the ball of her thumb, her lips pushed forward in a pout of concentration. Of course she had a lifetime of experience behind her while I was just learning, and it was inevitable that I seldom won. But I had done it tonight and I felt good.

My wife nudged me with her knee. 'Jim, I can't understand you. You never seem to do anything about it. And yet you say you like him.'

'Oh, I do, he's a grand chap, one of the best.' Everybody liked Granville, but at the same time there were many strong men who dived down alleys at the sight of him. I didn't like to tell Helen that every time I came into contact with him I got my wings singed. I fully realised that he meant well, that the whole thing was a natural extension of his extreme generosity. But it didn't help.

'And you said his wife was very nice, too.'

'Zoe? Oh yes, she's lovely.' And she was, too, but thanks to her husband she had never seen me in any other role than a drunken hulk. My toes curled under the blankets. Zoe was beautiful, kind and intelligent—just the kind of woman you wanted to observe you staggering and hiccuping all over the place. In the darkness I could feel the hot blush of shame on my cheeks.

'Well then,' Helen continued, with the persistence that is part of even the sweetest women. 'Why don't we accept their invitation? I'd rather like to meet them—and it's a bit embarrassing when they keep 'phoning.'

I turned on my side. 'Okay, we'll go one of these days, I promise.'

But if it hadn't been for the little papilloma on Sam's lip I don't think we would ever have got there. I noticed the thing —a growth smaller than a pea—near the left commissure when I was giving our beagle an illicit chocolate biscuit. It was a typical benign tumour and on anybody else's dog I should have administered a quick local and whipped it off in a minute. But since it was Sam I turned pale and phoned Granville.

I have always been as soppy as any old lady over my pets and I suspect many of my colleagues are the same. I listened apprehensively to the buzz-buzz at the far end, then the big voice came on the line.

'Bennett here.'

'Hello, Granville, it's . . ."

'Jim!' The boom of delight was flattering. 'Where have you been hiding yourself, laddie?'

He didn't know how near he was to the truth. I told him about Sam.

'Doesn't sound much, old son, but I'll have a look at him with pleasure. Tell you what. We've been trying to get you over here for a meal—why not bring the little chap with you?'

'Well . . .' A whole evening in Granville's hands—it was a daunting prospect.

'Now don't mess about, Jim. You know, there's a wonderful Indian restaurant in Newcastle. Zoe and I would love to take you both out there. It's about time we met your wife, isn't it?'

'Yes . . . of course it is. . . . Indian restaurant, eh?'

'Yes, laddie. Suberb curries—mild, medium or blast your bloody head off. Onion bhajis, bhuna lamb, gorgeous nan bread.'

My mind was working fast. 'Sounds marvellous, Granville.' It did seem fairly secure. He was most dangerous on his own territory and it would take forty-five minutes' driving each way to Newcastle. Then maybe an hour and a half in the restaurant. I should be reasonably safe for most of the evening. There was just the bit at his house before we left—that was the only worry.

It was uncanny how he seemed to read my thoughts. 'Before we leave, Jim, we'll have a little session in my garden.'

'Your garden?' It sounded strange in November.

'That's right, old lad.'

Ah well, maybe he was proud of his late chrysanthemums, and I couldn't see myself coming to much harm there. 'Well, fine, Granville. Maybe Wednesday night?'

'Lovely, lovely, lovely—can't wait to meet Helen.'

Wednesday was one of those bright frosty late autumn days which turn misty in the afternoon and by six o'clock the countryside was blanketed by one of the thickest fogs I had ever seen in Yorkshire.

Creeping along in our little car, my nose almost on the windscreen, I muttered against the glass.

'God's truth, Helen, we'll never get to Newcastle tonight! I know Granville's some driver but you can't see ten yards out there.'

Almost at walking pace we covered the twenty miles to the Bennett residence and it was with a feeling of relief that I saw the brightly lit doorway rising out of the mirk.

Granville, as vast and impressive as ever, was there in the hall with arms outspread. Bashfulness had never been one of his problems and he folded my wife in a bear-like embrace.

'Helen, my pet,' he said and kissed her fondly and lingeringly. He stopped to take a breath, regarded her for a moment with deep appreciation then kissed her again.

I shook hands decorously with Zoe and the two girls were introduced. They made quite a picture standing there. An attractive woman is a gift from heaven and it was a rare bonus to see two of them in close proximity. Helen very dark and blue-eyed, Zoe brown-haired with eyes of greyish-green, but both of them warm and smiling.

Zoe had her usual effect on me. That old feeling was welling up; the desire to look my best, in fact better than my best. I cast a furtive glance at the hall mirror. Immaculately suited, clean shirted, freshly shaven, I was sure I projected the desired image of the clean-limbed young veterinary surgeon, the newly married man of high principles and impeccable behaviour.

I breathed a silent prayer of thanks that at last she was seeing me stone cold sober and normal. Tonight I would expunge all her squalid memories of me from her mind.

'Zoe, my sweet,' carolled Granville. 'Take Helen into the garden while I see Jim's dog.'

I blinked. The garden in this fog. I just didn't get it, but I was too anxious about Sam to give the thing much thought. I opened the car door and the beagle trotted into the house.

My colleague greeted him with delight. 'Come inside, my little man.' Then he hollered at the top of his voice. 'Phoebles! Victoria! Yoo-hoo! Come and meet cousin Sam!'

The obese Staffordshire bull terrier waddled in, closely followed by the Yorkie, who bared her teeth in an ingratiating smile at all present.

After the dogs had met and exchanged pleasantries Granville lifted Sam into his arms.

'Is that what you mean, Jim? Is that what you're worried about?'

I nodded dumbly.

'Good God, I could take a deep breath and blow the damn thing off!' He looked at me incredulously and smiled. 'Jim, old lad, why are you so daft about your dog?'

'Why do you call Phoebe Phoebles?' I countered swiftly.

'Oh well . . .' He cleared his throat. 'I'll get my equipment. Hang on a minute.'

He disappeared and came back with a syringe and scissors. About half a cc was enough to numb the part, then he snipped off the papilloma, applied some styptic and put the beagle on the floor. The operation took about two minutes but even in that brief spell his unique dexterity was manifest.

'That'll be ten guineas, Mr Herriot,' he murmured, then gave a shout of laughter. 'Come on, let's get into the garden. Sam will be quite happy with my dogs.'

He led me out of the back door and we stumbled through the fog by a rockery and rose bushes. I was just wondering how on earth he expected to show me anything in this weather when we came up against a stone outhouse. He threw open the door and I stepped into a brightly lit, sparkling Aladdin's cave.

It was quite simply a fully fitted bar. At the far end a polished counter with beer handles and, behind, a long row of bottles of every imaginable liquor. A fire crackled in the hearth and hunting prints, cartoons and bright posters looked down from the walls. It was completely authentic.

Granville saw my astonished face and laughed. 'All right, eh, Jim? I thought it would be a nice idea to have my own little pub in the garden. Rather cosy, isn't it?'

'Yes . . . yes indeed . . . charming.'

'Good, good.' My colleague slipped behind the counter. 'Now what are you going to have?'

Helen and Zoe took sherry and I made a quick decision to stick to one fairly harmless drink.

'Gin and tonic, please, Granville.'

The girls received a normal measure of sherry but when the big man took my glass over to the gin bottle hanging on the wall his hand seemed to be overcome by an uncontrollable trembling. The bottle was upended with one of those little optic attachments you push up with the rim of the glass to give a single measure.

But as I say, as Granville inserted the neck of the bottle into the glass his whole arm jerked repeatedly as though he were going into a convulsion. It was obvious that the result would be about six gins instead of one and I was about to remonstrate when he took the glass away and topped it up quickly with tonic, ice and sliced lemon.

I looked at it apprehensively. 'Rather a big one, isn't it?'

'Not at all, laddie, nearly all tonic. Well, cheers, so nice to see you both.'

And it certainly was. They were generous, warm people and veterinary folk like ourselves. I felt a gush of gratitude for the friendliness they had always shown me and as I sipped my drink, which was chokingly strong, I felt as I had often done that these contacts were one of the brightest rewards of my job.

Granville held out his hand. 'Have another, laddie.'

'Well, hadn't we better be getting on our way? It's a terrible night—in fact I don't see us ever getting to Newcastle in this fog.'

'Nonsense, old son.' He took my glass, reached up to the gin bottle and again was seized with a series of violent tremors of the forearm. 'No problem, Jim. Straight along the north road —half an hour or so—know it like the back of my hand.'

The four of us stood around the fire. The girls clearly had a lot to say to each other and Granville and I, like all vets, talked shop. It is wonderful how easy veterinary practice is in a warm room with good company and a dollop of alcohol in the stomach.

'One for the road, Jim,' my colleague said.

'No really, Granville, I've had enough,' I replied firmly. 'Let's be off.'

'Jim, Jim.' The familiar hurt look was creeping over his face. 'There's no rush. Look, we'll just have this last one while I tell you about this gorgeous restaurant.'

Once more he approached the gin bottle and this time the

rigor lasted so long I wondered if he had some history of malaria.

Glass in hand he expounded. 'It's not just the curry, the cooking in general is exquisite.' He put his fingers to his lips and blew a reverent kiss into space. 'The flavours are unbelievable. All the spices of the orient, Jim.'

He went on at length and wished he would stop because he was making me hungry. I had had a hard day round the farms and had eaten very little with the evening's feast in view, and as my colleague waved his hand around and drew word pictures of how they blended the rare herbs with the meat and fish, then served it on a bed of saffron rice, I was almost drooling.

I was relieved when I got through the third massive drink and Granville squeezed round to the front of the bar as if ready to go. We were on our way out when a man's bulk loomed in the doorway.

'Raymond!' cried Granville in delight. 'Come in, I've been wanting you to meet Jim Herriot. Jim, this is one of my neighbours—likes a bit of gardening, don't you Raymond?'

The man replied with a fat chuckle. 'Right, old boy! Splendid garden, this!' Granville seemed to know a lot of large, red-faced hearty men and this was one more.

My friend was behind the counter again. 'We must just have one with Raymond.'

I felt trapped as he again pressed my glass against the bottle and went into another paroxysm, but the girls didn't seem to mind. They were still deep in conversation and seemed unaware of the passage of time or the ravages of hunger.

Raymond was just leaving when Tubby Pinder dropped in. He was another enthusiastic horticulturist and I wasn't surprised to see that he was large, red-faced and hearty.

We had to have one with Tubby and I noticed with some alarm that after another palsied replenishment of my glass he had to replace the empty gin bottle with a fresh one. If the first one had been full then I had consumed nearly all of it.

I could hardly believe it when at last we were in the hall putting on our coats. Granville was almost purring with contentment.

'You two are going to love this place. It will be a joy to lead you through the menu.'

Outside the fog was thicker than ever. My colleague backed his enormous Bentley from the garage and began to usher us inside with great ceremony. He installed Helen and Zoe in the back, clucking solicitously over them, then he helped me into the passenger seat in front as though I were a disabled old man, tucking my coat in, adjusting the angle of the seat for maximum comfort, showing me how the cigar lighter worked, lighting up the glove compartment, enquiring which radio programme I desired.

At last he himself was in residence behind the wheel, massive and composed. Beyond the windscreen the fog parted for a second to show a steep, almost vertical grassy bank opposite the house, then it closed down like a dirty yellow curtain cutting off everything.

'Granville,' I said. 'We'll never get to Newcastle in this. It's over thirty miles.'

He turned and gave me a gentle smile. 'Absolutely no problem, laddie. We'll be there in half an hour, sampling that wonderful food. Tandoori chicken, all the spices of the orient, old son. Don't worry about a thing—I really know these roads. No chance of losing my way.'

He started the engine and drove confidently off, but unfortunately instead of taking the orthodox route along the road he proceeded straight up the grassy bank. He didn't seem to notice as the nose of the great car rose steadily higher, but when we had achieved an angle of forty-five degrees Zoe broke in gently from the back.

'Granville, dear, you're on the grass.'

My colleague looked round in some surprise. 'Not at all, my love. The road slopes a little here if you remember.' He kept his foot on the throttle.

I said nothing as my feet rose and my head went back. There was a point when the Bentley was almost perpendicular and I thought we were going over backwards, then I heard Zoe again.

'Granville, darling.' There was a hint of urgency in her tone. 'You're going up the bank.'

This time it seemed her husband was prepared to concede a little.

'Yes . . . yes, my pet,' he murmured as we hung there, all

four of us gazing up at the fog-shrouded sky. 'Possibly I have strayed a little on to the verge.'

He took his foot off the brake and the car shot backwards at frightening speed into the darkness. We were brought up by a grinding crunch from the rear.

Zoe again: 'You've hit Mrs Thompson's wall, dear.'

'Have I, sweetheart? Ah, one moment. We'll soon be on our way.'

With undiminished aplomb he let in his clutch and we surged forward powerfully. But only for two seconds. From the gloom ahead there sounded a dull crash followed by a tinkling of glass and metal.

'Darling,' Zoe piped. 'That was the thirty miles an hour sign.'

'Was it really, my angel?' Granville rubbed his hand on the window. 'You know, Jim, the visibility isn't too good.' He paused for a moment. 'Perhaps it would be a good idea if we postponed our visit till another time.'

He manoeuvred the big car back into the garage and we got out. We had covered, I should think, about five yards on our journey to Newcastle.

Back in the garden bar, Granville was soon in full cry again. And I was all for it because my earlier trepidation had vanished entirely. I was floating in a happy haze and I offered no resistance as my colleague jerked and twitched more samples from the gin bottle.

Suddenly he held up a hand. 'I'm sure we're all starving. Let's have some hot dogs!'

'Hot dogs?' I cried. 'Splendid idea!' It was a long call from all the spices of the orient but I was ready for anything.

'Zoe, sweet,' he said. 'We can use the big can of saveloy sausages if you would just heat it up.'

His wife left for the kitchen and Helen touched my arm.

'Jim,' she said. 'Saveloys . . . ?'

I knew what she meant. I have a pretty good digestion but there are certain things I can't eat. A single saveloy was enough to bring my entire metabolism to a halt, but at that moment it seemed a pettifogging detail.

'Oh don't worry, Helen,' I whispered, putting my arm round her. 'They won't hurt me.'

When Zoe came back with the food Granville was in his

element, slicing the juicy smoked sausages lengthways, slapping mustard on them and enclosing them in rolls.

As I bit into the first one I thought I had never tasted anything so delicious. Chewing happily I found it difficult to comprehend my previous ridiculous prejudice.

'Ready for another, old son?' Granville held up a loaded roll.

'Sure! These are absolutely marvellous. Best hot dogs I've ever tasted!' I munched it down quickly and reached for a third.

I think it was when I had downed five of them that my friend prodded me in the ribs.

'Jim, lad,' he said between chews. 'We want a drop of beer to wash these down, don't you agree?'

I waved my arm extravagantly. 'Of course we do! Bloody gin's no good for this job!'

Granville pulled two pints of draught. Powerful delicious ale which flowed in a cooling wave over my inflamed mucous membranes, making me feel I had been waiting for it all my life. We each had three pints and another hot dog or two while waves of euphoria billowed around me.

The occasional anxious glance from Helen didn't worry me in the least. She was making signs that it was time to go home, but the very idea was unthinkable. I was having the time of my life, the world was a wonderful place and this little private pub was the finest corner of it.

Granville put down a half-eaten roll. 'Zoe, my precious, it would be nice to have something sweet to top this off. Why don't you bring out some of those little gooey things you made yesterday?'

She produced a plateful of very rich-looking cakelets. I do not have a sweet tooth and normally skip this part of the meal but I bit into one of Zoe's creations with relish. It was beautifully made and I could detect chocolate, marzipan, caramel and other things.

It was when I was eating the third that matters began to deteriorate. I found that my merry chatter had died and it was Granville doing all the talking, and as I listened to him owlishly I was surprised to see his face becoming two faces which floated apart and came together repeatedly. It was an astonishing phenomenon and it was happening with everything else in the room.

And I wasn't feeling so healthy now. That boundless vigour

was no longer surging through my veins and I felt only a great weariness and a rising nausea.

I lost count of time around then. No doubt the conversation went on among the four of us but I can't remember any of it and my next recollection was of the party breaking up. Granville was helping Helen on with her coat and there was a general air of cheerful departure.

'Ready, Jim?' my friend said briskly.

I nodded and got slowly to my feet and as I swayed he put his arm round me and assisted me to the door. Outside, the fog had cleared and a bright pattern of stars overhung the village, but the clean cold air only made me feel worse and I stumbled through the darkness like a sleepwalker. When I reached the car a long griping spasm drove through me, reminding me horribly of the sausages, the gin and the rest. I groaned and leaned on the roof.

'Maybe you'd better drive, Helen,' my colleague said. He was about to open the door when, with a dreadful feeling of helplessness, I began to slide along the metal.

Granville caught my shoulders. 'He'd be better in the back,' he gasped and began to lug me on to the seat. 'Zoe, sweetheart, Helen, love, grab a leg each, will you? Fine, now I'll get round the other side and pull him in.'

He trotted round to the far side, opened the door and hauled at my shoulders.

'Down a bit your side, Helen, dear. Now to me a little. Up a trifle your side, Zoe, pet. Now back to you a bit. Lovely, lovely.'

Clearly he was happy at his work. He sounded like an expert furniture remover and through the mists I wondered bitterly how many inert forms he had stuffed into their cars after an evening with him.

Finally they got me in, half lying across the back seat. My face was pressed against the side window and from the outside it must have been a grotesque sight with the nose squashed sideways and a solitary dead-mackerel eye staring sightlessly into the night.

With an effort I managed to focus and saw Zoe looking down at me anxiously. She gave a tentative wave of goodbye but I could produce only a slight twitch of the cheek in reply.

Granville kissed Helen fondly then slammed the car door. Moving back, he peered in at me and brandished his arms.

'See you soon, I hope, Jim. It's been a lovely evening!' His big face was wreathed in a happy smile and as I drove away my final impression was that he was thoroughly satisfied.

25

Being away from Darrowby and living a different life I was able to stand back and assess certain things objectively. I asked myself many questions. Why, for instance, was my partnership with Siegfried so successful?

Even now, as we still jog along happily after thirty-five years, I wonder about it. I know I liked him instinctively when I first saw him in the garden at Skeldale House on that very first afternoon, but I feel there is another reason why we get on together.

Maybe it is because we are opposites. Siegfried's restless energy impels him constantly to try to alter things while I abhor change of any kind. A lot of people would call him brilliant, while not even my best friends would apply that description to me. His mind relentlessly churns out ideas of all grades—excellent, doubtful and very strange indeed. I, on the other hand, rarely have an idea of any sort. He likes hunting, shooting and fishing; I prefer football, cricket and tennis. I could go on and on—we are even opposite physical types—and yet, as I say, we get along.

This of course doesn't mean that we have never had our differences. Over the years there have been minor clashes on various points.

One, I recall, was over the plastic calcium injectors. They were something new so Siegfried liked them, and by the same token I regarded them with deep suspicion.

My doubts were nourished by my difficulties with them. Their early troubles have now been ironed out but at the beginning I found the things so temperamental that I abandoned them.

My colleague pulled me up about it when he saw me washing out my flutter valve by running the surgery tap through it.

'For God's sake, James, you're not still using that old thing, are you?'

'Yes, I'm afraid I am.'

'But haven't you tried the new plastics?'

'I have.'

'Well . . . ?'

'Can't get away with them, Siegfried.'

'Can't . . . what on earth do you mean?'

I trickled the last drop of water through the tube, rolled it small and slipped it into its case. 'Well, the last time I used one the calcium squirted all over the place. And it's messy, sticky stuff. I had great white streaks down my coat.'

'But James!' He laughed incredulously. 'That's crazy! They're childishly simple to use. I haven't had the slightest trouble.'

'I believe you,' I said. 'But you know me. I haven't got a mechanical mind.'

'For heaven's sake, you don't need a mechanical mind. They're foolproof.'

'Not to me, they aren't. I've had enough of them.'

My colleague put his hand on my shoulder and his patient look began to creep across his face. 'James, James, you must persevere.' He raised a finger. 'There is another point at issue here, you know.'

'What's that?'

'The matter of asepsis. How do you know that length of rubber you have there is clean?'

'Well, I wash it through after use, I use a boiled needle, and . . .'

'But don't you see, my boy, you're only trying to achieve what already exists in the plastic pack. Each one is self-contained and sterilised.'

'Oh I know all about that, but what's the good of it if I can't get the stuff into the cow?' I said querulously.

'Oh piffle, James!' Siegfried assumed a grave expression. 'It only needs a little application on your part, and I must stress that you are behaving in a reactionary manner by being stubborn. I put it to you seriously that we have to move with the times and every time you use that antiquated outfit of yours it is a retrograde step.'

We stood, as we often did, eyeball to eyeball, in mutual disagreement till he smiled suddenly. 'Look, you're going out now, aren't you, to see that milk-fever cow I treated at John Tillot's. I understand it's not up yet.'

'That's right.'

'Well, as a favour to me, will you give one of the new packs a try?'

I thought for a moment. 'All right, Siegfried, I'll have one more go.'

When I reached the farm I found the cow comfortably ensconced in a field, in the middle of a rolling yellow ocean of buttercups.

'She's had a few tries to get on 'er feet,' the farmer said. 'But she can't quite make it.'

'Probably just wants another shot.' I went to my car which I had driven, rocking and bumping, over the rig and furrow of the field, and took one of the plastic packs from the boot.

Mr Tillot raised his eyebrows when he saw me coming back. 'Is that one o' them new things?'

'Yes, it is, Mr Tillot, the very latest invention. All completely sterilised.'

'Ah don't care what it is, ah don't like it!'

'You don't?'

'Naw!'

'Well . . . why not?'

'Ah'll tell ye. Mr Farnon used one this mornin'. Some of the stuff went in me eye, some went in 'is ear 'ole and the rest went down 'is trousers. Ah don't think t'bloody cow got any!'

There was another time Siegfried had to take me to task. An old-age pensioner was leading a small mongrel dog along the passage on the other end of a piece of string. I patted the consulting room table.

'Put him up here, will you?' I said.

The old man bent over slowly, groaning and puffing.

'Wait a minute.' I tapped his shoulder. 'Let me do it.' I hoisted the little animal on to the smooth surface.

'Thank ye, sir.' The man straightened up and rubbed his back and leg. 'I 'ave arthritis bad and I'm not much good at liftin'. My name's Bailey and I live at t'council houses.'

'Right, Mr Bailey, what's the trouble?'

'It's this cough. He's allus at it. And 'e kind of retches at t'end of it.'

'I see. How old is he?'

'He were ten last month.'

'Yes . . .' I took the temperature and carefully auscultated the chest. As I moved the stethoscope over the ribs Siegfried came in and began to rummage in the cupboard.

'It's a chronic bronchitis, Mr Bailey,' I said. 'Many older dogs suffer from it just like old folks.'

He laughed, 'Aye, ah'm a bit wheezy meself sometimes.'

'That's right, but you're not so bad, really, are you?'

'Naw, naw.'

'Well neither is your little dog. I'm going to give him an injection and a course of tablets and it will help him quite a bit. I'm afraid he'll never quite get rid of this cough, but bring him in again if it gets very bad.'

He nodded vigorously. 'Very good, sir. Thank ye kindly, sir.'

As Siegfried banged about in the cupboard I gave the injection and counted out twenty of the new M&B 693 tablets.

The old man gazed at them with interest then put them in his pocket. 'Now what do ah owe ye, Mr Herriot?'

I looked at the ragged tie knotted carefully over the frayed shirt collar, at the threadbare antiquity of the jacket. His trouser knees had been darned but on one side I caught a pink glimpse of the flesh through the material.

'No, that's all right, Mr Bailey. Just see how he goes on.'

'Eh?'

'There's no charge.'

'But . . .'

'Now don't worry about it—it's nothing, really. Just see he gets his tablets regularly.'

'I will, sir, and it's very kind of you. I never expected . . .'

'I know you didn't, Mr Bailey. Goodbye for now and bring him back if he's not a lot better in a few days.'

The sound of the old man's footsteps had hardly died away when Siegfried emerged from the cupboard. 'God, I've been ages hunting these down. I'm sure you deliberately hide things from me, James.'

I smiled but made no reply and as I was replacing my syringe on the trolley my colleague spoke again.

'James, I don't like to mention this, but aren't you rather rash, doing work for nothing?'

I looked at him in surprise. 'He was an old-age pensioner. Pretty hard up I should think.'

'Maybe so, but really, you know, you just cannot give your services free.'

'Oh but surely occasionally, Siegfried—in a case like this . . .'

'No, James, not even occasionally. It's just not practical.'

'But I've seen you do it—time and time again!'

'Me?' His eyes widened in astonishment. 'Never! I'm too aware of the harsh realities of life for that. Everything has become so frightfully expensive. For instance, weren't those M&B 693 tablets you were dishing out? Heaven help us, do you know those things are threepence each? It's no good—you must never work without charging.'

'But dammit, you're always doing it!' I burst out. 'Only last week there was that . . .'

Siegfried held up a restraining hand, 'Please, James, please. You imagine things, that's your trouble.'

I must have given him one of my most exasperated stares because he reached out and patted my shoulder.

'Believe me, my boy, I do understand. You acted from the highest possible motives and I have often been tempted to do the same. But you must be firm. These are hard times and one must be hard to survive. So remember in future—no more Robin Hood stuff, we can't afford it.'

I nodded and went on my way somewhat bemusedly, but I soon forgot the incident and would have thought no more about it had I not seen Mr Bailey about a week later.

His dog was once more on the consulting room table and Siegfred was giving it an injection. I didn't want to interfere so I went back along the passage to the front office and sat down to write in the day book. It was a summer afternoon, the window was open and through a parting in the curtain I could see the front steps.

As I wrote I heard Siegfried and the old man passing on their way to the front door. They stopped on the steps. The little dog, still on the end of its string, looked much as it did before.

'All right, Mr Bailey,' my colleague said. 'I can only tell you the same as Mr Herriot. I'm afraid he's got that cough for life, but when it gets bad you must come and see us.'

'Very good, sir,' the old man put his hand in his pocket. 'And what is the charge, please?'

'The charge, oh yes . . . the charge . . .' Siegfried cleared his throat a few times but seemed unable to articulate. He kept looking from the mongrel dog to the old man's tattered clothing and back again. Then he glanced furtively into the house and spoke in a hoarse whisper.

'It's nothing, Mr Bailey.'

'But Mr Farnon, I can't let ye . . .'

'Shh! Shh!' Siegfried waved a hand agitatedly in the old man's face. 'Not a word now! I don't want to hear any more about it.'

Having silenced Mr Bailey he produced a large bag.

'There's about a hundred M&B tablets in here,' he said, throwing an anxious glance over his shoulder. 'He's going to keep needing them, so I've given you a good supply.'

I could see my colleague had spotted the hole in the trouser knee because he gazed down at it for a long time before putting his hand in his jacket pocket.

'Hang on a minute.' He extracted a handful of assorted chattels. A few coins fell and rolled down the steps as he prodded in his palm among scissors, thermometers, pieces of string, bottle openers. Finally his search was rewarded and he pulled out a bank note.

'Here's a quid,' he whispered and again nervously shushed the man's attempts to speak.

Mr Bailey, realising the futility of argument, pocketed the money.

"Well, thank ye, Mr Farnon. Ah'll take t'missus to Scarborough wi' that.'

'Good lad, good lad,' muttered Siegfried, still looking around him guiltily. 'Now off you go.'

The old man solemnly raised his cap and began to shuffle painfully down the street.

'Hey, hold on, there,' my colleague called after him. 'What's the matter? You're not going very well.'

'It's this dang arthritis. Ah go a long way in a long time.'

'And you've got to walk all the way to the council houses?' Siegfried rubbed his chin irresolutely. 'It's a fair step.' He took a last wary peep down the passage then beckoned with his hand.

'Look, my car's right here,' he whispered. 'Nip in and I'll run you home.'

Some of our disagreements were sharp and short.

I was sitting at the lunch table, rubbing and flexing my elbow. Siegfried, carving enthusiastically at a joint of roast mutton, looked up from his work.

'What's the trouble, James—rheumatism?'

'No, a cow belted me with her horn this morning. Right on the funny bone.'

'Oh, bad luck. Were you trying to get hold of her nose?'

'No, giving her an injection.'

My colleague, transporting a slice of mutton to my plate, paused in mid-air. 'Injecting her? Up there?'

'Yes, in the neck.'

'Is that where you do it?'

'Yes, always have done. Why?'

'Because if I may say so, it's rather a daft place. I always use the rump.'

'Is that so?' I helped myself to mashed potatoes. 'And what's wrong with the neck?'

'Well, you've illustrated it yourself, haven't you? It's too damn near the horns for a start.'

'Okay, well the rump is too damn near the hind feet.'

'Oh, come now, James, you know very well a cow very seldom kicks after a rump injection.'

'Maybe so, but once is enough.'

'And once is enough with a bloody horn, isn't it?'

I made no reply, Siegfried plied the gravy boat over both our plates and we started to eat. But he had hardly swallowed the first mouthful when he returned to the attack.

'Another thing, the rump is so handy. Your way you have to squeeze up between the cows.'

'Well, so what?'

'Simply that you get your ribs squashed and your toes stood on, that's all.'

'All right.' I spooned some green beans from the tureen. 'But your way you stand an excellent chance of receiving a faceful of cow shit.'

'Oh rubbish, James, you're just making excuses!' He hacked violently at his mutton.

'Not at all,' I said. 'It's what I believe. And anyway, you haven't made out a case against the neck.'

'Made out a case? I haven't started yet. I could go on indefinitely. For instance, the neck is more painful.'

'The rump is more subject to contamination,' I countered.

'The neck is often thinly muscled,' snapped Siegfried. 'You haven't got a nice pad there to stick your neeedle into.'

'No, and you haven't got a tail either,' I growled.

'Tail? What the hell are you talking about?'

'I'm talking about the bloody tail! It's all right if you have somebody holding it but otherwise it's a menace, lashing about.'

Siegfried gave a few rapid chews and swallowed quickly. 'Lashing about? What in God's name has that got to do with it?'

'Quite a lot,' I replied. 'I don't like a whack across the face from a shitty tail, even if you do.'

There was a heavy-breathing lull then my colleague spoke in an ominously quite voice. 'Anything else about the tail?'

'Yes, there is. Some cows can whip a syringe out of your hand with their tails. The other day one caught my big fifty cc and smashed it against a wall. Broken glass everywhere.'

Siegfried flushed slightly and put down his knife and fork. 'James, I don't like to speak to you in these terms, but I am bound to tell you that you are talking the most unmitigated balls, bullshit and poppycock.'

I gave him a sullen glare. 'That's your opinion, is it?'

'It is indeed, James.'

'Right.'

'Right.'

'Okay.'

'Very well.'

We continued our meal in silence.

But over the next few days my mind kept returning to the conversation. Siegfried has always had a persuasive way with him and the thought kept recurring that there might be a lot in what he said.

It was a week later that I paused, syringe in hand, before pushing between two cows. The animals, divining my intent as they usually did, swung their craggy hind ends together and blocked my way. Yes, by God, Siegfried had a point. Why should I fight my way in there when the other end was ready and waiting?

I came to a decision. 'Hold the tail, please,' I said to the farmer and pushed my needle into the rump.

The cow never moved and as I completed the injection and pulled the needle out I was conscious of a faint sense of shame.

That lovely pad of gluteal muscle, the easy availability of the site—my colleague had been dead right and I had been a pig-headed fool. I knew what to do in future.

The farmer laughed as he stepped back across the dung channel. 'It's a funny thing how you fellers all have your different ways.'

'What do you mean?'

'Well, Mr Farnon was 'ere yesterday, injecting that cow over there.'

"He was?' A sudden light flashed in my mind. Could it be that Siegfried was not the only convincing talker in our practice . . . ? 'What about it?'

'Just that 'e had a different system from you. Had savage good arguments 'gainst goin' near the rump. He injected into the neck.'

Something in my expression must have conveyed a message to him. 'There now, Mr Herriot, ye mustn't let that bother ye.' He touched my arm sympathetically. 'You're still young. After all, Mr. Farnon is a man of experience.'

CHAPTER

26

I leaned on the handle of my spade, wiped away the sweat which had begun to run into my eyes and gazed around me at the hundreds of men scattered over the dusty green.

We were still on our toughening course. At least that's what they told us it was. I had a private suspicion that they just didn't know what to do with all the aircrews under training and that somebody had devised this method of getting us out of the way.

Anyway, we were building a reservoir near a charming little Shropshire town and a whole village of tents had sprung up to house us. Nobody was quite sure about the reservoir but we were supposed to be building something. They issued us with denim suits and pick-axes and spades and for hour after hour we pecked desultorily at a rocky hillside.

But, hot as I was, I couldn't help thinking that things could be a lot worse. The weather was wonderful and it was a treat to be in the open all day. I looked down the slope and away across the sweetly rolling countryside to where low hills rose in the blue distance; it was a gentler landscape than the stark fells and moors I had left behind in Yorkshire, but infinitely soothing.

And the roofs of the town showing above the trees held a rich promise. During the hours under the fierce sun, with the rock rust caking round our lips, we built up a gargantuan thirst which we nurtured carefully till the evening when we were allowed out of camp.

There, in cool taverns in the company of country folk, we slaked it with pints of glorious rough cider. I don't suppose you would find any there now. It is mostly factory-made cider which is drunk in the South of England these days, but many of the pubs used to have their own presses, where they squeezed the juice from the local apples.

To me, there was something disturbing about sleeping in a

tent. Each morning when I awoke with the early sun beating on the thin walls it was as if I were back in the hills above the Firth of Clyde long before the war was dreamed of. There was something very evocative about the tent smell of hot canvas and rubber groundsheet and crushed grass and the flies buzzing in a little cloud at the top of the pole. I was jerked back in an instant to Rosneath and when I opened my eyes I half expected to find Alex Taylor and Eddie Hutchison, the friends of my boyhood, lying there in their sleeping bags.

The three of us went camping at Rosneath every week-end from Easter to October, leaving the smoke and dirt of Glasgow behind us; and here in Shropshire, in the uncanny tent smell, when I closed my eyes I could see the little pine-wood behind the tent and the green hillside running down to the burn and, far below, the long blue mirror of the Gareloch glinting under the great mountains of Argyll. They have desecrated Rosneath and the Gareloch now, but to me, as a boy, it was a fairyland which led me into the full wonder and beauty of the world.

It was strange that I should dwell on that period when I was in my teens because Alex was in the Middle East, Eddie was in Burma and I was in another tent with a lot of different young men. And it was as though the time between had been rubbed away and Darrowby and Helen and all my struggles in veterinary practice had never happened. Yet those years in Darrowby had been the most important of my life. I used to sit up and shake myself, wondering at how my thoughts had been mixed up by the war.

But as I say, I quite enjoyed Shropshire. The only snag was that reservoir, or whatever it was that we were hacking out of the face of the hill. I could never get really involved with it. So that I pricked up my ears when our Flight Sergeant made an announcement one morning.

'Some of the local farmers want help with their harvest,' he called out at the early parade. 'Are there any volunteers?'

My hand was the first up and after a few moments' hesitation others followed, but none of my particular friends volunteered for the job. When everything had been sorted out I found I had been allotted to a farmer Edwards with three other airmen who were from a different flight and strangers to me.

Mr Edwards arrived the following day and packed the four of us into a typical big old-fashioned farmer's car. I sat in the front with him while the three others filled the back. He asked our names but nothing else, as though he felt that our station in civil life was none of his concern. He was about thirty-five with jet black hair above a sunburnt face in which his white teeth and clear blue eyes shone startlingly.

He looked us over with a good-humoured grin as we rolled into his farmyard.

'Well, here we are, lads,' he said. 'This is where we're going to put you through it.'

But I hardly heard him. I was looking around me at the scene which had been part of my life a few months ago. The cobbled yard, the rows of doors leading to cow byre, barn, pigsties and loose boxes. An old man was mucking out the byre and as the rich bovine smell drifted across, one of my companions wrinkled his nose. But I inhaled it like perfume.

The farmer led us all into the fields where a reaper and binder was at work, leaving the sheaves of corn lying in long golden swathes.

'Any of you ever done any stooking?' he asked.

We shook our heads dumbly.

'Never mind, you'll soon learn. You come with me, Jim.'

We spaced ourselves out in the big field, each of my colleagues with an old man while Mr Edwards took charge of me. It didn't take me long to realise that I had got the tough section.

The farmer grabbed a sheaf in each hand, tucked them under his arms, walked a few steps and planted them on end, resting against each other. I did the same till there were eight sheaves making up a stook. He showed me how to dig the stalks into the ground so that they stood upright and sometimes he gave a nudge with his knee to keep them in the right alignment.

I did my best but often my sheaves would fall over and I had to dart back and replace them. And I noticed with some alarm that Mr Edwards was going about twice as fast as the three old men. We had nearly finished the row while they were barely half way along, and my aching arms and back told me I was in for a testing time.

We went on like that for about two hours; bending, lifting, bending, lifting and shuffling forward without an instant's respite. One of the strongest impressions I had gained when I first came into country practice was that farming was the hardest way of all of making a living, and now I was finding out for myself. I was about ready to throw myself down on the stubble when Mrs Edwards came over the field with her young son and daughter. They carried baskets with the ingredients for our ten o'clock break; crusty apple tart and jugs of cider.

The farmer watched me quizzically as I sank gratefully down and began to drink like a parched traveller in the desert. The cider, from his own press, was superb, and I closed my eyes as I swallowed. The right thing, it seemed to me, would be to lie here in the sunshine for the rest of the day with about a gallon of this exquisite brew by my side, but Mr Edwards had other ideas. I was still chewing at the solid crust when he grasped a fresh pair of sheaves.

'Right, lad, must get on,' he grunted, and I was back on the treadmill.

With a pause at lunchtime for bread, cheese and more cider we went on at breakneck speed all day. I have always been grateful to the RAF for what they did for my physical well-being. When I was called up there was no doubt I was going slightly to seed under Helen's beneficent regime. Too much good cooking and the discovery of the charms of an armchair; I was getting fat. But the RAF changed all that and I don't think I have ever slipped back.

After the six months at Scarborough I am certain I didn't carry a surplus pound. Marching, drilling, PT, running—I could trot five miles along the beach and cliffs without trouble. When I arrived in Shropshire I was really fit. But I wasn't as fit as Mr Edwards.

He was a compact bundle of power. Not very big but with the wiry durability I remembered in the Yorkshire farmers. He seemed tireless, hardly breaking sweat as he moved along the rows, corded brown arms bulging from the sleeves of a faded collarless shirt, slightly bowed legs stumping effortlessly.

The sensible thing would have been to tell him straight that I couldn't go at his pace, but some demon of pride impelled me to keep up with him. I am quite sure he didn't mean to rub it in. Like any other farmer he had a job to do and was anxious to get on with it. At the lunch break he looked at me with some commiseration as I stood there, shirt sticking to my back, mouth hanging open, ribs heaving.

'You're doin' fine, Jim,' he said, then, as if noticing my distress for the first time, he shifted his feet awkwardly. 'I know you city lads ain't used to this kind of work and . . . well . . . it's not a question of strength, it's just knowin' how to do it.'

When we drove back to camp that night I could hear my companions groaning in the back of the car. They, too, had suffered, but not as badly as me.

After a few days I did begin to get the knack of the thing and though it still tested me to the utmost I was never on the border of collapse again.

Mr Edwards noticed the improvement and slapped me playfully on the shoulder. 'What did I tell you? It's just knowin' how to do it!'

But a new purgatory awaited me when we started to load the corn on to the stack. Forking the sheaves up on to the cart, roping them there then throwing them again, higher and higher as the stack grew in size. I realised with a jolt that stooking had been easy.

Mrs Edwards joined in this part. She stood on the top of the stack with her husband, expectly turning the sheaves towards him while he arranged them as they should be. I had the unskilled job way below, toiling as never before, back breaking, the handle of the fork blistering my palms.

I just couldn't go fast enough and Mr Edwards had to hop down to help me, grasping a fork and hurling the sheaves up with easy flicks of the wrist.

He looked at me as before and spoke the encouraging words. 'You're comin' along grand, Jim. It's just knowin' how to do it.'

But there were many compensations. The biggest was being among farming folk again. Mrs Edwards in her undemonstrative way was obviously anxious to show hospitality to these four rather bewildered city boys far from home, and set us down to a splendid meal every evening. She was dark like her husband, with large eyes which joined in her quick smile and a figure which managed to be thin and shapely at the same time. She hadn't much chance to get fat because she never stopped working. When she wasn't outside throwing the corn around like any man she was cooking and baking, looking after her children and scouring her great barn of a farmhouse.

Those evenings meals were something to look forward to and remember. Steaming rabbit pies with fresh green beans and potatoes from the garden. Bilberry tarts and apple crumble and a massive jug of thick cream to pour ad lib. Home-baked bread and farm cheese.

The four of us revelled in the change from the RAF fare. It was said the aircrews got the best food in the services and I believed it, but after a while it all began to taste the same. Maybe it was the bulk cooking but it palled in time.

Sitting at the farm table, looking at Mrs Edwards serving us, at her husband eating stolidly and at the two children, a girl of ten whose dark eyes showed promise of her mother's attractiveness and a sturdy, brown-limbed boy of eight, the thought recurred; they were good stock.

The clever economists who tell us that we don't need British agriculture and that our farms should be turned into national parks seem to ignore the rather obvious snag that an unfriendly country could starve us into submission in a week. But to me a greater tragedy still would be the loss of a whole community of people like the Edwards.

It was late one afternoon and I was feeling more of a weakling than ever, with Mr Edwards throwing the sheaves around as though they were weightless while I groaned and strained. The farmer was called away to attend to a calving cow and as he hopped blithely from the stack he patted my shoulder as I leaned on my fork.

'Never mind, Jim,' he laughed.

An hour later we were going into the kitchen for our meal when Mrs Edwards said, 'My husband's still on with that cow. He must be having difficulty with her.'

I hesitated in the doorway. 'Do you mind if I go and see how he's getting on?'

She smiled. 'All right, if you like. I'll keep your food warm for you.'

I crossed the yard and went into the byre. One of the old men was holding the tail of a big Red Poll and puffing his pipe placidly. Mr Edwards, stripped to the waist, had his arm in the cow up to the shoulder. But it was a different Mr Edwards. His back and chest glistened and droplets of sweat ran down his nose and dripped steadily from the end. His mouth gaped and he panted as he fought his private battle somewhere inside.

He turned glazed eyes in my direction. At first he didn't appear to see me in his absorption, then recognition dawned.

"Ullo, Jim,' he muttered breathlessly. 'I've got a right job on 'ere.'

'Sorry to hear that. What's the trouble?'

He began to reply then screwed up his face. 'Aaah! The old bitch! She's squeezin' the life out of me arm again! She'll break it afore she's finished!' He paused, head hanging down, to recover, then he looked up at me. 'The calf's laid wrong, Jim. There's just a tail comin' into the passage and I can't get the hind legs round.'

A breech. My favourite presentation but one which always defeated farmers. I couldn't blame them really because they had never had the opportunity to read Franz Benesch's classical work on *Veterinary Obstetrics* which explains the mechanics of parturition so lucidly. One phrase has always stuck in my mind: 'The necessity for simultaneous application of antagonistic forces'.

Benesch points out that in order to correct many malpresentations it is necessary to apply traction and repulsion at the same time, and to do that with one hand in a straining cow is impossible.

As though to endorse my thoughts Mr Edwards burst out once more. 'Dang it, I've missed it again! I keep pushin' the hock away then grabbin' for the foot but the old bitch just shoves it all back at me. I've been doin' this for an hour now and I'm about knackered.'

I never thought I would hear such words from this tough little man, but there was no doubt he had suffered. The cow was a massive animal with a back like a dining table and she was heaving the farmer back effortlessly every time she strained. We didn't see many Red Polls in Yorkshire but the ones I had met were self-willed and strong as elephants; the idea of pushing against one for an hour made me quail.

Mr Edwards pulled his arm out and stood for a moment leaning against the hairy rump. The animal was quite unperturbed by the interference of this puny human but the farmer was a picture of exhaustion. He worked his dangling fingers gingerly then looked up at me.

'By God!' he grunted. 'She's given me some stick. I've got hardly any feelin' left in this arm.'

He didn't have to tell me. I had known that sensation many a time. Even Benesch in the midst of his coldly scientific 'repositions', 'retropulsions', 'malpositions' and 'counteracting pressures' so far unbends as to state that 'Great demands are made upon the strength of the operator.' Mr Edwards would agree with him.

The farmer took a long shuddering breath and moved over to the bucket of hot water on the floor. He washed his arms then turned back to the cow with something like dread on his face.

'Look,' I said. 'Please let me help you.'

He gave me a pallid smile. 'Thanks, Jim, but there's nuthin' you can do. Those legs have got to come round.'

'That's what I mean. I can do it.'

'What . . . ?'

'With a bit of help from you. Have you got a piece of binder twine handy?'

'Aye, we've got yards of it, lad, but I'm tellin' you you need experience for this job. You know nuthin' about . . .'

He stopped because I was already pulling my shirt over my head. He was too tired to argue in any case.

Hanging the shirt on a nail on the wall, bending over the bucket and soaping my arms with the scent of the antiseptic coming up to me brought a rush of memories which was almost overwhelming. I held out my hand and Mr Edwards wordlessly passed me a length of twine.

I soaked it in the water, then quickly tied a slip knot at one end and inserted my hand into the cow. Ah yes, there was the tail, so familiar, hanging between the calf's pelvic bones. Oh, I did love a breech, and I ran my hand with almost voluptuous satisfaction along the hair of the limb till I reached the tiny foot. It was a moment's work to push the loop over the fetlock and tighten it while I passed the free end between the digits of the cloven foot.

'Hold that,' I said to the farmer, 'and pull it steadily when I tell you.'

I put my hand on the hock and began to push it away from me into the uterus.

'Now pull,' I said. 'But carefully. Don't jerk.'

Like a man in a dream he did as I said and within seconds the foot popped out of the vulva.

'Hell!' said Mr Edwards.

'Now for the other one,' I murmured as I removed the loop.

I repeated the procedure, the farmer, slightly pop-eyed, pulling on the twine. The second little hoof, yellow and moist, joined its fellow on the outside almost immediately.

'Bloody hell!' said Mr Edwards.

'Right,' I said. 'Grab a leg and we'll have him out in a couple of ticks.'

We each took a hold and leaned back, but the big cow did the job for us, giving a great heave which deposited the calf wet and wriggling into my arms. I staggered back and dropped with it on to the straw.

'Grand bull calf, Mr Edwards,' I said. 'Better give him a rub down.'

The farmer shot me a disbelieving glance then twisted some hay into a wisp and began to dry off the little creature.

'If you ever get stuck with a breech presentation again,' I said, 'I'll show you what you ought to do. You have to push and pull at the same time and that's where the twine comes in. As you repel the hock with your hand somebody else pulls the foot round, but you'll notice I have the twine between the calf's cleats and that's important. That way it lifts the sharp little foot up and prevents injury to the vaginal wall.'

The farmer nodded dumbly and went on with his rubbing. When he had finished he looked up at me in bewilderment and his lips moved soundlessly a few times before he spoke.

'What the . . . how . . . how the heck do you know all that?'

I told him.

There was a long pause then he exploded.

'You young bugger! You kept that dark, didn't you?'

'Well . . . you never asked me.'

He scratched his head. 'Well, I don't want to be nosey with you lads that helps me. Some folks don't like it. . . .' His voice trailed away.

We dried our arms and donned our shirts in silence. Before leaving he looked over at the calf, already making strenuous efforts to rise as its mother licked it.

'He's a lively little beggar,' he said. 'And we might have lost 'im. I'm right grateful to you.' He put an arm round my shoulders. 'Anyway, come on, Mister Veterinary Surgeon, and we'll 'ave some supper.'

Half way across the yard he stopped and regarded me ruefully. 'You know, I must have looked proper daft to you, fumblin' away inside there for an hour and damn near killin' myself, then you step up and do it in a couple of minutes. I feel as weak as a girl.'

'Not in the least, Mr Edwards,' I replied. 'It's . . .' I hesitated a moment. 'It's not a question of strength, it's just knowing how to do it.'

He nodded, then became very still and the seconds stretched out as he stared at me. Suddenly his teeth shone as the brown face broke into an ever-widening grin which developed into a great shout of laughter.

He was still laughing helplessly when we reached the house and as I opened the kitchen door he leaned against the wall and wiped his eyes.

'You young devil!' he said. 'I allus had a feeling there was something behind that innocent face of yours.'

CHAPTER

27

At last we were on our way to Flying School. It was at Windsor and that didn't seem far on the map, but it was a typical war-time journey of endless stops and changes and interminable waits. It went on all through the night and we took our sleep in snatches. I stole an hour's fitful slumber on the waiting-room table at a tiny nameless station and despite my hard pillowless bed I drifted deliciously back to Darrowby.

I was bumping along the rutted track to Nether Lees Farm, hanging on to the jerking wheel. I could see the house below me, its faded red tiles showing above the sheltering trees, and behind the buildings the scrubby hillside rose to the moor.

Up there the trees were stunted and sparse and dotted widely over the steep flanks. Higher still there was only scree and cliff and right at the top, beckoning in the sunshine, I saw the be-ginning of the moor—smooth, unbroken and bare.

A scar on the broad sweep of green showed where long ago they quarried the stones to build the massive farmhouses and the enduring walls which have stood against the unrelenting climate for hundreds of years. Those houses and those endlessly marching walls would still be there when I was gone and forgotten.

Helen was with me in the car. I loved it when she came with me on my rounds, and after the visit to the farm we climbed up the fell-side, panting through the scent of the warm bracken, feeling the old excitement as we neared the summit.

Then we were on the top, facing into the wide free moorland and the clean Yorkshire wind and the cloud shadows racing over the greens and browns. Helen's hand was warm in mine as we wandered among the heather through green islets nibbled to a velvet sward by the sheep. She raised a finger as a curlew's lonely cry sounded across the wild tapestry and the wonder in her eyes shone through the dark flurry of hair blowing across her face.

The gentle shaking at my shoulder pulled me back to wakefulness, to the hiss of steam and the clatter of boots. The table top was hard against my hip and my neck was stiff where it had rested on my pack.

'Train's in, Jim.' An airman was looking down at me. 'I hated to wake you—you were smiling.'

Two hours later, sweaty, unshaven, half asleep, laden with kit, we shuffled into the airfield at Windsor. Sitting in the wooden building we only half listened to the corporal giving us our introductory address. Then suddenly his words struck home.

'There's one other thing,' he said. 'Remember to wear your identity discs at all times. We had two prangs last week—couple of fellers burned beyond recognition and neither of 'em was wearing his discs. We didn't know who they were.' He spread his hands appealingly. 'This sort of thing makes a lot of work for us, so remember what I've told you.'

In a moment we were all wide awake and listening intently. Probably thinking as I was—that we had only been playing at being airmen up till now.

I looked through the window at the wind sock blowing over the long flat stretch of green, at the scattered aircraft, the fire tender, the huddle of low wooden huts. The playing was over now. This was where everything started.

28

This was a very different uniform. The wellingtons and breeches of my country vet days seemed far away as I climbed into the baggy flying suit and pulled on the sheepskin boots and the gloves—the silk ones first then the big clumsy pair on top. It was all new but I had a feeling of pride.

Leather helmet and goggles next, then I fastened on my parachute passing the straps over my shoulders and between my legs and buckling them against my chest before shuffling out of the flight hut on to the long stretch of sunlit grass.

Flying Officer Woodham was waiting for me there. He was to be my instructor and he glanced at me apprehensively as though he didn't relish the prospect. With his dark boyish good looks he resembled all the pictures I had seen of Battle of Britain pilots and in fact, like all our instructors, he had been through this crisis in our history. They had been sent here as a kind of holiday after their tremendous experience but it was said that they regarded their operations against the enemy as a picnic compared with this. They had faced the might of the Luftwaffe without flinching but we terrified them.

As we walked over the grass I could see one of my friends coming in to land. The little biplane slewed and weaved crazily in the sky, just missed a clump of trees then about fifty feet from the ground it dropped like a stone, bounced high on its wheels, bounced twice again then zig-zagged to a halt. The helmeted head in the rear cockpit jerked and nodded as though it were making some pointed remarks to the head in front. Flying Officer Woodham's face was expressionless but I knew what he was thinking. It was his turn next.

The Tiger Moth looked very small and alone on the wide stretch of green. I climbed up and strapped myself into the cockpit while my instructor got in behind me. He went through the drill which I would soon know by heart like a piece of poetry. A fitter gave the propellor a few turns for priming. Then 'Contact!' the fitter swung the prop, the engine roared, the chocks were pulled away from the wheels and we were away, bumping over the grass, then suddenly and miraculously lifting and soaring high over the straggle of huts into the summer sky with the patchwork of the soft countryside of southern England unfolding beneath us.

I felt a sudden elation, not just because I liked the sensation but because I had waited so long for this moment. The months of drilling and marching and studying navigation had been leading up to the time when I would take the air and now it had arrived.

F. O. Woodham's voice came over the intercom. 'Now you've got her. Take the stick and hold her steady. Watch the artificial horizon and keep it level. See that cloud ahead? Line yourself up with it and keep your nose on it.'

I gripped the joystick in my gauntleted hand. This was lovely. And easy, too. They had told me flying would be a simple matter and they had been right. It was child's play. Cruising along I glanced down at the grandstand of Ascot racecourse far below.

I was just beginning to smile happily when a voice crashed in my ear. 'Relax, for God's sake! What the hell are you playing at?'

I couldn't understand him. I felt perfectly relaxed and I thought I was doing fine, but in the mirror I could see my instructor's eyes glaring through his goggles.

'No, no, no! That's no bloody good! Relax, can't you hear me, relax!'

'Yes, sir,' I quavered and immediately began to stiffen up. I couldn't imagine what was troubling the man but as I began to stare with increasing desperation, now at the artificial horizon then at the nose of the aircraft against the cloud ahead, the noises over the intercom became increasingly apoplectic.

I didn't seem to have a single problem, yet all I could hear were curses and groans and on one occasion the voice rose to a scream. 'Get your bloody finger out, will you!'

I stopped enjoying myself and a faint misery welled in me. And as always when that happened I began to think of Helen and the happier life l had left behind. In the open cockpit the

wind thundered in my ears, lending vivid life to the picture forming in my mind.

The wind was thundering here, too, but it was against the
window of our bed-sitter. It was early November and a golden
autumn had changed with brutal suddenness to arctic cold. For
two weeks an icy rain had swept the grey towns and villages
which huddled in the folds of the Yorkshire Dales, turning the
fields into shallow lakes and the farmyards into squelching mud-
holes.

Everybody had colds. Some said it was flu, but whatever it
was it decimated the population. Half of Darrowby seemed to be
in bed and the other half sneezing at each other.

I myself was on a knife edge, crouching over the fire, sucking
an antiseptic lozenge and wincing every time I had to swallow.
My throat felt raw and there was an ominous tickling at the
back of my nose. I shivered as the rain hurled a drumming cascade of water against the glass. I was all alone in the practice.
Siegfried had gone away for a few days and I just daren't catch
cold.

It all depended on tonight. If only I could stay indoors and
then have a good sleep I could throw this off, but as I glanced
over at the phone on the bedside table it looked like a crouching
beast ready to spring.

Helen was sitting on the other side of the fire, knitting. She
didn't have a cold—she never did. And even in those early days
of our marriage I couldn't help feeling it was a little unfair.
Even now, thirty-five years later, things are just the same and,
as I go around sniffling, I still feel tight-lipped at her obstinate
refusal to join me.

I pulled my chair closer to the blaze. There was always a lot
of night work in our kind of practice but maybe I would be
lucky. It was eight o'clock with never a cheep and perhaps fate
had decreed that I would not be hauled out into that sodden
darkness in my weakened state.

Helen came to the end of a row and held up her knitting. It
was a sweater for me, about half done.

'How does it look, Jim?' she asked.

I smiled. There was something in her gesture that seemed to
epitomise our life together. I opened my mouth to tell her it was
simply smashing when the phone pealed with a suddenness
which made me bite my tongue.

Tremblingly I lifted the receiver while horrid visions of calving heifers floated before me. An hour with my shirt off would just tip me nicely over the brink.

'This is Sowden of Long Pasture,' a voice croaked.

'Yes, Mr Sowden?' I gripped the phone tightly. I would know my fate in a moment.

'I 'ave a big calf 'ere. Looks very dowly and gruntin' bad. Will ye come?'

A long breath of relief escaped me. A calf with probable stomach trouble. It could have been a lot worse.

'Right, I'll see you in twenty minutes,' I said.

As I turned back to the cosy warmth of the little room the injustice of life smote me.

'I've got to go out, Helen.'

'Oh, what a shame.'

'Yes, and I have this cold coming on,' I whimpered. 'And just listen to that rain!'

"Yes, you must wrap up well, Jim.'

I scowled at her. 'That place is ten miles away, and a cheerless dump if ever there was one. There's not a warm corner anywhere.' I fingered my aching throat. 'A trip out there's just what I need—I'm sure I've got a temperature.' I don't know if all veterinary surgeons blame their wives when they get an unwanted call, but heaven help me, I've done it all my life.

Instead of giving me a swift kick in the pants Helen smiled up at me. 'I'm really sorry, Jim, but maybe it won't take you long. And you can have a bowl of hot soup when you get back.'

I nodded sulkily. Yes, that was something to look forward to. Helen had made some brisket broth that day, rich and meaty, crowded with celery, leeks and carrots and with a flavour to bring a man back from the dead. I went over and kissed her and trailed off into the night.

Long Pasture Farm was in the little hamlet of Dowsett and I had travelled this narrow road many times. It snaked its way high into the wild country and on summer days the bare lonely hills had a serene beauty; treeless and austere, but with a clean wind sweeping over the grassy miles.

But tonight as I peered unhappily through the streaming windscreen the unseen surrounding black bulk pressed close and I could imagine the dripping stone walls climbing high to the summits where the rain drove across the moorland, drenching the heather and bracken, churning the dark mirrors of the bog water into liquid mud.

When I saw Mr Sowden I realised that I was really quite fit. He had obviously been suffering from the prevalent malady for some time, but like most farmers he just had to keep going at his hard ceaseless work. He looked at me from swimming eyes, gave a couple of racking coughs that almost tore him apart and led me into the buildings. He held an oil lamp high as we entered a lofty barn and in the feeble light I discerned various rusting farm implements, a heap of potatoes and another of turnips and in a corner a makeshift pen where my patient stood.

It wasn't the two week old baby calf I had half expected, but a little animal of six months, almost stirk age, but not well grown. It had all the signs of a 'bad doer'—thin and pot-bellied with its light roan coat hanging in a thick overgrown fringe below its abdomen.

'Allus been a poor calf,' Mr Sowden wheezed between coughs. 'Never seemed to put on flesh. Rain stopped for a bit this afternoon, so ah let 'im out for a bit of fresh air and now look at 'im.'

I climbed into the pen and as I slipped the thermometer into the rectum I studied the little creature. He offered no resistance as I gently pushed him to one side, his head hung down and he gazed apathetically at the floor from deep sunk eyes. Worst of all was the noise he was making. It was more than a grunt— rather a long, painful groan repeated every few seconds.

'It certainly looks like his stomach,' I said. 'Which field was he is this afternoon?'

'I nobbut let 'im have a walk round t'orchard for a couple of hours.'

'I see.' I looked at the thermometer. The temperature was subnormal. 'I suppose there's a bit of fruit lying around there.'

Mr Sowden went into another paroxysm, then leaned on the boards of the pen to recover his breath. 'Aye, there's apples and pears all over t'grass. Had a helluva crop this year.'

I put the stethoscope over the rumen and instead of the normal surge and bubble of the healthy stomach I heard only a deathly silence. I palpated the flank and felt the typical doughy fullness of impaction.

'Well, Mr Sowden, I think he's got a bellyful of fruit and it's brought his digestion to a complete halt. He's in a bad way.'

The farmer shrugged. 'Well, if 'e's just a bit bunged up a good dose of linseed oil 'ud shift 'im.'

'I'm afraid it's not as simple as that,' I said. 'This is a serious condition.'

'Well what are we goin' to do about it, then?' He wiped his nose and looked at me morosely.

I hesitated. It was bitterly cold in the old building and already I was feeling shivery and my throat ached. The thought of Helen and the bed-sitter and the warm fire was unbearably attractive. But I had seen impactions like this before and tried treating them with purgatives and it didn't work. This animal's temperature was falling to the moribund level and he had a sunken eye—if I didn't do something drastic he would be dead by morning.

'There's only one thing will save him,' I said. 'And that's a rumenotomy.'

'A what?'

'An operation. Open up his first stomach and clear out all the stuff that shouldn't be there.'

'Are ye sure? D'ye not think a good pint of oil would put 'im right. It 'ud be a lot easier.'

It would indeed. For a moment the fireside and Helen glowed like a jewel in a cave, then I glanced at the calf. Scraggy and long-haired, he looked utterly unimportant, infinitely vulnerable and dependent. It would be the easiest thing in the world to leave him groaning in the dark till morning.

'I'm quite sure, Mr Sowden. He's so weak that I think I'll do it under a local anaesthetic, so we'll need some help.'

The farmer nodded slowly. 'Awright, ah'll go down t'village and get George Hindley.' He coughed again, painfully. 'But by gaw, ah could do without this tonight. Ah'm sure I've got brown chitis.'

Brown chitis was a common malady among the farmers of those days and there was no doubt this poor man was suffering from it but my pang of sympathy faded as he left because he took the lamp with him and the darkness closed tightly on me.

There are all kinds of barns. Some of them are small, cosy and fragrant with hay, but this was a terrible place. I had been in here on sunny afternoons and even then the dank gloom of crumbling walls and rotting beams was like a clammy blanket and all warmth and softness seemed to disappear among the cobwebbed rafters high above. I used to feel that people with starry eyed notions of farming ought to take a look inside that barn. It was evocative of the grim comfortless other side of the agricultural life.

I had it to myself now, and as I stood there listening to the wind rattling the door on its latch a variety of draughts whistled round me and a remorseless drip-drip from the broken pantiles on the roof sent icy droplets trickling over my head and neck. And as the minutes ticked away I began to hop from foot to foot in a vain effort to keep warm.

Dales farmers are never in a hurry and I hadn't expected a quick return, but after fifteen minutes in the impenetrable blackness bitter thoughts began to assail me. Where the hell was the man? Maybe he and George Hindley were brewing a pot of tea for themselves or perhaps settling down to a quick game of dominoes. My legs were trembling by the time the oil lamp reappeared in the entrance and Mr Sowden ushered his neighbour inside.

'Good evening, George,' I said. 'How are you?'

'Only moderate, Mr Herriot,' the newcomer sniffled. 'This bloody caud's just—ah—ah—whoooosh—just gettin' a haud o' me.' He blew lustily into a red handkerchief and gazed at me blearily.

I looked around me. 'Well let's get started. We'll need an operating table. Perhaps you could stack up a few straw bales?'

The two men trailed out and returned, carrying a couple of bales apiece. When they were built up they were about the right height but rather wobbly.

'We could do with a board on top.' I blew on my freezing fingers and stamped my feet. 'Any ideas?'

Mr Sowden rubbed his chin. 'Aye, we'll get a door.' He shuffled out into the yard with his lamp and I watched him struggling to lift one of the cow byre doors from its hinges. George went to give him a hand and as the two of them pulled and heaved I thought wearily that veterinary operations didn't trouble me all that much but getting ready for them was a killer.

Finally the men staggered back into the barn, laid the door on top of the bales and the theatre was ready.

'Let's get him up,' I gasped.

We lifted the unresisting little creature on to the improvised table and stretched him on his right side. Mr Sowden held his head while George took charge of the tail and the rear end.

Quickly I laid out my instruments, removed coat and jacket and rolled up my shirt sleeves. 'Damn! We've no hot water. Will you bring some, Mr Sowden?'

I held the head and again waited interminably while the farmer went to the house. This time it was worse without my warm clothing and the cold ate into me as I pictured the farm kitchen and the slow scooping of the water from the side boiler into a bucket, then the unhurried journey back to the buildings.

When Mr Sowden finally reappeared I added antiseptic to the bucket and scrubbed my arms feverishly. Then I clipped the hair on the left side and filled the syringe with local anaesthetic. But as I infiltrated the area I felt my hopes sinking.

'I can hardly see a damn thing.' I looked helplessly at the oil lamp balanced on a nearby turnip chopper. 'That light's in the wrong place.'

Wordlessly Mr Sowden left his place and began to tie a length of plough cord to a beam. He threw it over another beam and made it fast before suspending the lamp above the calf. It was a big improvement but it took a long time and by the time he had finished I had abandoned all hope of ever throwing off my cold. I was frozen right through and a burning sensation had started in my chest. I would soon be in the same state as my helpers. Brown chitis was just round the corner.

Anyway, at least I could start now, and I incised skin, muscles, peritoneum and rumenal wall at record speed. I plunged an arm deep into the opened organ, through the fermenting mass of stomach contents, and in a flash all my troubles dissolved. Along the floor of the rumen apples and pears were spread in layers, some of them bitten but most of them whole and intact. Bovines take most of their food in big swallows and chew it over later at their leisure, but no animal could make cud out of this lot.

I looked up happily. 'It's just as I thought. He's full of fruit.'

'Hhrraaagh!' replied Mr Sowden. Coughs come in various forms but this one was tremendous and fundamental, starting at the soles of his hob-nailed boots and exploding right in my face. I hadn't realised how vulnerable I was with the farmer leaning over the calf's neck, his head a few inches from mine. 'Hhrraaagh!' he repeated, and a second shower of virus laden moisture struck me. Apparently Mr Sowden either didn't know or didn't care about droplet infection, but with my hands inside my patient there was nothing I could do about it.

Instinctively I turned my face a little in the other direction.

'Whoosh!' went George. It was a sneeze rather than a cough, but it sent a similar deadly spray against my other cheek. I realised there was no escape. I was hopelessly trapped between the two of them.

But as I say, my morale had received a boost. Eagerly I scooped out great handfuls of the offending fruit and within minutes the floor of the barn was littered with Bramley's seedlings and Conference pears.

'Enough here to start a shop,' I laughed.

'Hhrraaagh!' responded Mr Sowden.

'Whooosh!' added George, not to be outdone.

When I had sent the last apple and pear rolling into the darkness I scrubbed up again and started to stitch. This is the longest and most wearisome part of a rumenotomy. The excitement of diagnosis and discovery is over and it is a good time for idle chat, funny stories, anything to pass the time.

But there in the circle of yellow light with the wind whirling round my feet from the surrounding gloom and occasional icy trickles of rain running down my back I was singularly short of gossip, and my companions, sunk in their respective miseries, were in no mood for badinage.

I was half way down the skin sutures when a tickle mounted at the back of my nose and I had to stop and stand upright.

'Ah—ah—ashooo!' I rubbed my forearm along my nose.

'He's startin',' murmured George with mournful satisfaction.

'Aye, 'e's off,' agreed Mr Sowden, brightening visibly.

I was not greatly worried. I had long since come to the conclusion that my cause was lost. The long session of freezing in my shirt sleeves would have done it without the incessant germ bombardment from either side. I was resigned to my fate and besides, when I inserted the last stitch and helped the calf down from the table I felt a deep thrill of satisfaction. That horrible groan had vanished and the little animal was looking around him as though he had been away for a while. He wasn't cheerful yet, but I knew his pain had gone and that he would live.

'Bed him up well, Mr Sowden.' I started to wash my instruments in the bucket. 'And put a couple of sacks round him to keep him warm. I'll call in a fortnight to take out the stitches.'

That fortnight seemed to last a long time. My cold, as I had confidently expected, developed into a raging holocaust which settled down into the inevitable brown chitis with an accompanying cough that rivalled Mr Sowden's.

Mr Sowden was never an ebullient man but I expected him to look a little happier when I removed the stitches. Because the calf was bright and lively and I had to chase him around his pen to catch him.

Despite the fire in my chest I had that airy feeling of success.

'Well,' I said expansively. 'He's done very well. He'll make a good bullock some day.'

The farmer shrugged gloomily. 'Aye, reckon 'e will. But there was no need for all that carry on.'

'No need . . . ?'

'Naw. Ah've been talkin' to one or two folk about t'job and they all said it was daft to open 'im up like that. Ah should just 'ave given 'im a pint of oil like I said.'

'Mr Sowden, I assure you . . .'

'And now ah'll have a big bill to pay.' He dug his hands deep into his pockets.

'Believe me, it was worth it.'

'Nay, nay, never.' He started to walk away, then looked over his shoulder. 'It would've been better if you 'adn't come.'

I had done three circuits with F. O. Woodham and on this third one he had kept fairly quiet. Obviously I was doing all right now and I could start enjoying myself again. Flying was lovely.

The voice came over the intercom again. 'I'm going to let you land her yourself this time. I've told you how to do it. Right, you've got her.'

'I've got her,' I replied. He had indeed told me how to do it— again and again—and I was sure I would have no trouble.

As we lost height the tops of the trees appeared then the grass of the airfield came up to meet us. It was the moment of truth. Carefully I eased the stick back, then at what I thought was the right moment I slammed it back against my stomach. Maybe a bit soon because we bounced a couple of times and that made me forget to seesaw the rudder bar so that we careered from side to side over the turf before coming to a halt.

With the engine stilled I took a deep breath. That was my first landing and it hadn't been bad. In fact I had got better and better all the time and the conviction was growing in me that my instructor must have been impressed with my initial showing. We climbed out and after walking a few steps in silence F. O. Woodham halted and turned to me.

'What's your name?' he asked.

Ah yes, here was the proof. He knew I had done well. He was interested in me.

'Herriot, sir,' I replied smartly.

For a few moments he gave me a level stare. 'Well, Herriot,' he murmured. 'That was bloody awful.'

He turned and left me. I gazed down at my feet in their big sheepskin boots. Yes, the uniform was different, but things hadn't changed all that much.

29

Life in the R.A.F. reminded me of something I always knew: Men are like animals. I don't mean men are 'beastly'. The fact is I don't think animals are 'beastly'. What I mean is that no two are exactly alike. Many people think my farm patients are all the same, but cows, pigs, sheep and horses can be moody, placid, vicious, docile, spiteful, loving.

There was one particular pig called Gertrude, but before I come to her I must start with Mr Barge.

Nowadays the young men from the pharmaceutical companies who call on veterinary surgeons are referred to as 'reps', but nobody would have dreamed of applying such a term to Mr Barge. He was definitely a 'representative' of Cargil and Sons, Manufacturers of Fine Chemicals since 1850, and he was so old that he might have been in on the beginning.

It was a frosty morning in late winter when I opened the front door at Skeldale House and saw Mr Barge standing on the front step. He raised his black homburg a few inches above the sparse strands of silver hair and his pink features relaxed into a smile of gentle benevolence. He had always treated me as a favourite son and I took it as a compliment because he was a man of immense prestige.

'Mr Herriot,' he murmured, and bowed slightly. The bow was rich in dignity and matched the dark morning coat, striped trousers and shiny leather brief case.

'Please come in, Mr Barge,' I said, and ushered him into the house.

He always called at midday and stayed for lunch. My young boss, Siegfried Farnon, a man not easily overawed, invariably treated him with deference and in fact the visit was something of a state occasion.

The modern rep breezes in, chats briefly about blood levels of antibiotics and steroids, says a word or two about bulk discounts, drops a few data sheets on the desk and hurries away. In a way I feel rather sorry for these young men because, with a few exceptions, they are all selling the same things.

Mr Barge, on the other hand, like all his contemporaries, carried a thick catalogue of exotic remedies, each one peculiar to its own firm.

Siegfried pulled out the chair at the head of the dining table. 'Come and sit here, Mr Barge.'

'You are very kind.' The old gentleman inclined his head slightly and took his place.

As usual there was no reference to business during the meal and it wasn't until the coffee appeared that Mr Barge dropped his brochure carelessly on the table as though this part of the visit was an unimportant afterthought.

Siegfried and I browsed through the pages, savouring the exciting whiff of witchcraft which has been blown from our profession by the wind of science. At intervals my boss placed an order.

'I think we'd better have a couple of dozen electuaries, Mr Barge.'

'Thank you so much.' The old gentleman flipped open a leather-bound notebook and made an entry with a silver pencil.

'And we're getting a bit low on fever drinks, aren't we, James?' Siegfried glanced round at me. 'Yes, we'll need a gross of them if you please.'

'I am most grateful,' Mr Barge breathed, noting that down, too.

My employer murmured his requests as he riffled through the catalogue. A Winchester of spirits of nitre and another of formalin, castration clams, triple bromide, Stockholm tar—all the things we never use now—and Mr Barge responded gravely to each with 'I do thank you' or 'Thank you indeed,' and a flourish of his silver pencil.

Finally Siegfried lay back in his chair. 'Well now, Mr Barge, I think that's it—unless you have anything new.'

'As it happens, my dear Mr Farnon, we have.' The eyes in the pink face twinkled. 'I can offer you our latest product, Soothitt, an admirable sedative.'

In an instant Siegfried and I were all attention. Every animal doctor is keenly interested in sedatives. Anything which makes our patients more amenable is a blessing. Mr Barge extolled the unique properties of Soothitt and we probed for further information.

'How about unmaternal sows?' I asked. 'You know—the kind which savage their young. I don't suppose it's any good for that?'

'My dear young sir.' Mr Barge gave me the kind of sorrowing smile a bishop might bestow on an erring curate. 'Soothitt is a specific for this condition. A single injection to a farrowing sow and you will have no problems.'

'That's great,' I said. 'And does it have any effect on car sickness in dogs?'

The noble old features lit up with quiet triumph. 'Another classical indication, Mr Herriot. Soothitt comes in tablet form for that very purpose.'

'Splendid.' Siegfried drained his cup and stood up. 'Better send us a good supply then. And if you will excuse us, we must start the afternoon round, Mr Barge. Thank you so much for calling.'

We all shook hands, Mr Barge raised his homburg again on the front step and another gracious occasion was over.

Within a week the new supplies from Cargill and Sons arrived. Medicines were always sent in tea chests in those days and as I prised open the wooden lid I looked with interest at the beautifully packed phials and tablets of Soothitt. And it seemed uncanny that I had a call for the new product immediately.

That same day one of the town's bank managers, Mr Ronald Beresford, called to see me.

'Mr Herriot,' he said. 'As you know I have worked here for several years but I have been offered the managership of a bigger branch down south and I leave tomorrow for Portsmouth.' From his gaunt height he looked down at me with the unsmiling gaze which was characteristic of him.

'Portsmouth! Gosh, that's a long way.'

'Yes, it is—about three hundred miles. And I have a problem.'

'Really?'

'I have, I fear. I recently purchased a six month old cocker spaniel and he is an excellent little animal but for the fact that he behaves peculiarly in the car.'

'In what way?'

He hesitated. 'Well, he's outside now. If you've got a minute to spare I could demonstrate.'

'Of course,' I said. 'I'll come with you now.'

We went out to the car. His wife was in the passenger seat, as fat as her husband was thin, but with the same severe unbending manner. She nodded at me coldly but the attractive little animal on her lap gave me an enthusiastic welcome.

I stroked the long silky ears. 'He's a nice little fellow.'

Mr Beresford gave me a sidelong glance. 'Yes, his name is Coco and he really is quite charming. It's only when the engine is running that the trouble begins.'

I got in the back, he pressed the starter and we set off. And I saw immediately what he meant. The spaniel stiffened and raised his head till his nose pointed at the roof. He formed his lips into a cone and emitted a series of high-pitched howls.

'Hooo, hooo, hooo, hooo,' wailed Coco.

It really startled me because I had never heard anything quite like it. I don't know whether it was the perfectly even spacing of the hoots, their piercing, jarring quality, or the fact that they never stopped which drove the sound deep into my brain, but my head was singing after a two minute circuit of the town. I was vastly relieved when we drew up again outside the surgery.

Mr Beresford switched off the engine and it was as though he had switched off the noise, too, because the little animal relaxed instantly and began to lick my hand.

'Yes . . . ,' I said. 'You have a problem without a doubt.'

He pulled nervously at his tie. 'And it gets louder the longer you drive. Let me take you a bit farther round and . . .'

'No-no, no-no,' I put in hastily. 'That won't be necessary. I can see exactly how you are placed. But you say you haven't had Coco for long. He isn't much more than a pup. I'm sure he'll get used to the car in time.'

'Very possibly he will.' Mr Beresford's voice was taut with apprehension. 'But I'm thinking of tomorrow. I've got to drive all the way to Portsmouth with my wife and this dog and I've tried car sickness tablets without result.'

A full day with that appalling din was unthinkable but at that moment the image of Mr Barge rose before me. He had sprouted wings and floated in front of my eyes like an elderly guardian angel. What an incredible piece of luck!

'As it happens,' I said with a reassuring smile, 'there is something new for this sort of thing, and by a coincidence we have just received a batch of it today. Come in and I'll fix you up.'

'Well, thank heavens for that.' Mr Beresford examined the box of tablets, 'I just give one half an hour before the journey and all will be well?'

'That's the idea,' I replied cheerfully. 'I've given you a few extra for future journeys.'

'I am most grateful, you've taken a great load off my mind.' He went out to the car and I watched as he started the engine. As if in response to a signal the little brown head on the back seat went up and the lips pursed.

'Hooo, hooo, hooo, hooo,' Coco yowled, and his master shot me a despairing look as he drove away.

I stood on the steps for some time, listening incredulously. Many people in Darrowby didn't like Mr Beresford very much, probably because of his cold manner, but I felt he wasn't a bad chap and he certainly had my sympathy. Long after the car had disappeared round the corner of Trengate I could still hear Coco.

'Hooo, hooo, hooo, hooo.'

About seven o'clock that evening I had a phone call from Will Hollin.

'Gertrude's started farrowin'!' he said urgently. 'And she's tryin' to worry her pigs!'

It was bad news. Sows occasionally attacked their piglets after birth and in fact would kill them if they were not removed from their reach. And of course it meant that suckling was impossible.

It was a tricky problem at any time but particularly so in this case because Gertrude was a pedigree sow—an expensive animal Will Hollin had bought to improve his strain of pigs.

'How many has she had?' I asked.

'Four—and she's gone for every one.' His voice was tense.

It was then I remembered Soothitt and again I blessed the coming of Mr Barge.

I smiled into the receiver. 'There's a new product I can use, Mr Hollin. Just arrived today. I'll be right out.'

I trotted through to the dispensary, opened the box of phials and had a quick read at the enclosed pamphlet. Ah yes, there it was. 'Ten c.c.'s intramuscularly and the sow will accept the piglets within twenty minutes.'

It wasn't a long drive to the Hollin farm but as I sped through the darkness I could discern the workings of fate in the day's events. The Soothitt had arrived this morning and right away I had two urgent calls for it. There was no doubt Mr Barge had been sent for a purpose—living proof, perhaps, that everything in our lives is preordained. It gave me a prickling at the back of my neck to think about it.

I could hardly wait to get the injection into the sow and climbed eagerly into the pen. Gertrude didn't appreciate having a needle rammed into her thigh and she swung round on me with an explosive bark. But I got the ten c.c.'s in before making my escape.

'We just wait twenty minutes, then?' Will Hollin leaned on the rail and looked down anxiously at his pig. He was a hard-working smallholder in his fifties and I knew this meant a lot to him.

I was about to make a comforting reply when Gertrude popped out another pink, squirming piglet. The farmer leaned over and gently nudged the little creature towards the udder as the sow lay on her side, but as soon as the nose made contact with the teat the big pig was up in a flash, all growls and yellow teeth.

He snatched the piglet away quickly and deposited it with the others in a tall cardboard box. 'Well, you see how it is, Mr Herriot.'

'I certainly do. How many have you got in there now?'

'There's six. And they're grand pigs, too.'

I peered into the box at the little animals. They all had the classical long-bodied shape. 'Yes, they are. And she looks as though she has a lot more in her yet.'

The farmer nodded and we waited.

It seemed to take a long time for the twenty minutes to pass but finally I lifted a couple of piglets and clambered into the pen. I was about to put them to the sow when one of them squealed. Gertrude rushed across with a ferocious roar, mouth gaping, and I leaped to safety with an agility which surprised me.

'She don't look very sleepy,' Mr Hollin said.

'No . . . no . . . she doesn't, does she? Maybe we'd better wait a bit longer.'

We gave her another ten minutes and tried again with the

same result. I injected a further ten c.c.'s of the Soothitt, then about an hour later a third one. By nine o'clock Gertrude had produced fifteen beautiful young pigs and had chased me and her family from the pen six times. She was, if anything, livelier and fiercer than when I started.

'Well, she's cleansed,' Mr Hollin said gloomily. 'So it looks like she's finished.' He gazed, sad-faced, into the box. 'And now I've got fifteen pigs to rear without their mother's milk. I could lose all this lot.'

'Nay, nay.' The voice came from the open doorway. 'You won't lose 'em.'

I looked round. It was Grandad Hollin, his puckish features set in their customary smile. He marched to the pen and poked Gertrude's ribs with his stick.

She responded with a snarl and a malignant glare and the old man's smile grew broader.

'Ah'll soon fettle the awd beggar,' he said.

'Fettle her?' I shifted my feet uncomfortably. 'What do you mean?'

'Why, she just wants quietin', tha knaws.'

I took a long breath. 'Yes, Mr Hollin, that's exactly what I've been trying to do.'

'Aye, but you're not doin' it the right way, young man.'

I looked at him narrowly. The know-all with his liberal advice in a difficult situation is a familiar figure most veterinary surgeons have to tolerate, but in Grandad Hollin's case I didn't feel the usual irritation. I liked him. He was a nice man, the head of a fine family. Will was the eldest of his four sons and he had several farmer grandsons in the district.

Anyway, I had failed miserably. I was in no position to be uppity.

'Well, I've given her the latest injection,' I mumbled.

He shook his head. 'She don't want injections, she wants beer.'

'Eh?'

'Beer, young man. A drop o' good ale.' He turned to his son. 'Hasta got a clean bucket, Will, lad?'

'Aye, there's a new-scalded one in t'milk house.'

'Right, ah'll slip down to the pub. Won't be long.' Grandad swung on his heel and strode briskly into the night. He must have been around eighty but from the back he looked like a twenty five year old—upright, square-shouldered, jaunty.

Will Hollin and I didn't have much to say to each other. He was sunk in disappointment and I was awash with shame. It was a relief when Grandad returned bearing an enamel bucket brimming with brown liquid.

'By gaw,' he chuckled. 'You should've seen their faces down at t'Wagon and Horses. Reckon they've never heard of a two gallon order afore.'

I gaped at him. 'You've got two gallons of beer?'

'That's right, young man, and she'll need it all.' He turned again to his son. 'She hasn't had a drink for a bit, has she, Will?'

'Naw I was goin' to give her some water when sh'd finished piggin', but I haven't done it yet.'

Grandad poised his bucket. 'She'll be nice and thirsty, then.' He leaned over the rail and sent a dark cascade frothing into the empty trough.

Gertrude ambled moodily across and sniffed at the strange fluid. After some hesitation she dipped her snout and tried a tentative swallow, and within seconds the building echoed with a busy slobbering.

'By heck, she likes it!' Will exclaimed.

'She should,' Grandad murmured wistfully. 'It's John Smith's best bitter.'

It took the big sow a surprisingly short time to consume the two gallons and when she had finished she licked out every corner of the trough before turning away. She showed no inclination to return to her straw bed but began to saunter round the pen. Now and then she stopped at the trough to check that there was no more beer in it and from time to time she looked up at the three faces overhanging the timber walls.

On one of these occasions I caught her eye and saw with a sense of disbelief that the previously baleful little orb now registered only a gentle benevolence. In fact with a little effort I could have imagined she was smiling.

As the minutes passed her perambulations became increasingly erratic. There were times when she stumbled and almost fell and finally with an unmistakable hiccup she flopped on the straw and rolled on to her side.

Grandad regarded her expressionlessly for a few moments, whistling tunelessly, then he reached out again and pushed his stick against the fleshy thigh; but the only response he received from the motionless animal was a soft grunt of pleasure.

Gertrude was stoned to the wide.

The old man gestured towards the cardboard box. 'Put the little 'uns in now.'

Will went into the pen with a wriggling armful, then another, and like all new born creatures they didn't have to be told what to do. Fifteen ravenous little mouths fastened on to the teats and with mixed feelings I gazed at the sight which I had hoped to bring about with my modern veterinary skill, the long pink row filling their tiny stomachs with the life-giving fluid.

Well, I had fallen down on the job and an octogenarian farmer had wiped my eye with two gallons or strong ale. I didn't feel great.

Sheepishly I closed the box of Soothitt phials and was beating an unobtrusive retreat to my car when Will Hollin called after me.

'Come in and have a cup o' coffee afore you go, Mr Herriot.' His voice was friendly, with nothing to suggest that I had made no useful contribution all evening.

I made my way into the kitchen and as I went over to the table Will dug me in the ribs.

'Hey, look at this.' He held out the bucket in which a quantity of the good beer still sloshed around the bottom. 'There's summat better than coffee 'ere—enough for a couple of good drinks. I'll get two glasses.'

He was fumbling in the dresser when Grandad walked in. The old man hung his hat and stick on a hook on the wall and rubbed his hands.

'Tha can get another glass out, Will,' he said. 'Remember ah did the pourin' and ah left enough for three.'

Next morning I might have been inclined to dwell despondently on my chastening experience but I had a pre-breakfast call to a cow with a prolapsed uterus and there is nothing like an hour of feverish activity to rid the mind of brooding.

It was 8 a.m. when I drove back into Darrowby and I pulled into the market place petrol station which was just opening. With a pleasantly blank mind I was watching Bob Cooper running the petrol into my tank when I heard the sound in the distance.

'Hooo, hooo, hooo, hooo.'

Tremblingly I scanned the square. There was no other vehicle in sight but the dread ululation approached inexorably until Mr Beresford's car rounded the far corner, heading my way.

I shrank behind a petrol pump but it was of no avail. I had been spotted and the car bumped over the strip of cobbles before screeching to a halt beside me.

'Hooo, hooo, hooo, hooo.' At close quarters the noise was insupportable.

I peeped round the pump and into the bulging eyes of the bank manager as he lowered his window. He switched off the engine and Coco stopped his howling and gave me a friendly wag through the glass.

His master, however, did not look at all friendly.

'Good morning, Mr Herriot,' he said, grim-faced.

'Good morning,' I replied hoarsely, then working up a smile I bent at the window. 'And good morning to you, Mrs Beresford.'

The lady withered me with a look and was about to speak when her husband went on.

'I administered one of the wonderful new tablets early this morning on your advice.' His chin quivered slightly.

'Oh, yes . . . ?'

'Yes, I did, and it had no effect, so I gave him another.' He paused. 'Since this produced a similar result I tried a third and a fourth.'

I swallowed. 'Really . . . ?'

'Indeed.' He gave me a cold stare. 'So I am driven to the conclusion that the tablets are useless.'

'Well . . . er . . . it certainly does look . . .'

He held up a hand. 'I cannot listen to explanations. I have already wasted enough time and there are three hundred miles' driving in front of me.'

'I'm truly sorry . . .' I began, but he was already closing the window. He started the engine and Coco froze immediately into his miniature wolf position, nose high, lips puckered into a small circle. I watched the car roll across the square and turn out of sight on the road to the south. For quite a while after it had gone I could still hear Coco.

'Hooo, hooo, hooo, hooo.'

Feeling suddenly weak, I leaned against the pump. My heart went out to Mr Beresford. As I have said, I felt sure he was a decent man.

In fact I quite liked him, but for all that I was profoundly grateful that I would probably never see him again.

Our audiences with Mr Barge usually took place every three months and it was mid June before I saw him again at the head of our luncheon table. The silvery head gleamed under the summer sunshine as he sipped his coffee and murmured polite-nesses. At the end of the meal he dabbed his lips with a napkin and slid his brochure unhurriedly along the table cloth.

Siegfried reached for it and asked the inevitable question. 'Anything new, Mr Barge?'

'My dear sir.' The old gentleman's smile seemed to convey that the follies of the young, though incomprehensible to him, were still delightful. 'Cargill and Sons never send me to you without a host of new products, many of them specific, all of them efficient. I have many sovereign remedies to offer you.'

I must have uttered some sort of strangled sound because he turned and regarded me quizzically. 'Ah, Mr Herriot, did you say something, young sir?'

I swallowed a couple of times and opened my mouth as the waves of benevolence flowed over me, but against that dignity and presence I was helpless.

'No . . . not really, Mr Barge,' I replied. I knew I would never be able to tell him about the Soothitt.

Now that we were faced with the reality of life at flying school, the ties which bound me to my fellow airmen were strengthened. We had a common aim, a common worry.

The feeling of comradeship was very like my relationship with Siegfried and Tristan, back in Darrowby. But there, the pressures came not from learning to fly but from the daily challenge of veterinary practice. Our existence was ruled by sudden and unexpected alarms.

Tristan, however, didn't let it get him down. He and I were sitting in the big room at Skeldale House one night when the telephone burst into strident voice.

He reached from his chair and lifted the receiver.

'Allo, plis, oo is dis?' he enquired.

He listened attentively for a few moments then shook his head.

'Naw, naw, verree sorry, but Meester Farnon no at home. Yis, yis, I tell heem when he come. Hokey dokey, bye bye.'

I looked across at him wonderingly from the other side of the fireplace as he replaced the instrument. These strange accents were only one facet of his constant determination to extract amusement from every situation. He didn't do it all the time, only when the mood was on him, but it was not unusual for farmers to say that 'some foreign feller' had answered the phone.

Tristan settled comfortably behind his *Daily Mirror* and was fumbling for a Woodbine when the ringing started again. He stretched out once more.

'Yaas, yaas, goot efening, howdy do. Vat you vant, huh?'

I could just hear a deep rumble from the other end of the

line and Tristan suddenly snapped upright in his chair. His *Daily Mirror* and cigarettes slithered to the floor.

'Yes, Mr Mount,' he said smartly. 'No Mr Mount. Yes, indeed, Mr Mount, I shall pass on your message immediately. Thank you very much, goodbye.'

He fell back in the chair and blew out his cheeks. 'That was Mr Mount.'

'So I gathered. And he certainly wiped the smile off your face, Triss.'

'Yes . . . yes . . . just a little unexpected.' He recovered his Woodbines and lit one thoughtfully.

'Quite,' I said. 'What did he ring for, anyway?'

'Oh, he has a cart horse to see tomorrow morning. Something wrong with its hind feet.'

I made a note on the pad and turned back to the young man. 'I don't know how you find the time in your hectic love life, but you're running around with that chap's daughter, aren't you?'

Tristan took the cigarette from his mouth and studied the glowing end. 'Yes, as a matter of fact I have taken Deborah Mount out a few times. Why do you ask?'

'Oh, no particular reason. Her old man seems a bit formidable, that's all.'

I could picture Mr Mount the last time I saw him. He was well named; a veritable massif of a man towering several inches over six feet. From shoulders like the great buttresses of the fell which overhung his farm rose a beetling cliff of head with craggy outcrops of jaw and cheek and brow. He had the biggest hands I had ever seen—approximately three times the size of my own.

'Oh, I don't know,' Tristan said. 'He's not a bad sort.'

'I agree, I've nothing against him.' Mr Mount was deeply religious and had the reputation of being hard but fair. 'It's just that I wouldn't like him to come up to me and ask if I was trifling with his daughter's affections.'

Tristan swallowed, and anxiety flitted briefly in his eyes. 'Oh, that's ridiculous. Deborah and I have a friendly relationship, that's all.'

'Well I'm glad to hear it,' I said. 'I've been told her father is very protective about her and I'd hate to feel those big hands round my throat.'

Tristan gave me a cold stare. 'You're a sadistic bugger at times, Jim. Just because I occasionally enjoy a little female company . . .'

'Oh, forget it, Triss, I'm only kidding. You've nothing to worry about. When I see old Mount tomorrow I promise I won't mention that Deborah is one of your harem.' I dodged a flying cushion and went through to the dispensary to stock up for the next day's round.

But I realised next morning that my joke was barbed when I saw Mr Mount coming out of the farm house. For a moment his bulk filled the doorway then he advanced with measured tread over the cobbles till he loomed over me, blocking out the sunshine, throwing a large area around me into shade.

'That young man, Tristan,' he said without preamble. 'He was speakin' a bit funny like on the phone last night. What sort of a feller is he?'

I looked up at the great head poised above me, at the unwavering grey eyes probing into mine from beneath a bristling overhang of brow. 'Tristan?' I answered shakily. 'Oh, he's a splendid chap. A really fine type.'

'Mmm.' The huge man continued to look at me and one banana-like finger rubbed doubtfully along his chin. 'Does he drink?'

Mr Mount was renowned for his rigid antagonism to alcohol and I thought it unwise to reply that Tristan was a popular and esteemed figure at most of the local hostelries.

'Oh, er—' I said. 'Hardly at all . . . in the strictest moderation . . .'

At that moment Deborah came out of the house and began to walk across the yard.

She was wearing a flowered cotton dress. About nineteen, shining golden hair falling below her shoulders, she radiated the healthy buxom beauty of the country girl. As she went by she flashed a smile at me and I had a heart-lifting glimpse of white teeth and warm brown eyes. It was in the early days before I had met Helen and I had as sharp an interest in a pretty lass as anybody. I found myself studying her legs appreciatively after she had passed.

It was then that I had an almost palpable awareness of her father's gaze upon me. I turned and saw a new expression there

—a harsh disapproval which chilled me and left a deep conviction in my mind. Deborah was a little smasher all right, and she looked nice, too, but no . . . no . . . never. Tristan had more courage than I had.

Mr Mount turned away abruptly. 'This 'oss is in the stable,' he grunted.

In those late thirties the tractor had driven a lot of the draught horses from the land but most of the farmers kept a few around, perhaps because they had always worked horses and it was part of their way of life and maybe because of the sheer proud beauty of animals like the one which stood before me now.

It was a magnificent Shire gelding, standing all of eighteen hands. He was a picture of massively muscled power but when his master spoke, the great white-blazed face which turned to us was utterly docile.

The farmer slapped him on the rump. 'He's a good sort is Bobby and I think a bit about 'im. What ah noticed first was a strange smell about his hind feet and then ah had a look for meself. I've never seen owt like it.'

I bent and seized a handful of the long feathered hair behind the horse's pastern. Bobby did not resist as I lifted the huge spatulate foot and rested it on my knee. It seemed to occupy most of my lap but it was not the size which astonished me. Mr Mount had never seen owt like it and neither had I. The sole was a ragged, sodden mass with a stinking exudation oozing from the underrun horn, but what really bewildered me was the series of growths sprouting from every crevice.

They were like nightmare toadstools—long papillae with horny caps growing from the diseased surface. I had read about them in the books; they were called ergots, but I had never imagined them in such profusion. My thoughts raced as I moved behind the horse and lifted the other foot. It was just the same. Just as bad.

I had been qualified only a few months and was still trying to gain the confidence of the Darrowby farmers. This was just the sort of thing I didn't want.

'What is it?' Mr Mount asked, and again I felt that unwinking gaze piercing me.

I straightened up and rubbed my hands. 'It's canker, but a very bad case.' I knew all about the theory of the thing, in fact

I was bursting with theory, but putting it into practice with this animal was a bit different.

'How are you going to cure it?' Mr Mount had an uncomfortable habit of going straight to the heart of things.

'Well, you see, all that loose horn and those growths will have to be cut away and then the surface dressed with caustic,' I replied, and it sounded easy when I said it.

'It won't get better on its own, then?'

'No, if you leave it the sole will disintegrate and the pedal bone will come through. Also the discharge will work up under the wall of the hoof and cause separation.'

The farmer nodded. 'So he'd never walk again, and that would be the end of Bobby.'

'I'm afraid so.'

'Right, then.' Mr Mount threw up his head with a decisive gesture. 'When are you going to do it?'

It was a nasty question, because I was preoccupied at that moment not so much with when I would do it but how I would do it.

'Well now, let's see,' I said huskily. 'Would it be . . .'

The farmer broke in. 'We're busy hay-makin' all this week, and you'll be wantin' some men to help you. How about Monday next week?'

A wave of relief surged through me. Thank heavens he hadn't said tomorrow. I had a bit of time to think now.

'Very well, Mr Mount. That suits me fine. Don't feed him on the Sunday because he'll have to have an anaesthetic.'

Driving from the farm, a sense of doom oppressed me. Was I going to ruin that beautiful animal in my ignorance? Canker of the foot was unpleasant at any time and was not uncommon in the days of the draught horse, but this was something away out of the ordinary. No doubt many of my contemporaries have seen feet like Bobby's, but to the modern young veterinary surgeon it must be like a page from an ancient manual of farriery.

As is my wont when I have a worrying case I started mulling it over right away. As I drove, I rehearsed various procedures. Would that enormous horse go down with a chloroform muzzle? Or would I have to collect all Mr Mount's men and rope him and pull him down? But it would be like trying to pull down

St Paul's cathedral. And then how long would it take me to hack away all that horn—all those dreadful vegetations?

Within ten minutes my palms were sweating and I was tempted to throw the whole lot over to Siegfried. But I was restrained by the knowledge that I had to establish myself not only with the farmers but with my new boss. He wasn't going to think much of an assistant who couldn't handle a thing on his own.

I did what I usually did when I was worried; drove off the unfenced road, got out of the car and followed a track across the moor. The track wound beneath the brow of the fell which overlooked the Mount farm and when I had left the road far behind I flopped on the grass and looked down on the sunlit valley floor a thousand feet below.

In most places you could hear something—the call of a bird, a car in the distance—but here there was a silence which was absolute, except when the wind sighed over the hill top, rustling the bracken around me.

The farm lay in one of the soft places in a harsh countryside; lush flat fields where cattle grazed in comfort and the cut hay lay in long even swathes.

It was a placid scene, but it was up here in the airy heights that you found true serenity. Peace dwelt here in the high moorland, stealing across the empty miles, breathing from the silence and the tufted grass and the black, peaty earth.

The heady fragrance of the hay rose in the warm summer air and as always I felt my troubles dissolving. Even now, after all the years, I still count myself lucky that I can so often find tranquillity of mind in the high places.

As I rose to go I filled with a calm resolve. I would do the job somehow. Surely I could manage the thing without troubling Siegfried.

In any case Siegfried had other things on his mind when I met him over the lunch table.

'I looked in at Granville Bennett's surgery at Hartington this morning,' he said, helping himself to some new potatoes which had been picked that morning from the garden. 'And I must say I was very impressed with his waiting room. All those magazines. I know we don't have the numbers to cater for, but there's often a lot of farmers in there.' He poured gravy on to a corner of his plate. 'Tristan, I'll give you the job. Slip round to Garlow's and order a few suitable things to be delivered every week, will you?'

'Okay,' his student brother replied. 'I'll do it this afternoon.'

'Splendid.' Siegfried chewed happily. 'We must keep progressing in every way. Do have some more of these potatoes, James, they really are very good.'

Tristan went into action right away and within two days the table and shelves in our waiting room carried a tasteful selection of periodicals. *The Illustrated London News, The Farmer's Weekly, The Farmer and Stockbreeder, Punch*. But as usual he had to embroider the situation.

'Look at this, Jim,' he whispered one afternoon, guiding me through the door. 'I've been having a little harmless sport.'

'What do you mean?' I looked around me uncomprehendingly.

Tristan said nothing, but pointed to one of the shelves. There, among the innocent journals, was a German naturist magazine displaying a startling frontispiece of full frontal nudity. Even in these permissive days it would have caused a raised eyebrow but in rural Yorkshire in the thirties it was cataclysmic.

'Where the devil did you get this?' I gasped, leafing through it hurriedly. It was just the same inside. 'And what's the idea, anyway?'

Tristan repressed a giggle. 'A fellow at college gave it to me. And it's rather a lark to sneak in quietly and find some solid citizen having a peek when he thinks nobody's looking. I've had some very successful incursions. My best bags so far have been a town councillor, a Justice of the Peace and a lay preacher.'

I shook my head. 'I think you're sticking your neck out. What if Siegfried comes across it?'

'No fear of that,' he said. 'He rarely comes in here and he's always in too much of a hurry. Anyway, it's well out of the way.'

I shrugged. Tristan had been blessed with an agile intelligence which I envied, but so much of it was misapplied. However, at the moment I hadn't time for his tricks. My mind was feverishly preoccupied.

Mentally I had cast that horse by innumerable methods and operated on his feet a thousand times by night and day. In daylight, riding round in the car, it wasn't so bad, but the operations

I carried out in bed were truly bizarre. All the time I had the feeling that something was wrong, that there was some fatal flaw in the picture of myself carving awway those hideous growths in one session. Finally I buried my pride.

'Siegfried,' I said, one afternoon when the practice was slack. 'I have rather a weird horse case.'

My boss's eyes glinted and the mouth beneath the small sandy moustache crooked into a smile. The word 'horse' usually had this effect.

'Really James? Tell me.'

I told him.

'Yes . . . yes . . . ,' he murmured. 'Maybe we'd better have a look together.'

The Mount farm was deserted when we arrived. Everybody was in the hayfields working frantically while the sunshine lasted.

'Where is he?' Siegfried asked.

'In here.' I led the way to the stable.

My boss lifted a hind foot and whistled softly. Then he moved round and examined the other one. For a full minute he gazed down at the obscene fungi thrusting from the tattered stinking horn. When he stood up he looked at me expressionlessly.

It was a few seconds before he spoke. 'And you were just going to pop round here on Monday, tip this big fellow on to the grass and do the job?'

'Yes,' I replied. 'That was the idea.'

A strange smile spread over my employer's face. It held something of wonder, sympathy, amusement and a tinge of admiration. Finally he laughed and shook his head.

'Ah, the innocence of youth,' he murmured.

'What do you mean?' After all, I was only six years younger than Siegfried.

He came over and patted my shoulder. 'I'm not mocking you, James. This is the worst case of canker I've ever seen and I've seen a few.'

'You mean I couldn't do it at one go?'

'That's exactly what I mean. There's six weeks' work here, James.'

'Six weeks . . . ?'

'Yes, and there'll be three men involved. We'll have to get this horse in to one of the loose boxes at Skeldale House and then the two of us plus a blacksmith will have a go at him. After that his feet will have to be dressed every day in the stocks.'

'I see.'

'Yes, yes.' Siegfried was warming to his subject. 'We'll use the strongest caustic—nitric acid—and he'll be shod with special shoes with a metal plate to exert pressure on the sole.' He stopped, probably because I was beginning to look bewildered, then he continued in a gentler tone. 'Believe me, James, all this is necessary. The alternative is to shoot a fine horse, because he can't go on much longer than this.'

I looked at Bobby, at the white face again turned towards us. The thought of a bullet entering that noble head was unbearable.

'All right, whatever you say Siegfried,' I mumbled, and just then Mr Mount's vast bulk darkened the entrance to the stable.

'Ah, good afternoon to you, Mr Mount,' my boss said. 'I hope you're getting a good crop of hay.'

'Aye, thank ye, Mr Farnon. We're doing very nicely. We've been lucky with the weather.' The big man looked curiously from one of us to the other, and Siegfried went on quickly.

'Mr Herriot asked me to come and look at your horse. He's been thinking the matter over and has decided that it would be better to hospitalise him at our place for a few weeks. I must say I agree with him. It's a very bad case and the chances of a permanent cure would be increased.'

Bless you, Siegfried, I thought. I had expected to emerge from this meeting as the number one chump, but all was suddenly well. I congratulated myself, not for the first time, on having an employer who never let me down.

Mr Mount took off his hat and drew a forearm across his sweating brow. 'Aye well, if that's what you think, both of ye, we'd better do it. Ah want the best for Bobby. He's a favourite o' mine.'

'Yes, he's a grand sort, Mr Mount.' Siegfried went round the big animal, patting and stroking him, then as we walked back to the car he kept up an effortless conversation with the farmer. I had always found it difficult to speak to this formidable man, but in my colleague's presence he became quite chatty. In fact there were one or two occasions when he almost smiled.

Bobby came in to the yard at Skeldale House the following day and when I saw the amount of sheer hard labour which the operation entailed I realised the utter impossibility of a single man doing it at one go.

Pat Jenner the blacksmith with his full tool kit was pressed into service and between us, taking it in turns, we removed all the vegetations and diseased tissue, leaving only healthy horn. Siegfried applied the acid to cauterise the area, then packed the sole with twists of tow which were held in place by the metal plate Pat had made to fit under the shoe. This pressure from the tow was essential to effect a cure.

After a week I was doing the daily dressings myself. This was when I began to appreciate the value of the stocks with their massive timbers sunk deep into the cobbles of the yard. It made everything so much easier when I was able to lead Bobby into the stocks, pull up a foot and make it fast in any position I wished.

Some days Pat Jenner came in to check on the shoes and he and I were busy in the yard when I heard the familiar rattle of my little Austin in the back lane. The big double doors were open and I looked up as the car turned in and drew alongside us. Pat looked too, and his eyes popped.

'Bloody 'ell!' he exclaimed, and I couldn't blame him, because the car had no driver. At least it looked that way since there was nobody in the seat as it swung in from the lane.

A driverless car in motion is quite a sight, and Pat gaped open-mouthed for a few seconds. Then just as I was about to explain, Tristan shot up from the floor with a piercing cry.

'Hi there!' he shrieked.

Pat dropped his hammer and backed away. 'God 'elp us!' he breathed.

I was unaffected by the performance because it was old stuff to me. Whenever I was in the yard and a call came in, Tristan would drive my car round from the front street and this happened so many times that inevitably he grew bored and tried to find a less orthodox method.

After a bit of practice he mastered the driverless technique. He crouched on the floor with a foot on the accelerator and one hand on the wheel and nearly frightened the life out of me the first time he did it. But I was used to it now, and blasé.

Within a few days I was able to observe another of Tristan's little jokes. As I turned the corner of the passage at Skeldale House I found him lurking by the waiting room door which was slightly ajar.

'I think I've got a victim in there,' he whispered. 'Let's see what happens.' He gently pushed the door and tiptoed inside.

As I peeped through the crack I could see that he had indeed scored a success. A man was standing there with his back to him and he was poring over the nudist magazine with the greatest absorption. As he slowly turned the pages, his enthralment showed in the way he frequently moved the pictures towards the light from the french window, inclining his head this way and that to take in all the angles. He looked as though he would be happy to spend all day there but when he heard Tristan's exquisitely timed cough he dropped the magazine as though it was white hot, snatched hurriedly at the *Farmer's Weekly* and swung round.

That was when Tristan's victory went flat. It was Mr Mount.

The huge farmer loomed over him for a few seconds and the deep bass rumble came from between clenched teeth.

'It's you, is it?' He glanced quickly from the young man to the embarrassing magazine and back again and the eyes in the craggy face narrowed dangerously.

'Yes . . . yes . . . yes, Mr Mount,' Tristan replied unsteadily. 'And how are you, Mr Mount?'

'Ah'm awright.'

'Good . . . good . . . splendid.' Tristan backed away a few steps. 'And how is Deborah?'

The eyes beneath the sprouting bristles drew in further. 'She's awright.'

There was a silence which lingered interminably and I felt for my young friend. It was not a merry meeting.

At last he managed to work up a sickly smile. 'Ah well, yes, er . . . and what can we do for you, Mr Mount?'

'Ah've come to see me 'oss.'

'Yes, indeed, of course, certainly. I believe Mr Herriot is just outside the room.'

I led the big man down the long garden into the yard. His encounter with Tristan had clearly failed to improve his opinion of the young man and he glowered as I opened the loose box.

But his expression softened when he saw Bobby eating hay contentedly. He went in and patted the arching neck. 'How's he goin' on, then?'

'Oh, very well.' I lifted a hind foot and showed him the metal plate. 'I can take this off for you if you like.'

'Nay, nay, ah don't want to disturb the job. As long as all's well, that's all ah want to know.'

The dressings went on for a few more weeks till finally Siegfried was satisfied that the last remnants of the disease had been extirpated. Then he telephoned for Mr Mount to collect his horse the following morning.

It is always nice to be in on a little triumph, and I looked over my boss's shoulder as he lifted Bobby's feet and displayed the finished job to the owner. The necrotic jumble on the soles had been replaced by a clean, smooth surface with no sign of moisture anywhere.

Mr Mount was not enthusiastic by nature but he was obviously impressed. He nodded his head rapidly several times. 'Well now, that's champion. I'm right capped wi' that.'

Siegfried lowered the foot to the ground and straightened with a pleased smile. There was a general air of bonhomie in the yard, and then I heard my car in the back lane.

I felt a sudden tingle of apprehension. Oh no, Tristan, not this time, please. You don't know. . . . My toes curled as I waited but I realised all was lost when the car turned in through the double doors. It had no driver.

With a dreadful feeling of imminent catastrophe I watched as it stopped within a few feet of Siegfried and Mr Mount who were staring at it in disbelief.

Nothing happened for a few seconds, then without warning Tristan catapulted like a jack-in-the-box into the open window.

'Yippeeee!' he screeched, but his happy grin froze as he found himself gazing into the faces of his brother and Mr Mount. Siegfried's expression of exasperation was familiar to me, but the farmer's was infinitely more menacing. The eyes in the stony visage were mere slits, the jaw jutted, the great tangle of eyebrows bristled fiercely. There was no doubt he had finally made up his mind about Tristan.

I felt the young man had suffered enough, and I kept off the subject for a week or two afterwards, but we were sitting in the big room at Skeldale House when he mentioned casually that he wouldn't be taking Deborah out any more.

'Seems her father has forbidden it,' he said.

I shrugged in sympathy, but said nothing. After all, it had been an ill-starred romance from the beginning.

CHAPTER

31

'Circuits and bumps' they called it. Taking off, circling the field and landing, over and over and over. After an hour of it with F. O. Woodham in full voice I had had enough and it was a blessed relief when we climbed out at the end.

As my instructor walked away, one of his fellow officers strolled by his side. 'How are you getting on with that chap, Woody?' he asked, smiling.

F. O. Woodham did not pause in his stride or turn his head. 'Oh God!' he said with a hollow groan, and that was all.

I knew I wasn't meant to hear the words but they bit deep. My spirits did not rise till I entered the barrack hut and was greeted by the cheerful voices of my fellow airmen.

'Hello, Jim!' 'How's it going, Jim?' The words were like balm.

I looked around at the young men sprawled on their beds, reading or smoking and I realised that I needed them and their friendship.

Animals are the same. They need friends. Have you ever watched two animals in a field? They may be of different species —a pony and a sheep—but they hang together. This comradeship between animals has always fascinated me, and I often think of Jack Sanders' two dogs as a perfect example of mutual devotion.

One of them was called Jingo and as I injected the local anaesthetic alongside the barbed wire tear in his skin the powerful white bull terrier whimpered just once. Then he decided to resign himself to his fate and looked stolidly to the front as I depressed the plunger.

Meanwhile his inseparable friend, Skipper the corgi, gnawed gently at Jingo's hind leg. It was odd to see two dogs on the table at once, but I knew the relationship between them and made no comment as their master hoisted them both up.

After I had infiltrated the area around the wound I began to stitch and Jingo relaxed noticeably when he found that he could feel nothing.

'Maybe this'll teach you to avoid barbed wire fences in future, Jing,' I said.

Jack Sanders laughed. 'I doubt if it will, Mr Herriot. I thought the coast was clear when I took him down the lane this morning, but he spotted a dog on the other side of the fence and he was through like a bullet. Fortunately it was a greyhound and he couldn't catch it.'

'You're a regular terror, Jing.' I patted my patient, and the big Roman-nosed face turned to me with an ear-to-ear grin and at the other end the tail whipped delightedly.

'Yes, it's amazing, isn't it?' his master said. 'He's always looking for a fight, yet people and children can do anything with him. He's the best natured dog in the world.'

I finished stitching and dropped the suture needle into a kidney dish on the trolley. 'Well, you've got to remember that the bull terrier is the original English fighting dog and Jing is only obeying an age-old instinct.'

'Oh I realise that. I'll just have to go on scanning the horizon every time I let him off the lead. No dog is safe from him.'

'Except this one, Jack.' I laughed and pointed to the little corgi who had tired of his companion's leg and was now chewing his ear.

'Yes, isn't it marvellous. I think he could bite Jing's ear off without reprisal.'

It was indeed rather wonderful. The corgi was eleven years old and beginning to show his age in stiffness of movement and impairment of sight while the bull terrier was only three, at the height of his strength and power. A squat, barrel-chested bundle of bone and muscle, he was a formidable animal. But when the ear-chewing became too violent, all he did was turn and gently engulf Skipper's head in his huge jaws till the little animal desisted. Those jaws could be as merciless as a steel trap but they held the tiny head in a loving embrace.

Ten days later their master brought both dogs back to the surgery for the removal of the stitches. He looked worried as he lifted the animals on to the table.

'Jingo isn't at all well, Mr Herriot,' he said. 'He's been off his food for a couple of days and he looks miserable. Could that wound make him ill if it turned septic?'

'Yes it could, of course.' I looked down anxiously at the area of the flank where I had stitched, and my fingers explored the long scar. 'But there's not the slightest sign of infection here. No swelling, no pain. He's healed beautifully.'

I stepped back and looked at the bull terrier. He was strangely disconsolate, tail tucked down, eyes gazing ahead with total lack of interest. Not even the busy nibbling of his friend at one of his paws relieved his apathy.

Clearly Skipper didn't like being ignored in this fashion. He transferred his operations to the front end and started on the big dog's ear. As his efforts still went unnoticed he began to chew and tug harder, dragging the massive head down to one side, but as far as Jingo was concerned he might as well not have been there.

'Hey, that's enough, Skipper,' I said. 'Jing isn't in the mood for rough stuff to-day.' I lifted him gently to the floor where he paced indignantly around the table legs.

I examined the bull terrier thoroughly and the only significant finding was an elevated temperature.

'It's a hundred and five, Jack. He's very ill, there's no doubt about that.'

'But what's the matter with him?'

'With a high fever like that he must have some acute infection. But at the moment it's difficult to pinpoint.' I reached out and stroked the broad skull, running my fingers over the curving white face as my thoughts raced.

For an instant the tail twitched between his hocks and the friendly eyes rolled round to me and then to his master. It was that movement of the eyes which seized my whole attention. I quickly raised the upper lid. The conjunctiva appeared to be a normal pink, but in the smooth white sclera I could discern the faintest tinge of yellow.

'He's got jaundice,' I said. 'Have you noticed anything peculiar about his urine?'

Jack Sanders nodded. 'Yes, now you mention it. I saw him cock his leg in the garden and his water looked a bit dark.'

'Those are bile pigments.' I gently squeezed the abdomen and the dog winced slightly. 'Yes, he's definitely tender in there.'

'Jaundice?' His master stared at me across the table. 'Where would he get that?'

I rubbed my chin. 'Well, when I see a dog like this I think firstly of two things—phosphorus poisoning and leptospirosis. In view of the high temperature I go for the leptospirosis.'

'Would he catch it from another dog?'

'Possibly, but more likely from rats. Does he come into contact with any rats?'

'Yes, now and then. There's a lot of them in an old hen house at the foot of the lane and Jing sometimes gets in there after them.'

'Well that's it.' I shrugged. 'I don't think we need to look any further for the cause.'

He nodded slowly. 'Anyway, it's something to know what's wrong with him. Now you can set about putting him right.'

I looked at him for a moment in silence. It wasn't like that at all. I didn't want to upset him, but on the other hand he was a highly intelligent and sensible man in his forties, a teacher at the local school. I felt I had to tell him the whole truth.

'Jack,' I said. 'This is a terrible condition to treat. If there's one thing I hate to see it's a jaundiced dog.'

'You mean it's serious?'

'I'm afraid so. In fact the mortality rate is very high.'

I felt for him when I saw the sudden pain and concern in his face, but a warning now was better than a shock later, because I knew that Jingo could be dead within a few days. Even now, thirty years later, I quail when I see that yellowish discolouration in a dog's eyes. Penicillin and other antibiotics have some effect against the causal organism of leptospirosis but the disease is still very often fatal.

'I see . . . I see . . .' He was collecting his thoughts. 'But surely you can do something?'

'Yes, yes, of course,' I said briskly. 'I'm going to give him a big shot of antileptospiral serum and some medicine to administer by the mouth. It isn't completely hopeless.'

I injected the serum in the knowledge that it didn't have much effect at this stage, but I had nothing else to offer. I gave Skipper a shot, too, with the happier feeling that it would protect him against the infection.

'One thing, more, Jack,' I added. 'This disease also affects humans, so please take all hygienic precautions when handling Jingo. All right?'

He nodded and lifted the bull terrier from the table. The big dog, as most of my patients do, tried to hurry away from the disturbing white-coat-and-antiseptic atmosphere of the surgery. As he trotted along the passage his master turned to me eagerly.

'Look at that! He doesn't seem too bad, does he?'

I didn't say anything. I hoped with all my heart that he was right, but I was fighting off the conviction that this nice animal was doomed. At any rate I would soon know.

I knew, in fact, next day. Jack Sanders was on the phone before nine o'clock in the morning.

'Jing's not so good,' he said, but the tremor in his voice belied the lightness of his words.

'Oh.' I experienced the familiar drooping of the spirits. 'What is he doing?'

'Nothing, I'm afraid. Won't eat a thing . . . lying around . . . just lifeless. And every now and then he vomits.'

It was what I expected, but I still felt like kicking the desk by my side. 'Very well, I'll be right round.'

There were no tail wags from Jing to-day. He was crouched before the fire, gazing listlessly into the coals. The yellow in his eyes had deepened to a rich orange and his temperature still soared. I repeated the serum injection, but the big dog did not heed the entry of the needle. Before I left I ran my hand over the smooth white body and Skipper as ever kept burrowing in on his friend, but Jingo's thoughts were elsewhere, sunk in his inner misery.

I visited him daily and on the fourth day I found him stretched almost comatose on his side. The conjunctiva, sclera, and the mucous membranes of the mouth were a dirty chocolate colour.

'Is he suffering?' Jack Sanders asked.

I hesitated for a moment. 'I honestly don't think he's in pain. Sickness, nausea, yes, but I'd say that's all.'

'Well I'd like to keep on trying,' he said. 'I don't want to put him down even though you think it's hopeless. You do . . . don't you?'

I made a non-committal gesture. I was watching Skipper who seemed bewildered. He had given up his worrying tactics and was sniffing round his friend in a puzzled manner. Only once did he pull very gently at the unresponsive ear.

I went through the motions with a feeling of helplessness and left with the unpleasant intuition that I would never see Jingo alive again.

And even though I was waiting for it, Jack Sanders' phone call next morning was a bad start to the day.

'Jing died during the night, Mr Herriot. I thought I'd better let you know. You said you were coming back this morning.' He was trying to be matter-of-fact.

'I'm sorry, Jack,' I said. 'I did rather expect . . .'

'Yes, I know. And thank you for what you did.'

It made it worse when people were nice at these times. The Sanders were a childless couple and devoted to their animals. I knew how he was feeling.

I stood there with the receiver in my hand. 'Anyway, Jack, you've still got Skipper.' It sounded a bit lame, but it did help to have the comfort of one remaining dog, even though he was old.

'That's right,' he replied. 'We're very thankful for Skipper.'

I went on with my work. Patients died sometimes and once it was over it was almost a relief, especially when I knew in Jingo's case that the end was inevitable.

But this thing wasn't over. Less than a week later Jack Sanders was on the phone again.

'It's Skipper,' he said. 'He seems to be going the same way as Jing.'

A cold hand took hold of my stomach and twisted it.

'But . . . but . . . he can't be! I gave him the protective injection!'

'Well, I don't know, but he's hanging around miserably and hardly eats a thing. He seems to be going down fast.'

I ran out and jumped into my car. And as I drove to the edge of the town where the Sanders lived my heart thudded and panicky thoughts jostled around in my mind. How could he have got the infection? I had little faith in the serum as a cure but as a prevention I felt it was safe. I had even given him a second shot to make sure. The idea of these people losing both their dogs was bad enough but I couldn't bear the thought that the second one might be my fault.

The little corgi trailed unhappily across the carpet when he saw me and I lifted him quickly on to the kitchen table. I almost snatched at his eyelids in my anxiety but there was no sign of jaundice in the sclera nor in the mucous membranes of the mouth. The temperature was dead normal and I felt a wave of relief.

'He hasn't got leptospirosis, anyway,' I said.

Mrs Sanders clasped her hands. 'Oh thank God for that. We were sure it was the same thing. He looks so awful.'

I examined the little animal meticulously and when I finished I put my stethoscope in my pocket. 'Well, I can't find much wrong here. He's got a bit of a heart murmur but you've known about that for some time. He's old, after all.'

'Do you think he could be fretting for Jing?' Jack Sanders asked.

'Yes, I do. They were such friends. He must feel lost.'

'But he'll get over that, won't he?'

'Oh of course he will. I'll leave some mild sedatives tablets for him and I'm sure they'll help.'

I met Jack a few days later in the market place.

'How is Skipper?' I asked.

He blew out his cheeks. 'About the same. Maybe a bit worse. The trouble is he eats practically nothing—he's getting very thin.'

I didn't see what else I could do but on the following day I looked in at the Sanders' as I was passing.

I was shocked at the little corgi's appearance. Despite his age he had been so cocky and full of bounce, and when Jing was alive he had been indisputably the boss dog. But now he was utterly deflated. He looked at me with lack-lustre eyes as I came in, then crept stiffly to his basket where he curled himself as though wishing to shut out the world.

I examined him again. The heart murmur seemed a little more pronounced but there was nothing else except that he looked old and decrepit and done.

'You know, I'm beginning to wonder if he really is fretting,' I said. 'It could be just his age catching up on him. After all, he'll be twelve in the spring, won't he?'

Mrs Sanders nodded. 'That's right. Then you think . . . this could be the end?'

'It's possible.' I knew what she was thinking. A couple of weeks ago two healthy dogs rolling around and playing in this house and now there could soon be none.

'But isn't there anything else you can do?'

'Well I can give him a course of digitalis for his heart. And perhaps you would bring in a sample of his urine. I want to see how his kidneys are functioning."

I tested the urine. There was a little albumen, but no more than you would expect in a dog of his age. I ruled out nephritis as a cause.

As the days passed I tried other things; vitamins, iron tonics, organo-phosphates, but the little animal declined steadily. It was about a month after Jing's death that I was called to the house again.

Skipper was in his basket and when I called to him he slowly raised his head. His face was pinched and fleshless and the filmed eyes regarded me without recognition.

'Come on, lad,' I said encouragingly. 'Let's see you get out of there.'

Jack Sanders shook his head. 'It's no good, Mr Herriot. He never leaves his basket now and when we lift him out he's almost too weak to walk. Another thing . . . he makes a mess down here in the kitchen during the night. That's something he's never done.'

It was like the tolling of a sad bell. Everything he said pointed to a dog in the last stages of senility. I tried to pick my words.

'I'm sorry, Jack, but it all sounds as if the old chap has come to the end of the road. I don't think fretting could possibly cause all this.'

He didn't speak for a moment. He looked at his wife then down at the forlorn little creature. 'Well of course this has been in the back of our minds. But we've kept hoping he would start to eat. What . . . what do you suggest?'

I could not bring myself to say the fateful words. "It seems to me that we can't stand by and let him suffer. He's just a little skeleton and I can't think he's getting any pleasure out of his life now.'

'I see,' he said. 'And I agree. He lies there all day—he has no interest in anything.' He paused and looked at his wife again. 'I tell you what, Mr Herriot. Let us think it over till tomorrow. But you do think there's no hope?'

'Yes, Jack, I do. Old dogs often go this way at the end. Skipper has just cracked up . . . he's finished, I'm afraid.'

He drew a long breath. 'Right, if you don't hear from me by

eight o'clock tomorrow morning, please come and put him to sleep.'

I had small hope of the call coming and it didn't. In those early days of our marriage Helen worked as a secretary for one of the local millers. We often started our day together by descending the long flights of stairs from our bed-sitter and I would see her out of the front door before getting ready for my round.

This morning she gave me her usual kiss before going out into the street but then she looked at me searchingly. 'You've been quiet all through breakfast, Jim. What's the matter?'

'It's nothing, really. Just part of the job,' I said. But when she kept her steady gaze on me I told her quickly about the Sanders.

She touched my arm. 'It's such a shame, Jim, but you can't let your sad cases depress you. You'd never survive.'

'Aagh, I know that. But I'm a softy, that's my trouble. Sometimes I think I should never have been a vet.'

'You're wrong there,' she said. 'I couldn't imagine you as anything else. You'll do what you have to do, and you'll do it the right way.' She kissed me again, turned and ran down the steps.

It was mid morning before I drew up outside the Sanders' home. I opened the car boot and took out the syringe and the bottle of concentrated anaesthetic which would give the old dog a peaceful and painless end.

The first thing I saw when I went into the kitchen was a fat little white puppy waddling across the floor.

I looked down in astonishment. 'What's this . . . ?'

Mrs Sanders gave me a strained smile 'Jack and I had a talk yesterday. We couldn't bear the idea of not having a dog at all, so we went round to Mrs Palmer who bred Jing and found she had a litter for sale. It seemed like fate. We've called him Jingo, too.'

'What a splendid idea!' I lifted the pup which squirmed in my hand, grunted in an obese manner and tried to lick my face. This, I felt, would make my unpleasant task easier. 'I think you've been very sensible.'

I lifted the bottle of anaesthetic unobtrusively from my pocket and went over to the basket in the corner. Skipper was still curled in the unheeding ball of yesterday and the comforting thought came to me that all I was going to do was push him a little further along the journey he had already begun.

I pierced the rubber diaphragm on the bottle with my needle and was about to withdraw the barbiturate when I saw that Skipper had raised his head. Chin resting on the edge of the basket, he seemed to be watching the pup. Wearily his eyes followed the tiny creature as it made its way to a dish of milk and began to lap busily. And there was something in his intent expression which had not been there for a long time.

I stood very still as the corgi made a couple of attempts then heaved himself to a standing position. He almost fell out of the basket and staggered on shaking legs across the floor. When he came alongside the pup he remained there, swaying, for some time, a gaunt caricature of his former self, but as I watched in disbelief, he reached forward and seized the little white ear in his mouth.

Stoicism is not a characteristic of pups and Jingo the Second yelped shrilly as the teeth squeezed. Skipper, undeterred, continued to gnaw with rapt concentration.

I dropped bottle and syringe back in my pocket. 'Bring him some food,' I said quietly.

Mrs Sanders hurried to the pantry and came back with a few pieces of meat on a saucer. Skipper continued his ear-nibbling for a few moments then sniffed the pup unhurriedly from end to end before turning to the saucer. He hardly had the strength to chew but he lifted a portion of meat and his jaws moved slowly.

'Good heavens!' Jack Sanders burst out. 'That's the first thing he's eaten for days!'

His wife seized my arm. 'What's happened, Mr Herriot? We only got the puppy because we couldn't have a house without a dog.'

'Well, it looks to me as though you've got two again.' I went over to the door and smiled back at the two people watching fascinated as the corgi swallowed then started determinedly on another piece of meat.

About eight months later, Jack Sanders came into the surgery and put Jingo Two on the table. He was growing into a fine animal with the wide chest and powerful legs of the breed. His good-natured face and whipping tail reminded me strongly of his predecessor.

'He's got a bit of eczema between his pads,' Jack said, then he bent and lifted Skipper up.

At that moment I had no eyes for my patient. All my attention was on the corgi, plump and bright-eyed, nibbling at the big white dog's hind limbs with all his old bounce and vigour.

'Just look at that!' I murmured. 'It's like turning the clock back.'

Jack Sanders laughed. 'Yes, isn't it. They're tremendous friends—just like before.'

'Come here, Skipper.' I grabbed the little corgi and looked him over. When I had finished I held him for a moment as he tried to wriggle his way back to his friend. 'Do you know, I honestly think he'll go on for years yet.'

'Really?' Jack Sanders looked at me with a mischievous light in his eyes. 'But I seem to remember you saying quite a long time ago that his days were over—he was finished.'

I held up a hand. 'I know, I know. But sometimes it's lovely to be wrong.'

'To-day,' said F. O. Woodham, 'we're going to try a few new things. Spinning, side-slipping and how to come out of a stall.' His voice was gentle, and before he pulled on his helmet he turned his dark, fine-featured face towards me and smiled. Walking over the grass I thought what a likeable chap he was. I could have made a friend of him.

But he was always like that on the ground. He was altogether different in the air.

Yet I could never understand it. Flying was no trouble at all, and as we spun and dropped and soared about the summer sky his instructions appeared simple and easy to carry out. But the rot, as always, began to set in very soon.

'Didn't I tell you opposite rudder and stick to sideslip?' he bawled over the intercom.

'Yes sir,' was all I replied, instead of more appropriate 'That's just what I'm doing, you stupid bugger!' which I might have used in civil life.

The goggled eyes bulged in the mirror. 'Well, why the bloody hell aren't you doing it?' His voice rose to a wild shriek.

'Sorry, sir.'

'Well take her up. We'll try again. And for God's sake keep your wits about you!'

It was the same with the spins and stalls. I hadn't the slightest difficulty in pulling out of them but at times I thought my instructor was going out of his mind.

Berserk cries rang in my ears. 'Full opposite rudder and centralise the stick! Centralise it! Can't you hear me? Oh God, God!'

And of course the panic gradually crept in and I began to crack. One moment I could see a railway station in front of me whirling around in crazy circles, then there was nothing but the empty heavens and within seconds fields and trees would start to rush at me. Everything kept changing bewilderingly except the enraged eyes in the mirror and the exasperated yells.

'Centralise it, you bloody fool! Keep your eyes on that cloud! Watch your artificial horizon! Don't you know what the altimeter's for? I told you to keep at 1,000 feet but it's like talking to a bloody wall!'

After a while a kind of numbness took over and the words rang meaninglessly in my head, one sentence seeming to contradict another. Desperately I tried to sort out the volleys of advice, but the whole thing began to slip from my grasp.

Back on the ground and still dizzy, not from the flight but from the bewildering cataract of words, it occurred to me that I had felt like this somewhere before. There was a familiar ring about this jumble in my brain. Then it came back to me. It was like being back at the Birtwhistles.

The trouble with the Birtwhistles was that they all spoke at once. Mr Birtwhistle invariably discussed his livestock, his wife concentrated on family matters and Len, their massive eighteen year old son, talked of nothing but football.

I was examining Nellie, the big white cow that always stood opposite the doorway in the grey stone byre. She had been lame for over a week and I didn't like the look of her.

'Lift her foot, will you, Len,' I said. It was wonderful to have a muscular giant to hoist the hind limb instead of going through the tedious business of hauling it up with a rope over a beam.

With the cloven hoof cradled in the great hands I could see that my fears were realised. The space between the cleats was clear but there was a significant swelling around the interphalangeal joint.

I looked up from my stooping position. 'Can you see that, Mr Birtwhistle? The infection is spreading upwards.'

'Aye . . . aye . . .' The farmer thrust a finger against the tumefied area and Nellie flinched. 'It's going' up her leg on that side right enough. Ah thought it was nowt but a bit 'o foul and I've been puttin . . .'

'By gaw,' Len interjected. 'The lads 'ad a good win against Hellerby on Saturday. Johnnie Nudd got another couple o' goals and . . .'

'. . . puttin' that caustic lotion between 'er cleats.' Mr Birtwhistle didn't appear to have heard his son, but it was always like that. 'Done it regular night and mornin'. And ah'll tell ye the best way to do it. Get a hen feather an' . . .'

'. . . ah wouldn't be surprised if 'e scores a few more this Saturday,' continued Len unheedingly. 'He's a right bobby dazzler when 'e . . .'

'. . . ye just dip it in t'lotion and push the feather in between t'cleats. It works like a . . .'

'. . . gets that ball on 'is right foot. He just whacks 'em in . . .'

I raised a hand. 'Wait a minute. You must realise this cow hasn't got foul. She has suppurative arthritis in this little joint just at the coronet here. I don't want to use a lot of big words but she has pus—matter—right inside the joint cavity, and it's a very nasty thing.'

Mr Birtwhistle nodded slowly. 'Sort of a abscess, you mean? Well, maybe it ud be best to lance it. Once you let t'matter out it would . . .'

'. . . just like a rocket,' went on Len. 'Ah'll tell ye, Johnnie could get a trial for Darlington one o' these days and then . . .'

I always think it is polite to look at a person when they are talking to you, but it is difficult when they are both talking at once, especially when one of them is bent double and the other standing behind you.

'Thank you, Len,' I said. 'You can put her foot down now.' I straightened up and directed my gaze somewhere between them. 'The trouble with this condition is that you can't just stick a knife into it and relieve it. Very often the smooth surfaces of the joint are eaten away and it's terribly painful.'

Nellie would agree with me. It was the outside cleat which was affected and she was standing with her leg splayed sideways in an attempt to take the weight on the healthy inner digit.

The farmer asked the inevitable question. 'Well, what are we goin' to do?'

I had an uncomfortable conviction that it wasn't going to make much different what we did, but I had to make an effort.

'We'll give her a course of sulphanilamide powders and I also want you to put a poultice on that foot three times daily.'

'Poultice?' The farmer brightened. 'Ah've been doin' that. Ah've been . . .'

'If Darlington signed Johnnie Nudd I reckon . . .'

'Hold on, Len,' I said. 'What poultice have you been using, Mr Birtwhistle?'

'Cow shit,' the farmer replied confidently. 'Ye can't beat a good cow shit poultice to bring t'bad out. Ah've used it for them bad cases o' . . .'

'. . . ah'd have to go through to Darlington now and then instead of watchin' the Kestrels,' Len broke in. 'Ah'd have to see how Johnnie was gettin' on wi' them professionals because . . .'

I managed a twisted smile. I like football myself and I found it touching that Len ignored the great panorama of league football to concentrate on a village team who played in front of about twenty spectators. 'Yes, yes, Len, I quite understand how you feel.' Then I turned to his father. 'I was thinking of a rather different type of poultice, Mr Birtwhistle.'

The farmer's face lengthened and the corners of his mouth drooped. 'Well, ah've never found owt better than cow shit and ah've been among stock all me life.'

I clenched my teeth. This earthy medicament was highly regarded among the Dales Farmers of the thirties and the damnable thing was that it often achieved its objective. There was no doubt that a sackful of bovine faeces applied to an inflamed area set up a tremendous heat and counter-irritation. In those days I had to go along with many of the ancient cures and keep my tongue between my teeth but I had never prescribed cow shit and I wasn't going to start now.

'Maybe so,' I said firmly, 'but what I was thinking of was kaolin. You could call down at the surgery for some. You just heat the tin in a pan of hot water and apply the poultice to the foot. It keeps its heat for several hours."

Mr Birtwhistle showed no great enthusiasm so I tried again. 'Or you could use bran. I see you've got a sack over there.'

He cheered up a little. 'Aye . . . that's right.'

'Okay, put on some hot bran three times a day and give her the powders and I'll see her again in a few days.' I knew the farmer would do as I said, because he was a conscientious stockman, but I had seen cases like this before and I wasn't happy. Nothing seems to pull a good cow down quicker than a painful foot. Big fat animals could be reduced to skeletons within weeks because of the agony of septic arthritis. I could only hope.

'Very good, Mr Herriot,' Mr Birtwhistle said. 'And now come into the house. T'missus has a cup o' tea ready for you.'

I seldom refuse such an invitation but as I entered the kitchen I knew this was where the going got really tough.

'Now then, Mr. Herriot,' the farmer's wife said, beaming as she handed me a steaming mug. 'I was talkin' to your good lady in the market place yesterday, and she said . . .'

'And ye think them powders o' yours might do the trick?' Her husband looked at me seriously. 'I 'ope so, because Nellie's a right good milker. Ah reckon last lactation she gave . . .'

'Kestrels is drawn agin Dibham in t'Hulton cup.' Len chimed in. 'It'll be some game. Last time . . .'

Mrs Birtwhistle continued without drawing breath. '. . . you were nicely settled in at top of Skeldale House. It must be right pleasant up there with the lovely view and . . .'

'. . . five gallons when she fust calved and she kept it up for . . .'

'. . . they nearly kicked us off t'pitch, but by gaw ah'll tell ye, we'll . . .'

'. . . you can see right over Darrowby. But it wouldn't do for a fat body like me. I was sayin' to your missus that you 'ave to be young and slim to live up there. All them stairs and . . .'

I took a long draught from my cup. It gave me a chance to focus my eyes and attention on just one thing as the conversation crackled unceasingly around me. I invariably found it wearing trying to listen to all three Birtwhistles in full cry and of course it was impossible to look at them all simultaneously and adjust my expression to their different remarks.

The thing that amazed me was that none of them ever became angry at the others butting in. Nobody ever said, 'I'm speaking, do you mind?' or 'Don't interrupt!' or 'For Pete's sake, shut up!' They lived together in perfect harmony with all of them talking at once and none paying the slightest heed to what the other was saying.

When I saw the cow during the following week she was worse. Mr Birtwhistle had followed my instructions faithfully but Nellie could scarcely hobble as he brought her in from the field.

Len was there to lift the foot and I gloomily surveyed the increased swelling. It ran right round the coronet from the heel to the interdigital cleft in front, and the slightest touch from my finger caused the big cow to jerk her leg in pain.

I didn't say much, because I knew what was in store for

Nellie, and I knew too that Mr Birtwhistle wasn't going to like it when I told him.

When I visited again at the end of the week I had only to look at the farmer's face to realise that everything had turned out as I feared. For once he was on his own and he led me silently into the byre.

Nellie was on three legs now, not daring even to bring the infected foot into momentary contact with the cobble flooring. And worse, she was in an advanced state of emaciation, the sleek healthy animal of two weeks ago reduced to little more than bone and hide.

'I doubt she's 'ad it,' Mr Birtwhistle muttered.

Cow's hind feet are difficult to lift, but today I didn't need any help because Nellie had stopped caring. I examined the swollen digit. It was now vast—a great ugly club of tissue with a trickle of pus discharging down the wall.

'I see it's bust there,' the farmer poked a finger at the ragged opening. 'But it hasn't given 'er no relief.'

'Well, I wouldn't expect it to,' I said. 'Remember I told you the trouble is all inside the joint.'

'Well, these things 'appen,' he replied. 'Ah might as well tele-phone for Mallock. She's hardly givin' a drop o' milk, poor awd lass, she's nowt but a screw now.'

I always had to wait for the threat of the knacker man's hu-mane killer before I said what I had to say now. Right from the start this had been a case for surgery, but it would have been a waste of time to suggest it at the beginning. Amputation of the bovine digit has always filled farmers with horror and even now I knew I would have trouble convincing Mr Birtwhistle.

'There's no need to slaughter her," I said. 'There's another way of curing this.'

'Another way? We've tried 'ard enough, surely.'

I bent and lifted the foot again. 'Look at this.' I seized the inner cleat and moved it freely around. 'This side is perfectly healthy. There's nothing wrong with it. It would bear Nellie's full weight.'

'Aye, but . . . how about t'other 'orrible thing?'

'I could remove it.'

'You mean . . . cut it off?'

'Yes.'

He shook his head vigorously. 'Nay, nay, I'm not havin' that.

She's suffered enough. Far better send for Jeff Mallock and get the job over.'

Here it was again. Farmers are anything but shrinking violets, but there was something about this business which appalled them.

'But Mr Birtwhistle,' I said. 'Don't you see—the pain is immediately relieved. The pressure is off and all the weight rests on the good side.'

'Ah said no, Mr Herriot, and ah mean no. You've done your best and I thank ye, but I'm not havin' her foot cut off and that's all about it.' He turned and began to walk away.

I looked after him helplessly. One thing I hate to do is talk a man into an operaiton on one of his beasts for the simple reason that if anything goes wrong I get the blame. But I was just about certain that an hour's work could restore this good cow to her former state. I couldn't let it go at this.

I trotted from the byre. The farmer was already half way across the yard on his way to the phone.

I panted up to him as he reached the farmhouse door. 'Mr Birtwhistle, listen to me for a minute. I never said anything about cutting off her foot. Just one cleat.'

'Well that's half a foot, isn't it?' he looked down at his boots. 'And it's ower much for me.'

'But she wouldn't know a thing,' I pleaded. 'She'd be under a general anaesthetic. And I'm nearly sure it would be a success.'

'Mr Herriot, I just don't fancy it. I don't like t'idea. And even if it did work it would be like havin' a crippled cow walkin' about.'

'Not at all. She would grow a little stump of horn there and I'd like to bet you'd never notice a thing.'

He gave me a long sideways look and I could see he was weakening.

'Mr Birtwhistle,' I said, pressing home the attack. 'Within a month Nellie could be a fat cow again, giving five gallons of milk a day.'

This was silly talk, not to be recommended to any veterinary surgeon, but I was seized by a kind of madness. I couldn't bear the thought of that cow being cut up for dog food when I was convinced I could put her right. And there was another thing; I was already savouring the pleasure, childish perhaps, of instantly relieving an animal's pain, of bringing off a spectacular cure. There aren't many operations in the field of bovine surgery where you can do this but digit amputation is one of them.

Something of my fervour must have been communicated to the farmer because he looked at me steadily for a few moments then shrugged.

'When do you want to do it?' he asked.

'Tomorrow.'

'Right. Will you need a lot o' fellers to help?'

'No, just you and Len. I'll see you at ten o'clock."

Next day the sun was warm on my back as I laid out my equipment on a small field near the house. It was a typical setting for many large animal operations I have carried out over the years; the sweet stretch of green, the grey stone buildings and the peaceful bulk of the fells rising calm and unheeding into the white scattering of clouds.

It took a long time for them to lead Nellie out, though she didn't have far to go, and as the bony scarecrow hopped painfully towards me, dangling her useless limb, the brave words of yesterday seemed foolhardy.

'All right,' I said. 'Stop there. That's a good spot.' On the grass, nearby, lay my tray with the saw, chloroform, bandages, cotton wool and iodoform. I had my long casting rope too, which we used to pull cattle down, but I had a feeling Nellie wouldn't need it.

I was right. I buckled on the muzzle, poured some chloroform on to the sponge and the big white cow sank almost thankfully on to the cool green herbage.

'Kestrels had a smashin' match on Wednesday night,' Len chuckled happily. 'Johnnie Nudd didn't score but Len Bottomley . . .'

'I 'ope we're doin' t'right thing,' muttered Mr Birtwhistle. 'The way she staggered out 'ere I'd say it was a waste of time to . . .'

'. . . cracked in a couple o' beauties.' Len's face lit up at the memory. 'Kestrels is lucky to 'ave two fellers like . . .'

'Get hold of that bad foot, Len!' I barked, playing them at their own game. 'And keep it steady on that block of wood. And you, Mr Birtwhistle, hold her head down. I don't suppose she'll move, but if she does we'll have to give her more chloroform.'

Cows are good subjects for chloroform anaesthesia but I don't like to keep them laid out too long in case of regurgitation of food. I was in a hurry.

I quickly tied a bandage above the hoof, pulling it tight to serve as a tourniquet, then I reached back to the tray for the saw. The books are full of sophisticated methods of digit amputation with much talk of curved incisions, reflections of skin to expose the region of the articulations, and the like. But I have whipped off hundreds of cleats with a few brisk strokes of the saw below the coronary band with complete success.

I took a long breath. 'Hold tight, Len.' And set to work.

For a few moments there was silence except for the rhythmic grating of metal on bone, then the offending digit was lying on the grass, leaving a flat stump from which a few capillary vessels spurted. Using curved scissors I speedily disarticulated the remains of the pedal bone from the second phalanx and held it up.

'Look at that!' I cried. 'Almost eaten away.' I pointed to the necrotic tissue in and around the joint. 'And d'you see all that rubbish? No wonder she was in pain.' I did a bit of quick curetting, dusted the surface with iodoform, applied a thick pad of cotton wool and prepared to bandage.

And as I tore the paper from the white rolls I felt a stab of remorse. In my absorption I had been rather rude. I had never replied to Len's remark about his beloved team. Maybe I could pass the next few minutes with a little gentle banter.

'Hey, Len,' I said. 'When you're talking about the Kestrels you never mention the time Willerton beat them five nil. How is that?'

In reply the young man hurled himself unhesitatingly at me, butting me savagely on the forehead. The assault of the great coarse-haired head against my skin was like being attacked by a curlypolled bull, and the impact sent me flying backwards on to the grass. At first the inside of my cranium was illuminated by a firework display but as consciousness slipped away my last sensation was of astonishment and disbelief.

I loved football myself but never had I thought that Len's devotion to the Kestrels would lead him to physical violence. He had always seemed a most gentle and harmless boy.

I suppose I was out for only a few seconds but I fancy I might have spent a good deal longer lying on the cool turf but for the fact that something kept hammering out the message that I was in the middle of a surgical procedure. I blinked and sat up.

Nellie was still sleeping peacefully against the green back-ground of hills. Mrs Birtwhistle, hands on her neck, was regard-ing me anxiously, and Len was lying unconscious face down across the cow's body.

'Has he hurt tha, Mr Herriot?'

'No . . . no . . . not really. What happened?'

'I owt to have told ye. He can't stand the sight o' blood. Great daft beggar.' The farmer directed an exasperated glare at his slumbering son. 'But ah've never seen 'im go down as fast as that. Pitched right into you, 'e did!'

I rolled the young man's inert form to one side and began again. I bandaged slowly and carefully because of the danger of post operative haemorrhage. I finished with several layers of zinc oxide plaster then turned to the farmer.

'You can take her muzzle off now, Mr Birtwhistle. The job's done."

I was starting to wash my instruments in the bucket when Len sat up almost as suddenly as he had slumped down. He was deathly pale but he looked at me with his usual friendly smile.

'What was that ye were sayin' about t'Kestrels, Mr Herriot?'

'Nothing, Len,' I replied hastily. 'Nothing at all.'

After three days I returned and removed the original dressing which was caked hard with blood and pus. I dusted the stump with powder again and bandaged on a clean soft pad of cotton wool.

'She'll feel a lot more comfortable now,' I said, and indeed Nellie was already looking vastly happier. She was taking some weight on the affected foot—rather gingerly, as though she couldn't believe that terrible thing had gone from her life.

As she walked away I crossed my fingers. The only thing that can ruin these operations is if the infection spreads to the other side. The inevitable result then is immediate slaughter and ter-rible disappointment.

But it never happened to Nellie. When I took off the second dressing she was almost sound and I didn't see her again until about five weeks after the operation.

I had finished injecting one of Mr Birtwhistle's pigs when I asked casually, 'And how's Nellie?'

'Come and 'ave a look at her,' the farmer replied. 'She's just in that field at side of t'road.'

We walked together over the grass to where the white cow was standing among her companions, head down, munching busily. And she must have done a lot of that since I saw her because she was fat again.

'Get on, lass.' The farmer gently nudged her rump with his thumb and she ambled forward a few places before setting to work on another patch of grass. There wasn't the slightest trace of lameness.

'Well, that's grand,' I said. 'And is she milking well, too?'

'Aye, back to five gallons.' He pulled a much dented tobacco tin from his pocket, unscrewed the lid and produced an ancient watch. 'It's ten o'clock, young man. Len'll have gone into t'house for his tea, and lowance. Will ye come in and have a cup?"

I squared my shoulders and followed him inside, and the barrage began immediately.

'Summat right funny happened on Saturday,' Len said with a roar of laughter. 'Walter Gimmet was refereein' and 'e gave two penalties agin t'Kestrels. So what did the lads do, they . . .'

'Eee, wasn't it sad about old Mr Brent?' Mrs Birtwhistle put her head on one side and looked at me piteously. 'We buried 'im on Saturday and . . .'

'You know, Mr Herriot,' her husband put in. 'Ah thought you were pullin' ma leg when you said Nellie would be givin' five gallons again. I never . . .'

'. . . dumped the beggar in a 'oss trough. He won't give no more penalties agin t'Kestrels. You should 'ave seen . . .'

'. . . it would 'ave been his ninetieth birthday today, poor old man. He was well liked in t'village and there was a big congregation. Parson said . . .'

'. . . expected owt like that. Ah thought she might maybe put on a bit of flesh so we could get 'er off for beef. Ah'm right grateful to . . .'

At that moment, fingers clenched tensely around my cup, I happened to catch sight of my reflection in a cracked mirror above the kitchen sink. It was a frightening experience because I was staring glassily into space with my features contorted almost out of recognition. There was something of an idiot smile as I acknowledged the humour of Walter in the horse trough, a touch of sorrow at Mr Brent's demise, and, I swear, a suggestion of gratification at the successful outcome of Nellie's operation. And since I was also trying to look in three directions at once, I had to give myself full marks for effort.

But as I say, I found it a little unnerving and excused myself soon afterwards. The men were still busy with Mrs Birtwhistle's apple pie and scones and the conversation was raging unabated when I left. The closure of the door behind me brought a sudden peace. The feeling of tranquillity stayed with me as I got into my car and drove out of the yard and onto the narrow country road. It persisted as I stopped the car after less than a hundred yards and wound down the window to have a look at my patient.

Nellie was lying down now. She had eaten her fill and was resting comfortably on her chest as she chewed her cud. To a doctor of farm animals there is nothing more reassuring than that slow lateral grinding. It means contentment and health. She gazed at me across the stone wall and the placid eyes in the white face added to the restfulness of the scene, accentuating the silence after the babel of voices in the farmhouse.

Nellie couldn't talk, but those calmly moving jaws told me all I wanted to know.

33

To me there are few things more appealing than a dog begging. This one was tied to a lamp post outside a shop in Windsor. Its eyes were fixed steadfastly on the shop doorway, willing its owner to come out, and every now and then it sat up in mute entreaty.

Flying had been suspended for an afternoon. It gave us all a chance to relax and no doubt it eased the frayed nerves of our instructors, but as I looked at that dog all the pressures of the R.A.F. fell away and I was back in Darrowby.

It was when Siegfried and I were making one of our market day sorties that we noticed the little dog among the stalls.

When things were quiet in the surgery we often used to walk together across the cobbles and have a word with the farmers gathered round the doorway of the Drovers' Arms. Sometimes we collected a few outstanding bills or drummed up a bit of work for the forthcoming week—and if nothing like that happened we still enjoyed the fresh air.

The thing that made us notice the dog was that he was sitting up begging in front of the biscuit stall.

'Look at that little chap,' Siegfried said. 'I wonder where he's sprung from.'

As he spoke, the stallholder threw a biscuit which the dog devoured eagerly but when the man came round and stretched out a hand the little animal trotted away.

He stopped, however, at another stall which sold produce; eggs, cheese, butter cakes and scones. Without hesitation he sat up again in the begging position, rock steady, paws dangling, head pointing expectantly.

I nudged Siegfried. 'There he goes again.'

My colleague nodded. 'Yes, he's an engaging little thing, isn't he? What breed would you call him?'

'A cross, I'd say. He's like a little brown sheepdog, but there's a touch of something else—maybe terrier.'

It wasn't long before he was munching a bun, and this time we walked over to him. And as we drew near I spoke gently.

'Here, boy,' I said, squatting down a yard away. 'Come on, let's have a look at you.'

He faced me and for a moment two friendly brown eyes gazed at me from a singularly attractive little face. The fringed tail waved in response to my words but as I inched nearer he turned and ambled unhurriedly among the market day crowd till he was lost to sight. I didn't want to make a thing out of the encounter because I could never quite divine Siegfried's attitude to the small animals. He was eminently wrapped up in his horse work and often seemed amused at the way I rushed around after dogs and cats.

At that time, in fact, Siegfried was strongly opposed to the whole idea of keeping animals as pets. He was quite vociferous on the subject—said it was utterly foolish—despite the fact that five assorted dogs travelled everywhere with him in his car. Now, thirty-five years later, he is just as strongly *in favour* of keeping pets, though he now carries only one dog in his car. So, as I say, it was difficult to assess his reactions in this field and I refrained from following the little animal.

I was standing there when a young policeman came up to me.

'I've been watching that little dog begging among the stalls all morning,' he said. 'But like you, I haven't been able to get near him.'

'Yes, it's strange. He's obviously friendly, yet he's afraid. I wonder who owns him.'

'I reckon he's a stray, Mr Herriot. I'm interested in dogs myself and I fancy I know just about all of them around here. But this 'un's a stranger to me.'

I nodded. 'I bet you're right. So anything could have happened to him. He could have been ill-treated by somebody and run away, or he could have been dumped from a car.'

'Yes,' he replied. 'There's some lovely people around. It beats me how anybody can leave a helpless animal to fend for itself like that. I've had a few goes at catching him myself but it's no good.'

The memory stayed with me for the rest of the day and even when I lay in bed that night I was unable to dispel the disturbing image of the little brown creature wandering in a strange world, sitting up asking for help in the only way he knew.

I was still a bachelor at that time and on the Friday night of the same week Siegfried and I were arraying ourselves in evening dress in preparation for the Hunt Ball at East Hirdsley, about ten miles away.

It was a tortuous business because those were the days of starched shirt fronts and stiff high collars and I kept hearing explosions of colourful language from Siegfried's room as he wrestled with his studs.

I was in an even worse plight because I had outgrown my suit and even when I had managed to secure the strangling collar I had to fight my way into the dinner jacket which nipped me cruelly under the arms. I had just managed to don the complete outfit and was trying out a few careful breaths when the phone rang.

It was the same young policeman I had been speaking to earlier in the week.

'We've got that dog round here, Mr Herriot. You know—the one that was begging in the market place.'

'Oh yes? Somebody's managed to catch him, then?'

There was a pause. 'No, not really. One of our men found him lying by the roadside about a mile out of town and brought him in. He's been in an accident.'

I told Siegfried. He looked at his watch. 'Always happens, doesn't it, James. Just when we're ready to go out. It's nine o'clock now and we should be on our way.' He thought for a moment. 'Anyway, slip round there and have a look and I'll wait for you. It would be better if we could go to this affair together.'

As I drove round to the Police Station I hoped fervently that there wouldn't be much to do. This Hunt Ball meant a lot to my boss because it would be a gathering of the horse-loving fraternity of the district and he would have a wonderful time just chatting and drinking with so many kindred spirits even though he hardly danced at all. Also, he maintained, it was good for business to meet the clients socially.

The kennels were at the bottom of a yard behind the Station and the policeman led me down and opened one of the doors.

The little dog was lying very still under the single electric bulb and when I bent and stroked the brown coat his tail stirred briefly among the straw of his bed.

'He can still manage a wag, anyway,' I said.

The policeman nodded. 'Aye, there's no doubt he's a good-natured little thing.'

I tried to examine him as much as possible without touching. I didn't want to hurt him and there was no saying what the extent of his injuries might be. But even at a glance certain things were obvious; he had multiple lacerations, one hind leg was crooked in the unmistakable posture of a fracture and there was blood on his lips.

This could be from damaged teeth and I gently raised the head with a view to looking into his mouth. He was lying on his right side and as the head came round it was as though somebody had struck me in the face.

The right eye had been violently dislodged from its socket and it sprouted like some hideous growth from above the cheek bone, a great glistening orb with the eyelids tucked behind the white expanse of sclera.

I seemed to squat there for a long time, stunned by the obscenity, and as the seconds dragged by I looked into the little dog's face and he looked back at me—trustingly from one soft brown eye, glaring meaninglessly from the grotesque ball on the other side.

The policeman's voice broke my thoughts. 'He's a mess, isn't he?'

'Yes . . . yes . . . must have been struck by some vehicle —maybe dragged along by the look of all those wounds.'

'What d'you think, Mr Herriot?'

I knew what he meant. It was the sensible thing to ease this lost unwanted creature from the world. He was grievously hurt and he didn't seem to belong to anybody. A quick overdose of anaesthetic—his troubles would be over and I'd be on my way to the dance.

But the policeman didn't say anything of the sort. Maybe, like me, he was looking into the soft depths of that one trusting eye.

I stood up quickly. 'Can I use your phone?'

At the other end of the line Siegfried's voice crackled with impatience. 'Hell, James, it's half past nine! If we're going to this thing we've got to go now or we might as well not bother. A stray dog, badly injured. It doesn't sound such a great problem.'

'I know, Siegfried. I'm sorry to hold you up but I can't make up my mind. I wish you'd come round and tell me what you think.'

There was a silence then a long sigh. 'All right, James. See you in five minutes.'

He created a slight stir as he entered the Station. Even in his casual working clothes Siegfried always managed to look distinguished, but as he swept into the station newly bathed and shaved, a camel coat thrown over the sparkling white shirt and black tie, there was something ducal about him.

He drew respectful glances from the men sitting around, then my young policeman stepped forward.

'This way, sir,' he said, and we went back to the kennels.

Siegfried was silent as he crouched over the dog, looking him over as I had done without touching him. Then he carefully raised the head and the monstrous eye glared.

'My God!' he said softly, and at the sound of his voice the long fringed tail moved along the ground.

For a few seconds he stayed very still looking fixedly at the dog's face while in the silence, the whisking tail rustled the straw.

Then he straightened up. 'Let's get him round there,' he murmured.

In the surgery we anaesthetised the little animal and as he lay unconscious on the table we were able to examine him thoroughly. After a few minutes Siegfried stuffed his stethoscope into the pocket of his white coat and leaned both hands on the table.

'Luxated eyeball, fractured femur, umpteen deep lacerations, broken claws. There's enough here to keep us going till midnight, James.'

I didn't say anything.

My boss pulled the knot from his black tie and undid the front stud. He peeled off the stiff collar and hung it on the cross bar of the surgery lamp.

"By God, that's better," he muttered, and began to lay out suture materials.

I looked at him across the table. 'How about the Hunt Ball?'

'Oh bugger the Hunt Ball,' Siegfried said. 'Let's get busy.'

We were busy, too, for a long time. I hung up my collar next to my colleague's and we began on the eye. I know we both felt the same—we wanted to get rid of that horror before we did anything else.

I lubricated the great ball and pulled the eyelids apart while Siegfried gently manoeuvered it back into the orbital cavity. I sighed as everything slid out of sight, leaving only the cornea visible.

Siegfried chuckled with satisfaction. 'Looks like an eye again, doesn't it.' He seized an ophthalmoscope and peered into the depths.

'And there's no major damage—could be as good as new again. But we'll just stitch the lids together to protect it for a few days.'

The broken ends of the fractured tibia were badly displaced and we had a struggle to bring them into apposition before applying the plaster of paris. But at last we finished and started on the long job of stitching the many cuts and lacerations.

We worked separately for this, and for a long time it was quiet in the operating room except for the snip of scissors as we clipped the brown hair away from the wounds. I knew and Siegfried knew that we were almost certainly working without payment, but the most disturbing thought was that after all our efforts we may still have to put him down. He was still in the care of the police and if nobody claimed him within ten days it meant euthanasia. And if his late owners were really interested in his fate, why hadn't they tried to contact the police before now . . . ?

By the time we had completed our work and washed the instruments it was after midnight. Siegfried dropped the last suture needle into its tray and looked at the sleeping animal.

'I think he's beginning to come round,' he said. 'Let's take him through to the fire and we can have a drink while he recovers.'

We stretchered the dog through to the sitting room on a blanket and laid him on the rug before the brightly burning coals. My colleague reached a long arm up to the glass-fronted cabinet above the mantlepiece and pulled down the whisky bottle and two glasses. Drinks in hand, collarless, still in shirt sleeves, with our starched white fronts and braided evening trousers to remind us of the lost dance we lay back in our chairs on either side of the fireplace and between us our patient stretched peacefully.

He was a happier sight now. One eye was closed by the protecting stitches and his hind leg projected stiffly in its white cast, but he was tidy, cleaned up, cared for. He looked as though he belonged to somebody—but then there was a great big doubt about that.

It was nearly one o'clock in the morning and we were getting well down the bottle when the shaggy brown head began to move.

Siegfried leaned forward and touched one of the ears and immediately the tail flapped against the rug and a pink tongue lazily licked his fingers.

'What an absolutely grand little dog,' he murmured, but his voice had a distant quality. I knew he was worried too.

I took the stitches out of the eyelids in two days and was delighted to find a normal eye underneath.

The young policeman was as pleased as I was. 'Look at that!' he exclaimed. 'You'd never know anything had happened there.'

'Yes, it's done wonderfully well. All the swelling and inflammation has gone.' I hesitated for a moment. 'Has anybody enquired about him?'

He shook his head. 'Nothing yet. But there's another eight days to go and we're taking good care of him here.'

I visited the Police Station several times and the little animal greeted me with undisguised joy, all his fear gone, standing upright against my legs on his plastered limb, his tail swishing.

But all the time my sense of foreboding increased, and on the tenth day I made my way almost with dread to the police kennels. I had heard nothing. My course of action seemed inevitable. Putting down old or hopelessly ill dogs was often an act of mercy but when it was a young healthy dog it was terrible. I hated it, but it was one of the things veterinary surgeons had to do.

The young policeman was standing in the doorway.

'Still no news?' I asked, and he shook his head.

I went past him into the kennel and the shaggy little creature stood up against my legs as before, laughing into my face, mouth open, eyes shining.

I turned away quickly. I'd have to do this right now or I'd never do it.

'Mr Herriot.' The policeman put his hand on my arm. 'I think I'll take him.'

'You?' I stared at him.

'Aye, that's right. We get a lot o' stray dogs in here and though I feel sorry for them you can't give them all a home, can you?'

'No, you can't,' I said. 'I have the same problem.'

He nodded slowly. 'But somehow this 'un's different, and it seems to me he's just come at the right time. I have two little girls and they've been at me for a bit to get 'em a dog. This little bloke looks just right for the job.'

Warm relief began to ebb through me. 'I couldn't agree more. He's the soul of good nature. I bet he's be wonderful with children.'

'Good. That's settled then. I thought I'd ask your advice first.' He smiled happily.

I looked at him as though I had never seen him before. 'What's your name?'

'Phelps,' he replied. 'P. C. Phelps.'

He was a good-looking young fellow, clear-skinned, with cheerful blue eyes and a solid dependable look about him. I had to fight against an impulse to wring his hand and thump him on the back. But I managed to preserve the professional exterior.

'Well, that's fine.' I bent and stroked the little dog. 'Don't forget to bring him along to the surgery in ten days for removal of the stitches, and we'll have to get that plaster off in about a month.'

It was Siegfried who took out the stitches, and I didn't see our patient again until four weeks later.

P. C. Phelps had his little girls, aged four and six, with him as well as the dog.

'You said the plaster ought to come off about now,' he said, and I nodded.

He looked down at the children. 'Well, come on, you two, lift him on the table.'

Eagerly the little girls put their arms around their new pet and as they hoisted him the tail wagged furiously and the wide mouth panted in delight.

'Looks as though he's been a success,' I said.

He smiled. 'That's an understatement. He's perfect with these two. I can't tell you what pleasure he's given us. He's one of the family.'

I got out my little saw and began to hack at the plaster.

'It's worked both ways, I should say. A dog loves a secure home.'

'Well, he couldn't be more secure.' He ran his hand along the brown coat and laughed as he addressed the little dog. 'That's what you get for begging among the stalls on market day, my lad. You're in the hands of the law now.'

CHAPTER
34

When I entered the R.A.F. I had a secret fear. All my life I have suffered from vertigo and even now I have only to look down from the smallest height to be engulfed by that dreadful dizziness and panic. What would I feel, then, when I started to fly?

As it turned out, I felt nothing. I could gaze downwards from the open cockpit through thousands of feet of space without a qualm, so my fear was groundless.

I had my fears in veterinary practice, too, and in the early days the thing which raised the greatest terror in my breast was the Ministry of Agriculture.

An extraordinary statement, perhaps, but true. It was the clerical side that scared me—all those forms. As to the practical Ministry work itself, I felt in all modesty that I was quite good at it. My thoughts often turned back to all the tuberculin testing I used to do—clipping a clean little area from just the right place in the cow's neck, inserting the needle into the thickness of the skin and injecting one tenth of a c.c. of tuberculin.

It was on Mr Hill's farm, and I watched the satisfactory intradermal 'pea' rise up under my needle. That was the way it should be, and when it came up like that you knew you were really doing your job and testing the animal for tuberculosis.

'That 'un's number 65,' the farmer said, then a slightly injured look spread over his face as I checked the number in the ear.

'You're wastin' your time, Mr Herriot. I 'ave the whole list, all in t'correct order. Wrote it out special for you so you could take it away with you.'

I had my doubts. All farmers were convinced that their herd records were flawless but I had been caught out before. I seemed to have the gift of making every possible clerical mistake and I didn't need any help from the farmers.

But still . . . it was tempting. I looked at the long list of figures dangling from the horny fingers. If I accepted it I would save a lot of time. There were still more than fifty animals to test here and I had to get through two more herds before lunch time.

I looked at my watch. Damn! I was well behind my programme and I felt the old stab of frustration.

'Right, Mr Hill, I'll take it and thank you very much.' I stuffed the sheet of paper into my pocket and began to move along the byre, clipping and injecting at top speed.

A week later the dread words leaped out at me from the open day book. 'Ring Min.' The cryptic phrase in Miss Harbottle's writing had the power to freeze my blood quicker than anything else. It meant simply that I had to telephone the Ministry of Agriculture office, and whenever our secretary wrote those words in the book it meant that I was in trouble again. I extended a trembling hand towards the receiver.

As always, Kitty Pattison answered my call and I could detect the note of pity in her voice. She was the attractive girl in charge of the office staff and she knew all about my misdemeanours. In fact when it was something very trivial she sometimes brought it to my attention herself, but when I had really dropped a large brick I was dealt with by the boss, Charles Harcourt the Divisional Inspector.

'Ah, Mr Herriot,' Kitty said lightly. I knew she sympathised with me but she couldn't do a thing about it. 'Mr Harcourt wants a word with you.'

There it was. The terrible sentence that always set my heart thumping.

'Thank you,' I said huskily, and waited an eternity as the phone was switched through.

'Herriot!' The booming voice made me jump.

I swallowed. 'Good morning, Mr Harcourt. How are you?'

'I'll tell you how I am, I'm bloody annoyed!' I could imagine vividly the handsome, high-coloured, choleric face flushing deeper, the greenish eyes glaring. 'In fact I'm hopping bloody mad!'

'Oh.'

'It's no use saying "oh." That's what you said the last time when you tested that cow of Frankland's that had been dead for two years! That was very clever—I don't know how you managed it. Now I've been going over your test at Hill's of High View and there are two cows here that you've tested—numbers 74 and 103. Now our records show that he sold both of them at Brawton Auction Mart six months ago, so you've performed another miracle.'

'I'm sorry . . .'

'Please don't be sorry, it's bloody marvellous how you do it. I have all the figures here—skin measurements, the lot. I see you found they were both thin-skinned animals even though they were about fifteen miles away at the time. Clever stuff!'

'Well I . . .'

'All right, Herriot, I'll dispense with the comedy. I'm going to tell you once more, for the last time, and I hope you're listening.' He paused and I could almost see the big shoulders hunching as he barked into the phone. 'LOOK IN THE BLOODY EARS IN FUTURE!'

I broke into a rapid gabble. 'I will indeed, Mr Harcourt, I assure you from now on . . .'

'All right, all right, but there's something else.'

'Something else?'

'Yes, I'm not finished yet.' The voice took on a great weariness. 'Can I ask you to cast your mind back to that cow you took under the T.B. order from Wilson of Low Parks?'

I dug my nails into my palm. We were heading for deep water. 'Yes—I remember it.'

'Well now, Herriot, lad, do you remember a little chat we had about the forms?' Charles was trying to be patient, because he was a decent man, but it was costing him dearly. 'Didn't anything I told you sink in?'

'Well yes, of course.'

'Then why, why didn't you send me a receipt for slaughter?'

'Receipt for . . . didn't I . . . ?'

'No, you didn't,' he said. 'And honestly I can't understand it. I went over it with you step by step last time when you forgot to forward a copy of the valuation agreement.'

'Oh dear, I really am sorry.'

A deep sigh came from the other end. 'And there's nothing to it.' He paused. 'Tell you what we'll do. Let's go over the procedure once more, shall we?'

'Yes, by all means.'

'Very well,' he said. 'First of all, when you find an infected animal you serve B. 205.D.T., Form A., which is the notice requiring detention and isolation of the animal. Next,' and I could hear the slap of finger on palm as he enumerated his points. 'Next, there is B. 207 D.T., Form C., Notice of intended slaughter. Then B. 208 D.T., Form D., Post Mortem Certificate. Then B. 196 D.T., Veterinary Inspector's report. Then B. 209 D.T., Valuation agreement, and in cases where the owner objects, there is B. 213 D.T., Appointment of valuer. Then we have B. 212 D.T., Notice to owner of time and place of slaughter, followed by B. 227 D.T., Receipt for animal for slaughter, and finally B. 230 D.T., Notice requiring cleansing and disinfection. Dammit, a child could understand that. It's perfectly simple, isn't it?'

'Yes, yes, certainly, absolutely.' It wasn't simple to me, but I didn't mention the fact. He had calmed down nicely and I didn't want to inflame him again.

'Well thank you, Mr. Harcourt,' I said. 'I'll see it doesn't happen again.' I put down the receiver with the feeling that things could have turned out a lot worse, but for all that my nerves didn't stop jangling for some time. The trouble was that the Ministry work was desperately important to general practitioners. In fact, in those precarious days it was the main rent payer.

This business of the Tuberculosis Order. When a veterinary surgeon came upon a cow with open T.B. it was his duty to see that the animal was slaughtered immediately because its milk could be a danger to the public. That sounds easy, but unfortunately the law insisted that the demise of each unhappy creature be commemorated by a confetti-like shower of the doom-laden forms.

It wasn't just that there were so many of these forms, but they had to be sent to an amazing variety of people. Sometimes I used to think that there were very few people in England who didn't get one. Apart from Charles Harcourt, other recipients included the farmer concerned, the police, the Head Office of the Ministry, the knacker man, the local authority. I nearly always managed to forget one of them. I used to have nightmares about standing in the middle of the market place, throwing the forms around me at the passers-by and laughing hysterically.

Looking back, I can hardly believe that for all this wear and tear on the nervous system the payment was one guinea plus ten and sixpence for the post mortem.

It was a mere two days after my interview with the Divisional Inspector that I had to take another cow under the T.B. Order. When I came to fill in the forms I sat at the surgery desk in a dither of apprehension, going over them again and again, laying them out side by side and enclosing them one by one in their various envelopes. This time there must be no mistake.

I took them over to the post myself and uttered a silent prayer as I dropped them into the box. Charles would have them the following morning, and I would soon know if I had done it again. When two days passed without incident I felt I was safe, but midway through the third morning I dropped in at the surgery and read the message in letters of fire. 'RING MIN!'

Kitty Pattison sounded strained. She didn't even try to appear casual. 'Oh yes, Mr Herriot,' she said hurriedly. 'Mr Harcourt asked me to call you. I'm putting you through now.'

My heart almost stopped as I waited for the familiar bellow, but when the quiet voice came on the line it frightened me even more.

'Good morning, Herriot.' Charles was curt and impersonal. 'I'd like to discuss that last cow you took under the Order.'

'Oh yes?' I croaked.

'But not over the telephone. I want to see you here in the office.'

'In the . . . the office?'

'Yes, right away if you can.'

I put down the phone and went out to the car with my knees knocking. Charles was really upset this time. There was a kind of restrained fury in his words, and this business of going to the office—that was reserved for serious transgressions.

Twenty minutes later my footsteps echoed in the corridor of the Ministry building. Marching stiffly like a condemned man I passed the windows where I could see the typists at work, then I read 'Divisional Inspector' on the door at the end.

I took one long shuddering breath then knocked.

'Come in.' The voice was still quiet and controlled.

Charles looked up unsmilingly from his desk as I entered. He motioned me to a chair and directed a cold stare at me.

'Herriot,' he said unemotionally. 'You're really on the carpet this time.'

Charles had been a Major in the Punjabi Rifles and he was very much the Indian Army officer at this moment. A fine looking man, clear-skinned and ruddy, with massive cheek bones above a powerful jaw. Looking at the dangerously glinting eyes it struck me that only a fool would trifle with somebody like him—and I had a nasty feeling that I had been trifling.

Dry-mouthed, I waited.

'You know, Herriot,' he went on. 'After our last telephone conversation about T.B. forms I thought you might give me a little peace.'

'Peace . . .?'

'Yes, yes, it was silly of me, I know, but when I took all that time to go over the procedure with you I actually thought you were listening.'

'Oh I was, I was!'

'You were? Oh good.' He gave me a mirthless smile. 'Then I suppose it was even more foolish of me to expect you to act upon my instructions. In my innocence I thought you cared about what I was telling you.'

'Mr Harcourt, believe me, I do care, I . . .'

'THEN WHY,' he bawled without warning, bringing his great hand flailing down on the desk with a crash that made pens and inkwells dance. 'WHY THE BLOODY HELL DO YOU KEEP MAKING A BALLS OF IT?'

I resisted a strong impulse to run away. 'Making a . . . I don't quite understand.'

'You don't?' He kept up his pounding on the desk. 'Well I'll tell you. One of my veterinary officers was on that farm, and he found that you hadn't served a Notice of Cleansing and Disinfection!'

'Is that so?'

'Yes, it bloody well is so! You didn't give one to the farmer but you sent one to me. Maybe you want me to go and disinfect the place, is that it? Would you like me to slip along there and get busy with a hosepipe—I'll go now if it'll make you feel any happier!'

'Oh no, no, no . . . no.'

Charles was apparently not satisfied with the thunderous noise he was making because he began to use both hands, bringing them down simultaneously with sickening force on the wood while he glared wildly.

'Herriot!' he shouted. 'There's just one thing I want to know from you—do you want this bloody work or don't you? Just say the word and I'll give it to another practice and then maybe we'd both be able to live a quiet life!'

'Please, Mr Harcourt, I give you my word, I . . . we . . . we do want the work very much.' And I meant it with all my heart.

The big man slumped back in his chair and regarded me for a few moments in silence. Then he glanced at his wrist watch.

'Ten past twelve,' he murmured. 'They'll be open at the Red Lion. Let's go and have a beer.'

In the pub lounge he took a long pull at his glass, placed it carefully on the table in front of him, then turned to me with a touch of weariness.

'You know, Herriot, I do wish you'd stop doing this sort of thing. It takes it out of me.'

I believed him. His face had lost a little of its colour and his hand trembled slightly as he raised his glass again.

'I'm truly sorry, Mr Harcourt, I don't know how it happened. I did try to get it right this time and I'll do my best to avoid troubling you in future.'

He nodded a few times then clapped me on the shoulder. 'Good, good—let's just have one more.'

He moved over to the bar, brought back the drinks then fished out a brown paper parcel from his pocket.

'Little wedding present, Herriot. Understand you're getting married soon—this is from my missus and me with our best wishes.'

I didn't know what to say. I fumbled the wrapping away and uncovered a small square barometer.

Shame engulfed me as I muttered a few words of thanks. This man was the head of the Ministry in the area while I was the newest and lowest of his minions. Not only that, but I was pretty sure I caused him more trouble than all the others put together —I was like a hair shirt to him. There was no earthly reason why he should give me a barometer.

This last experience deepened my dread of form filling to the extent that I hoped it would be a long time before I encountered another tuberculous animal, but fate decreed that I had some concentrated days of clinical inspections and it was with a feeling of inevitability that I surveyed Mr Moverley's Ayrshire cow.

It was the soft cough which made me stop and look at her

more closely, and as I studied her my spirits sank. This was another one. The skin stretched tightly over the bony frame, the slightly accelerated respirations and that deep careful cough. Mercifully you don't see cows like that now, but in those days they were all too common.

I moved along her side and examined the wall in front of her. The tell-tale blobs of sputum were clearly visible on the rough stones and I quickly lifted a sample and smeared it on a glass slide.

Back at the surgery I stained the smear by Ziehl-Nielson's method and pushed the slide under the microscope. The red clumps of tubercle bacilli lay among the scattered cells, tiny, iridescent and deadly. I hadn't really needed the grim proof but it was there.

Mr Moverley was not amused when I told him next morning that the animal would have to be slaughtered.

'It's nobut got a bit of a chill,' he grunted. The farmers were never pleased when one of their milk producers was removed by a petty bureaucrat like me. 'But ah suppose it's no use arguin'.'

'I assure you, Mr Moverley, there's no doubt about it. I examined that sample last night and . . .'

'Oh never mind about that.' The farmer waved an impatient hand. 'If t'bloody government says me cow's got to go she's got to go. But ah get compensation, don't I?'

'Yes, you do.'

'How much?'

I thought rapidly. The rules stated that the animal be valued as if it were up for sale in the open market in its present condition. The minimum was five pounds and there was no doubt that this emaciated cow came into that category.

'The statutory value is five pounds,' I said.

'Shit!' replied Mr Moverley.

'We can appoint a valuer if you don't agree.'

'Oh 'ell, let's get t'job over with.' He was clearly disgusted and I thought it imprudent to tell him that he would only get a proportion of the five pounds, depending on the post mortem.

'Very well,' I said. 'I'll tell Jeff Mallock to collect her as soon as possible.'

The fact that I was unpopular with Mr Moverley didn't worry me as much as the prospect of dealing with the dreaded forms.

The very thought of sending another batch winging hopefully on its way to Charles Harcourt brought me out in a sweat.

Then I had a flash of inspiration. Such things don't often happen to me, but this struck me as brilliant. I wouldn't send off the forms till I'd had them vetted by Kitty Pattison.

I couldn't wait to get the plan under way. Almost gleefully I laid the papers out in a long row, signed them and laid them by their envelopes, ready for their varied journeys. Then I phoned the Ministry office.

Kitty was patient and kind. I am sure she realised that I did my work conscientiously but that I was a clerical numbskull and she sympathised.

When I had finished going through the list she congratulated me. 'Well done, Mr Herriot, you've got them right this time! All you need now is the knacker man's signature and your post mortem report and you're home and dry.'

'Bless you, Kitty,' I said. 'You've made my day.'

And she had. The airy sensation of relief was tremendous. The knowledge that there would be no come-back from Charles this time was like the sun bursting through dark clouds. I felt like singing as I went round to Mallock's yard and arranged with him to pick up the cow.

'Have her ready for me to inspect tomorrow, Jeff,' I said, and went on my way with a light heart.

I couldn't understand it when Mr Moverley waved me down from his farm gate next day. As I drew up I could see he was extremely agitated.

'Hey!' he cried. 'Ah've just got back from the market and my missus tells me Mallock's been!'

I smiled. 'That's right, Mr Moverley. Remember I told you I was going to send him round for your cow.'

'Aye, ah know all about that!' He paused and glared at me. 'But he's took the wrong one!'

'Wrong . . . wrong what?'

'Wrong cow, that's what! He's off wi' the best cow in me herd. Pedigree Ayrshire—ah bought 'er in Dumfries last week and they only delivered 'er this mornin'."

Horror drove through me in a freezing wave. I had told the knacker man to collect the Ayrshire which would be isolated in the loose box in the yard. The new animal would be in a box, too, after her arrival. I could see Jeff and his man leading her up the ramp into his wagon with a dreadful clarity.

'This is your responsibility, tha knaws!' The farmer waved a threatening finger. 'If he kills me good cow you'll 'ave to answer for it!'

He didn't have to tell me. I'd have to answer for it to a lot of people, including Charles Harcourt.

'Get on the phone to the knacker yard right away!' I gasped.

The farmer waved his arms about. 'Ah've tried that and there's no reply. Ah tell ye he'll shoot 'er afore we can stop 'im. Do you know how much ah paid for that cow?'

'Never mind about that! Which way did he go?'

'T'missus said he went towards Grampton—about ten minutes ago.'

I started my engine. 'He'll maybe be picking up other beasts—I'll go after him.'

Teeth clenched, eyes popping, I roared along the Grampton road. The enormity of this latest catastrophe was almost more than I could assimilate. The wrong form was bad enough, but the wrong cow was unthinkable. But it had happened. Charles would crucify me this time. He was a good bloke but he would have no option, because the higher-ups in the Ministry would get wind of an immortal boner like this and they would howl for blood.

Feverishly but vainly I scanned each farm entrance in Grampton village as I shot through, and when I saw the open countryside ahead of me again the tension was almost unbearable. I was telling myself that the thing was hopeless when in the far distance above a row of trees I spotted the familiar top of Mallock's wagon.

It was a high, wooden-sided vehicle and I couldn't mistake it. Repressing a shout of triumph I put my foot on the boards and set off in that direction with the fanatical zeal of the hunter. But it was a long way off and I hadn't travelled a mile before I realised I had lost it.

Over the years many things have stayed in my memory, but the Great Cow Chase is engraven deeper than most. The sheer terror I felt is vivid to this day. I kept sighting the wagon among the maze of lanes and side roads but by the time I had cut across country my quarry had disappeared behind a hillside or dipped into one of the many hollows in the wide vista. I was constantly deceived by the fact that I expected him to be turning towards Darrowby after passing through a village, but he never did. Clearly he had other business on the way.

The whole thing seemed to last a very long time and there was no fun in it for me. I was gripped throughout by a cold dread, and the violent swings—the alternating scents of hope and despair—were wearing to the point of exhaustion. I was utterly drained when at last I saw the tall lorry rocking along a straight road in front of me.

I had him now! Forcing my little car to the limit, I drew abreast of him, sounding my horn repeatedly till he stopped. Breathlessly I pulled up in front of him and ran round to offer my explanations. But as I looked up into the driver's cab my eager smile vanished. It wasn't Jeff Mallock at all. I had been following the wrong man.

It was the 'ket feller'. He had exactly the same type of wagon as Mallock and he went round a wide area of Yorkshire picking up the nameless odds and ends of the dead animals which even the knacker men didn't want. It was a strange job and he was a strange-looking man. The oddly piercing eyes glittered uncannily from under a tattered army peaked cap.

'Wot's up, guvnor?' He removed a cigarette from his mouth and spat companionably into the roadway.

My throat was tight. 'I—I'm sorry. I thought you were Jeff Mallock.'

The eyes did not change expression, but the corner of his mouth twitched briefly. 'If tha wants Jeff he'll be back at his yard now, ah reckon.' He spat again and replaced his cigarette.

I nodded dully. Jeff would be there now all right—long ago. I had been chasing the wrong wagon for about an hour and that cow would be dead and hanging up on hooks at this moment. The knacker man was a fast and skilful worker and wasted no time when he got back with his beasts.

'Well, ah'm off 'ome now,' the ket feller said. 'So long, boss.' He winked at me, started his engine and the big vehicle rumbled away.

I trailed back to my car. There was no hurry now. And strangely, now that all was lost my mood relaxed. In fact, as I drove away, a great calm settled on me and I began to assess my future with cool objectivity. I would be drummed out of the

Ministry's service for sure, and idly I wondered if they had any special ceremony for the occasion—perhaps a ritual stripping of the Panel Certificates or something of the sort.

I tried to put away the thought that more than the Ministry would be interested in my latest exploit. How about the Royal College? Did they strike you off for something like this? Well, it was possible, and in my serene state of mind I toyed with the possibilities of alternative avenues of employment. I had often thought it must be fun to run a second hand book shop and now that I began to consider it seriously I felt sure there was an opening for one in Darrowby. I experienced a comfortable glow at the vision of myself sitting under the rows of dusty volumes, pulling one down from the shelf when I felt like it or maybe just looking out into the street through the window from my safe little world where there were no forms or telephones or messages saying 'Ring Min.'

In Darrowby I drove round without haste to the knacker yard. I left my car outside the grim little building with the black smoke drifting from its chimney. I pulled back the sliding door and saw Jeff seated at his ease on a pile of cow hides, holding a slice of apple pie in blood-stained fingers. And, ah yes, there, just behind him hung the two great sides of beef and on the floor, the lungs, bowels and other viscera—the sad remnants of Mr Moverley's pedigree Ayrshire.

'Hello, Jeff,' I said.

'Now then, Mr Herriot.' He gave me the beatific smile which mirrored his personality so well. 'Ah'm just havin' a little snack. I allus like a bite about this time.' He sank his teeth into the pie and chewed appreciatively.

'So I see.' I sorrowfully scanned the hanging carcase. Just dog meat and not even much of that. Ayrshires were never very fat. I was wondering how to break the news to him when he spoke again.

'Ah'm sorry you've caught me out this time, Mr Herriot,' he said, reaching for a greasy mug of tea.

'What do you mean?'

'Well, I allus reckon to have t'beast dressed and ready for you but you've come a bit early.'

I stared at him. 'But . . . everything's here, surely.' I waved a hand around me.

'Nay, nay, that's not 'er.'

'You mean . . . that isn't the cow from Moverley's.'

'That's right.' He took a long draught from the mug and wiped his mouth with the back of his hand. 'I 'ad to do this 'un first. Moverley's cow's still in t'wagon out at the back.'

'Alive?'

He looked mildly surprised. 'Aye, of course. She's never had a finger on 'er. Nice cow for a screw, too.'

I could have fainted with relief. 'She's no screw, Jeff. That's the wrong cow you've got there!'

'Wrong cow?' Nothing ever startled him but he obviously desired more information. I told him the whole story.

When I had finished, his shoulders began to shake gently and the beautiful clear eyes twinkled in the pink face.

'Well, that's a licker,' he murmured, and continued to laugh gently. There was nothing immoderate in his mirth and indeed nothing I had said disturbed him in the least. The fact that he had wasted his journey or that the farmer might be annoyed was of no moment to him.

Again, looking at Jeff Mallock, it struck me, as many times before, that there was nothing like a lifetime of dabbling among diseased carcases and lethal bacteria for breeding tranquillity of mind.

'You'll slip back and change the cow?' I said.

'Aye, in a minute or two. There's nowt spoilin'. Ah never likes to hurry me grub.' He belched contentedly. 'And how about you, Mr Herriot? You could do with summat to keep your strength up.' He produced another mug and broke off a generous wedge of pie which he offered to me.

'No . . . no . . . er . . . no, thank you, Jeff It's kind of you, but no . . . no . . . not just now.'

He shrugged his shoulders and smiled as he stretched an arm for his pipe which was balanced on a sheep's skull. Flicking away some shreds of stray tissue from the stem he applied a match and settled down blissfully on the hides.

'I'll see ye later, then,' he said. 'Come round tonight and everything'll be ready for you.' He closed his eyes and again his shoulders quivered. 'Ah'd better get the right 'un this time.'

It must be more than twenty years since I took a cow under the T.B. Order, because the clinical cases so rarely exist now. 'Ring Min.' no longer has the power to chill my blood, and the dread forms which scarred my soul lie unused and yellowing in the bottom of a drawer.

All these things have gone from my life. Charles Harcourt has gone too, but I think of him every day when I look at the little barometer which still hangs on my wall.

35

The food was so good at the Winckfield flying school that it was said that those airmen whose homes were within visiting distance wouldn't take a day's leave because they might miss some culinary speciality. Difficult to believe, maybe, but I often think that few people in wartime Britain fared as well as the handful of young men in the scatter of wooden huts on that flat green stretch outside Windsor.

It wasn't as though we had a French chef, either. The cooking was done by two grizzled old men—civilians who wore cloth caps and smoked pipes and went about their business with unsmiling taciturnity.

It was rumoured that they were two ex-army cooks from the first world war, but whatever their origins they were artists. In their hands, simple stews and pies assumed a new significance and it was possible to rhapsodise even over the perfect flouriness of their potatoes.

So it was surprising when at lunch time my neighbour on the left threw down his spoon, pushed away his plate and groaned. We ate on trestle tables, sitting in rows on long forms, and I was right up against the young man.

'What's wrong?' I asked. 'This apple dumpling is terriffic.'

'Ah, it's not the grub.' He buried his face in his hands for a few seconds then looked at me with tortured eyes. 'I've been doing circuits and bumps this morning with Routledge and he's torn the knackers off me—all the time, it never stopped.'

Suddenly my own meal lost some of its flavour. I knew just what he meant. F. O. Woodham did the same to me.

He gave me another despairing glance then stared straight ahead.

'I know one thing, Jim. I'll never make a bloody pilot.'

His words sent a chill through me. He was voicing the conviction which had been gradually growing in me. I never seemed to make any progress—whatever I did was wrong, and I was losing heart. Like all the others I was hoping to be graded pilot, but after every session with F. O. Woodham the idea of ever flying an aeroplane all on my own seemed more and more ludicrous. And I had another date with him at 2 p.m.

He was as quiet and charming as ever when I met him—till we got up into the sky and the shouting started again.

'Relax! For heavens sake, relax!' or 'Watch your height! Where the hell d'you think you're going?' or 'Didn't I tell you to centralise the stick? Are you bloody deaf or something?' And finally, after the first circuit when we juddered to a halt on the grass, 'That was an absolutely bloody ropy landing! Take off again!'

On the second circuit he fell strangely silent. And though I should have felt relieved I found something ominous in the unaccustomed peace. It could mean only one thing—he had finally given me up as a bad job. When we landed he told me to switch off the engine and climbed out of the rear cockpit. I was about to unbuckle my straps and follow him when he signalled me to remain in my seat.

'Stay where you are,' he said. 'You can take her up now.'

I stared down at him through my goggles. 'What . . .?'

'I said take her up.'

'You mean, on my own . . . ? Go solo . . . ?'

'Yes, of course. Come and see me in the flight hut after you've landed and taxied in.' He turned and walked away over the green. He didn't look back.

After a few minutes a fitter came over to where I sat trembling in my seat. He spat on the turf then looked at me with deep distaste.

'Look, mate,' he said. 'That's a——good aircraft you've got there.'

I nodded agreement.

'Well I don't want it——well smashed up, okay?'

'Okay.'

He gave me a final disgusted glance then went round to the propellor.

Panic-stricken though I was, I did not forget the cockpit drill which had been dinned in to me so often. I never thought I'd have to use it in earnest but now I automatically tested the controls—rudder, ailerons and elevator. Fuel on, switches off, throttle closed, then switches on, throttle slightly open.

'Contact!' I cried.

The fitter swung the propellor and the engine roared. I pushed the throttle full open and the Tiger Moth began to bump its way over the grass. As we gathered speed I eased the stick forward to lift the tail, then as I pulled it back again the bumping stopped and we climbed smoothly into the air with the long dining hut at the end of the airfield flashing away beneath.

I was gripped by exhilaration and triumph. The impossible had happened. I was up here on my own, flying, really flying at last. I had been so certain of failure that the feeling of relief was overpowering. In fact it intoxicated me, so that for a long time I just sailed along, grinning foolishly to myself.

When I finally came to my senses I looked down happily over the side. It must be time to turn now, but as I stared downwards cold reality began to roll over me in a gathering flood. I couldn't recognise a thing in the great hazy tapestry beneath me. And everything seemed smaller than usual. Dry-mouthed, I looked at the altimeter. I was well over 2,000 feet.

And suddenly it came to me that F. O. Woodham's shouts had not been meaningless; he had been talking sense, giving me good advice, and as soon as I got up in the air by myself I had ignored it all. I hadn't lined myself up on a cloud, I hadn't watched my artificial horizon, I hadn't kept an eye on the altimeter. And I was lost.

It was a terrible feeling, this sense of utter isolation as I desperately scanned the great chequered landscape for a familiar object. What did you do in a case like this? Soar around southern England till I found some farmer's field big enough to land in, then make my own abject way back to Winckfield? But that way I was going to look the complete fool, and also I'd stand an excellent chance of smashing up that fitter's beloved aeroplane and maybe myself.

It seemed to me that one way or another I was going to make a name for myself. Funny things had happened to some of the other lads—many had been air-sick and vomited in the cockpit, one had gone through a hedge, another on his first solo had circled the airfield again and again—seven times he had gone round—trying to find the courage to land while his instructor sweated blood and cursed on the ground. But nobody had really got lost like me. Nobody had flown off into the blue and returned on foot without his aeroplane.

My visions of my immediate fate were reaching horrific proportions and my heart was hammering uncontrollably when far away on my left I spotted the dear familiar bulk of the big stand on Ascot racecourse. Almost weeping with joy, I turned towards it and within minutes I was banking above its roof as I had done so often.

And there, far below and approaching with uncomfortable speed was the belt of trees which fringed the airfield and beyond, the windsock blowing over the wide green. But I was still far too high—I could never drop down there in time to hit that landing strip, I would have to go round again.

The ignominy of it went deep. They would all be watching on the ground and some would have a good laugh at the sight of Herriot over-shooting the field by several hundred feet and cruising off again into the clouds. But what was I thinking about? There was a way of losing height rapidly and, bless you, F. O. Woodham, I knew how to do it.

Opposite rudder and stick. He had told me a hundred times how to side slip and I did it now as hard as I could, sending the little machine slewing like an airborne crab down, down towards those trees.

And by golly it worked! The green copse rushed up at me and before I knew I was almost skimming the branches. I straightened up and headed for the long stretch of grass. At fifty feet I rounded out then checked the stick gradually back till just above the ground when I slammed it into my abdomen. The undercarriage made contact with the earth with hardly a tremor and I worked the rudder bar to keep straight until I came to a halt. Then I taxied in, climbed from the cockpit and walked over to the flight hut.

F. O. Woodham was sitting at a table, cup in hand, and he looked up as I entered. He had got out of his flying suit and was wearing a battle dress jacket with the wings we all dreamed about and the ribbon of the D.F.C.

'Ah, Herriot, I'm just having some coffee. Will you join me?'
'Thank you, sir.'

I sat down and he pushed a cup towards me.

'I saw your landing,' he said. 'Delightful, quite delightful.'
'Thank you, sir.'

'And that side-slip.' One corner of his mouth twitched upwards. 'Very good indeed, really masterly.'

He reached for the coffee pot and went on. 'You've done awfully well, Herriot. Solo after nine hours' instruction, eh? Splendid. But then I never had the slightest doubt about you at any time.'

He poised the pot over my cup. 'How do you like your coffee —black or white?'

36

I was only the third man in our Flight of fifty to go solo and it was a matter of particular pride to me because so many of my comrades were eighteen and nineteen year olds. They didn't say so but I often had the impression that they felt that an elderly gentleman like me in my twenties with a wife and baby had no right to be there, training for aircrew. In the nicest possible way they thought I was past it.

Of course, in many ways they had a point. The pull I had from home was probably stronger than theirs. When our sergeant handed out the letters on the daily parade I used to secrete mine away till I had a few minutes of solitude to read about how fast little Jimmy was growing, how much he weighed, the unmistakeable signs of outstanding intelligence, even genius, which Helen could already discern in him.

I was missing his babyhood and it saddened me. It was something I deeply regret because it comes only once and is gone so quickly. But I still have the bundles of letters which his proud mother wrote to keep me in touch with every fascinating stage, and when I read them now it is almost as though I had been there to see it all.

At the time, those letters pulled me back almost painfully to the comforts of home. On the other hand there were occasions when life in Darrowby hadn't been all that comfortable. . . .

I think it was the early morning calls in the winter which were the worst. It was a fairly common experience to be walking sleepy-eyed into a cow byre at 6 a.m. for a calving but at Mr Blackburn's farm there was a difference. In fact several differences.

Firstly, there was usually an anxious-faced farmer to greet me with news of how the calf was coming, when labour had started, but today I was like an unwelcome stranger. Secondly, I had grown accustomed to the sight of a few cows tied up in a cobbled byre with wooden partitions and an oil lamp, and now I was gazing down a long avenue of concrete under blazing electric light with a seemingly endless succession of bovine backsides protruding from tubular metal standings. Thirdly, instead of the early morning peace there was a clattering of buckets, the rhythmic pulsing of a milking machine and the blaring of a radio loudspeaker. There was also a frantic scurrying of white-coated, white-capped men, but none of them paid the slightest attention to me.

This was one of the new big dairy farms. In place of a solitary figure on a milk stool, head buried in the cow's side, pulling forth the milk with a gentle 'hiss-hiss', there was this impersonal hustle and bustle.

I stood just inside the doorway while out in the yard a particularly cold snow drifted from the blackness above. I had left a comfortable bed and a warm wife to come here and it seemed somebody ought at least to say 'hello'. Then I noticed the owner hurrying past with a bucket. He was moving as fast as any of his men.

'Hey, Mr Blackburn!' I cried. 'You rang me—you've got a cow calving?'

He stopped and looked at me uncomprehendingly for a moment. 'Oh aye . . . aye . . . she's down there on t'right.' He pointed to a light roan animal half way along the byre. She was easy to pick out—the only one lying down.

'How long has she been on?' I asked, but when I turned round Mr Blackburn had gone. I trotted after him, cornered him in the milk house and repeated my question.

'Oh, she should've calved last night. Must be summat amiss.' He began to pour his bucket of milk over the cooler into the churn.

'Have you had a feel inside her?'

'Nay, haven't had time.' He turned harassed eyes towards me. 'We're a bit behind with milkin' this mornin'. We can't be late for t'milk man.'

I knew what he meant. The drivers who collected the churns for the big dairy companies were a fierce body of men. Probably kind husbands and fathers at normal times but subject to violent outbursts of rage if they were kept waiting even for an instant. I couldn't blame them, because they had a lot of territory to cover and many farms to visit, but I had seen them when provoked and their anger was frightening to behold.

'All right,' I said. 'Can I have some hot water, soap and a towel, please?'

Mr Blackburn jerked his head at the corner of the milk house. 'You'll 'ave to help yourself. There's everythin' there. Ah must get on.' He went off again at a brisk walk. Clearly he was more in fear of the milk man than he was of me.

I filled a bucket, found a piece of soap and threw a towel over my shoulder. When I reached my patient I looked in vain for some sign of a name. So many of the cows of those days had their names printed above their stalls but there were no Marigolds, Alices or Snowdrops here, just numbers.

Before taking off my jacket I looked casually in the ear where the tattoo marks stood out plainly against the creamy white surface. She was number eighty seven.

I was in more trouble when I stripped off my shirt. In a modern byre like this there were no nails jutting from the walls to serve as hangers. I had to roll my clothes into a ball and carry them through to the milk house. There I found a sack which I tied round my middle with a length of binder twine.

Still ignored by everybody, I returned, soaped my arm and inserted it into the cow. I had to go a long way in to reach the calf, which was strange considering the birth should have taken place last night. It was the top of the little creature's head I touched first; the nose was tucked downwards instead of thrusting its way along the vagina towards the outside world, and the legs were similarly coiled under the body.

And I noticed something else. The entry of my arm did not provoke any answering strain from the cow, nor did she try to rise to her feet. There was something else troubling Number Eighty Seven.

Lying flat on the concrete, still buried to the shoulder in the cow, I raised my head and looked along the shaggy back with its speckle of light red and white hairs, and when I reached the neck I knew I need seek no further. The lateral kink was very obvious. Number Eighty Seven, slumped on her chest, was gazing wearily and without interest at the wall in front of her but there was that funny little bend in her neck that told me everything.

I got up, washed and dried my arm and looked for Mr Blackburn. I found him bending by the side of a fat brown animal, pulling the cups from her teats. I tapped him on the shoulder.

'She's got milk fever,' I said.

'Oh aye,' he replied, then he hoisted the bucket, brushed past me and made off down the byre.

I kept pace with him. 'That's why she can't strain. Her uterus has lost its tone. She'll never calve till she gets some calcium.'

'Right.' He still didn't look at me. 'Ye'll give 'er some then?'

'Yes,' I said to his retreating back.

The snow still swirled in the outer darkness and I toyed with the idea of getting dressed. But I'd only have to strip again so I decided to make a dash for it. With the car boot open it seemed to take a long time to fish out the bottles and flutter valve with the flakes settling thickly on my naked flesh.

Back in the byre I looked around for a spare man to help me but there was no lessening of the feverish activity. I would have to roll this cow onto her side and inject into her milk vein without assistance. It all depended on how comatose she was.

And she must have been pretty far gone because when I braced my feet against the tubular steel and pushed both hands against her shoulder she flopped over without resistance. To keep her there I lay on top of her as I pushed in the needle and ran the calcium into the vein.

One snag was that my sprawling position took me right underneath the neighbouring cow on the right, a skittish sort of animal who didn't welcome the rubber-booted legs tangling with her hind feet. She expressed her disapproval by treading painfully on my ankles and giving me a few smart kicks on the thigh, but I daren't move because the calcium was flowing in beautifully.

When the bottle was empty I kneed my patient back onto her chest and ran another bottle of calcium magnesium and phosphorus under her skin. By the time I had finished and rubbed away the subcutaneous fluid Number Eighty Seven was looking decidedly happier.

I didn't hurry over cleaning and putting away my injection outfit and re-soaping my arms because I knew that every minute would bring back strength to my patient.

The lightning response to intravenous calcium has always afforded me a simple pleasure and when I pushed my arm in again the difference was remarkable. The previously flaccid uterus gripped at my hand and as the cow went into a long expulsive effort she turned her head, looked back at me and opened her mouth in a muffled bellow. It was not a sound of pain but rather as though she was saying, 'I'm back in business now.'

'All right, my lass,' I replied. 'I'll stay with you till it's all over.'

At other times I might have been a little chary of being overheard conversing with a cow, but with the clamour of buckets and the nonstop blasting of the radio there was no chance of that happening.

I knew that I had to guide the calf back into the correct position and that it would take time, but I had a strange sense of oneness with this animal because neither of us seemed to be of the slightest importance in the present setting. As I lay there face down on the concrete which grew harder all the time and with the milkers stumbling over my prostrate form I felt very much alone. There was just myself and Number Eighty Seven for it.

Another thing I missed was the sense of occasion. There was a compensation in many an arduous calving in the feeling of a little drama being enacted; the worried farmer, attentive stocksmen, the danger of losing the calf or even the mother—it was a gripping play and there was no doubt the vet was the leading man. He may even be the villain but he was number one. And here I was now, a scrabbling nonentity with hardly a mention in the cast. It was the shape of things to come.

And yet . . . and yet . . the job was still there. I lifted the calf's lower jaw and as the cow gave a heave I eased it over the brim of the pelvis. Then I groped for the tiny legs and straightened them as another expulsive effort pushed the little creature towards me. He was definitely on his way now.

I didn't rush things—just lay there and let the cow get on with it. My worst moment was when one of the men came to put the milking machine on the temperamental animal on my right. As he tried to step up beside her she swung round, cocked her tail and sent a jet of faeces cascading across my back.

The man pushed her back into place, slipped on the teat cups then lifted the hose which was lying ready for swilling down the byre. A moment later I felt the icy flow of water playing from my shoulders to my hips then the application of a spare udder cloth as the helpful fellow cleaned me off.

'Thanks very much,' I gasped. And I was really grateful. It was the only attention I had received all morning.

Within half an hour the feet appeared at the vulva followed by a wet nose whose nostrils twitched reassuringly. But they were big feet—this would be a bull calf and his final entry into the world could be a tight squeeze.

I got into a sitting position and gripped a slippery cloven hoof in each hand. Leaning back, feet against the dung channel, I addressed Number Eighty Seven again.

'Come on, old lass. A couple of good shoves and we're there.'

She responded with a mighty inflation of the abdomen and the calf surged towards me as I pulled, giving me a glimpse of a broad forehead and a pair of slightly puzzled eyes. For a moment I thought the ears were going to slip through but then the cow relaxed and the head disappeared back inside.

'Once more, girl!' I pleaded, and this time it seemed that she had decided to stop playing around and get the job over with. She gave a prolonged strain which sent head and shoulders through, and as I hauled away I had only that momentary panic I always feel that the hips might jam in the pelvis. But this one didn't stick and came sliding beautifully on to my lap.

Puffing slightly, I got to my feet and parted the hind legs. Sure enough the little scrotum was there; he was a fine bull calf. I pulled some hay from the rack and dried him off and within minutes he was sitting up, sniffing and snorting, looking around him with interest.

He wasn't the only interested party. His mother, craning round in her neck chain, gazed fascinatedly at the new arrival before releasing a deafening bellow. I seized the front feet again and pulled the calf up to the front of the stall where the cow after a brief examination began to lick him from head to tail. Then as I watched, entranced, she suddenly rose to her feet so that she could reach some of the little creature's more inaccessible corners.

I smiled to myself. So that was that. She had got over the milk fever and had a nice live calf, too. All was well with Number Eighty Seven.

Mr Blackburn came up and stood by my side and I realised that the noise in the byre had subsided. The milking was finished.

The farmer took off his white hat and wiped away the sweat from his brow. 'By gaw, that was a rush, We were short-handed this mornin' and I was sure we were goin' to miss that milk feller. He's a terror—won't wait a minute, and I've had to chase after 'im in a tractor with the churns afore now."

As he finished speaking a hen leaped with a squawk from the rack. Mr Blackburn reached forward and lifted a warm new-laid egg out of the hay.

He inspected it for a moment then turned to me. 'Have you 'ad your breakfast?'

'No, of course not.'

'Well tell your missus to put this in the fryin' pan,' he said, handing me the egg.

'Oh, thank you very much, Mr Blackburn, I'll enjoy that.'

He nodded and continued to stand there, gazing at the cow and calf. Dairy farming is one of the hardest ways of making a living and this pre-dawn turmoil was an every day occurrence in his life. But I knew he was pleased with my efforts because he faced me suddenly and his weathered features broke into a delighted grin. Without warning he gave me a friendly thump on the chest.

'Good old Jim!' he said, and walked away.

I dressed, got into the car and placed my egg with the utmost care on the dash, then I eased myself gingerly on to the seat, because that hosing had sent a pint or two of dirty water down into my underpants and sitting down was intensely uncomfortable.

As I drove away the darkness was thinning into the grey beginning of a new day and around me the white bulk of the fells began to lift from the half light—massive, smooth and inexpressibly cold.

I looked at the egg rocking gently on the dash, and smiled to myself. I could still see Mr. Blackburn's sudden grin, still feel his punch on the chest, and my main sensation was of reassurance.

Systems may be changing, but cows and calves and Yorkshire farmers were just the same.

CHAPTER

37

On my wage of seven and threepence a day, out of which was deducted maintenance for wife and child, I was unable to indulge in high living even if I had wanted to, but one evening in Windsor I decided to allow myself the luxury of one glass of beer, and as I pushed open the pub doorway the first thing I saw was a man sitting at the corner of the bar with a small dog under his chair.

Little things like that could lift me effortlessly back to my old life, and I could almost hear George Wilks, the auctioneer, in the Drovers' Arms at Darrowby.

'I reckon that's the best Pub Terrier I've ever seen.' He bent down from the bar counter and patted Theo's shaggy head as it protruded from beneath his master's stool.

It struck me that 'Pub Terrier' wasn't a bad description. Theo was small and mainly white, though there were odd streaks of black on his flanks, and his muzzle had a bushy outgrowth of hair which made him undeniably attractive but still more mysterious.

I warmed to a Scottish colleague recently who, when pressed by a lady client to diagnose her dog's breed and lineage replied finally, 'Madam, I think it would be best to call him a wee broon dug.'

By the same token Theo could with safety be described as a wee white dug, but in Yorkshire the expression 'Pub Terrier' would be more easily understood.

His master, Paul Cotterell, looked down from his high perch. 'What's he saying about you, old chap?' he murmured languidly, and at the sound of his voice the little animal leaped, eager and wagging, from his retreat.

Theo spent a considerable part of his life between the four metal legs of that stool, as did his master on the seat. And it often seemed to me to be a waste of time for both of them. I often took my own dog, Sam, into pubs and he would squat beneath my seat, but whereas it was an occasional thing with me—maybe once or twice a week—with Paul Cotterel it was an unvarying ritual. Every night from eight o'clock onwards he could be found sitting there at the end of the bar of the Drovers' Arms, pint glass in front of him, little curly pipe drooping over his chin.

For a young man like him—he was a bachelor in his late thirties—and a person of education and intelligence, it seemed a sterile existence.

He turned to me as I approached the counter. 'Hello, Jim, let me get you a drink."

'That's very kind of you, Paul,' I replied. 'I'll have a pint.'

'Splendid.' He turned to the barmaid with easy courtesy. 'Could I trouble you, Moyra?'

We sipped our beer and we chatted. This time it was about the music festival at Brawton and then we got on to music in general. As with any other topic I had discussed with him he seemed to know a lot about it.

'So you're not all that keen on Bach?' he enquired lazily.

'No, not really. Some of it, yes, but on the whole I like something a bit more emotional. Elgar, Beethoven, Mozart. Even Tchaikovsky—I suppose you highbrows look down your noses at him?'

He shrugged, puffed his little pipe and regarded me with a half smile, one eyebrow raised. He often looked like that and it made me feel he ought to wear a monocle. But he didn't enthuse about Bach, though it seemed he was his favourite composer. He never enthused about anything, and he listened with that funny look on his face while I rhapsodised about the Elgar violin concerto.

Paul Cotterell was from the south of England, but the locals had long since forgiven him for that because he was likeable, amusing, and always ready to buy anybody a drink from his corner in the Drovers. To me, he had a charm which was very English; casual, effortless. He never got excited, he was always polite and utterly self contained.

'While you're here, Jim,' he said. 'I wonder if you'd have a look at Theo's foot?'

'Of course.' It is one of a vet's occupational hazards that

wherever he goes socially it is taken for granted that there is nothing he would rather do than dole out advice or listen to symptoms. 'Let's have him up.'

'Here, boy, come on.' Paul patted his knee and the little dog jumped up and sat there, eyes sparkling with pleasure. And I thought as I always did that Theo should be in pictures. He was the perfect film dog with that extraordinarily fuzzy laughing face. People paid good money to see dogs just like him in cinemas all over the world.

'All right, Theo,' I said, scooping him from his master's knee. 'Where's the trouble?'

Paul indicated the right fore foot with the stem of his pipe. 'It's that one. He's been going a bit lame off and on for the last few days.'

'I see.' I rolled the little animal on his back and then laughed. 'Oh, he's only got a broken claw. There's a little bit hanging off here. He must have caught it on a stone. Hang on a minute.' I delved in my pocket for the scissors which always dwelt there. A quick snip and the job was done.

'Is that all?' asked Paul.

'Yes, that's it.'

One eyebrow went up mockingly as he looked at Theo. 'So that's what you were making all the fuss about, eh? Silly old trout.' He snapped his fingers. 'Back you go.'

The little dog obediently leaped to the carpet and disappeared into his sanctuary beneath the stool. And at that moment I had a flash of intuition about Paul—about his charm which I had often admired and envied. He didn't really care. He was fond of his dog, of course. He took him everywhere with him, exercised him regularly by the river, but there was none of the anxiety, the almost desperate concern which I had so often seen in the eyes of my clients when I dealt with even the most trivial of their ailments. They cared too much—as I have always done with my own animals.

And of course he was right. It was an easier and more comfortable way to live. Caring made you vulnerable while Paul cruised along, impregnable. That attractive casualness, the nonchalant good manners, the imperturbability—they all had their roots in the fact that nothing touched him very deeply.

And despite my snap diagnosis of his character I still envied him. I have always been blown around too easily by my emotions; it must be lovely to be like Paul. And the more I thought about it the more I realised how everything fitted in. He had never cared enough to get married. Even Bach, with his mathematical music, was part of the pattern.

'I think that major operation deserves another pint, Jim.' He smiled his lop-sided smile. 'Unless you demand a higher fee?'

I laughed. I would always like him. We are all different and we have to act as we are made, but as I started my second glass I thought again of his carefree life. He had a good job in the government offices in Brawton, no domestic responsibilities, and every night he sat on that same stool drinking beer with his dog underneath. He hadn't a worry in the world.

Anyway, he was part of the Darrowby scene, part of something I liked, and since I have always hated change it was in a sense reassuring to know that no matter what night you went into the Drovers you would find Paul Cotterell in the corner and Theo's shaggy muzzle peeping from below.

I felt like that one night when I dropped in near closing time.

'D'you think he's got worms?' The question was typically off-hand.

'I don't know, Paul. Why do you ask?'

He drew on his pipe. 'Oh I just thought he looked a bit thin lately. Come up, Theo!'

The little dog, perched on his master's knee, looked as chirpy as ever and when I reached over and lifted him he licked my hand. But his ribs did feel rather prominent.

'Mmm, yes,' I said. 'Maybe he has lost a bit of weight. Have you noticed him passing any worms?'

'I haven't, actually.'

'Not even little bits—whitish segments sticking round his rear?'

'No, Jim.' He shook his head and smiled. 'But I haven't looked all that closely, old boy.'

'Okay,' I said. 'Let's worm him, just in case. I'll bring in some tablets tomorrow night. You'll be here . . . ?'

The eyebrow went up. 'I think that's highly probable.'

Theo duly got his worm tablets and after that there was a space of several weeks when I was too busy to visit the Drovers. When I finally did get in it was a Saturday night and the Athletic Club dance was in full spate. A rhythmic beat drifted from the ballroom, the little bar was packed, and the domino players were under pressure, squashed into a corner by the crush of dinner jackets and backless dresses.

In the noise and heat I struggled towards the bar, thinking that the place was unrecognisable. But there was one feature unchanged—Paul Cotterell on his stool at the far end of the counter.

I squeezed in next to him and saw he was wearing his usual tweed jacket. 'Not dancing, Paul?'

He half closed his eyes, shook his head slowly and smiled at me over his bent little pipe. 'Not for me, old boy,' he murmured. 'Too much like work.'

I glanced down and saw that something else hadn't changed. Theo was there, too, keeping his nose well clear of the milling feet. I ordered two beers and we tried to converse, but it was difficult to shout above the babel. Arms kept poking between us towards the counter, red faces pushed into ours and shouted greetings. Most of the time we just looked around us.

Then Paul leaned close and spoke into my ear. 'I gave Theo those pills but he's still getting thinner.'

'Really?' I shouted back. 'That's unusual.'

'Yes . . . perhaps you'd have a look at him?'

I nodded, he snapped his fingers and the little dog was on his knee in an instant. I reached and lifted him onto mine and I noticed immediately that he was lighter in my hands.

'You're right,' I said. 'He's still losing weight.'

Balancing the dog in my lap, I pulled down an eyelid and saw that the conjunctiva was pale.

I shouted again. 'He's anaemic.' I felt my way back over his face and behind the angle of the jaw I found that the post pharyngeal lymph glands were very enlarged. This was strange. Could he have some form of mouth or throat infection? I looked helplessly around me, wishing fervently that Paul wouldn't invariably consult me about his dog in a pub. I wanted to examine the animal, but I couldn't very well deposit him among the glasses on the bar.

I was trying to get a better grip with a view to looking down his throat when my hand slipped behind his fore leg and my heart gave a sudden thump as I encountered the axillary gland. It, too, was grossly enlarged. I whipped my fingers back into his groin and there was the inguinal gland, prominent as an egg. The prescapular was the same, and as I groped around feverishly

I realised that every superficial lymph gland was several times its normal size.

Hodgkin's disease. For a few moments I was oblivious of the shouting and laughter, the muffled blare of music. Then I looked at Paul who was regarding me calmly as he puffed his pipe. How could I tell him in these surroundings? He would ask me what Hodgkin's disease was and I would have to explain that it was a cancer of the lymphatic system and that his dog was surely going to die.

As my thoughts raced I stroked the shaggy head and Theo's comic whiskered face turned towards me. People jostled past, hands reached out and bore gins and whiskies and beers past my face, a fat man threw his arm round my neck.

I leaned across. 'Paul,' I said.

'Yes, Jim?'

'Will you . . . will you bring Theo round to the surgery tomorrow morning. It's ten o'clock on a Sunday.'

Momentarily the eyebrow twitched upwards, then he nodded.

'Right, old boy.'

I didn't bother to finish my drink. I began to push my way towards the door and as the crush closed around me I glanced back. The little dog's tail was just disappearing under the stool.

Next day I had one of those early waking mornings when I started tossing around at six o'clock and finished by staring at the ceiling.

Even after I had got my feet on the ground and brought Helen a cup of tea the waiting was interminable until the moment arrived which I had been dreading—when I faced Paul across the surgery table with Theo standing between us.

I told him straight away. I couldn't think of any easy way to lead up to it.

His expression did not change, but he took his pipe out of his mouth and looked steadily at me, then at the dog and back again at me.

'Oh,' he said at last. 'I see.'

I didn't say anything and he slowly ran his hand along the little animal's back. 'Are you quite sure, Jim?'

'Absolutely. I'm terribly sorry.'

'Is there no treatment?'

'There are various palliatives, Paul, but I've never seen any of them do any good. The end result is always the same.'

'Yes . . .' He nodded slowly. 'But he doesn't look so bad. What will happen if we don't do anything?'

I paused. 'Well, as the internal glands enlarge, various things will happen. Ascites—dropsy—will develop in the abdomen. In fact you can see he's a little bit pot-bellied now.'

'Yes . . . I do see, now you mention it. Anything else?'

'As the thoracic glands get bigger he'll begin to pant.'

'I've noticed that already. He's breathless after a short walk.'

'And all the time he'll get thinner and thinner and more debilitated.'

Paul looked down at his feet for a few moments then faced me. 'So what it amounts to is that he's going to be pretty miserable for the rest of his life.' He swallowed. 'And how long is that going to be?'

'A few weeks. It varies. Maybe up to three months.'

'Well, Jim.' He smoothed back his hair. 'I can't let that happen. It's my responsibility. You must put him to sleep now, before he really starts to suffer. Don't you agree?'

'Yes, Paul, it's the kindest thing to do.'

'Will you do it immediately—as soon as I am out of that door?'

'I will,' I replied. 'And I promise you he won't know a thing.'

His face held a curious fixity of expression. He put his pipe in his mouth, but it had gone out so he stuffed it into his pocket. Then he leaned forward and patted his dog once on the head. The bushy face with the funny shock of hair round the muzzle turned to him and for a few seconds they looked at each other.

Then, 'Goodbye, old chap,' he muttered and strode quickly from the room.

I kept my promise.

'Good lad, good old Theo,' I murmured, and stroked the face and ears again and again as the little creature slipped peacefully away. Like all vets I hated doing this, painless though it was, but to me there has always been a comfort in the knowledge that the last thing these helpless animals knew was the sound of a friendly voice and the touch of a gentle hand.

Sentimental, maybe. Not like Paul. He had been practical and utterly rational in the way he had acted. He had been able to do the right thing because he was not at the mercy of his emotions.

Later, over a Sunday lunch which I didn't enjoy as much as usual I told Helen about Theo.

I had to say something because she had produced a delicious pot roast on the gas ring which was our only means of cooking and I wasn't doing justice to her skill.

Sitting at our bench I looked down at her. It was my turn for the high stool.

'You know, Helen,' I said. 'That was an object lesson for me. The way Paul acted, I mean. If I'd been in his position I'd have shilly-shallied—tried to put off something which was inevitable.'

She thought for a moment. 'Well, a lot of people would.'

'Yes, but he didn't.' I put down my knife and fork and stared at the wall. 'He behaved in a mature way. I suppose Paul has one of those personalities you read about. Well-adjusted, completely adequate.'

'Come on, Jim, eat your lunch. I know it was a sad thing but it had to be done and you mustn't start criticising yourself. Paul is Paul and you are you.'

I started again on the meat but I couldn't repress the rising sense of my own inadequacy. Then as I glanced to one side I saw that my wife was smiling up at me.

I felt suddenly reassured. It seemed that she at least didn't seem to mind that I was me.

That was on the Sunday, and on Tuesday morning I was handing out some wart lotion to Mr Sangster who kept a few dairy cows down by the station.

'Dab that on the udder night and morning after milking,' I said. 'I think you'll find that the warts will start to drop off after a week or two.'

'Thank ye.' He handed over half a crown and I was dropping it into the desk drawer when he spoke again.

'Bad job about Paul Cotterell, wasn't it?'

'What do you mean?'

'Ah thought you'd have heard,' he said. 'He's dead.'

'Dead!' I stared at him stupidly. 'How . . . what . . . ?'

'Found 'im this mornin'. He did away with 'isself.'

I leaned with both hands on the desk. 'Do you mean . . . suicide?'

'Aye, that's what they say. Took a lot o' pills. It's all ower t'town.'

I found myself hunching over the day book, sightlessly scan-

ning the list of calls while the farmer's voice seemed to come
from far away.

'It's a bad job, right enough. He were a nice feller. Reckon
everybody liked 'im.'

Later that day I was passing Paul's lodgings when I saw his
landlady, Mrs Clayton, in the doorway. I pulled up and got out
of the car.

'Mrs Clayton,' I said. 'I still can't believe this.'

'Nor can I, Mr Herriot, it's terrible.' Her face was pale, her
eyes red. 'He was with me six years, you know—he was like a
son.'

'But why on earth . . . ?'

'Oh, it was losin' his dog that did it. He just couldn't stand
it.'

A great wave of misery rose and engulfed me and she put her
hand on my arm.

'Don't look like that, Mr Herriot. It wasn't your fault. Paul
told me all about it and nobody could have saved Theo. People
die of that, never mind dogs.'

I nodded dumbly and she went on.

'But I'll tell you something in confidence, Mr Herriot. Paul
wasn't able to stand things like you or me. It was the way he
was made—you see he suffered from depression.'

'Depression! Paul . . . ?'

'Oh yes, he's been under the doctor for a long time and takin'
pills regular. He allus put a brave face on, but he's had nervous
trouble off and on for years.'

'Nervous trouble . . . I'd never have dreamed . . .'

'No, nobody would, but that's how it was. He had an unhappy
childhood from what I made out. Maybe that's why he was so
fond of his dog. He got too attached to him, really.'

'Yes . . . yes . . .'

She took out a screwed up handkerchief and blew her nose.
'Well, as I said, the poor lad had a rough time most of his life,
but he was brave.'

There didn't seem anything else to say. I drove away out of
the town and the calm green hills offered a quiet contrast to
the turmoil which can fill a man's mind. So much for Herriot
as a judge of character. I couldn't have been more wrong, but
Paul had fought his secret battle with a courage which had deceived everybody.

I thought of the object lesson which I thought he had given me, but in fact it was a lesson of another kind and one which I have never forgotten; that there are countless people like Paul who are not what they seem.

38

The shock of Paul Cotterell's death stayed with me for a long time, and in fact I know I have never quite got over it because even now when the company in the bar of the Drover has changed and I am one of the few old faces left from thirty five years ago I can still see the jaunty figure on the corner stool and the bushy face peeping from beneath.

It was the kind of experience I didn't want repeated in my lifetime yet, uncannily, I ran into the same sort of thing almost immediately afterwards.

It couldn't have been more than a week after Paul's funeral that Andrew Vine brought his fox terrier to the surgery.

I put the little dog on the table and examined each of his eyes carefully in turn.

'I'm afraid he's getting worse,' I said.

Without warning the man slumped across the table and buried his face in his hands.

I put my hand on his shoulder. 'What is it, Andrew? What on earth's the matter?'

At first he did not answer but stayed there, huddled grotesquely by the side of his dog as great sobs shook his body.

When he spoke at last it was into his hands and his voice was hoarse and desperate. 'I can't stand it! If Digger goes blind I'll kill myself!'

I looked down at the bowed head in horrified disbelief. It couldn't be happening again. Not so soon after Paul. And yet there were similarities. Andrew was another bachelor in his thirties and the terrier was his constant companion. He lived in lodgings and appeared to have no worries though he was a shy, diffident man with a fragile look about his tall stooping frame and pallid face.

He had first consulted me about Digger several months ago.

'I call him that because he's dug large holes in the garden ever since his puppy days,' he said with a half smile, looking at me almost apprehensively from large dark eyes.

I laughed. 'I hope you haven't brought him to me to cure that, because I've never read anything in the books about it.'

'No, no, it's about something else—his eyes. And he's had that trouble since he was a pup, too.'

'Really? Tell me.'

'Well, when I first got him he had sort of mattery eyes, but the breeder said he'd probably just got some irritant in them and it would soon clear up. And in fact it did. But he's never been quite right. He always seems to have a little discomfort in his eyes.'

'How do you mean?'

'He rubs the side of his face along the carpet and he blinks in bright light.'

'I see.' I pulled the little animal's face around towards me and looked intently at the eyelids. My mind had been busy as he spoke and I was fairly sure I should find either entropion (inversion of the eyelids) or distichiasis (an extra row of lashes rubbing against the eyeball) but there was no sign of either. The surface of the cornea, too, looked normal, except perhaps that the deeper structures of lens and iris were not as easy to define as usual.

I moved over to a cupboard for the ophthalmoscope. 'How old is he now?'

'About a year.'

'So he's had this for about ten months?'

'Yes, about that. But it varies a lot. Most of the time he seems normal then there are days when he goes and lies in his basket with his eyes half closed and you can tell there's something wrong. Not pain, really. More like discomfort as I said.'

I nodded and hoped I was looking wise but none of this added up to anything familiar. I switched on the little light on the ophthalmoscope and peered into the depths of that most magical and delicate of all organs, down through the lens to the brilliant tapestry of the retina with its optic papilla and branching blood vessels. I couldn't find a thing wrong.

'Does he still dig holes?' I asked. When baffled I often snatch at straws and I wondered if the dog was suffering from a soil irritation.

Andrew shook his head. 'No, very seldom now, and anyway, his bad days are never associated with his digging.'

'Is that so?' I rubbed my chin. The man was obviously ahead of me with his thinking and I had an uncomfortable feeling of bewilderment. People were always bringing their dogs in with 'bad eyes' and there was invariably something to be seen, some cause to be found. 'And would you say that this was one of his bad days?'

'Well I thought so this morning, but he seems a bit better now. Still, he's a bit blinky, don't you think?'

'Yes . . . maybe so.' Digger did appear to be reluctant to open his eyes fully to the sunshine streaming through the surgery window. And occasionally he kept them closed for a second or two as though he wasn't very happy. But damn it, nothing gave me the slightest clue.

I didn't tell the owner that I hadn't the faintest idea what was wrong with his dog. Such remarks do not inspire confidence. Instead, I took refuge in businesslike activity.

'I'm going to give you some lotion,' I said briskly. 'Put a few drops into his eyes three times daily. And let me know how he goes on. It's possible he has some long-standing infection in there.'

I handed over a bottle of 2% boric acid solution and patted Digger's head. 'I hope that will clear things up for you, lad,' I said, and the stumpy tail wagged in reply. He was a sharp looking little animal, attractive and good-natured and a fine specimen of the smooth-haired breed with his long head and neck, pointed nose and beautifully straight limbs.

He jumped from the table and leaped excitedly around his master's legs.

I laughed. 'He's eager to go, like most of my patients.' I bent and slapped him playfully on the rump. 'My word, doesn't he look fit!'

'He is fit.' Andrew smiled proudly. 'In fact I often think that apart from those eyes he's a perfect little physical machine. You should see him out in the fields—he can run like a whippet.'

'I'll bet he can. Keep in touch, will you?' I waved them out of the door and turned to my other work, mercifully unaware that I had just embarked on one of the most frustrating cases of my career.

After that first time I took special notice of Digger and his owner. Andrew, a sensitive likeable man, was a representative for a firm of agricultural chemists and, like myself, spent most of his time driving around the Darrowby district. His dog was always with him and I had been perfunctorily amused by the fact that the little animal was invariably peering intently through the windscreen, his paws either on the dash or balanced on his master's hand as he operated the gear lever.

But now that I was personally interested I could discern the obvious delight which the little animal derived from taking in every detail of his surroundings. He missed nothing in his daily journeys. The road ahead, the houses and people, trees and fields which flashed by the windows—these made up his world.

I met him one day when I was exercising Sam up on the high moors which crown the windy summits of the fells. But this was May, the air was soft and a week's hot sunshine had dried the green paths which wandered among the heather. I saw Digger flashing like a white streak over the velvet turf and when he spotted Sam he darted up to him, set himself teasingly for a moment then shot back to Andrew who was standing in a natural circular glade among the harsh brown growth.

Here gorse bushes blazed in full yellow glory and the little dog hurtled round and round the arena, exulting in his health and speed.

'That's what I'd call sheer joy of living,' I said.

Andrew smiled shyly. 'Yes, isn't he beautiful,' he murmured.

'How are the eyes?' I asked.

He shrugged. 'Sometimes good, sometimes not so good. Much the same as before. But I must say he seems easier whenever I put the drops in.'

'But he still has days when he looks unhappy?'

'Yes . . . I have to say yes. Some days they bother him a lot.'

Again the frustration welled in me. 'Let's walk back to the car,' I said. 'I might as well have a look at him.'

I lifted Digger on to the bonnet and examined him again. There wasn't a single abnormality in the eyelids—I had wondered if I had missed something last time—but as the bright sunshine slanted across the eyeballs I could just discern the faintest cloudiness in the cornea. There was a slight keratitis there which hadn't been visible before. But why . . . why?

'He'd better have some stronger lotion.' I rummaged in the car boot. 'I've got some here. We'll try silver nitrate this time.'

Andrew brought him in about a week later. The corneal discolouration had gone—probably the silver nitrate had moved it —but the underlying trouble was unchanged. There was still something sadly wrong. Something I couldn't diagnose.

That was when I started to get really worried. As the weeks passed I bombarded those eyes with everything in the book; oxide of mercury, chinosol, zinc sulphide, ichthyol and a host of other things which are now buried in history.

I had none of the modern sophisticated antibiotic and steroid applications but it would have made no difference if I had. I know that now.

The real nightmare started when I saw the first of the pigment cells beginning to invade the cornea. Sinister brown specks gathering at the limbus and pushing out dark tendrils into the smooth membrane which was Digger's window on the world. I had seen cells like them before. When they came they usually stayed. And they were opaque.

Over the next month I fought them with my pathetic remedies, but they crept inwards, slowly but inexorably, blurring and narrowing Digger's field of vision. Andrew noticed them too, and when he brought the little dog into the surgery he clasped and unclasped his hands anxiously.

'You know, he's seeing less all the time, Mr Herriot. I can tell. He still looks out of the car windows but he used to bark at all sorts of things he didn't like—other dogs for instance—and now he just doesn't spot them. He's—he's losing his sight.'

I felt like screaming or kicking the table, but since that wouldn't have helped I just looked at him.

'It's that brown stuff isn't it?' he said. 'What is it?'

'It's called pigmentary keratitis, Andrew. It sometimes happens when the cornea—the front of the eyeball—has been inflamed over a long period, and it is very difficult to treat. I'll do the best I can.'

My best wasn't enough. That slow, creeping tide was pitiless, and as the pigment cells were laid down thicker and thicker the resulting layer was almost black, lowering a dingy curtain between Digger and all the things he had gazed at so eagerly.

And all the time I suffered a long gnawing worry, a helpless wretchedness as I contemplated the inevitable.

It was when I examined the eyes five months after I had first seen them that Andrew broke down. There was hardly anything to be seen of the original corneal structure now; just a brown-black opacity which left only minute chinks for moments of sight. Blindness was not far away.

I patted the man's shoulder again. 'Come on, Andrew. Come over here and sit down.' I pulled over the single wooden chair in the consulting room.

He staggered across the floor and almost collapsed on the seat. He sat there, head in hands, for some time then raised a tear-stained face to me. His expression was distraught.

'I can't bear the thought of it,' he gasped. 'A friendly little thing like Digger—he loves everybody. What has he ever done to deserve this?'

'Nothing, Andrew. It's just one of the sad things which happen. I'm terribly sorry.'

He rolled his head from side to side. 'Oh God, but it's worse for him. You've seen him in the car—he's so interested in everything. Life wouldn't be worth living for him if he lost his sight. And I don't want to live any more either!'

'You mustn't talk like that, Andrew,' I said. 'That's going too far.' I hesitated. 'Please don't be offended, but you ought to see your doctor.'

'Oh I'm always at the doctor,' he replied dully. 'I'm full of pills right now. He tells me I have a depression.'

The word was like a mournful knell. Coming so soon after Paul it sent a wave of panic through me.

'How long have you been like this?'

'Oh, weeks. I seem to be getting worse.'

'Have you ever had it before?'

'No, never.' He wrung his hands and looked at the floor. 'The doctor says that if I keep on taking the pills I'll get over it, but I'm reaching the end of my tether now.'

'But the doctor is right, Andrew. You've got to stick it and you'll be as good as new.'

'I don't believe it,' he muttered. 'Every day lasts a year. I never enjoy anything. And every morning when I wake up I dread having to face the world again.'

I didn't know what to say or how to help. 'Can I get you a glass of water?'

'No . . . no thanks.'

He turned his deathly pale face up to me again and the dark eyes held a terrible blankness. 'What's the use of going on? I know I'm going to be miserable for the rest of my life.'

I am no psychiatrist but I knew better than to tell somebody in Andrew's condition to snap out of it. And I had a flash of intuition.

'All right,' I said. 'Be miserable for the rest of your life, but while you're about it you've got to look after this dog.'

'Look after him? What can I do? He's going blind. There's nothing anybody can do for him now.'

'You're wrong, Andrew. This is where you start doing things for him. He's going to be lost without your help.'

'How do you mean?'

'Well, you know all those walks you take him—you've got to get him used to the same tracks and paths so that he can trot along on familiar ground without fear. Keep him clear of holes and ditches.'

He screwed up his face. 'Yes, but he won't enjoy the walks any more.

'He will,' I said. 'You'll be surprised.'

'Oh, but . . .'

'And that nice big lawn at the back of your house where he runs. You'll have to be on the lookout all the time in case there are things left lying around on the grass that he might bump into. And the eye drops—you say they make him more comfortable. Who's going to put them in if you don't?'

'But Mr. Herriot . . . you've seen how he always looks out of the car when he's with me . . .'

'He'll still look out.'

'Even if he can't see?'

'Yes.' I put my hand on his arm. 'You must understand, Andrew, when an animal loses his sight he doesn't realise what's happened to him. It's a terrible thing, I know, but he doesn't suffer the mental agony of a human being.'

He stood up and took a long shuddering breath. 'But I'm having the agony. I've been dreading this happening for so long. I haven't been able to sleep for thinking about it. It seems so cruel and unjust for this to strike a helpless animal—a little creature who's never done anybody any harm.' He began to wring his hands again and pace about the room.

'You're just torturing yourself!' I said sharply. 'That's part of your trouble. You're using Digger to punish yourself instead of doing something useful.'

'Oh but what can I do that will really help? All those things you talked about—they can't give him a happy life.'

'Oh but they can. Digger can be happy for years and years if you really work at it. It's up to you.'

Like a man in a dream he bent and gathered his dog into his arms and shuffled along the passage to the front door. As he went down the steps into the street I called out to him.

'Keep in touch with your doctor, Andrew. Take your pills regularly—and remember.' I raised my voice to a shout. 'Remember you've got a job to do with that dog!'

After Paul I was on a knife edge of apprehension but this time there was no tragic news to shatter me. Instead I saw Andrew Vine frequently, sometimes in the town with Digger on a lead, occasionally in his car with the little white head framed always in the windscreen, and most often in the fields by the river where he seemed to be carrying out my advice by following the good open tracks again and again.

It was by the river that I stopped him one day. 'How are things going, Andrew?'

He looked at me unsmilingly. 'Oh, he's finding his way around not too badly. I keep my eye on him. I always avoid that field over there—there's a lot of boggy places in it.'

'Good, that's the idea. And how are you yourself?'

'Do you really want to know?'

'Yes, of course.'

He tried to smile. 'Well this is one of my good days. I'm just tense and dreadfully unhappy. On my bad days I'm terror-stricken, despairing, utterly desolate.'

'I'm sorry, Andrew.'

He shrugged. 'Don't think I'm wallowing in self pity. You asked me. Anyway, I have a system. Every morning I look at myself in the mirror and I say, 'Okay, Vine, here's another bloody awful day coming up, but you're going to do your job and you're going to look after your dog.'

'That's good, Andrew. And it will all pass. The whole thing will go away and you'll be all right one day.'

'That's what the doctor says.' He gave me a sidelong glance. 'But in the meantime . . .' He looked down at his dog. 'Come on, Digger.'

He turned and strode away abruptly with the little dog trotting after him, and there was something in the set of the man's shoulders and the forward thrust of his head which gave me hope. He was a picture of fierce determination.

My hopes were fulfilled. Both Andrew and Digger won through. I knew that within months, but the final picture in my mind is of a meeting I had with the two of them about two years later. It was on the flat table-land above Darrowby where I had first seen Digger hurtling joyously among the gorse bushes.

He wasn't doing so badly now, running freely over the smooth green turf, sniffing among the herbage, cooking a leg now and then with deep contentment against the drystone wall which ran along the hillside.

Andrew laughed when he saw me. He had put on weight and looked a different person. 'Digger knows every inch of this walk,' he said. 'I think it's just about his favourite spot—you can see how he's enjoying himself.'

I nodded. 'He certainly looks a happy little dog.'

'Yes, he's happy all right. He has a good life and honestly I often forget that he can't see.' He paused. 'You were right, that day in your surgery. You said this would happen.'

'Well that's great, Andrew.' I said. 'And you're happy, too, aren't you?'

'I am, Mr. Herriot. Thank God, I am.' A shadow crossed his face. 'When I think how it was then, I can't believe my luck. It was like being in a dark valley, and bit by by I've climbed out into the sunshine.'

'I can see that. You're as good as new, now.'

He smiled. 'I'm better than that—better than I was before. That terrible experience did me good. Remember you said I was torturing myself? I realised I had spent all my days doing that. I used to take every little mishap of life and beat myself over the head with it.'

'You don't have to tell me, Andrew,' I said ruefully. 'I've always been pretty good at that myself.'

'Well yes, I suppose a lot of us are. But I became an expert and look where it got me. It helped so much to have Digger to look after.' His face lit up and he pointed over the grass. 'Just look at that!'

The little dog had been inspecting an ancient fence, a few rotting planks which were probably part of an old sheep fold, and as we watched he leaped effortlessly between the spars to the other side.

'Marvellous!' I said delightedly. 'You'd think there was nothing wrong with him.'

Andrew turned to me. 'Mr. Herriot, when I see a thing like that it makes me wonder. Can a blind dog do such a thing. Do you think . . . do you think there's a chance he can see just a little?'

I hesitated. 'Maybe he can see a bit through that pigment, but it can't be much—a flicker of light and shade, perhaps. I really don't know. But in any case, he's become so clever in his familiar surroundings that it doesn't make much difference.'

'Yes . . . yes.' He smiled philosophically. 'Anyway, we must get on our way. Come on, Digger!'

He snapped his fingers and set off along a track which pushed a vivid green finger through the heather, pointing clean and unbroken to the sunny skyline. His dog bounded ahead of him, not just at a trot but at a gallop.

I have made no secret of the fact that I never really knew the cause of Digger's blindness, but in the light of modern developments in eye surgery I believe it was a condition called keratitis sicca. This was simply not recognised in those early days and anyway, if I had known I could have done little about it. The name means 'dryness of the cornea' and it occurs when the dog is not producing enough tears. At the present time it is treated by instilling artificial tears or by an intricate operation whereby the salivary ducts are transferred to the eyes. But even now, despite these things, I have seen that dread pigmentation taking over in the end.

When I look back on the whole episode my feeling is of thankfulness. All sorts of things help people to pull out of a depression. Mostly it is their family—the knowledge that wife and children are dependent on them—sometimes it is a cause to work for, but in Andrew Vine's case it was a dog.

I often think of the dark valley which closed around him at that time and I am convinced he came out of it on the end of Digger's lead.

Now that I had done my first solo I was beginning to appreciate the qualities of my instructor. There was no doubt F. O. Woodham was a very good teacher.

There was a war on and no time for niceties. He had to get green young men into the air on their own without delay and he had done it with me.

I used to fancy myself as a teacher, too, with the boys who came to see practice in Darrowby. I could see myself now, smiling indulgently at one of my pupils.

'You don't see this sort of thing in country practice, David,' I said. He was one of the young people who occasionally came with me on my rounds. Fifteen years old, and like all the others he thought he wanted to be a veterinary surgeon. But at the moment he looked a little bewildered.

I really couldn't blame him. It was his first visit and he had expected to spend a day with me in the rough and tumble of large animal practice in the Yorkshire Dales and now there was this lady with the poodle and Emmeline. The lady's progress along the passage to the consulting room had been punctuated by a series of squeaking noises produced by her squeezing a small rubber doll. At each squeak Lucy advanced a few reluctant steps until a final pressure lured her on to the table. There she stood trembling and looking soulfully around her.

'She won't go anywhere without Emmeline,' the lady explained.

'Emmeline?'

'The doll.' She held up the rubber toy. 'Since this trouble started Lucy has become devoted to her.'

'I see. And what trouble is that?'

'Well, it's been going on for about two weeks now. She's so listless and strange, and she hardly eats anything.'

I reached behind me to the trolley for the thermometer. 'Right, we'll have a look at her. There's something wrong when a dog won't eat.'

The temperature was normal. I went over her chest thoroughly with my stethoscope without finding any unusual sounds. The heart thudded steadily in my ears. Careful palpation of the abdomen revealed nothing out of the way.

The lady stroked Lucy's curly poll and the little animal looked up at her with sorrowful liquid eyes. 'I'm getting really worried about her. She doesn't want to go for walks. In fact we can't even entice her from the house without Emmeline.'

'Eh?'

'I say she won't take a step outside unless we squeak Emmeline at her, and then they both go out together. Even then she just trails along like an old dog, and she's only three after all. You know how lively she is normally.'

I nodded. I did know. This little poodle was a bundle of energy. I had seen her racing around the fields down by the river, jumping to enormous heights as she chased a ball. She must be suffering from something pretty severe, but so far I was baffled.

And I wished the lady wouldn't keep on about Emmeline and the squeaking. I shot a side glance at David. I had been holding forth to him, telling him how ours was a scientific profession and that he would have to be really hot at physics, chemistry and biology to gain entrance to a veterinary school, and it didn't fit in with all this.

Maybe I could guide the conversation along more clinical lines.

'Any more symptoms?' I asked. 'Any cough, constipation, diarrhoea? Does she ever cry out in pain?'

The lady shook her head. 'No. nothing like that. She just looks around looking at us with such a pitiful expression and searching for Emmeline.'

Oh dear, there it was again. I cleared my throat. 'She never vomits at all? Especially after a meal?'

'Never. When she does eat a little she goes straight away to find Emmeline and takes her to her basket.'

'Really? Well I can't see that that has anything to do with it. Are you sure she isn't lame at times?'

The lady didn't seem to be listening. 'And when she gets

Emmeline into her basket she sort of circles around, scratching the blanket as though she was making a bed for the little thing.'

I gritted my teeth. Would she never stop? Then a light flashed in the darkness.

'Wait a minute,' I said. 'Did you say making a bed?'

'Yes, she scratches around for ages then puts Emmeline down.'

'Ah yes.' The next question would settle it. 'When was she last in season?'

The lady tapped a finger against her cheek. 'Let me see. It was in the middle of May—that would be about nine weeks ago.'

There wasn't a mystery any more.

'Roll her over, please,' I said.

With Lucy stretched on her back, her eyes regarding the surgery ceiling with deep emotion, I ran my fingers over the mammary glands. They were turgid and swollen. I gently squeezed one of the teats and a bead of milk appeared.

'She's got false pregnancy,' I said.

'What on earth is that?' The lady looked at me, round-eyed.

'Oh, it's quite common in bitches. They get the idea they are going to have pups and around the end of the gestation period they start this business. Making a bed for the pups is typical, but some of them actually swell in the abdomen. They do all sorts of peculiar things.'

'My goodness, how extraordinary!' The lady began to laugh. 'Lucy, you silly little thing, worrying us over nothing.' She looked at me across the table. 'How long is she going to be like this?'

I turned on the hot tap and began to wash my hands. 'Not for long. I'll give you some tablets for her. If she's not much better in a week come back for more. But you needn't worry—even if it takes a bit longer she'll be her old self in the end.'

I went through to the dispensary, put the tablets in a box and handed them over. The lady thanked me then turned to her pet who was sitting on the tiled floor looking dreamily into space.

'Come along Lucy,' she said, but the poodle took no notice. 'Lucy! Do you hear me? We're going now!' She began to walk briskly along the passage but the little animal merely put her head on one side and appeared to be hearkening to inward music. After a minute her mistress reappeared and regarded her with some exasperation. 'Oh really, you are naughty. I suppose there's only one way.' She opened her handbag and produced the rubber toy.

'Squeak-squeak,' went Emmeline and the poodle raised her eyes with misty adoration. 'Squeak-squeak, squeak-squeak.' The sound retreated along the passage and Lucy followed entranced until she disappeared round the corner.

I turned to David with an apologetic grin. 'Right,' I said. 'We'll get out on the road. I know you want to see farm practice and I assure you it's vastly different from what you've seen here."

Sitting in the car, I continued. 'Mind you, don't get me wrong. I'm not decrying small animal work. In fact I'd have to admit that it is the most highly skilled branch of the profession and I personally think that small animal surgery is tremendously demanding. Just don't judge it all by Emmeline. Anyway, we have one doggy visit before we go out into the country.'

'What's that?' the lad asked.

'Well, I've had a call from a Mr Rington to say that his dalmation bitch has completely altered her behaviour. In fact she's acting so strangely that he doesn't want to bring her to the surgery.'

'What do you think that might be?'

I thought for a moment. 'It seems a bit silly, but the first thing that comes to my mind is rabies. This is the most dreadful dog disease of all, but thank heaven we've managed to keep it out of this country so far by strict quarantine regulations. But at college it was hammered into us so forcibly that it is always at the back of my mind even though I don't really expect to see it. But this case of the dalmation could be anything. I only hope she hasn't turned savage because that's the sort of thing that leads to a dog being put down and I hate that.'

Mr Rington's opening remark didn't cheer me.

'Tessa's become really fierce lately, Mr Herriot. Started moping about and growling a few days ago and frankly I daren't trust her with strangers now. She nailed the postman by the ankle this morning. Most embarrassing.'

My spirits sank lower. 'Actually bit somebody!' Mr. Rington went on. 'It's unbelievable—she's such a softie. I've always been able to do anything with her.'

'I know, I know,' he muttered. 'She's marvellous with children, too. I can't understand it. But come and have a look at her.'

The dalmation was sitting in a corner of the lounge and she glanced up sulkily as we entered. She was a favourite patient and I approached her confidently.

'Hello, Tessa,' I said, and held out my hand. I usually had a tail-lashing, tongue-lolling welcome from this animal but today she froze into complete immobility and her lips withdrew silently from her teeth. It wasn't an ordinary snarl—it was as though the upper lip was operated by strings and there was something unnerving about it.

'What's the matter, old girl?' I enquired, and again the gleaming incisors were soundlessly exposed. And as I stared uncomprehendingly I could see that the eyes were glaring at me with blazing primitive hatred. Tessa was unrecognizable.

'Mr Herriot.' Her owner looked at me apprehensively. 'I don't think I'd go any nearer if I were you.'

I withdrew a pace. 'Yes, I'm inclined to agree with you. I don't think she'd cooperate if I tried to examine her. But never mind, tell me all about her.'

'Well, there's really nothing more to tell,' Mr Rington said helplessly. 'She's just different—like this.'

'Appetite good?'

'Yes, fine. Eats everything in front of her.'

'No unusual symptoms at all?'

'None, apart from the altered temperament. The family can handle her, but quite frankly I think she'd bite any stranger who came too near.'

I ran my fingers through my hair. 'Any change in family circumstances? New baby? Different domestic help? Unusual people coming to the house?'

'No, nothing like that. There's been no change.'

'I ask because animals sometimes act like this out of jealousy or disapproval.'

'Sorry.' Mr Rington shrugged his shoulders. 'Everything is just as it's always been. Only this morning my wife was wondering if Tessa was still cross with us because we kept her indoors for three weeks while she was in season. But that was a long time ago—about two months now.'

I whipped round and faced him. 'Two months?'

'Yes, about that.'

Surely not again! I gestured to the owner. 'Would you please lift her up so that she's standing on her hind legs?'

'Like this?' He put his arms round the dalmation's chest and hoisted till she was in the upright position with her abdomen facing me.

And it was as if I knew beforehand. Because I felt not the slightest surprise when I saw the twin row of engorged teats. It was unnecessary, but I leaned forward, grasped a little nipple and sent a white jet spurting.

'She's bulging with milk,' I said.

'Milk?'

'Yes, she's got false pregnancy. This is one of the more unusual side effects, but I'll give you some tablets and she'll soon be the docile Tessa again.'

As we got back into the car I had a good idea what the schoolboy was thinking. He would be wondering where the chemistry, physics and biology came in.

'Sorry about that, David,' I said. 'I've been telling you all about the constant variety of a vet's life and the first two cases you see are the same condition. But we are going out to the farms now and as I said, you'll find it very different. I mean, those two cases were really psychological things. You don't get that in country practice. It's a bit rough but it's real and down to earth.'

As we drove into the farmyard I saw the farmer carrying a bag of meal over the cobbles.

I got out of the car with David. 'You've got a pig ill, Mr Fisher?'

'Aye, a big sow. She's in 'ere.' He led the way into a pen and pointed to a huge white pig lying on her side.

'She's been off it for a few days,' he said. 'Hardly eats owt—just picks at her food. And she just lays there all t'time. Ah don't think she's got strength to get to her feet.'

My thermometer had been in the pig's rectum as he spoke and I fished it out and read the temperature. It was 102-2—dead normal. I auscultated the chest and palpated the abdomen with growing puzzlement. Nothing wrong. I looked over at the trough nearby. It was filled to the brim with fresh meal and water—untouched. And pigs do love their food.

I nudged her thigh with my fist. 'Come on, lass, get up.' And I followed it with a brisk slap across the rump. A healthy pig would have leaped to her feet but the sow never moved.

I tried not to scratch my head. There was something very funny here. 'Has she ever been ill before, Mr Fisher?'

'Nay, never ailed a thing and she's allus been a real lively pig, too. Ah can't reckon it up.'

Nor could I. 'What beats me,' I said, 'is that she doesn't look like a sick animal. She's not trembling or anxious, she's lying there as if she hadn't a care in the world.'

'Aye, you're right, Mr Herriot. She's as 'appy as Larry, but she'll neither move nor eat. It's a rum 'un, isn't it?'

It was very rum indeed. I squatted on my heels, watching the big sow. She reached forward and pushed gently with her snout at the straw bedding round her head. Sick pigs never did that. It was a gesture of well-being. And those little grunts which issued from deep in her chest. They were grunts of deep contentment and there was something familiar about the sound of them . . . something lurking at the back of my mind which wouldn't come forward. It was the same with the way the sow eased herself further on to her side, pushing the great stretch of abdomen outward as though in offering.

I had heard and seen it so many times before—the happy sounds, the careful movements. Then I remembered. Of course! She was like a sow with a litter, only there was no litter.

A wave of disbelief flowed over me. Oh no, no, please not a third time! It was dark in the pen and I couldn't get a clear view of the mammary glands.

I turned to the farmer. 'Open the door a little will you, please.'

As the sunshine flooded in everything was obvious. It was mere routine to reach out to the long tumefied udder and squirt the milk against the wall.

I straightened up wearily and was about to make my now commonplace announcement when David did it for me.

'False pregnancy?' he said.

I nodded dumbly.

'What was that?' enquired Mr Fisher.

'Well your sow has got it into her head that she is pregnant,' I said. 'Not only that, but she thinks she has given birth to a litter and she's suckling the imaginary piglets now. You can see it, can't you?'

The farmer gave a long soft whistle. 'Aye . . . aye . . . you're right. That's what she's doin' . . . enjoyin' it, too.' He took off his cap, rubbed the top of his head and put the cap on again. 'Well, there's allus summat new, isn't there?'

It wasn't new to David, of course. Old stuff, in fact, and I didn't want to bore him further with a lengthy dissertation.

'Nothing to worry about, Mr Fisher,' I said hastily. 'Call down to the surgery and I'll give you something to put in her food. She'll soon be back to normal.'

As I left the pen the sow gave a deep sigh of utter fulfilment and moved her position with the utmost care to avoid crushing her phantom family. I looked back at her and I could almost see the long pink row of piglets sucking busily. I shook my head to dispel the vision and went out to the car.

I was opening the door when the farmer's wife trotted towards me. 'I've just had a phone call from your surgery, Mr Herriot. They want you to go to Mr Rogers of East Farm. There's a cow calving.'

An emergency like this in the middle of a round was usually an irritant, but today the news came as a relief. I had promised this schoolboy some genuine country practice and I was beginning to feel embarrassed.

'Well, David,' I said with a light laugh as we drove away. 'You must be thinking all my patients are neurotic. But you're going to see a bit of the real thing now—there's nothing airy-fairy about a calving cow. This is where the hard work of our job comes in. It's often pretty tough fighting against a big straining cow, because you must remember the vet only sees the difficult cases where the calf is laid wrong.'

The situation of East Farm seemed to add weight to my words. We were bumping up the fellside along a narrow track which was never meant for motor cars and I winced as the exhaust grated against the jutting rocks.

The farm was perched almost on the edge of the hilltop and behind it the sparse fields, stolen from the moorland, rolled away to the skyline. The crumbling stonework and broken roof tiles testified to the age of the squat grey house.

I pointed to some figures, faintly visible on the massive stone lintel above the front door. 'What does that date mean to you, David?'

'Sixteen sixty six, the great fire of London,' he replied promptly.

'Well done. Strange to think they were building this place in the same year as old London burned down.'

Mr Rogers appeared, carrying a steaming bucket and a towel. 'She's out in t'field, Mr Herriot, but she's a quiet cow and easy to catch.'

'All right.' I followed him through the gate. It was another little annoyance when the farmer didn't have the cow inside for me but again I felt that if David wanted to be a vet he ought to know that a lot of our work was carried out in the open, often in the cold and rain.

Even now on this July morning a cool breeze whipped round my chest and back as I pulled off my shirt. It was never very warm in the high country of the Dales but I felt at home here. With the cow standing patiently as the farmer held her halter, the bucket perched among the tufts of wiry grass, and only a few stunted wind-bent trees breaking the harsh sweep of green, it seemed that at last this boy was seeing me in my proper place.

I soaped my arms to the shoulder. 'Hold the tail, will you, David. This is where I find out what kind of job it's going to be.'

As I slipped my hand into the cow it struck me that it would be no bad thing if it was a hard calving. If the lad saw me losing a bit of sweat it would give him a truer picture of the life in front of him.

'Sometimes these jobs take an hour or more,' I said. 'But you have the reward of delivering a new living creature. Seeing a calf wriggling on the ground at the end of it is the biggest thrill in practice.'

I reached forward, my mind alive with the possibilities. Posterior? Head back? Breech? But as I groped through the open cervix into the uterus I felt a growing astonishment. There was nothing there.

I withdrew my arm and leaned for a moment on the hairy rump. The day's events were taking on a dreamlike quality. Then I looked up at the farmer.

'There's no calf in this cow, Mr. Rogers.'

'Eh?'

'She's empty. She's calved already.'

The farmer gazed around him, scanning the acres of bare grass. 'Well where the hangment is the thing? This cow was messin' about last night and I thought she'd calve, but there was nowt to find this mornin'.'

His attention was caught by a cry from the right.

'Hey, Willie! Just a minute, Willie!' It was Bob Sellars from the next farm. He was leaning over the drystone wall about twenty yards away.

'What's matter, Bob?'

'Ah thowt ah'd better tell ye. Ah saw that cow hidin' her calf this mornin'.'

'Hidin' . . . ? What are ye on about?'

'Ah'm not jokin' nor jestin', Willie. She hid it in yon gutter over there and every time t'calf tried to get out she pushed it back in again.'

'But . . . nay, nay, I can't 'ave that. I've never heard of such a thing. Have you, Mr Herriot?"

I shook my head, but the whole thing seemed to fit in with the air of fantasy which had begun to pervade the day's work.

Bob Sellars began to climb over the wall. 'Awright, if ye won't believe me I'l show ye.'

He led the way to the far end of the field where a dry ditch ran along the base of the wall. 'There 'e is!' he said triumphantly.

And there indeed he was. A tiny red and white calf half concealed by the long herbage. He was curled comfortably in his grassy bed, his nose resting on his fore legs.

When the little creature saw his mother he staggered to his feet and clambered shakily up the side of the ditch, but no sooner had he gained the level of the field than the big cow, released now from her halter, lowered her head and gently nudged him back in again.

Bob waved his arm. 'There y'are, she's hiding it, isn't she?'

Mr Rogers said nothing and I merely shrugged my shoulders, but twice more the calf managed to scramble from the ditch and twice more his mother returned him firmly with her head.

'Well it teks a bit o' believin',' the farmer murmured, half to himself. 'She's had five calves afore this and we've taken 'em straight away from 'er as we allus do. Maybe she wants to keep this 'un for 'erself? I dunno . . . I dunno . . .' His voice trailed away.

Later, as we rattled down the stony track, David turned to me. 'Do you think that cow really hid her calf . . . so that she could keep it for herself?'

I stared helplessly through the glass of the windscreen. 'Well, anybody would tell you it's impossible, but you saw what happened. I'm like Mr Rogers, I just don't know.' I paused as the car dipped into a deep rut and sent us bobbing about. 'But you see some funny things at our job.'

The schoolboy nodded thoughtfully. 'Yes, it seems to me that yours is a funny life altogether.'

40

The doctor put down the folder containing my case history and gave me a friendly smile across the desk.

'I'm sorry, Herriot, but you've got to have an operation.'

His words, though gentle, were like a slap in the face. After flying school we had been posted to Heaton Park, Manchester, and I heard within two days that I had been graded pilot. Everything seemed at last to be going smoothly.

'An operation . . . are you sure?'

'Absolutely, I'm afraid,' he said, and he looked like a man who knew his business. He was a Wing Commander, almost certainly a specialist in civil life, and I had been sent to him after a medical inspection by one of the regular doctors.

'This old scar they mention in your documents,' he went on. 'You've already had surgery there, haven't you?'

'Yes, a few years ago.'

'Well, I'm afraid the thing is opening up again and needs attention.'

I seemed to have run out of words and could think of only one.

'When?'

'Immediately. Within a few days, anyway.'

I stared at him. 'But my flight's going overseas at the end of the week.'

'Ah well, that's a pity.' He spread his hands and smiled again. 'But they'll be going without you. You will be in hospital.'

I had a sudden feeling of loss, of something coming to an end, and it lingered after I had left the Wing Commander's office. I realised painfully that the fifty men with whom I had sweated my way through all those new experiences had become my friends. The first breaking-in at St. John's Wood in London, the hard training at Scarborough I.T.W., the 'toughening course' in

Shropshire and the final flying instruction at Winckfield; it had bound us together and I had come to think of myself not as an individual but as part of a group. My mind could hardly accept the fact that I was going to be on my own.

The others were sorry, too, my own particular chums looking almost bereaved, but they were all too busy to pay me much attention. They were being pushed around all over the place, getting briefed and kitted out for their posting and it was a hectic time for the whole flight—except me. I sat on my bed in the Nissen hut while the excitement billowed around me.

I thought my departure would go unnoticed but when I got my summons and prepared to leave I found, tucked in the webbing of my pack, an envelope filled with the precious coupons with which we drew our ration of cigarettes in those days. It seemed that nearly everybody had chipped in and the final gesture squeezed at my throat as I made my lonely way from the camp.

The hospital was at Creden Hill, near Hereford, and I suppose it is one of the consolations of service life that you can't feel lonely for very long. The beds in the long ward were filled with people like myself who had been torn from their comrades and were eager to be friendly.

In the few days before my operation we came to know each other pretty well. The young man in the bed on my left spent his time writing excruciating poetry to his girl friend and insisted on reading it out to me, stanza by stanza. The lad on the right seemed a pensive type. Everybody addressed him as 'Sammy' but he replied only in grunts.

When he found out I was a vet he leaned from the sheets and beckoned to me.

'I get fed up wi' them blokes callin' me Sammy,' he muttered in a ripe Birmingham accent. 'Because me name's not Sammy, it's Desmond.'

'Really? Why do they do it, then?'

He leaned out further. 'That's what I want to talk to you about. You bein' a vet—you'll know about these things. It's because of what's wrong with me—why I'm in 'ere.'

'Well, why are you here? What's your trouble?'

He looked around him then spoke in a confidential whisper. 'I gotta big ball.'

'A what?'

'A big ball. One of me balls is a right whopper.'

'Ah, I see, but I still don't understand . . .'

'Well, it's like this,' he said. 'All the fellers in the ward keep sayin' the doctor's goin' to cut it off—then I'd be like Sammy Hall.'

I nodded in comprehension. Memories from my college days filtered back. It had been a popular ditty at the parties. 'My name is Sammy Hall and I've only got one ball . . .'

'Oh, nonsense, they're pulling your leg,' I said. 'An enlarged testicle can be all sorts of things. Can you remember what the doctor called it?'

He screwed up his face. 'It was a funny name. Like vorry or varry something.'

'Do you mean varicocele?'

'That's it!' He threw up an arm. 'That's the word!'

'Well, you can stop worrying,' I said. 'It's quite a simple little operation. Trifling, in fact.'

'You mean they won't cut me ball off?'

'Definitely not. Just remove a few surplus blood vessels, that's all. No trouble.'

He fell back on the pillow and gazed ecstatically at the ceiling. 'Thanks, mate,' he breathed. 'You've done me a world o' good. I'm gettin' done tomorrow and I've been dreadin' it.'

He was like a different person all that day, laughing and joking with everybody, and next morning when the nurse came to give him his pre-med injection he turned to me with a last appeal in his eyes.

'You wouldn't kid me, mate, would you? They're not goin' to . . .?'

I held up a hand. 'I assure you, Sammy—er—Desmond, you've nothing to worry about. I give you my word.'

Again the beatific smile crept over his face and it stayed there until the 'blood wagon', the operating room trolley pushed by a male orderly, came to collect him.

The blood wagon was very busy each morning and it was customary to raise a cheer as each man was wheeled out. Most of the victims responded with a sleepy wave before the swing doors closed behind them, but when I saw Desmond grinning cheerfully and giving the thumbs-up sign I felt I had really done something.

Next morning it was my turn. I had my injection at around

eight o'clock and by the time the trolley appeared I was pleasantly woozy. They removed my pyjamas and arrayed me in a sort of nightgown with laces at the neck and pulled thick woollen socks over my feet. As the orderly wheeled me away the inmates of the ward broke into a ragged chorus of encouragement and I managed the ritual flourish of an arm as I left.

It was a cheerless journey along white-tiled corridors until the trolley pushed its way into the anaesthetics room. As I entered, the doors at the far end parted as a doctor came towards me bearing a loaded syringe. I had a chilling glimpse of the operating theatre beyond, with the lights beating on the long table and the masked surgeons waiting.

The doctor pushed up my sleeve and swabbed my forearm with surgical spirit. I decided I had seen enough and closed my eyes, but an exclamation from above made me open them.

'Good God, it's Jim Herriot!'

I looked up at the man with the syringe. It was Teddy McQueen. He had been in my class at school and I hadn't seen him since the day I left.

My throat was dry after the injection but I felt I had to say something.

'Hello, Teddy,' I croaked.

His eyes were wide. 'What the hell are you doing here?'

'What the hell do you think?' I rasped crossly. 'I'm going in there for an operation.'

'Oh, I know that—I'm the anaesthetist here—but I remember you telling me at school that you were going to be a vet.'

'That's right. I am a vet.'

'You are?' His face was a picture of amazement. 'But what the devil is a vet doing in the R.A.F.?'

It was a good question. 'Nothing very much, Teddy,' I replied.

He began to laugh. Obviously he found the whole situation intriguing.

'Well, Jim, I can't get over this!' He leaned over me and giggled uncontrollably. 'Imagine our meeting here after all these years. I think it's an absolute hoot!' His whole body began to shake and he had to dab away the tears from his eyes.

Lying there on the blood wagon in my nightie and woolly socks I didn't find it all that funny, and my numbed brain was searching for a withering riposte when a voice barked from the theatre.

'What's keeping you, McQueen? We can't wait all morning!'

Teddy stopped laughing. 'Sorry, Jim old chum,' he said. 'But your presence is requested within.' He pushed the needle into my vein and my last memory as I drifted away was of his lingering amused smile.

I spent three weeks at Creden Hill and towards the end of that time those of us who were almost fully recovered were allowed out to visit the nearby town of Hereford. This was embarrassing because we were all clad in the regulation suit of hospital blue with white shirt and red tie and it was obvious from the respectful glances we received that people thought we had been wounded in action.

When a veteran of the first war came up to me and asked, 'Where did you get your packet, mate?' I stopped going altogether.

I left the R.A.F. hospital with a feeling of gratitude—particularly towards the hard-working, cheerful nurses. They gave us many a tongue lashing for chattering after lights out, for smoking under the blankets, for messing up our beds, but all the time I marvelled at their dedication.

I used to lie there and wonder what it was in a girl's character that made her go in for the arduous life of nursing. A concern for people's welfare? A natural caring instinct? Whatever it was, I am sure a person is born with it.

This trait is part of the personalities of some animals and it was exemplified in Eric Abbot's sheepdog, Judy.

I first met Judy when I was treating Eric's bullock for wooden tongue. The bullock was only a young one and the farmer admitted ruefully that he had neglected it because it was almost a walking skeleton.

'Damn!' Eric grunted. 'He's been runnin' out with that bunch in the far fields and I must have missed 'im. I never knew he'd got to this state.'

When actinobacillosis affects the tongue it should be treated right at the start, when the first symptoms of salivation and swelling beneath the jaw appear. Otherwise the tongue becomes harder and harder till finally it sticks out of the front of the mouth, as unyielding as the wood which gives the disease its ancient name.

This skinny little creature had reached that stage, so that he not only looked pathetic but also slightly comic as though he were making a derisive gesture at me. But with a tongue like that he just couldn't eat and was literally starving to death. He lay quietly as though he didn't care.

'There's one thing, Eric,' I said. 'Giving him an intravenous injection won't be any problem. He hasn't the strength to resist.'

The great new treatment at that time was sodium iodide into the vein—modern and spectacular. Before that the farmers used to paint the tongue with tincture of iodine, a tedious procedure which sometimes worked and sometimes didn't. The sodium iodide was a magical improvement and showed results within a few days.

I inserted the needle into the jugular and tipped up the bottle of clear fluid. Two drachms of the iodide I used to use, in eight ounces of distilled water and it didn't take long to flow in. In fact the bottle was nearly empty before I noticed Judy.

I had been aware of a big dog sitting near me all the time, but as I neared the end of the injection a black nose moved ever closer till it was almost touching the needle. Then the nose moved along the rubber tube up to the bottle and back again, sniffing with the utmost concentration. When I removed the needle the nose began a careful inspection of the injection site. Then a tongue appeared and began to lick the bullock's neck methodically.

I squatted back on my heels and watched. This was something more than mere curiosity; everything in the dog's attitude suggested intense interest and concern.

'You know, Eric,' I said. 'I have the impression that this dog isn't just watching me. She's supervising the whole job.'

The farmer laughed. 'You're right there. She's a funny old bitch is Judy—sort of a nurse. If there's anything amiss she's on duty. You can't keep her away.'

Judy looked up quickly at the sound of her name. She was a handsome animal; not the usual colour, but a variegated brindle with waving lines of brown and grey mingling with the normal black and white of the farm collie. Maybe there was a cross somewhere but the result was very attractive and the effect was heightened by her bright-eyed, laughing-mouthed friendliness.

I reached out and tickled the backs of her ears and she

wagged mightily—not just her tail but her entire rear end. 'I suppose she's just good-natured.'

'Oh aye, she is,' the farmer said. 'But it's not only that. It sounds daft but I think Judy feels a sense of responsibility to all the stock on t'farm.'

I nodded. 'I believe you. Anyway, let's get this beast on to his chest.'

We got down in the straw and with our hands under the back bone, rolled the bullock till he was resting on his sternum. We balanced him there with straw bales on either side then covered him with a horse rug.

In that position he didn't look as moribund as before, but the emaciated head with the useless jutting tongue lolled feebly on his shoulders and the saliva drooled uncontrolled on to the straw. I wondered if I'd ever see him alive again.

Judy however didn't appear to share my pessimism. After a thorough sniffing examination of rug and bales she moved to the front, applied an encouraging tongue to the shaggy forehead then stationed herself comfortably facing the bullock, very like a night nurse keeping an eye on her patient.

'Will she stay there?' I closed the half door and took a last look inside.

'Aye, nothing'll shift her till he's dead or better,' Eric replied. 'She's in her element now.'

'Well, you never know, she may give him an interest in life, just sitting there. He certainly needs some help. You must keep him alive with milk or gruel till the injection starts to work. If he'll drink it it'll do him most good but otherwise you'll have to bottle it into him. But be careful—you can choke a beast that way.'

A case like this had more than the usual share of the old fascination because I was using a therapeutic agent which really worked—something that didn't happen too often at that time. So I was eager to get back to see if I had been able to pull that bullock from the brink of death. But I knew I had to give the drug a chance and kept away for five days.

When I walked across the yard to the box I knew there would be no further doubts. He would either be dead or on the road to recovery.

The sound of my steps on the cobbles hadn't gone unnoticed.

Judy's head, ears cocked, appeared above the half door. A little well of triumph brimmed in me. If the nurse was still on duty then the patient must be alive. And I felt even more certain when the big dog disappeared for a second then came soaring effortlessly over the door and capered up to me, working her hind end into convolutions of delight. She seemed to be doing her best to tell me all was well.

Inside the box the bullock was still lying down but he turned to look at me and I noticed a strand of hay hanging from his mouth. The tongue itself had disappeared behind the lips.

'Well, we're winnin', aren't we?' Eric Abbot came in from the yard.

'Without a doubt,' I said. 'The tongue's much softer and I see he's been trying to eat hay.'

'Aye, can't quite manage it yet, but he's suppin' the milk and gruel like a good 'un. He's been up a time or two but he's very wobbly on his pins."

I produced another bottle of sodium iodide and repeated the injection with Judy's nose again almost touching the needle as she sniffed avidly. Her eyes were focused on the injection site with fierce concentration and so intent was she on extracting the full savour that she occasionally blew out her nostrils with a sharp blast before recommencing her inspection.

When I had finished she took up her position at the head and as I prepared to leave I noticed a voluptuous swaying of her hips which were embedded in the straw. I was a little puzzled until I realised she was wagging in the sitting position.

'Well, Judy's happy at the way things are going,' I said.

The farmer nodded. 'Yes, she is. She likes to be in charge. Do you know, she gives every new-born calf a good lick over as soon as it comes into t'world and it's the same whenever one of our cats 'as kittens.'

'Bit of a midwife, too, eh?'

'You could say that. And another funny thing about 'er—she lives with the livestock in the buildings. She's got a nice warm kennel but she never bothers with it—sleeps with the beasts in the straw every night.

I revisited the bullock a week later and this time he galloped round the box like a racehorse when I approached him. When I finally trapped him in a corner and caught his nose I was breathless but happy. I slipped my fingers into his mouth; the tongue was pliable and almost normal.

'One more shot, Eric,' I said. 'Wooden tongue is the very devil for recurring if you don't get it cleared up thoroughly.' I began to unwind the rubber tube. 'By the way, I don't see Judy around.'

'Oh, I reckon she feels he's cured now, and anyway, she has summat else on her plate this mornin'. Can you see her over there?'

I looked through the doorway. Judy was stalking importantly across the yard. She had something in her mouth—a yellow, fluffy object.

I craned out further. 'What is she carrying?'

'It's a chicken.'

'A chicken?'

'Aye, there's a brood of them runnin' around just now. They're only a month old and t'awd bitch seems to think they'd be better off in the stable. She's made a bed for them in there and she keeps tryin' to curl herself round them. But the little things won't 'ave it.'

I watched Judy disappear into the stable. Very soon she came out, trotted after a group of tiny chicks which were pecking happily among the cobbles and gently scooped one up. Busily she made her way back to the stable but as she entered the previous chick reappeared in the doorway and pottered over to rejoin his friends.

She was having a frustrating time but I knew she would keep at it because that was the way she was. Judy the nurse dog was still on duty.

41

My experience in the R.A.F. hospital made me think. As a veterinary surgeon I had become used to being on the other end of the knife and I preferred it that way.

As I remembered, I was quite happy that morning a couple of years ago as I poised my knife over a swollen ear. Tristan, one elbow leaning wearily on the table, was holding an anaesthetic mask over the nose of the sleeping dog when Siegfried came into the room.

He glanced briefly at the patient. 'Ah yes, that haematoma you were telling me about, James.' Then he looked across the table at his brother. 'Good God, you're a lovely sight this morning! When did you get in last night?'

Tristan raised a pallid countenance. His eyes were bloodshot slits between puffy lids. 'Oh, I don't quite know. Fairly late, I should think.'

'Fairly late! I got back from a farrowing at four o'clock and you hadn't arrived then. Where the hell were you, anyway?'

'I was at the Licensed Victuallers' Ball. Very good do, actually.'

'I bet it was!' Siegfried snorted. 'You don't miss a thing, do you? Darts Team Dinner, Bellringers' Outing, Pigeon Club Dance and now it's the Licensed Victuallers' Ball. If there's a good booze-up going on anywhere you'll find it.'

When under fire Tristan always retained his dignity and he drew it around him now like a threadbare cloak.

'As a matter of fact,' he said, 'many of the Licensed Victuallers are my friends.'

His brother flushed. 'I believe you. I should think you're the best bloody customer they've ever had!'

Tristan made no reply but began to make a careful check of the flow of oxygen into the ether bottle.

'And another thing,' Siegfried continued. 'I keep seeing you slinking around with about a dozen different women. And you're supposed to be studying for an exam.'

'That's an exaggeration.' The young man gave him a pained look. 'I admit I enjoy a little female company now and then—just like yourself.'

Tristan believed in attack as the best form of defence, and it was a telling blow because there was a constant stream of attractive girls laying siege to Siegfried at Skeldale House.

But the elder brother was only temporarily halted. 'Never mind me!' he shouted. 'I've passed all my exams. I'm talking about you! Didn't I see you with that new barmaid from the Drovers' the other night? You dodged rapidly into a shop doorway but I'm bloody sure it was you.'

Tristan cleared his throat. 'It quite possibly was. I have recently become friendly with Lydia—she's a very nice girl.'

'I'm not saying she isn't. What I am saying is that I want to see you indoors at night with your books instead of boozing and chasing women. Is that clear?'

'Quite.' The young man inclined his head gracefully and turned down the knob on the anaesthetic machine.

His brother regarded him balefully for a few moments, breathing deeply. These remonstrations always took it out of him. Then he turned away quickly and left.

Tristan's facade crumbled as soon as the door closed.

'Watch the anaesthetic for a minute, Jim,' he croaked. He went over to the basin in the corner, filled a measuring jar with cold water and drank it at a long gulp. Then he soaked some cotton wool under the tap and applied it to his brow.

'I wish he hadn't come in just then. I'm in no mood for the raised voices and angry words.' He reached up to a large bottle of aspirins, swallowed a few and washed them down with another gargantuan draught. 'All right then, Jim,' he murmured as he returned to the table and took over the mask again. 'Let's go.'

I bent once more over the sleeping dog. He was a Scottie called Hamish and his mistress, Miss Westerman, had brought him in two days ago.

She was a retired school teacher and I always used to think she must have had little trouble in keeping her class in order. The chilly pale eyes looking straight into mine reminded me that she was as tall as I was and the square jaw between the muscular shoulders completed a redoubtable presence.

'Mr Herriot,' she barked. 'I want you to have a look at Hamish. I do hope it's nothing serious but his ear has become very swollen and painful. They don't get—er—cancer there, do they?' For a moment the steady gaze wavered.

'Oh that's most unlikely.' I lifted the little animal's chin and looked at the left ear which was drooping over the side of his face. His whole head, in fact, was askew as though dragged down by pain.

Carefully I lifted the ear and touched the tense swelling with a forefinger. Hamish looked round at me and whimpered.

'Yes, I know, old chap. It's tender, isn't it?' As I turned to Miss Westerman I almost bumped into the close-cropped iron-grey head which was hovering close over the little dog.

'He's got an aural haematoma,' I said.

'What on earth is that?'

'It's when the little blood vessels between the skin and cartilage of the ear rupture and the blood flows out and causes this acute distension.'

She patted the jet black shaggy coat. 'But what causes it?'

'Canker, usually. Has he been shaking his head lately?'

'Yes, now you mention it he has. Just as though he had got something in his ear and was trying to get rid of it.'

'Well that's what bursts the blood vessels. I can see he has a touch of canker though it isn't common in this breed.'

She nodded. 'I see. And how can you cure it?'

'Only by an operation, I'm afraid.'

'Oh dear!' She put her hand to her mouth. 'I'm not keen on that.'

'There's nothing to worry about,' I said. 'It's just a case of letting the blood out and stitching the layers of the ear together. If we don't do this soon he'll suffer a lot of pain and finish up with a cauliflower ear, and we don't want that because he's a bonny little chap.'

I meant it, too. Hamish was a proud-strutting, trim little dog. The Scottish terrier is an attractive creature and I often lament that there are so few around in these modern days.

After some hesitation Miss Westerman agreed and we fixed a date two days from then. When she brought him in for the operation she deposited Hamish in my arms, stroked his head again and again then looked from Tristan to me and back again.

'You'll take care of him, won't you,' she said, and the jaw jutted and the pale blue eyes stabbed. For a moment I felt like a little boy caught in mischief, and I think my colleague felt the same because he blew out his breath as the lady departed.

'By gum, Jim, that's a tough baby,' he muttered. 'I wouldn't like to get on the wrong side of her.'

I nodded. 'Yes, and she thinks all the world of this dog, so let's make a good job of him.'

After Siegfried's departure I lifted the ear which was now a turgid cone and made an incision along the inner skin. As the pent up blood gushed forth I caught it in an enamel dish, then I squeezed several big clots through the wound.

'No wonder the poor little chap was in pain,' I said softly. 'He'll feel a lot better when he wakes up.'

I filled the cavity between skin and cartilage with sulphanila-mide then began to stitch the layers together, using a row of buttons. You had to do something like this or the thing filled up again within a few days. When I first began to operate on aural haematomata I used to pack the interior with gauze then bandage the ear to the head. The owners often made little granny-hats to try to keep the bandage in place, but a frisky dog usually had it off very soon.

The buttons were a far better idea and kept the layers in close contact, lessening the chance of distortion.

By lunch time Hamish had come round from the anaesthetic and though still slightly dopey he already seemed to be relieved that his bulging ear had been deflated. Miss Westerman had gone away for the day and was due to pick him up in the evening. The little dog, curled in his basket, waited philosophically.

At tea time, Siegfried glanced across the table at his brother. 'I'm going off to Brawton for a few hours, Tristan,' he said. 'I want you to stay in the house and give Miss Westerman her dog when she arrives. I don't know just when she'll come.' He scooped out a spoonful of jam. 'You can keep an eye on the patient and do a bit of studying, too. It's about time you had a night at home.'

Tristan nodded. 'Right, I'll do that.' But I could see he wasn't enthusiastic.

When Siegfried had driven away Tristan rubbed his chin and

gazed reflectively through the french window into the darkening garden. 'This is distinctly awkward, Jim.'

'Why?'

'Well, Lydia has tonight off and I promised to see her.' He whistled a few bars under his breath. 'It seems a pity to waste the opportunity just when things are building up nicely. I've got a strong feeling that girl fancies me. In fact she's nearly eating out of my hand.'

I looked at him wonderingly. 'My God, I thought you'd want a bit of peace and quiet and an early bed after last night!'

'Not me,' he said. 'I'm raring to go again.'

And indeed he looked fresh and fit, eyes sparkling, roses back in his cheeks.

'Look, Jim,' he went on. 'I don't suppose you could stick around with this dog?'

I shrugged. 'Sorry, Triss. I'm going back to see that cow of Ted Binns'—right at the top of the Dale. I'll be away for nearly two hours.'

For a few moments he was silent, then he raised a finger. 'I think I have the solution. It's quite simple, in fact it's perfect. I'll bring Lydia in here.'

'What! Into the house?'

'Yes, into this very room. I can put Hamish in his basket by the fire and Lydia and I can occupy the sofa. Marvellous! What could be nicer on a cold winter's night. Cheap, too.'

'But Triss! How about Siegfried's lecture this morning? What if he comes home early and catches the two of you here?'

Tristan lit a Woodbine and blew out an expansive cloud. 'Not a chance. You worry about such tiny things, Jim. He's always late when he goes to Brawton. There's no problem at all.'

'Well, please yourself,' I said. 'But I think you're asking for trouble. Anyway, shouldn't you be doing a bit of bacteriology? The exams are getting close.'

He smiled seraphically through the smoke. 'Oh, I'll have a quick read through it all in good time.'

I couldn't argue with him there. I always had to go over a thing about six times before it finally sunk in, but with his brain the quick read would no doubt suffice. I went out on my call.

I got back about eight o'clock and as I opened the front door my mind was far from Tristan. Ted Binns' cow wasn't responding to my treatment and I was beginning to wonder if I was on the right track. When in doubt I liked to look the subject up and the books were on the shelves in the sitting room. I hurried along the passage and threw open the door.

For a moment I stood there bewildered, trying to reorientate my thoughts. The sofa was drawn close to the bright fire, the atmosphere was heavy with cigarette smoke and the scent of perfume, but there was nobody to be seen.

The most striking feature was the long curtain over the french window. It was wafting slowly downwards as though some object had just hurtled through it at great speed. I trotted over the carpet and peered out into the dark garden. From somewhere in the gloom I heard a scuffling noise, a thud and a muffled cry, then there was a pitter-patter followed by a shrill yelping. I stood for some time listening, then as my eyes grew accustomed to the darkness I walked down the long path under the high brick wall to the yard at the foot. The yard door was open as were the big double doors into the back lane, but there was no sign of life.

Slowly I retraced my steps to the warm oblong of light at the foot of the tall old house. I was about to close the french window when I heard a stealthy movement and an urgent whisper.

'Is that you, Jim?'

'Triss! Where the hell have you sprung from?'

The young man tiptoed past me into the room and looked around him anxiously. 'It was you, then, not Siegfried?'

'Yes, I've just come in.'

He flopped on the sofa and sunk his head in his hands. 'Oh damn! I was just lying here a few minutes ago with Lydia in my arms. At peace with the world. Everything was wonderful. Then I heard the front door open.'

'But you knew I was coming back.'

'Yes, and I'd have given you a shout, but for some reason I thought, "God help us, it's Siegfried!" It sounded like his step in the passage.'

'Then what happened?'

He churned his hair around with his fingers. 'Oh, I panicked. I was whispering lovely things into Lydia's ear, then the next second I grabbed her, threw her off the couch and out of the french window.'

'I heard a thud . . .'

'Yes, that was Lydia falling into the rockery.'

'And then some sort of high-pitched cries . . .'

He sighed and closed his eyes. 'That was Lydia in the rose bushes. She doesn't know the geography of the place, poor lass.'

'Gosh, Triss,' I said. 'I'm really sorry. I shouldn't have burst in on you like that. I was thinking of something else.'

He rose wearily and put a hand on my shoulder. 'Not your fault, Jim, not your fault. You did warn me.' He reached for his cigarettes. 'I don't know how I'm going to face that girl again. I just chucked her out into the lane and told her to beat it home with all speed. She must think I'm stone balmy.' He gave a hollow groan.

I tried to be cheerful. 'Oh, you'll get round her again. You'll have a laugh about it later.'

But he wasn't listening. His eyes, wide with horror, were staring past me. Slowly he raised a trembling finger and pointed towards the fireplace. His mouth worked for a few seconds before he spoke.

'Christ, Jim, it's gone!' he gasped.

For a moment I thought the shock had deranged him. 'Gone . . . ? What's gone?'

'The bloody dog! He was there when I dashed outside. Right there!'

I looked down at the empty basket and a cold hand clutched at me. 'Oh no! He must have got out through the open window. We're in trouble.'

We rushed into the garden and searched in vain. We came back for torches and searched once more, prowling around the yard and back lane, shouting the little dog's name with diminishing hope.

After ten minutes we trailed back to the brightly lit room and stared at each other.

Tristan was the first to voice our thoughts. 'What do we tell Miss Westerman when she calls?'

I shook my head. My mind fled from the thought of informing that lady that we had lost her dog.

Just at that moment the front door bell pealed in the passage and Tristan almost leaped in the air.

'Oh God!' he quavered. 'That'll be her now. Go and see her,

Jim. Tell her it was my fault—anything you like—but I daren't face her.'

I squared my shoulders, marched over the long stretch of tiles and opened the door. It wasn't Miss Westerman, it was a well-built platinum blonde and she glared at me angrily.

'Where's Tristan?' she rasped in a voice which told me we had more than one tough female to deal with tonight.

'Well, he's—er—.'

'Oh, I know he's in there!' As she brushed past me I noticed she had a smear of soil on her cheek and her hair was sadly disarranged. I followed her into the room where she stalked up to my friend.

'Look at my bloody stockings!' she burst out. 'They're ruined!'

Tristan peered nervously at the shapely legs. 'I'm sorry, Lydia. I'll get you another pair. Honestly, love, I will.'

'You'd better, you bugger!' she replied. 'And don't "love" me —I've never been so insulted in my life. What did you think you were playing at?'

'It was all a misunderstanding. Let me explain . . .' Tristan advanced on her with a brave attempt at a winning smile, but she backed away.

'Keep your distance,' she said frigidly. 'I've had enough of you for one night.'

She swept out and Tristan leaned his head against the mantelpiece. 'The end of a lovely friendship, Jim.' Then he shook himself. 'But we've got to find that dog. Come on.'

I set off in one direction and he went in the other. It was a moonless night of impenetrable darkness and we were looking for a jet black dog. I think we both knew it was hopeless but we had to try.

In a little town like Darrowby you are soon out on the country roads where there are no lights and as I stumbled around peering vainly over invisible fields the utter pointlessness of the activity became more and more obvious.

Occasionally I came within Tristan's orbit and heard his despairing cries echoing over the empty landscape. 'Haamiish! Haamiish! Haamiish . . . !'

After half an hour we met at Skeldale House. Tristan faced me and as I shook my head he seemed to shrink within himself. His chest heaved as he fought for breath. Obviously he had been running while I had been walking and I suppose that was natural enough. We were both in an awkward situation but the final devastating blow would inevitably fall on him.

'Well, we'd better get out on the road again,' he gasped, and as he spoke the front door bell rang again.

The colour drained rapidly from his face and he clutched my arm. 'That must be Miss Westerman this time. God almighty, she's coming in!'

Rapid footsteps sounded in the passage and the sitting room door opened. But it wasn't Miss Westerman, it was Lydia again. She strode over to the sofa, reached underneath and extracted her handbag. She didn't say anything but merely shrivelled Tristan with a sidelong glance before leaving.

'What a night!' he moaned, putting a hand to his forehead. 'I can't stand much more of this.'

Over the next hour we made innumerable sorties but we couldn't find Hamish and nobody else seemed to have seen him. I came in to find Tristan collapsed in an armchair. His mouth hung open and he showed every sign of advanced exhaustion. I shook my head and he shook his then I heard the telephone.

I lifted the receiver, listened for a minute and turned to the young man. 'I've got to go out, Triss. Mr Drew's old pony has colic again.'

He reached out a hand from the depths of his chair. 'You're not going to leave me, Jim?'

'Sorry, I must. But I won't be long. It's only a mile away.'

'But what if Miss Westerman comes?'

I shrugged. 'You'll just have to apologise. Hamish is bound to turn up—maybe in the morning.'

'You make it sound easy . . .' He ran a hand inside his collar. 'And another thing—how about Siegfried? What if he arrives and asks about the dog? What do I tell him?'

'Oh, I shouldn't worry about that.' I replied airily. 'Just say you were too busy on the sofa wth the Drovers' barmaid to bother about such things. He'll understand.'

But my attempt at jocularity fell flat. The young man fixed me with a cold eye and ignited a quivering Woodbine. 'I believe I've told you this before, Jim, but there's a nasty cruel streak in you.'

Mr Drew's pony had almost recovered when I got there but I

gave it a mild sedative injection before turning for home. On the way back a thought struck me and I took a road round the edge of the town to the row of modern bungalows where Miss Westerman lived. I parked the car and walked up the path of number ten.

And there was Hamish in the porch, coiled up comfortably on the mat, looking up at me with mild surprise as I hovered over him.

'Come on, lad,' I said. 'You've got more sense than we had. Why didn't we think of this before?'

I deposited him on the passenger seat and as I drove away he hoisted his paws on to the dash and gazed out interestedly at the road unfolding in the headlights. Truly a phlegmatic little hound.

Outside Skeldale House I tucked him under my arm and was about to turn the handle of the front door when I paused. Tristan had notched up a long succession of successful pranks against me—fake telephone calls, the ghost in my bedroom and many others—and in fact, good friends as we were, he never neglected a chance to take the mickey out of me. In this situation, with the positions reversed, he would be merciless. Instead of walking straight in as I always did, I put my finger on the bell and leaned on it for several long seconds.

For some time there was neither sound nor movement from within and I pictured the cowering figure mustering his courage before marching to his doom. Then the light came on in the passage and as I peered expectantly through the glass a nose appeared round the far corner followed very gingerly by a wary eye. By degrees the full face inched into view and when Tristan recognised my grinning countenance he unleashed a cry of rage and bounded along the passage with upraised fist.

I really think that in his distraught state he would have attacked me, but the sight of Hamish banished all else. He grabbed the hairy creature and began to fondle him.

'Good little dog, nice little dog,' he crooned as he trotted through to the sitting room. 'What a beautiful thing you are.' He laid him lovingly in the basket, and Hamish, after a 'heigh-ho, here we are again' glance around him, put his head along his side and promptly went to sleep.

Tristan fell limply into the armchair and gazed at me with glazed eyes.

'Well, we're saved, Jim,' he whispered. 'But I'll never be the same after tonight. I've run bloody miles and I've nearly lost my voice with shouting. I tell you I'm about knackered.'

I too was vastly relieved, and the nearness of catastrophe was brought home to us when Miss Westerman arrived within ten minutes.

'Oh, my darling!' she cried as Hamish leaped at her, mouth open, short tail wagging furiously. 'I've been so worried about you all day.'

She looked tentatively at the ear with its rows of buttons. 'Oh, it does look a lot better without that horrid swelling—and what a nice neat job you have made. Thank you, Mr Herriot, and thank you, too, young man.'

Tristan, who had staggered to his feet, bowed slightly as I showed the lady out.

'Bring him back in six weeks to have the stitches out,' I called to her as she left, then I rushed back into the room.

'Siegfried's just pulled up outside! You'd better look as if you've been working.'

He rushed to the book shelves, pulled down Gaiger and Davis's *Bacteriology* and a notebook and dived into a chair When his brother came in he was utterly engrossed.

Siegfried moved over to the fire and warmed his hands. He looked pink and mellow.

'I've just been speaking to Miss Westerman,' he said. 'She's really pleased. Well done, both of you.'

'Thank you,' I said, but Tristan was too busy to reply, scanning the pages anxiously and scribbling repeatedly in the notebook.

Siegfried walked behind the young man's chair and looked down at the open volume.

'Ah yes, Clostridium septique," he murmured, smiling indulgently. 'That's a good one to study. Keeps coming up in exams.' He rested a hand briefly on his brother's shoulder. 'I'm glad to see you at work. You've been raking about too much lately and it's getting you down. A night at your books will have been good for you.'

'Am I not right, James?' he said to me across the room. 'Tell him. Few more nights like this will put him right.'

'Right.'
'Put him just where he ought to be.'
'Right.'
'Quite.' And Siegfried went off to bed.

CHAPTER

42

When I was discharged from hospital I expected to be posted straight overseas and I wondered if I would be able to catch up with my old flight and my friends.

However, I learned with surprise that I had to go to a convalescent home for a fortnight before any further action could be taken. This was in Puddlestone, near Leominster—a lovely mansion house in acres of beautiful gardens. It was presided over by a delightful old matron with whom we fortunate airmen played sedate games of croquet or walked in the cool woods; it was easy to imagine there was no such thing as a war. Two weeks of this treatment left me feeling revitalised. It wouldn't be long, I felt, before I was back on the job.

From Puddlestone it was back to Manchester and Heaton Park again and this time it was strange to think that in all the great sprawl of huts and the crowding thousands of men in blue there wasn't a soul who knew me.

Except, of course, the Wing Commander who had sent me to hospital in the first place. I had an interview with him on my arrival and he came straight to the point.

'Herriot,' he said. 'I'm afraid you can't fly any more.'

'But . . . I've had the operation . . . I'm a lot better.'

'I know that, but you can no longer be classed as 100% fit. You have been officially downgraded and I'm sure you realise that pilots have to be grade one.'

'Yes . . . of course.'

He glanced at the file in his hand. 'I see you are a veterinary surgeon. Mmm—this poses a problem. Normally when an aircrew man is grounded he remusters on the ground staff, but yours is a reserved occupation. You really can't serve in any capacity but aircrew. Yes . . . yes . . . we'll have to see.'

It was all very impersonal and businesslike. Those few words coming from a man like him left no room for argument and they obliterated at a stroke every picture I had ever had of my future in the R.A.F.

I was fairly certain that if my flying days were over I would be discharged from the service and as I left the Wing Commander's office and walked slowly back to my hut at the other end of the park I pondered on my contribution to the war effort.

I hadn't fired a shot in anger. I had peeled mountains of potatoes, washed countless dishes, shovelled coke, mucked out pigs, marched for miles, drilled interminably, finally and magically learned to fly and now it was all for nothing. I passed the big dining hall and the R.A.F. march blared out at me from the loudspeakers.

The familiar sound reminded me of so many experiences, so many friends, and suddenly I felt intensely lonely and cut off. It was a new sensation for me, and there, in those unlikely surroundings, I began to think of old Mr Potts from my veterinary days. He must have felt like that.

'How are you, Mr Herriot?'

Ordinary words, but the eagerness, almost desperation in the old man's voice made them urgent and meaningful.

I saw him nearly every day. In my unpredictable life it was difficult to do anything regularly but I did like a stroll by the river before lunch and so did my beagle, Sam. That was when we met Mr Potts and Nip, his elderly sheepdog—they seemed to have the same habits as we did. His house backed on to the riverside fields and he spent a lot of time just walking around with his dog.

Many retired farmers kept a bit of land and a few stock to occupy their minds and ease the transition from their arduous existence to day-long leisure, but Mr Potts had bought a little bungalow with a scrap of garden and it was obvious that time dragged.

Probably his health had dictated this. As he faced me he leaned on his stick and his bluish cheeks rose and fell with his breathing. He was a heart case if ever I saw one.

'I'm fine, Mr Potts,' I replied. 'And how are things with you?'

'Nobbut middlin', lad. Ah soon get short o' wind.' He coughed a couple of times then asked the inevitable question.

'And what have you been doin' this mornin'?' That was when his eyes grew intent and wide. He really wanted to know.

I thought for a moment. 'Well now, let's see.' I always tried to give him a detailed answer because I knew it meant a lot to him and brought back the life he missed so much. 'I've done a couple of cleansings, seen a lame bullock, treated two cows with mastitis and another with milk fever.'

He nodded eagerly at every word.

'By gaw!' he exclaimed. 'It's a beggar, that milk fever. When I were a lad, good cows used to die like flies with it. Allus good milkers after their third or fourth calf. Couldn't get to their feet and we used to dose 'em with all sorts, but they died, every one of 'em.'

'Yes,' I said. 'It must have been heartbreaking in those days.'

'But then.' He smiled delightedly, digging a forefinger into my chest. 'Then we started blowin' up their udders wi' a bicycle pump, and d'you know—they jumped up and walked away. Like magic it were.' His eyes sparkled at the memory.

'I know, Mr Potts, I've blown up a few myself, only I didn't use a bicycle pump—I had a special little inflation apparatus.'

That black box with its shining cylinders and filter is now in my personal museum, and it is the best place for it. It had got me out of some difficult situations but in the background there had always been the gnawing dread of transmitting tuberculosis. I had heard of it happening and was glad that calcium borogluconate had arrived.

As we spoke, Sam and Nip played on the grass beside us. I watched as the beagle frisked round the old animal while Nip pawed at him stiff-jointedly, his tail waving with pleasure. You could see that he enjoyed these meetings as much as his master and for a brief time the years fell away from him as he rolled on his back with Sam astride him, nibbling gently at his chest.

I walked with the old farmer as far as the little wooden bridge, then I had to turn for home. I watched the two of them pottering slowly over the narrow strip of timber to the other side of the river. Sam and I had our work pressing, but they had nothing else to do.

I used to see Mr Potts at other times, too. Wandering aimlessly among the stalls on market days or standing on the fringe of the group of farmers who always gathered in front of the Drovers Arms to meet cattle dealers, cow feed merchants, or just to talk business among themselves.

Or I saw him at the auction mart, leaning on his stick, listening to the rapid-fire chanting of the auctioneer, watching list-lessly as the beasts were bought and sold. And all the time I knew there was an emptiness in him, because there were none of his cattle in the stalls, none of his sheep in the long rows of pens. He was out of it all, old and done.

I saw him the day before he died. It was in the usual place and I was standing at the river's edge watching a heron rising from a rush-lined island and flapping lazily away over the fields.

The old man stopped as he came abreast of me and the two dogs began their friendly wrestling.

'Well now, Mr Herriot.' He paused and bowed his head over the stick which he had dug into the grass of his farm for half a century. 'What have you been doin' today?'

Perhaps his cheeks were a deeper shade of blue and the breath whistled through his pursed lips as he exhaled, but I can't recall that he looked any worse than usual.

'I'll tell you, Mr Potts,' I said. 'I'm feeling a bit weary. I ran into a real snorter of a foaling this morning—took me over two hours and I ache all over.'

'Foaling, eh? Foal would be laid wrong, I reckon?'

'Yes, cross-ways on, and I had a struggle to turn it.'

'By gaw, yes, it's hard work is that.' He smiled reminiscently. 'Doesta remember that Clydesdale mare you foaled at ma place? Must 'ave been one of your first jobs when you came to Dar-rowby.'

'Of course I do,' I replied. And I remembered too, how kind the old man had been. Seeing I was young and green and unsure of myself he had taken pains, in his quiet way, to put me at my ease and give me confidence. 'Yes,' I went on. 'It was late on a Sunday night and we had a right tussle with it. There was just the two of us but we managed, didn't we?'

He squared his shoulders and for a moment his eyes looked past me at something I couldn't see. 'Aye, that's right. We made a job of 'er, you and me. Ah could push and pull a bit then.'

'You certainly could. There's no doubt about that.'

He sucked the air in with difficulty and blew it out again with that peculiar pursing of the lips. Then he turned to me with a strange dignity.

'They were good days, Mr Herriot, weren't they?'

'They were, Mr Potts, they were indeed.'

'Aye, aye.' He nodded slowly. 'Ah've had a lot o' them days.

Hard but good.' He looked down at his dog. 'And awd Nip shared 'em with me, didn't ye, lad?'

His words took me back to the very first time I had seen Mr Potts. He was perched on a stool, milking one of his few cows, his cloth-capped head thrusting into the hairy flank, and as he pulled at the teats old Nip dropped a stone on the toe of his boot. The farmer reached down, lifted the stone between two fingers and flicked it out through the open door into the yard. Nip scurried delightedly after it and was back within seconds, dropping the stone on the boot and panting hopefully.

He wasn't disappointed. His master repeated the throw automatically as if it was something he did all the time, and as I watched it happening again and again I realised that this was a daily ritual between the two. I had a piercing impression of infinite patience and devotion.

'Right, then, Mr Herriot, we'll be off,' Mr Potts said, jerking me back to the present. 'Come on, Nip.' He waved his stick and I watched him till a low-hanging willow branch hid man and dog from my sight.

That was the last time I saw him. Next day the man at the petrol pumps mumbled casually, 'See old Mr Potts got his time in, eh?'

And that was it. There was no excitement, and only a handful of his old friends turned up at the funeral.

For me it was a stab of sorrow. Another familiar face gone, and I should miss him as my busy life went on. I knew our daily conversations had cheered him but I felt with a sad finality that there was nothing else I could do for Mr Potts.

It was about a fortnight later and as I opened the gate to let Sam into the riverside fields I glanced at my watch. Twelve thirty—plenty of time for our pre-lunch walk and the long stretch of green was empty. Then I noticed a single dog away on the left. It was Nip, and as I watched he got up, took a few indeterminate steps over the grass then turned and sat down again at the gate of his back garden.

Instead of taking my usual route I cut along behind the houses till I reached the old dog. He had been looking around him aimlessly but when we came up to him he seemed to come to life, sniffing Sam over and wagging his tail at me.

On the other side of the gate Mrs Potts was doing a bit of weeding, bending painfully as she plied her trowel.

'How are you, Mrs Potts ?' I said.

With an effort she straightened up. 'Oh, not too bad, thank you, Mr Herriot.' She came over and leaned on the gate. 'I see you're lookin' at the awd dog. My word he's missin' his master.'

I didn't say anything and she went on. 'He's eating all right and I can give him plenty of good food, but what I can't do is take 'im for walks.' She rubbed her back. 'I'm plagued with rheumatics, Mr Herriot, and it takes me all my time to get around the house and garden.'

'I can understand that,' I said. 'And I don't suppose he'll walk by himself.'

'Nay, he won't. There's the path he went along every day.' She pointed to the winding strip of beaten earth among the grass. 'But he won't go more'n a few yards.'

'Ah well, dogs like a bit of company just the same as we do.' I bent and ran my hand over the old animal's head and ears. 'How would you like to come with us, Nip?'

I set off along the path and he followed unhesitatingly, trotting alongside Sam with swinging tail.

'Eee, look!' the old lady cried. 'Isn't that grand to see!'

I followed his usual route down to the river where the water ran dark and silent under the branches of the gnarled willows. Then we went over the bridge and in front of us the river widened into pebbly shallows and murmured and chattered among the stones.

It was peaceful down there with only the endless water sound and the piping of birds in my ears and the long curtain of leaves parting here and there to give glimpses of the green flanks of the fells.

I watched the two dogs frisking ahead of me and the decision came to me quite naturally; I would do this regularly. From that day I altered my route and went along behind the houses first. Nip was happy again, Sam loved the whole idea, and for me there was a strange comfort in the knowledge that there was still something I could do for Mr Potts.

CHAPTER

43

I looked around me at the heap of boots, the piled mounds of shirts, the rows of empty shelves and pigeon holes. I was employed in the stores at Heaton Park, living proof that the R.A.F. was finding me something of a problem.

The big war machine was rumbling along pretty smoothly by this time, turning out pilots, navigators, air-gunners in a steady stream and slotting them into different jobs if they failed to make the grade. It ticked over like a well-oiled engine as long as nothing disturbed the rhythm.

I was like a speck of sand in the works, and I could tell from various interviews that I had caused the administrators a certain amount of puzzlement. I don't suppose Mr Churchill was losing any sleep over me but since I wasn't allowed to fly and was ineligible for the ground staff I was obviously a bit of a nuisance. Nobody seemed to have come across a grounded vet before.

Of course it was inevitable that I would be sent back to my practice, but I could see that it was going to take some time for the R.A.F. to regurgitate me into civil life. Apparently I had to go through the motions even though some of them were meaningless.

One of the interviews was with three officers. They were very nice and they sat behind a table, beaming, friendly, reassuring. Their task, apparently, was to find out what ground staff job might suit me. I think they were probably psychologists and they asked me all kinds of questions, nodding and smiling kindly all the time.

'Well now, Herriot,' the middle officer said. 'We are going to put you through a series of aptitude tests. It will last two days, starting tomorrow, and by the end of it I think we'll know all about you.' He laughed. 'It's nothing to worry about. You might rather enjoy it.'

I did enjoy it, in fact. I filled up great long sheets with my answers, I drew diagrams, fitted odd-shaped pieces of wood into holes. It was fun.

I had to wait another two days before I was called before the tribunal again. The three were if anything more charming than before and I seemed to sense an air of subdued excitement about them this time. They were all smiling broadly as the middle one spoke.

'Herriot, we have really found out something about you,' he said.

'You have?'

'Yes, indeed. We have found that you have an outstanding mechanical aptitude.'

I stared at him. This was a facer, because if ever there was a mechanical idiot that man is J. Herriot. I have a loathing for engines, wheels, pistons, cylinders, cogs. I can't mend anything and if a garage mechanic tries to explain something to me I just can't take it in.

I told the officers this and the three smiles became rather fixed.

'But surely,' said the one on the left, 'you drive a car in the course of your professional work?'

'Yes, sir, I do. I've driven one for years, but I still don't know how it works and if I break down I have to scream for help.'

'I see, I see.' The smiles were very thin now and the three heads came together for a whispered consultation.

Finally the middle one leaned across the table.

'Tell you what, Herriot. How would you like to be a meteorologist?'

'Fine,' I replied.

I sympathised with them, because they were obviously kind men, but I've never had any faith in aptitude tests since then.

Of course there was never the slightest chance of my becoming a meteorologist and I suppose that's how I landed in the stores. It was one of the bizarre periods of my life, mercifully brief but vivid. They had told me to report to corporal Weekes at the stores hut and I made my way through the maze of roads of a Heaton Park populated by strangers.

Corporal Weekes was fat and he gave me a quick look over with crafty eyes.

'Herriot, eh? Well you can make yourself useful around 'ere. Not much to do, really. This ain't a main stores—we deal mainly wiv laundry and boot repairs.'

As he spoke a fair-haired young man came in.

'AC2 Morgan, corporal,' he said. 'Come for my boots. They've been re-soled.'

Weekes jerked his head and I had my first sight of the boot mountain. 'They're in there. They'll be labelled.'

The young man looked surprised but he came round behind the counter and began to delve among the hundreds of identical black objects. It took him nearly an hour to find his own pair during which the corporal puffed at cigarettes with a total lack of interest. When the boots were finally unearthed he wordlessly ticked off the name on a long list.

'This is the sort of thing you'll be doin',' he said to me. 'Nothin' to it.'

He wasn't exaggerating. There was nothing to life in those stores. It took me only a day or two to realise the sweet existence Weekes had carved out for himself. Store-bashing is an honourable trade but not the way he did it. The innumerable compartments, niches and alcoves around the big hut were all marked with letters or numbers and there is no doubt the incoming boots and shirts should have been tucked away in order for easy recovery. But that would have involved work and the corporal was clearly averse to that.

When the boots came in they were tipped out in the middle of the floor and the string-tied packages of laundry were stacked, shirts-uppermost where they formed a blue tumulus reaching almost to the roof.

After three days I could stand it no longer.

'Look,' I said. 'It would pass the time if I had something to do. Do you mind if I start putting all this stuff on the shelves? It would be a lot easier to hand out.'

Weekes continued to study his magazine—he was a big reader —and at first I thought he hadn't heard me. Then he tongued his cigarette to the corner of his mouth and glanced at me through the smoke.

'Now just get this through your 'ead, mate,' he drawled. 'If I want any —— thing doin' I'll —— well tell you. I'm the boss in 'ere and I give the —— orders, awright?' He resumed his perusal of the magazine.

I subsided in my chair. Clearly I had offended my overseer and I would have to leave things as they were.

But overseer is a misnomer for Weekes because on the following day, after a final brain-washing that the procedure must remain unchanged he disappeared and except for a few minutes each morning he left me on my own. I had nothing to do but sit there behind the wooden counter, ticking off the comings and goings of the boots and shirts and I had the feeling that I was only one of many displaced persons who had fallen under his thrall.

I found it acutely embarrassing to watch the lads scrabbling for their belongings and the strongest impression left with me was of the infinite tolerance of the British race. Since I was in charge they thought I was responsible for the whole system but despite the fact that I was of lowly rank nobody attacked me physically. Most of them muttered and grumbled as they searched and one large chap came over to the counter and said, 'You should be filing away these boots in their proper order instead of sitting there on your arse, you lazy sod!' But he didn't punch me on the nose and I marvelled at it.

But still, the knowledge that great numbers of decent young men shared his opinion was uncomfortable and I found I was developing a permanently ingratiating smile.

The only time I came very near to being lynched was when a mob suddenly appeared one afternoon. An unexpected leave pass had been granted and there were hundreds of men milling around on the tarmac and grass outside the stores. They wanted their laundry—and quick, because they had trains to catch.

For a moment panic seized me. I couldn't let them all inside to fight for their shirts. Then inspiration came. I grabbed an armful of the flat packets from the table and shouted the name on the label.

'Walters!' And from somewhere among the surging heads an eager voice replied, 'Here!'

I located the source, held the packet between thumb and finger and with a back-handed flick sent it skimming over the crowd.

'Reilly!'
'Here!'
'McDonald!'
'Here!'

'Gibson!'

'Here!'

I was getting quite skilful at it, propelling the blue oblongs unerringly towards their owners, but it was a slow method of distribution. Also, there were occasional disasters when the strings broke in mid-air, sending a shower of collars on the upturned faces. Sometimes the shirts themselves burst free from their wrappings and plunged to earth.

It wasn't long before the voices had turned from eager to angry. As my projectiles planed and glided, volleys of abuse came back at me.

'You've made me miss my train, you useless bugger!'

'Bloody skiver, you want locking up!'

Much of it was in stronger language which I would rather not record here, but I have a particularly vivid memory of one young man scraping up his laundry from the dusty ground and approaching me with rapid strides. He pushed his face to within inches of mine. Despite the rage which disfigured it I could see it was a gentle, good-natured face. He looked a well-bred lad, the type who didn't even swear, but as he stared into my eyes his lips trembled and his cheeks twitched.

'This is a . . .' he stammered. 'This is a . . . a BASTARD system!'

He spat the words out and strode away.

I agreed entirely with him, of course, but continued to hurl the packets doggedly while somewhere in the back of my mind a little voice kept enquiring how James Herriot, Member of the Royal College of Veterinary Surgeons and traniee pilot, had ever got into this.

After half an hour there was no appreciable diminution in the size of the multitude and I began to be aware of an increasing restlessness among the medley of waiting faces.

Suddenly there was a concerted movement and the packed mass of men surged at me in a great wave. I shrank back, clutching an armful of shirts, quite certain that this was when they rushed me and beat me up, but my fears were groundless. All they wanted was a speedier delivery and about a dozen of them swept past me behind the counter and began to follow my example.

Whereas there had been only a single missile winging over the heads the sky was now dark with the flying objects. Mid-air collisions were frequent. Collars sprayed, handkerchiefs fluttered, underpants parachuted gracefully, but after an unbearably long period of chaos the last airman had picked up his scattered laundry, given me a disgusted glance and departed.

I was left alone in the hut with the sad knowledge that my prestige was very low and the equally sad conviction that the R.A.F. still did not know what to do with me.

Occasionally my period in limbo was relieved when I was
allowed out of camp into the city of Manchester. And I suppose
it was the fact that I was a new-fangled parent that made me
look at the various prams in the streets. Mostly the prams were
pushed by women but now and then I saw a man doing the job.

I suppose it isn't unusual to see a man pushing a pram in a
town, but on a lonely moorland road the sight merits a second
glance. Especially when the pram contains a large dog.

That was what I saw in the hills above Darrowby one morning
and I slowed down as I drove past. I had noticed the strange
combination before—on several occasions over the last few
weeks—and it was clear that man and dog had recently moved
into the district.

As the car drew abreast of him the man turned, smiled and
raised his hand. It was a smile of rare sweetness in a very brown
face. A forty year old face, I thought, above a brown neck
which bore neither collar and tie, and a faded striped shirt lying
open over a bare chest despite the coldness of the day.

I couldn't help wondering who or what he was. The outfit of
scuffed suede golf jacket, corduroy trousers and sturdy boots
didn't give much clue. Some people might have put him down
as an ordinary tramp, but there was a businesslike energetic look
about him which didn't fit the term.

I wound the window down and the thin wind of a Yorkshire
March bit at my cheeks.

'Nippy this morning,' I said.

The man seemed surprised. 'Aye,' he replied after a moment.
'Aye, reckon it is.'

I looked at the pram, ancient and rusty, and at the big animal
sitting upright inside it. He was a lurcher, a cross-bred greyhound, and he gazed back at me with unruffled dignity.

'Nice dog,' I said.

'Aye, that's Jake.' The man smiled again, showing good regular teeth. 'He's a grand 'un.'

I waved and drove on. In the mirror I could see the compact figure stepping out briskly, head up, shoulders squared, and, rising like a statue from the middle of the pram, the huge brindled form of Jake.

I didn't have to wait long to meet the unlikely pair again. I was examining a carthorse's teeth in a farmyard when on the hillside beyond the stable I saw a figure kneeling by a dry stone wall. And by his side, a pram and a big dog sitting patiently on the grass.

'Hey, just a minute.' I pointed at the hill. 'Who is that?'

The farmer laughed. 'That's Roddy Travers. D'you ken 'im?'

'No, no I don't. I had a word with him on the road the other day, that's all.'

'Aye, on the road.' He nodded knowingly. 'That's where you'd see Roddy, right enough.'

'But what is he? Where does he come from?'

'He comes from somewhere in Yorkshire, but ah don't rightly know where and ah don't think anybody else does. But I'll tell you this—he can turn 'is hand to anything.'

'Yes,' I said, watching the man expertly laying the flat slabs of stone as he repaired a gap in the wall. 'There's not many can do what he's doing now.'

'That's true. Wallin' is a skilled job and it's dying out, but Roddy's a dab hand at it. But he can do owt—hedgin', ditchin', lookin' after stock, it's all the same to him.'

I lifted the tooth rasp and began to rub a few sharp corners off the horse's molars. 'And how long will he stay here?'

'Oh, when he's finished that wall he'll be off. Ah could do with 'im stoppin' around for a bit but he never stays in one place for long.'

'But hasn't he got a home anywhere?'

'Nay, nay.' The farmer laughed again. 'Roddy's got nowt. All 'e has in the world is in that there pram.'

Over the next weeks as the harsh spring began to soften and the sunshine brought a bright speckle of primroses on to the grassy banks I saw Roddy quite often, sometimes on the road, occasionally wielding a spade busily on the ditches around the fields. Jake was always there, either loping by his side or watching him at work. But we didn't actually meet again till I was inoculating Mr Pawson's sheep for pulpy kidney.

There were three hundred to do and they drove them in batches into a small pen where Roddy caught and held them for me. And I could see he was an expert at this, too. The wild hill sheep whipped past him like bullets but he seized their fleece effortlessly, sometimes in mid-air, and held the fore leg up to expose that bare clean area of skin behind the elbow that nature seemed to provide for the veterinary surgeon's needle.

Outside, on the windy slopes the big lurcher sat upright in typical pose, looking with mild interest at the farm dogs prowling intently around the pens, but not interfering in any way.

'You've got him well trained,' I said.

Roddy smiled. 'Yes, ye'll never find Jake dashin' about, annoyin' people. He knows 'e has to sit there till I'm finished and there he'll sit.'

'And quite happy to do so, by the look of him.' I glanced again at the dog, a picture of contentment. 'He must live a wonderful life, travelling everywhere with you.'

'You're right there,' Mr Pawson broke in as he ushered another bunch of sheep into the pen. 'He hasn't a care in t'world, just like his master.'

Roddy didn't say anything, but as the sheep ran in he straightened up and took a long steady breath. He had been working hard and a little trickle of sweat ran down the side of his forehead but as he gazed over the wide sweep of moor and fell I could read utter serenity in his face. After a few moments he spoke.

'I reckon that's true. We haven't much to worry us, Jake and me.'

Mr Pawson grinned mischievously. 'By gaw, Roddy, you never spoke a truer word. No wife, no kids, no life insurance, no overdraft at t'bank—you must have a right peaceful existence.'

'Ah suppose so,' Roddy said. 'But then ah've no money either.'

The farmer gave him a quizzical look. 'Aye, how about that, then? Wouldn't you feel a bit more secure, like, if you had a bit o' brass put by?'

'Nay, nay. Ye can't take it with you and any road, as long as a man can pay 'is way, he's got enough.'

There was nothing original about the words, but they have

stayed with me all my life because they came from his lips and were spoken with such profound assurance.

When I had finished the inoculations and the ewes were turned out to trot back happily over the open fields I turned to Roddy. 'Well, thanks very much. It makes my job a lot quicker when I have a good catcher like you.' I pulled out a packet of Gold Flake. 'Will you have a cigarette?'

'No, thank ye, Mr Herriot. I don't smoke.'

'You don't?'

'No—don't drink either.' He gave me his gentle smile and again I had the impression of physical and mental purity. No drinking, no smoking, a life of constant movement in the open air without material possessions or ambitions—it all showed in the unclouded eyes, the fresh skin and the hard muscular frame. He wasn't very big but he looked indestructible.

'C'mon, Jake, it's dinner time,' he said and the big lurcher bounded around him in delight. I went over and spoke to the dog and he responded with tremendous body-swaying wags, his handsome face looking up at me, full of friendliness.

I stroked the long pointed head and tickled the ears. 'He's a beauty, Roddy—a grand 'un, as you said.'

I walked to the house to wash my hands and before I went inside I glanced back at the two of them. They were sitting in the shelter of a wall and Roddy was laying out a thermos flask and a parcel of food while Jake watched eagerly. The hard bright sunshine beat on them as the wind whistled over the top of the wall. They looked supremely comfortable and at peace.

'He's independent, you see,' the farmer's wife said as I stood at the kitchen sink. 'He's welcome to come in for a bit o' dinner but he'd rather stay outside with his dog.'

I nodded. 'Where does he sleep when he's going round the farms like this.'

'Oh, anywhere,' she replied. 'In hay barns or granaries or sometimes out in the open, but when he's with us he sleeps upstairs in one of our rooms. Ah know for a fact any of the farmers would be willin' to have him in the house because he allus keeps himself spotless clean.'

'I see.' I pulled the towel from behind the door. 'He's quite a character, isn't he?'

She smiled ruminatively. 'Aye, he certainly is. Just him and his dog!' She lifted a fragrant dishful of hot roast ham from the oven and set it on the table. 'But I'll tell you this. The feller's all right. Everybody likes Roddy Travers—he's a very nice man.'

Roddy stayed around the Darrowby district throughout the summer and I grew used to the sight of him on the farms or pushing his pram along the roads. When it was raining he wore a tattered over-long gaberdine coat, but at other times it was always the golf jacket and corduroys. I don't know where he had accumulated his wardrobe. It was a safe bet he had never been on a golf course in his life and it was just another of the little mysteries about him.

I saw him early one morning on a hill path in early October. It had been a night of iron frost and the tussocky pastures beyond the walls were held in a pitiless white grip with every blade of grass stiffly ensheathed in rime.

I was muffled to the eyes and had been beating my gloved fingers against my knees to thaw them out, but when I pulled up and wound down the window the first thing I saw was the bare chest under the collarless unbuttoned shirt.

'Mornin', Mr Herriot,' he said. 'Ah'm glad I've seen ye.' He paused and gave me his tranquil smile. 'There's a job along t'road for a couple of weeks, then I'm movin' on.'

'I see.' I knew enough about him now not to ask where he was going. Instead I looked down at Jake who was sniffing the herbage. 'I see he's walking this morning.'

Roddy laughed. 'Yes, sometimes 'e likes to walk, sometimes 'e likes to ride. He pleases 'imself.'

'Right, Roddy,' I said. 'No doubt we'll meet again. All the best to you.'

He waved and set off jauntily over the icebound road and I felt that a little vein of richness had gone from my life.

But I was wrong. That same evening about eight o'clock the front door bell rang. I answered it and found Roddy on the front door steps. Behind him, just visible in the frosty darkness, stood the ubiquitous pram.

'I want you to look at me dog, Mr Herriot,' he said.

'Why, what's the trouble?'

'Ah don't rightly know. He's havin' sort of . . . faintin' fits.'

'Fainting fits? That doesn't sound like Jake. Where is he, anyway?'

He pointed behind him. 'In t'pram, under t'cover.'

'All right.' I threw the door wide. 'Bring him in.'

Roddy adroitly manhandled the rusty old vehicle up the steps and pushed it, squeaking and rattling, along the passage to the consulting room. There, under the bright lights he snapped back the fasteners and threw off the cover to reveal Jake stretched beneath.

His head was pillowed on the familiar gaberdine coat and around him lay his master's worldly goods; a string-tied bundle of spare shirt and socks, a packet of tea, a thermos, knife and spoon and an ex-army haversack.

The big dog looked up at me with terrified eyes and as I patted him I could feel his whole frame quivering.

'Let him lie there a minute, Roddy,' I said. 'And tell me exactly what you've seen.'

He rubbed his palms together and his fingers trembled. 'Well it only started this afternoon. He was right as rain, larkin' about on the grass, then he went into a sort o' fit.'

'How do you mean?'

'Just kind of seized up and toppled over on 'is side. He lay there for a bit, gaspin' and slaverin'. Ah'll tell ye, I thought he was a goner.' His eyes widened and a corner of his mouth twitched at the memory.

'How long did that last?'

'Nobbut a few seconds. Then he got up and you'd say there was nowt wrong with 'im.'

'But he did it again?'

'Aye, time and time again. Drove me near daft. But in between 'e was normal. Normal, Mr. Herriot!'

It sounded ominously like the onset of epilepsy. 'How old is he?' I asked.

'Five gone last February.'

Ah well, it was a bit old for that. I reached for a stethoscope and auscultated the heart. I listened intently but heard only the racing beat of a frightened animal. There was no abnormality. My thermometer showed no rise in temperature.

'Let's have him on the table, Roddy. You take the back end.'

The big animal was limp in our arms as we hoisted him on to the smooth surface, but after lying there for a moment he looked timidly around him then sat up with a slow and careful movement. As we watched he reached out and licked his master's face while his tail flickered between his legs.

'Look at that!' the man exclaimed. 'He's all right again. You'd think he didn't ail a thing.'

And indeed Jake was recovering his confidence rapidly. He peered tentatively at the floor a few times then suddenly jumped down, trotted to his master and put his paws against his chest.

I looked at the dog standing there, tail wagging furiously. 'Well, that's a relief, anyway. I didn't like the look of him just then, but whatever's been troubling him seems to have righted itself. I'll . . .'

My happy flow was cut off. I stared at the lurcher. His fore legs were on the floor again and his mouth was gaping as he fought for breath. Frantically he gasped and retched then he blundered across the floor, collided with the pram wheels and fell on his side.

'What the hell . . . ! Quick, get him up again!' I grabbed the animal round the middle and we lifted him back on to the table.

I watched in disbelief as the huge form lay there. There was no fight for breath now—he wasn't breathing at all, he was un-conscious. I pushed my fingers inside his thigh and felt the pulse. It was still going, rapid and feeble, but yet he didn't breathe.

He could die any moment and I stood there helpless, all my scientific training useless. Finally my frustration burst from me and I struck the dog on the ribs with the flat of my hand.

'Jake!' I yelled. 'Jake, what's the matter with you?'

As though in reply, the lurcher immediately started to take great wheezing breaths, his eyelids twitched back to conscious-ness and he began to look about him. But he was still mortally afraid and he lay prone as I gently stroked his head.

There was a long silence while the animal's terror slowly sub-sided, then he sat up on the table and regarded us placidly.

'There you are,' Roddy said softly. 'Same thing again. Ah can't reckon it up and ah thought ah knew summat about dogs.'

I didn't say anything. I couldn't reckon it up either, and I was supposed to be a veterinary surgeon.

I spoke at last. 'Roddy, that wasn't a fit. He was choking. Something was interfering with his air flow.' I took my hand torch from my breast pocket. 'I'm going to have a look at his throat.'

I pushed Jake's jaws apart, depressed his tongue with a forefinger and shone the light into the depths. He was the kind of good-natured dog who offered no resistance as I prodded around, but despite my floodlit view of the pharynx I could find nothing wrong. I had been hoping desperately to come across a bit of bone stuck there somewhere but I ranged feverishly over pink tongue, healthy tonsils and gleaming molars without success. Everything looked perfect.

I was tilting his head a little further when I felt him stiffen and heard Roddy's cry.

'He's goin' again!'

And he was, too. I stared in horror as the brindled body slid away from me and lay prostrate once more on the table. And again the mouth strained wide and froth bubbled round the lips. As before, the breathing had stopped and the rib cage was motionless. As the seconds ticked away I beat on the chest with my hand but it didn't work this time. I pulled the lower eyelid down from the staring orb—the conjunctiva was blue, Jake hadn't long to live. The tragedy of the thing bore down on me. This wasn't just a dog, he was this man's family and I was watching him die.

It was at that moment that I heard the faint sound. It was a strangled cough which barely stirred the dog's lips.

'Damn it!' I shouted. 'He IS choking. There must be something down there.'

Again I seized the head and pushed my torch into the mouth and I shall always be thankful that at that very instant the dog coughed again, opening the cartilages of the larynx and giving me a glimpse of the cause of all the trouble. There, beyond the drooping epiglottis I saw for a fleeting moment a smooth round object no bigger than a pea.

'I think it's a pebble,' I gasped. 'Right inside his larynx.'

'You mean, in 'is Adam's apple?'

'That's right, and it's acting like a ball valve, blocking his windpipe every now and then.' I shook the dog's head. 'You see, look, I've dislodged it for the moment. He's coming round again.'

Once more Jake was reviving and breathing steadily.

Roddy ran his hand over the head, along the back and down the great muscles of the hind limbs. 'But . . . but . . . it'll happen again, won't it?'

I nodded. 'I'm afraid so.'

'And one of these times it isn't goin' to shift and that'll be the end of 'im?' He had gone very pale.

'That's about it, Roddy, I'll have to get that pebble out.'

'But how . . . ?'

'Cut into the larynx. And right now—it's the only way.'

'All right.' He swallowed. 'Let's get on. I don't think ah could stand it if he went down again.'

I knew what he meant. My knees had begun to shake, and I had a strong conviction that if Jake collapsed once more then so would I.

I seized a pair of scissors and clipped away the hair from the ventral surface of the larynx. I dare not use a general anaesthetic and infiltrated the area with local before swabbing with antiseptic. Mercifully there was a freshly boiled set of instruments lying in the steriliser and I lifted out the tray and set it on the trolley by the side of the table.

'Hold his head steady,' I said hoarsely, and gripped a scalpel.

I cut down through skin, fascia and the thin layers of the sterno-hyoid and omo-hyoid muscles till the ventral surface of the larynx was revealed. This was something I had never done to a live dog before, but desperation abolished any hesitancy and it took me only another few seconds to incise the thin membrane and peer into the interior.

And there it was. A pebble right enough—grey and glistening and tiny, but big enough to kill.

I had to fish it out quickly and cleanly without pushing it into the trachea. I leaned back and rummaged in the tray till I found some broad-bladed forceps then I poised them over the wound. Great surgeons' hands, I felt sure, didn't shake like this, nor did such men pant as I was doing. But I clenched my teeth, introduced the forceps and my hand magically steadied as I clamped them over the pebble.

I stopped panting, too. In fact I didn't breathe at all as I bore the shining little object slowly and tenderly through the opening and dropped it with a gentle rat-tat on the table.

'Is that it?' asked Roddy, almost in a whisper.

'That's it.' I reached for needle and suture silk. 'All is well now.'

The stitching took only a few minutes and by the end of it

Jake was bright-eyed and alert, paws shifting impatiently, ready for anything. He seemed to know his troubles were over.

Roddy brought him back in ten days to have the stitches removed. It was, in fact, the very morning he was leaving the Darrowby district, and after I had picked the few loops of silk from the nicely healed wound I walked with him to the front door while Jake capered round our feet.

On the pavement outside Skeldale House the ancient pram stood in all its high, rusted dignity. Roddy pulled back the cover.

'Up, boy,' he murmured, and the big dog leaped effortlessly into his accustomed place.

Roddy took hold of the handle with both hands and as the autumn sunshine broke suddenly through the clouds it lit up a picture which had grown familiar and part of the daily scene. The golf jacket, the open shirt and brown chest, the handsome animal sitting up, looking around him with natural grace.

'Well, so long, Roddy,' I said. 'I suppose you'll be round these parts again.'

He turned and I saw that smile again. 'Aye, reckon ah'll be back.'

He gave a push and they were off, the strange vehicle creaking, Jake swaying gently as they went down the street. The memory came back to me of what I had seen under the cover that night in the surgery. The haversack, which would contain his razor, towel, soap and a few other things. The packet of tea and the thermos. And something else—a creased old photograph of a young woman which slipped from an envelope in the scuffle. It added a little more mystery to the man . . . and explained other things, too.

That farmer was right. All Roddy possessed was in that pram. And it seemed it was all he desired, too, because as he turned the corner and disappeared from my view I could hear him whistling.

I have never been much good at small talk but as I sat in the stores day after day without seeing a friendly face I realised how much I used to enjoy chatting with the farmers during my veterinary calls.

It is one of the nicest things about country practice, but you have to keep your mind on the job at the same time or you could be in trouble. And at Mr Duggleby's I nearly landed in the biggest trouble of all. He was a smallholder who kept a few sows and reared the litters to pork weight in some ramshackle sheds behind the railway line outside Darrowby.

He was also a cricket fanatic, steeped in the lore and history of the game, and he would talk about it for hours on end. He never tired of it.

I was a willing listener because cricket has always fascinated me, even though I grew up in Scotland where it is little played. As I moved among the young pigs only part of my attention was focused on the little animals—most of me was out on the great green oval at Headingly with the Yorkshire heroes.

'By gaw, you should've seen Len Hutton on Saturday,' he breathed reverently. 'A hundred and eighty and never gave a chance. It was lovely to watch 'im.' He gave a fair imitation of the great man's cover drive.

'Yes, I can imagine it.' I nodded and smiled. 'You said these pigs were lame, Mr Duggleby?'

'Aye, noticed a few of 'em hoppin' about with a leg up this mornin'. And you know, Maurice Leyland was nearly as good. Not as classy as Len, tha knows, but by heck 'e can clump 'em.'

'Yes, he's a lion-hearted little player is Maurice,' I said. I reached down, grabbed a pig by the tail and thrust my thermometer into its rectum. 'Remember him and Eddie Paynter in the test match against Australia?'

He gave a dreamy smile. 'Remember it? By gaw, that's summat I'll never forget. What a day that was!'

I withdrew the thermometer. 'This little chap's got a temperature of a hundred and five. Must be some infection somewhere —maybe a touch of joint ill.' I felt my way along the small pink limbs. 'And yet it's funny, the joints aren't swollen.'

'Ah reckon Bill Bowes'll skittle Somerset out when they start their innings today. This wicket's just to 'is liking.'

'Yes, he's a great bowler, isn't he?' I said. 'I love watching a good fast bowler. I suppose you'll have seen them all—Larwood, Voce, G. O. Allen and the rest?'

'Aye, that I have. I could go on all day about those men.'

I caught another of the lame pigs and examined it. 'This is rather strange, Mr Duggleby. About half the pigs in this pen seem to be lame but there's nothing to see.'

'Aye well, happen it's like you said—joint ill. You can give 'em a jab for that, can't you? And while you're doin' it I'll tell you of the time I saw Wilfred Rhodes take eight wickets in an afternoon.'

I filled a syringe. 'Right, we'd better give them all a shot. Have you got a marking pencil there?'

The farmer nodded and lifted one of the little animals which promptly unleashed a protesting scream. 'There was never anybody like awd Wilfred,' he shouted above the noise. 'It was about half past two and the wicket had had a shower of rain on it when t'skipper threw 'im the ball.'

I smiled and raised my syringe. It passed the time so pleasantly listening to these reminiscences. Well content, I was about to plunge the needle into the pink thigh when one of the pigs began to nibble at the heel of my wellington. I looked down at a ring of the little creatures all looking up at me, alarmed by the shrill screeches of their friend.

My mind was still with Wilfred Rhodes when I noticed what looked like a small white knob on one of the uptilted snouts. And there was another on that one—and that one . . . I had been unable to see their faces until now because they had been trying to run away from me, but a warning bell clanged suddenly in my head.

I reached down and seized a pig, and as I squeezed the swelling on the snout a cold wind blew through me, scattering the gentle vision of cricket and sunshine and green grass. It wasn't a knob, it was a vesicle, a delicate blister which ruptured easily on pressure.

I could feel my arms shaking as I turned the piglet up and began to examine the tiny cloven feet. There were more vesicles there, flatter and more diffuse, but telling the same dread story.

Dry mouthed, I lifted two other pigs. They were just the same. As I turned to the farmer I felt bowed down by a crushing weight of pity, almost of guilt. He was still smiling eagerly, anxious to get on with his tale, and I was about to give him the worst news a veterinary surgeon can give a stocksman.

'Mr Duggleby,' I said. 'I'm afraid I'll have to telephone the Ministry of Agriculture.'

'The Ministry . . . ? What for?'

'To tell them I have a case of suspected Foot and Mouth Disease.'

'Foot and Mouth? Never!'

'Yes, I'm terribly sorry.'

'Are you sure?'

'It's not up to me to be definite about it, Mr Duggleby. One of the Ministry officers will have to do that—I must phone them right away.'

It was an unlikely place to find a telephone but Mr Duggleby ran a little coal delivery round on the side. I was quickly through to the Ministry and I spoke to Neville Craggs, one of the full time officers.

He groaned. 'Sounds awful like it, Jim. Anyway, stay put till I see you.'

In the farm kitchen Mr Duggleby looked at me enquiringly. 'What now?'

'You'll just have to put up with me for a bit,' I said. 'I can't leave till I get the verdict.'

He was silent for a moment. 'What happens if it's what you think?'

'I'm afraid your pigs will have to be slaughtered.'

'Every one of 'em?'

'That is the law—I'm sorry. But you'll get compensation.'

He scratched his head. 'But they can get better. Why do you have to kill 'em all?'

'You're quite right.' I shrugged. 'Many animals do recover, but Foot and Mouth is fiercely infectious. While you were treating them it would have spread to neighbouring farms, then all over the country.'

'Aye, but look at the expense. Slaughtering must cost thousands o' pounds.'

'I agree, but it would cost a lot more the other way. Apart from the animals that die, just think of the loss of milk, loss of flesh in cows, pigs and sheep. It would come to millions every year. It's lucky Britain is an island.'

'Reckon you'll be right.' He felt for his pipe. 'And you're pretty sure I've got it?'

'Yes.'

'Aye well,' he murmured. 'These things 'appen.'

The old Yorkshire words. I had heard them so often under circumstances that would make most city folk, including myself, beat their heads against a wall. Mr Duggleby's smallholding would soon be a silent place of death, but he just chewed his pipe and said, 'These things 'appen.'

It didn't take the Ministry long to make up their minds. The source of the infection was almost certainly some imported meat that Mr Duggleby hadn't boiled properly with his swill. The disease was confirmed and a fifteen mile radius standstill order was imposed. I disinfected myself and my car and went home. I undressed, my clothes were taken away for fumigation and I climbed into a hot antiseptic bath.

Lying there in the steam, I pondered on what might have been. If I had failed to spot the disease I would have gone merrily on my way, spreading destruction and havoc. I always washed my boots before leaving a farm, but how about those little pigs nibbling round the hem of my long coat, how about my syringe, even my thermometer? My next call was to have been to Terence Bailey's pedigree herd of dairy shorthorns— two hundred peerless cows, a strain built up over generations. Foreigners came from all over the world to buy them and I could have been the cause of their annihilation.

And then there was Mr Duggleby himself. I could picture him rattling around the farms in his coal wagon. He would have done his bit of spreading, too. And like as not he would have taken a few store pigs to the auction mart this week, sending the deadly contagion all over Yorkshire and beyond. It was easy to see how a major outbreak could have started—a disaster of national importance costing millions.

If I hadn't been sweating already I would have started now at the very thought of it. I would have joined the unhappy band of practitioners who had missed Foot and Mouth.

I knew of some of these people and my heart bled for them. It could happen so easily. Busy men trying to examine kicking, struggling animals in dark buildings with perhaps part of their mind on the list of calls ahead. And the other hazards—the total unexpectedness, the atypical case, various distractions. My distraction had been cricket and it had nearly caused my downfall. But I had escaped and, huddling lower in the hot water, I said a silent prayer of thanks.

Later, with a complete change of clothes and instruments, I continued on my rounds and as I stood in Terence Bailey's long byre I realised my luck again. The long rows of beautiful animals meticulously groomed, firm high udders pushing between their hocks, delicate heads, fine legs deep in straw; they were a picture of bovine perfection and quite irreplaceable.

Once Foot and Mouth is confirmed in a district there is a tense period of waiting. Farmers, veterinary surgeons and most of all, Ministry officials are on the rack, wondering if there has been any dissemination before diagnosis, bracing themselves against the telephone message that could herald the raging spread they dreaded and which would tear their lives apart.

To the city dwellers a big Foot and Mouth outbreak is something remote they read about in the newspapers. To the country folk it means the transformation of the quiet farms and fields into charnel houses and funeral pyres. It means heartbreak and ruin.

We waited in Darrowby. And as the days passed and no frightening news of lame or salivating animals came over the wires it seemed that the Duggleby episode was what we hoped —an isolated case caused by a few shreds of imported meat.

I almost bathed in disinfectant on every farm, sloshing a strong solution of Lysol over my boots and protective clothing so that my car reeked of the stuff and I caused wrinkled noses when I entered a shop, the post office, the bank.

After nearly two weeks I had begun to feel reasonably safe but when I had a call from the famous Bailey farm I felt a twinge of apprehension.

It was Terence Bailey himself. 'Will you come and see one of my cows, Mr Herriot. She's got blisters on one of her teats.'

'Blisters!' My heart went bump. 'Is she slavering, is she lame?'

'Nay, nay, she just has these nasty blisters. Seem to have fluid in them.'

I was breathless as I put down the receiver. One nasty blister would be enough. It sometimes started like that in cows. I almost ran out to my car and on the journey my mind beat about like a trapped bird.

Bailey's was the farm I had visited straight from Duggleby's. Could I possibly have carried it there? But the change of clothes, the bath, the fresh thermometer and instruments. What more could I do? How about my car wheels? Well, I had disinfected them, too—I couldn't possibly be blamed, but . . . but . . . .

It was Mr Bailey's wife who met me.

'I noticed this cow when I was milking this morning, Mr Herriot.' The herd was still hand-milked and in the hard-working family tradition Mrs Bailey did her stint night and morning with her husband and the farm men.

'As soon as I got hold of the teats I could see the cow was uneasy,' she continued. 'Then I saw there was a lot of little blisters and one big one. I managed to milk her and most of the little blisters burst, but the big one's still there.'

I bent and peered anxiously at the udder. It was as she said—lots of small ruptured vesicles and one large one, intact and fluctuating. It was all horribly evocative and without speaking I moved along, grasped the cow's nose and pulled her head round. I prised the mouth open and stared desperately at lips, cheek and dental pad. I think I would have fainted if I had found anything in there but it was all clean and normal.

I lifted each forefoot in turn and scrubbed out the clefts with soap and water—nothing. I tied a rope round the hind leg, threw it over a beam and with the help of one of the men pulled the foot up. More scrubbing and searching without success then the same with the other hind foot. When I finished I was perspiring but no further forward.

I took the temperature and found it slightly elevated, then I walked up and down the byre.

'Is there any trouble among these other cows?' I asked.

Mrs Bailey shook her head. 'No, there's just this one.' She

was a good-looking woman in her thirties with the red, roughened complexion of the outdoor worker. 'What do you think it
is?'

I didn't dare tell her. I had a cow with vesicles on the teats
right in the middle of a district under Foot and Mouth restrictions. I just couldn't take a chance. I had to bring the Ministry
in.

Even then I was unable to speak the dread words. All I could
say was, 'Can I use your phone, please?'

She looked surprised, but smiled quickly. 'Yes, of course.
Come into the house.'

As I walked down the byre I looked again at the beautiful
cows and then beyond, at the fold yard where I could see the
young heifers and the tiny calves in their pens. All of them carrying the Bailey blood which had been produced and perfected
by generations of careful breeding and selection. But a humane
killer is no respecter of such things and if my fears were realised
a quick series of bang-bangs would wipe out all this in an hour
or two.

We went into the farm kitchen and Mrs Bailey pointed to
the door at the far end.

'The phone's through there in the front room,' she said.

I kicked off my wellingtons and was padding across the floor
in my stockinged feet when I almost fell over Giles, the lusty
one year old baby of the family, as he waddled across my path.
I bent to ease him out of the way and he looked up at me with
an enormous cheesy grin.

His mother laughed. 'Just look at him. Full of the devil, and
he's had such a painful arm since his smallpox vaccination.'

'Poor lad,' I said absently, patting his head as I opened the
door, my mind already busy with the uncomfortable conversation ahead. I had taken a few strides over the carpet beyond,
when I halted abruptly.

I turned and looked back into the kitchen. 'Did you say smallpox vaccination?'

'Yes, all our other children have been done when they were
this age but they've never reacted like this. I've had to change
his dressing every day.'

'You changed his dressing . . . and you milked that cow?'

'Yes, that's right.'

A great light beamed suddenly, spilling sunshine into my dark troubled world. I returned to the kitchen and closed the door behind me.

Mrs Bailey looked at me for a moment in silence, then she spoke hesitantly. 'Aren't you going to use the phone?'

'No . . . no . . .' I replied. 'I've changed my mind.'

'I see.' She raised her eyebrows and seemed at a loss for words. Then she smiled and lifted the kettle. 'Well maybe you'll have a cup of tea, then?'

'Thank you, that would be lovely.' I sank happily on to one of the hard wooden chairs.

Mrs Bailey put the kettle on and turned to me. 'By the way, you've never told me what's wrong with that cow.'

'Oh yes, of course, I'm sorry,' I said airily as though I'd just forgotten to mention it. 'She's got cow pox. In fact you gave it to her.'

'I gave it . . .? What do you mean?'

'Well, the vaccine they use for babies is made from the cow pox virus. You carried it on your hands from the baby to the cow.' I smiled, enjoying my big moment.

Her mouth fell open slightly, then she began to giggle. 'Oh dear, I don't know what my husband's going to say. I've never heard of anything like that.' She wiggled her fingers in front of her eyes. 'And I'm always so careful, too. But I've been a bit harassed with the poor little chap's arm.'

'Oh well, it isn't serious,' I said. 'I've got some ointment in the car which will cure it quite quickly.'

I sipped my tea and watched Giles's activities. In a short time he had spread chaos throughout the kitchen and at the moment was busily engaged in removing all the contents of a cupboard in the corner. Bent double, small bottom outthrust, he hurled pans, lids, brushes behind him with intense dedication till the cupboard was empty. Then, as he looked around for further employment, he spotted me and tacked towards me on straddled legs.

My stocking-clad toes seemed to fascinate him and as I wiggled them at him he grasped at them with fat little hands. When he had finally trapped my big toe he looked up at me with his huge grin in which four tiny teeth glittered.

I smiled back at him with sincere affection as the relief flowed through me. It wasn't just that I was grateful to him—I really liked him. I still like Giles today. He is one of my clients, a burly farmer with a family of his own, a deep love and knowledge of pedigree cows and the same big grin, except that there are a few more teeth in it.

But he'll never know how near his smallpox vaccination came to giving me heart failure.

CHAPTER

46

They had sent me to Eastchurch on the Isle of Sheppey and I knew it was the last stop.

As I looked along the disorderly line of men I realised I wouldn't be taking part in many more parades. And it came to me with a pang that at the Scarborough I.T.W. this would not have been classed as a parade at all. I could remember the ranks of blue outside the Grand Hotel, straight as the Grenadier Guards and every man standing stiffly, looking neither to left nor right. Our boots gleaming, buttons shining like gold and not a movement anywhere as the flight sergeant led the officer round on morning inspection.

I had moaned as loudly as anybody at the rigid discipline, the 'bull', the scrubbing and polishing, marching and drilling, but now that it had all gone it seemed good and meaningful and I missed it.

Here the files of airmen lounged, chatted among themselves and occasionally took a surreptitious drag at a cigarette as a sergeant out in front called the names from a list and gave us our leisurely instructions for the day.

This particular morning he was taking a long time over it, consulting sheaves of papers and making laboured notes with a pencil. A big Irishman on my right was becoming increasingly restive and finally he shouted testily:

'For——sake, sergeant, get us off this——square. Me ——feet's killin' me!'

The sergeant didn't even look up. 'Shut your mouth, Brady,' he replied. 'You'll get off the square when I say so and not before.'

It was like that at Eastchurch, the great filter tank of the R.A.F. where what I had heard described as the 'odds and sods' were finally sorted out. It was a big sprawling camp filled with a widely varied mixture of airmen who had one thing in common; they were all waiting—some of them for remuster, but most for discharge from the service.

There was a resigned air about the whole place, an acceptance of the fact that we were all just putting in time. There was a token discipline but it was of the most benign kind. And as I said, every man there was just waiting . . . waiting. . . .

Little Ned Finch in his remote corner of the high Yorkshire Dales always seemed to me to be waiting, too. I could remember his boss yelling at him.

'For God's sake, shape up to t'job! You're not framin' at all!' Mr Daggett grabbed hold of a leaping calf and glared in exasperation.

Ned gazed back at him impassively. His face registered no particular emotion, but in the pale blue eyes I read the expression that was always there—as though he was waiting for something to happen, but without much hope. He made a tentative attempt to catch a calf but was brushed aside, then he put his arms round the neck of another one, a chunky little animal of three months, and was borne along a few yards before being deposited on his back in the straw.

'Oh, dang it, do this one, Mr Herriot!' Mr Daggett barked, turning the hairy neck towards me. 'It looks as though I'll have to catch 'em all myself.'

I injected the animal. I was inoculating a batch of twenty with preventive pneumonia vaccine and Ned was suffering. With his diminutive stature and skinny, small-boned limbs he had always seemed to me to be in the wrong job; but he had been a farm worker all his life and he was over sixty now, grizzled, balding and slightly bent, but still battling on.

Mr Daggett reached out and as one of the shaggy creatures sped past he scooped the head into one of his great hands and seized the ear with the other. The little animal seemed to realise it was useless to struggle and stood unresisting as I inserted the needle. At the other end Ned put his knee against the calf's rear and listlessly pushed it against the wall. He wasn't doing much good and his boss gave him a withering glance.

We finished the bunch with hardly any help from the little

man, and as we left the pen and came out into the yard Mr Daggett wiped his brow. It was a raw November day but he was sweating profusely and for a moment he leaned his gaunt six foot frame against the wall as the wind from the bare moorland blew over him.

'By gaw, he's a useless little beggar is that,' he grunted. 'Ah don't know how ah put up with 'em.' He muttered to himself for a few moments then gave tongue again. 'Hey, Ned!'

The little man who had been trailing aimlessly over the cobbles turned his pinched face and looked at him with his submissive but strangely expectant eyes.

'Get them bags o' corn up into the granary!' his boss ordered.

Wordlessly Ned went over to a cart and with an effort shouldered a sack of corn. As he painfully mounted the stone steps to the granary his frail little legs trembled and bent under the weight.

Mr Daggett shook his head and turned to me. His long cadaverous face was set in its usual cast of melancholy.

'You know what's wrong wi' Ned?' he murmured confidentially.'

'What do you mean?'

'Well, you know why 'e can't catch them calves?'

My own view was that Ned wasn't big enough or strong enough and anyway he was naturally ineffectual, but I shook my head.

'No,' I said. 'Why is it?'

'Well I'll tell ye.' Mr Daggett glanced furtively across the yard then spoke from behind his hand. 'He's ower fond of t'bright lights.'

'Eh?'

'Ah'm tellin' ye, he's crazed over t'bright lights.'

'Bright . . . what . . . where . . .?"

Mr Daggett leaned closer. 'He gets over to Briston every night.'

'Briston . . .?" I looked across from the isolated farm to the village three miles away on the other side of the Dale. It was the only settlement in that bleak vista—a straggle of ancient houses dark and silent against the green fellside. I could recall that at night the oil lamps made yellow flickers of light in the windows but they weren't very bright. 'I don't understand.'

'Well . . . 'e gets into t'pub.'

'Ah, the pub.'

Mr Daggett nodded slowly and portentously but I was still puzzled. The Hulton Arms was a square kitchen where you could get a glass of beer and where a few old men played dominoes of an evening. It wasn't my idea of a den of vice.

'Does he get drunk there?' I asked.

'Nay, nay.' The farmer shook his head. 'It's not that. It's the hours 'e keeps.'

'Comes back late, eh?'

'Aye, that 'e does!' The eyes widened in their cavernous sockets. 'Sometimes 'e doesn't get back till 'alf past nine or ten o'clock!'

'Gosh, is that so?'

'Sure as ah'm standin' here. And there's another thing. He can't get out of 'is bed next day. Ah've done half a day's work before 'e starts.' He paused and glanced again across the yard. 'You can believe me or believe me not, but sometimes 'e isn't on the job till seven o'clock in t'morning!'

'Good heavens!'

He shrugged wearily. 'Aye well, you see how it is. Come into t'house, you'll want to wash your hands.'

In the huge flagged kitchen I bent low over the brown earthenware sink. Scar Farm was four hundred years old and the various tenants hadn't altered it much since the days of Henry the Eighth. Gnarled beams, rough whitewashed walls and hard wooden chairs. But comfort had never been important to Mr Daggett or his wife who was ladling hot water from the primitive boiler by the side of the fire and pouring it into her scrubbing bucket.

She clopped around over the flags in her clogs, hair pulled back tightly from her weathered face into a bun, a coarse sacking apron tied round her waist. She had no children but her life was one of constant activity; indoors or outside, she worked all the time.

At one end of the room wooden steps led up through a hole in the ceiling to a loft where Ned slept. That had been the little man's room for nearly fifty years ever since he had come to work for Mr Daggett's father as a boy from school. And in all that time he had never travelled further than Darrowby, never done anything outside his daily routine. Wifeless, friendless, he plodded through his life, endlessly milking, feeding and mucking out, and waiting, I suspected with diminishing hope for something to happen.

With my handle on the car door I looked back at Scar Farm, at the sagging roof tiles, the great stone lintel over the door. It typified the harshness of the lives of the people within. Little Ned was no bargain as a stocksman, and his boss's exasperation was understandable. Mr Daggett was not a cruel or an unjust man. He and his wife had been hardened and squeezed dry by the pitiless austerity of their existence in this lonely corner of the high Pennines.

There was no softness up here, no frills. The stone walls, sparse grass and stunted trees; the narrow road with its smears of cow muck. Everything was down to fundamentals, and it was a miracle to me that most of the Dalesmen were not like the Daggetts but cheerful and humorous.

But as I drove away, the sombre beauty of the place overwhelmed me. The lowering hillsides burst magically into life as a shaft of sunshine stabbed through the clouds, flooding the bare flanks with warm gold. Suddenly I was aware of the delicate shadings of green, the rich glowing bronze of the dead bracken spilling from the high tops, the whole peaceful majesty of my work-a-day world.

I hadn't far to drive to my next call—just about a mile— and it was in a vastly different atmosphere. Miss Tremayne, a rich lady from the south, had bought a tumbledown manor house and spent many thousands of pounds in converting it into a luxury home. As my feet crunched on the gravel I looked up at the large windows with their leaded panes, at the smooth, freshly-painted stones.

Elsie opened the door to me. She was Miss Tremayne's cook-housekeeper, and one of my favourite people. Aged about fifty, no more than five feet high and as round as a ball with short bandy legs sticking out from beneath a tight black dress.

'Good morning, Elsie,' I said, and she burst into a peal of laughter. This, more than her remarkable physical appearance, was what delighted me. She laughed uproariously at every statement and occurrence; in fact she laughed at the things she said herself.

'Come in, Mr Herriot, ha-ha-ha,' she said. 'It's been a bit nippy today, he-he, but I think it'll get out this afternoon, ho-ho-ho.'

All the mirth may have seemed somewhat unnecessary, and indeed, it made her rather difficult to understand, but the general effect was cheering. She led me into the drawing room and her mistress rose with some difficulty from her chair.

Miss Tremayne was elderly and half crippled with arthritis but bore her affliction without fuss.

'Ah, Mr Herriott,' she said. 'How good of you to come.' She put her head on one side and beamed at me as though I was the most delightful thing she had seen for a long time.

She, too, had a bubbling, happy personality, and since she owned three dogs, two cats and an elderly donkey I had come to know her very well in her six months' residence in the Dale.

My visit was to dress the donkey's overgrown hooves, and a pair of clippers and a blacksmith's knife dangled from my right hand.

'Oh, put those grisly instruments down over there,' she said. 'Elsie's bringing some tea—I'm sure you've time for a cup.'

I sank willingly into one of the brightly covered armchairs and was looking round the comfortable room when Elsie reappeared, gliding over the carpet as though on wheels. She put the tray on the table by my side.

'There's yer tea,' she said, and went into a paroxysm so hearty that she had to lean on the back of my chair. She had no visible neck and the laughter caused the fat little body to shake all over.

When she had recovered she rolled back into the kitchen and I heard her clattering about with pans. Despite her idiosyncrasies she was a wonderful cook and very efficient in all she did.

I spent a pleasant ten minutes with Miss Tremayne and the tea, then I went outside and attended to the donkey. When I had finished I made my way round the back of the house and as I was passing the kitchen I saw Elsie at the open window.

'Many thanks for the tea, Elsie,' I said.

The little woman gripped the sides of the sink to steady herself. 'Ha-ha-ha, that's all right. That's, he-he, quite all right, ha-ha-ho-ho-ho.'

Wonderingly I got into the car and as I drove away, the disturbing thought came to me that one day I might say something really witty to Elsie and cause her to do herself an injury.

I was called back to Mr Daggett's quite soon afterwards to see a cow which wouldn't get up. The farmer thought she was paralysed.

I drove there in a thin drizzle and the light was fading at about four o'clock in the afternoon when I arrived at Scar Farm.

Whn I examined the cow I was convinced she had just got herself into an awkward position in the stall with her legs jammed under the broken timbers of the partition.

'I think she's sulking, Mr Daggett,' I said. 'She's had a few goes at rising and now she's decided not to try any more. Some cows are like that.'

'Maybe you're right,' the farmer replied. 'She's allus been a stupid bitch.'

'And she's a big one, too. She'll take a bit of moving.' I lifted a rope from the byre wall and tied it round the hocks. 'I'll push the feet from the other side while you and Ned pull the legs round.'

'Pull?' Mr. Daggett gave the little man a sour look. 'He couldn't pull the skin off a rice puddin'.'

Ned said nothing, just gazed dully to his front, arms hanging limp. He looked as though he didn't care, wasn't even there with us. His mind was certainly elsewhere if his thoughts were mirrored in his eyes—vacant, unheeding, but as always, expectant.

I went behind the partition and thrust steadily at the feet while the men pulled. At least Mr Daggett pulled, mouth open, gasping with effort, while Ned leaned languidly on the rope.

Inch by inch the big animal came round till she was lying almost in the middle of the stall, but as I was about to call a halt the rope broke and Mr Daggett flew backwards on to the hard cobbles. Ned of course did not fall down because he hadn't been trying, and his employer, stretched flat, glared up at him with frustrated rage.

'Ye little bugger, ye let me do that all by meself! Ah don't know why ah bother with you, you're bloody useless.'

At that moment the cow, as I had expected, rose to her feet, and the farmer gesticulated at the little man. 'Well, go on, dang ye, get some straw and rub her legs! They'll be numb.'

Meekly Ned twisted some straw into a wisp and began to do a bit of massage. Mr Daggett got up stiffly, felt gingerly along his back then walked up beside the cow to make sure the chain hadn't tightened round her neck. He was on his way back when the big animal swung round suddenly and brought her cloven hoof down solidly on the farmer's toe.

If he had been wearing heavy boots it wouldn't have been so bad, but his feet were encased in ancient cracked wellingtons which offered no protection.

'Ow! Ow! Ow!' yelled Mr Daggett, beating on the hairy back with his fists. 'Gerroff, ye awd bitch!' He heaved, pushed and writhed but the ten hundredweight of beef ground down inexorably.

The farmer was only released when the cow slid off his foot, and I know from experience that that sliding is the worst part.

Mr Daggett hopped around on one leg, nursing the bruised extremity in his hands. 'Bloody 'ell,' he moaned. 'Oh, bloody 'ell.'

Just then I happened to glance towards Ned and was amazed to see the apathetic little face crinkle suddenly into a wide grin of unholy glee. I couldn't recall him even smiling before, and my astonishment must have shown in my face because his boss whipped round suddenly and stared at him. As if by magic the sad mask slipped back into place and he went on with his rubbing.

Mr Daggett hobbled out to the car with me and as I was about to leave he nudged me.

'Look at 'im,' he whispered.

Ned, milk pail in hand, was bustling along the byre with unwonted energy.

His employer gave a bitter smile. 'It's t'only time 'e ever hurries. Can't wait to get out to t'pub.'

'Oh well, you say he doesn't get drunk. There can't be any harm in it.'

The deep sunk eyes held me. 'Don't you believe it. He'll come tiv a bad end gaddin' about the way 'e does.'

'But surely the odd glass of beer . . .'

'Ah but there's more than that to it.' He glanced around him. 'There's women!'

I laughed incredulously. 'Oh come now, Mr Daggett, what women?'

'Over at t'pub,' he muttered. 'Them Bradley lasses.'

'The landlord's daughters? Oh really, I can't believe . . .'

'All right, ye can say what ye like. He's got 'is eye on 'em. Ah knaw—ah've only been in that pub once but ah've seen for meself.'

I didn't know what to say, but in any case I had no opportunity because he turned and strode into the house.

Alone in the cold darkness I looked at the gaunt silhouette of the old farmhouse above me. In the dying light of the November day the rain streamed down the rough stones and the wind caught at the thin tendril of smoke from the chimney, hurling it in ragged streamers across the slate blue pallor of the western sky. The fell hung over everything, a black featureless bulk, oppressive and menacing.

Through the kitchen window I could see the old lamp casting its dim light over the bare table, the cheerless hearth with its tiny flicker of fire. In the shadows at the far end the steps rose into Ned's loft and I could imagine the little figure clambering up to get changed and escape to Briston.

Across the valley the single street of the village was a broken grey thread in the gloom but in the cottage windows the lamps winked faintly. These were Ned Finch's bright lights and I could understand how he felt. After Scar Farm, Briston would be like Monte Carlo.

The image stayed in my mind so vividly that after two more calls that evening I decided to go a few miles out of my way as I returned homeward. I cut across the Dale and it was about half past eight when I drove into Briston. It was difficult to find the Hulton Arms because there was no lighted entrance, no attempt to advertise its presence, but I persevered because I had to find out what was behind Mr Daggett's tale of debauchery.

I located it at last. Just like the door of an ordinary house with a faded wooden sign hanging above it. Inside, the usual domino game was in progress, a few farmers sat chatting quietly. The Misses Bradley, plain but pleasant-faced women in their forties, sat on either side of the fire, and sure enough there was Ned with a half pint glass in front of him.

I sat down by his side. 'Hello, Ned.'

'Now then, Mr Herriott,' he murmured absently, glancing at me with his strange expectant eyes.

One of the Bradley ladies put down her knitting and came over.

'Pint of bitter, please,' I said. 'What will you have, Ned?'

'Nay, thank ye, Mr Herriot. This'll do for me. It's me second and ah'm not a big drinker, tha knows.'

Miss Bradley laughed. 'Yes, he nobbut has 'is two glasses a night, but he enjoys them, don't you, Ned?'

'That's right, ah do.' He looked up at her and she smiled kindly down at him before going for my beer.

He took a sip at his glass. "Ah really come for t'company, Mr Herriot.'

'Yes, of course,' I said. I knew what he meant. He probably sat on his own most of the time, but around him was warmth and comfort and friendliness. A great log sent flames crackling up to the wide chimney, there was electric light and shining mirrors with whisky slogans painted on their surface. It wasn't anything like Scar Farm.

The little man said very little. He spun out his drink for another hour, looking around him as the dominoes clicked and I lowered another contemplative pint. The Misses Bradley knitted and brewed tea in a big black kettle over the fire and when they had to get up to serve their customers they occasionally patted Ned playfully on the cheek as they passed.

By the time he tipped down the last drop and rose to go it was a quarter to ten and he still had to cycle across to the other side of the Dale. Another late night for Ned.

It was a Tuesday lunchtime in early spring. Helen always cooked steak and kidney pie on Tuesdays and I used to think about it all morning on my rounds. My thoughts that morning had been particularly evocative because lambing had started and I had spent most of the time in my shirt sleeves in the biting wind as my hunger grew and grew.

Helen cut into her blissful creation and began to scoop the fragrant contents on to my plate.

'I met Miss Tremayne in the market place this morning, Jim.'

'Oh yes?' I was almost drooling as my wife stopped shovelling out the pie, sliced open some jacket potatoes and dropped pats of farm butter on to the steaming surfaces.

'Yes, she wants you to go out there this afternoon and put some canker drops in Wilberforce's ears if you have time.'

'Oh I have time for that,' I said. Wilberforce was Miss Tremayne's ancient tabby cat and it was just the kind of job I wanted after my arm-aching morning.

I was raising a luscious forkful when Helen spoke again. 'Oh, and she had an interesting item of news.'

'Really?' But I had begun to chew and my thoughts were distant.

'It's about the little woman who works for her—Elsie. You know her?'

I nodded and took another mouthful. 'Of course, of course.'

'Well it's quite unexpected, I suppose, but Elsie's getting married.'

I choked on my pie. 'What!'

'It's true. And maybe you know the bridegroom.'

'Tell me.'

'He works on one of the neighbouring farms. His name is Ned Finch.'

This time my breath was cut off completely and Helen had to beat me on the back as I spluttered and retched. It wasn't until an occluding morsel of potato skin had shot down my nose that I was able to utter a weak croak. 'Ned Finch?'

'That's what she said.'

I finished my lunch in a dream, but by the end of it I had accepted the extraordinary fact. Helen and Miss Tremayne were two sensible people—there couldn't be any mistake. And yet . . . even as I drew up outside the old Manor House a feeling of unreality persisted.

Elsie opened the door as usual. I looked at her for a moment. 'What's this I hear, Elsie?'

She started a giggle which rapidly spread over her spherical frame.

I put my hand on her shoulder. 'Is it true?'

The giggle developed into a mighty gale of laughter, and if she hadn't been holding the handle I am sure she would have fallen over.

'Aye, it's right enough,' she gasped. 'Ah've found a man at

last and ah'm goin' to get wed!' She leaned helplessly on the door.

'Well, I'm pleased to hear it, Elsie. I hope you'll be very happy.'

She hadn't the strength to speak but merely nodded as she lay against the door. Then she led me to the drawing room. 'In ye go,' she chuckled. 'Ah'll bring ye some tea.'

Miss Tremayne rose to greet me with parted lips and shining eyes. 'Oh, Mr. Herriot, have you heard?'

'Yes, but how . . . ?'

'It all started when I asked Mr Daggett for some fresh eggs. He sent Ned on his bicycle with the eggs and it was like fate.'

'Well, how wonderful.'

'Yes, and I actually saw it happen. Ned walked in that door with his basket, Elsie was clearing the table here, and, Mr Herriot.' She clasped her hands under her chin, smiled ecstatically and her eyes rolled upwards. 'Oh, Mr Herriot, it was love at first sight!'

'Yes . . . yes, indeed. Marvellous!'

'And ever since that day Ned has been calling round and now he comes every evening and sits with Elsie in the kitchen. Isn't it romantic!'

'It certainly is. And when did they decide to get married?'

'Oh, he popped the question within a month, and I'm so happy for Elsie because Ned is such a dear little man, don't you think so?'

'Yes he is.' I said. 'He's a very nice chap.'

Elsie simpered and tittered her way in with the tea then put her hand over her face and fled in confusion, and as Miss Tremayne began to pour I sank into one of the armchairs and lifted Wilberforce on to my lap.

The big cat purred as I instilled a few drops of lotion into his ear. He had a chronic canker condition—not very bad but now and then it became painful and needed treatment. It was because Miss Tremayne didn't like putting the lotion in that I was pressed into service.

As I turned the ear over and gently massaged the oily liquid into the depths, Wilberforce groaned softly with pleasure and rubbed his cheek against my hand. He loved this anointing of the tender area beyond his reach and when I had finished he curled up on my knee.

I leaned back and sipped my tea. At that moment, with my back and shoulders weary and my hands red and chapped with countless washings on the open hillsides this seemed to be veterinary practice at its best.

Miss Tremayne continued. 'We shall have a little reception after the wedding and then the happy couple will take up residence here.'

'You mean, in this house?'

'Yes, of course. There's heaps of room in this big old place, and I have furnished two rooms for them on the east side. I'm sure they'll be very comfortable. Oh, I'm so excited about it all!'

She refilled my cup. 'Before you go you must let Elsie show you where they are going to live.'

On my way out the little woman took me through to the far end of the house.

'This, hee-hee-hee,' she said, 'is where we'll sit of a night, and this, ha-ha-ho-ho, oh dear me, is our bedroom.' She staggered around for a bit, wiped her eyes and turned to me for my opinion.

'It's really lovely, Elsie,' I said.

There were bright carpets, chairs with flowered covers and a fine mahogany-ended bed. It was nothing like the loft.

And as I looked at Elsie I realised the things Ned would see in his bride. Laughter, warmth, vivacity, and—I had no doubt at all—beauty and glamour.

I seemed to get round to most farms that lambing time and in due course I landed at Mr Daggett's. I delivered a fine pair of twins for him but it didn't seem to cheer him at all. Lifting the towel from the grass he handed it to me.

'Well, what did ah tell ye about Ned, eh? Got mixed up wi' a woman just like ah said.' He sniffed disapprovingly. 'All that rakin' and chasin' about—ah knew he'd get into mischief at t'finish.'

I walked back over the sunlit fields to the farm and as I passed the byre door Ned came out pushing a wheelbarrow.

'Good morning, Ned,' I said.

He glanced up at me in his vague way. 'How do, Mr. Herriot.'

There was something different about him and it took me a few moments to discern what it was; his eyes had lost the expectant look which had been there for so long, and, after all, that was perfectly natural.

Because it had happened at last for Ned.

I had plenty of time on my hands at Eastchurch, plenty of time to think, and like most servicemen I thought of home. Only my home wasn't there any more.

When I left Darrowby Helen had gone back to live with her father and the little rooms under the tiles of Skeldale House would be empty and dusty now. But they lived on in my mind, clear in every detail.

I could see the ivy-fringed window looking over the tumble of roofs to the green hills, our few pieces of furniture, the bed and side table and the old wardrobe which only stayed shut with the aid of one of my socks jammed in the door. Strangely, it was that dangling woollen toe which gave me the sharpest stab as I remembered.

And even though it was all gone I could hear the bedside radio playing, my wife's voice from the other side of the fire and on that winter evening Tristan shouting up the stairs from the passage far below.

'Jim! Jim!'

I went out and stuck my head over the bannisters. 'What is it, Triss?'

'Sorry to bother you, Jim, but could you come down for a minute?' The upturned face had an anxious look.

I went down the long flights of steps two at a time and when I arrived slightly breathless on the ground floor Tristan beckoned me through to the consulting room at the back of the house. A teenage girl was standing by the table, her hand resting on a stained roll of blanket.

'It's a cat,' Tristan said. He pulled back a fold of the blanket and I looked down at a large, deeply striped tabby. At least he would have been large if he had had any flesh on his bones, but ribs and pelvis stood out painfully through the fur and as I passed my hand over the motionless body I could feel only a thin covering of skin.

Tristan cleared his throat. 'There's something else, Jim.'

I looked at him curiously. For once he didn't seem to have a joke in him. I watched as he gently lifted one of the cat's hind legs and rolled the abdomen into view. There was a gash on the ventral surface through which a coiled cluster of intestines spilled grotesquely on to the cloth. I was still shocked and staring when the girl spoke.

'I saw this cat sittin' in the dark, down Brown's yard. I thought 'e looked skinny, like, and a bit quiet and I bent down to give 'im a pat. Then I saw 'e was badly hurt and I went home for a blanket and brought 'im round to you.'

'That was kind of you,' I said. 'Have you any idea who he belongs to?'

The girl shook her head. 'No, he looks like a stray to me.'

'He does indeed.' I dragged my eyes away from the terrible wound. 'You're Marjorie Simpson, aren't you?'

'Yes.'

'I know your Dad well. He's our postman.'

'That's right.' She gave a half smile then her lips trembled.

'Well, I reckon I'd better leave 'im with you. You'll be goin' to put him out of his misery. There's nothing anybody can do about . . . about that?'

I shrugged and shook my head. The girl's eyes filled with tears, she stretched out a hand and touched the emaciated animal then turned and walked quickly to the door.

'Thanks again, Marjorie,' I called after the retreating back. 'And don't worry—we'll look after him.'

In the silence that followed, Tristan and I looked down at the shattered animal. Under the surgery lamp it was all too easy to see. He had almost been disembowelled and the pile of intestines was covered in dirt and mud.

'What d'you think did this?' Tristan said at length. 'Has he been run over?'

'Maybe,' I replied. 'Could be anything. An attack by a big dog or somebody could have kicked him or struck him.' All things were possible with cats because some people seemed to regard them as fair game for any cruelty.

Tristan nodded. 'Anyway, whatever happened, he must have

been on the verge of starvation. He's a skeleton. I bet he's wandered miles from home.'

'Ah well,' I sighed. 'There's only one thing to do. Those guts are perforated in several places. It's hopeless.'

Tristan didn't say anything but he whistled under his breath and drew the tip of his forefinger again and again across the furry cheek. And, unbelievably, from somewhere in the scraggy chest a gentle purring arose.

The young man looked at me, round eyed. 'My God, do you hear that?'

'Yes . . . amazing in that condition. He's a good natured cat.'

Tristan, head bowed, continued his stroking. I knew how he felt because, although he preserved a cheerfully hard-boiled attitude to our patients he couldn't kid me about one thing; he had a soft spot for cats. Even now, when we are both around the sixty mark, he often talks to me over a beer about the cat he has had for many years. It is a typical relationship—they tease each other unmercifully—but it is based on real affection.

'It's no good, Triss,' I said gently. 'It's got to be done.' I reached for the syringe but something in me rebelled against plunging a needle into that mutilated body. Instead I pulled a fold of the blanket over the cat's head.

'Pour a little ether on to the cloth.' I said. 'He'll just sleep away.'

Wordlessly Tristan unscrewed the cap of the ether bottle and poised it above the head. Then from under the shapeless heap of blanket we heard it again; the deep purring which increased in volume till it boomed in our ears like a distant motor cycle.

Tristan was like a man turned to stone, hand gripping the bottle rigidly, eyes staring down at the mound of cloth from which the purring rose in waves of warm friendly sound.

At last he looked up at me and gulped. 'I don't fancy this much, Jim. Can't we do something?'

'You mean, put that lot back?'

'Yes.'

'But the bowels are damaged—they're like a sieve in parts.'

'We could stitch them, couldn't we?'

I lifted the blanket and looked again. 'Honestly, Triss, I wouldn't know where to start. And the whole think is filthy.'

He didn't say anything, but continued to look at me steadily. And I didn't need much persuading. I had no more desire to pour ether on to that comradely purring than he had.

'Come on, then,' I said. 'We'll have a go.'

With the oxygen bubbling and the cat's head in the anaesthetic mask we washed the whole prolapse with warm saline. We did it again and again but it was impossible to remove every fragment of caked dirt. Then we started the painfully slow business of stitching the many holes in the tiny intestines, and here I was glad of Tristan's nimble fingers which seemed better able to manipulate the small round-bodied needles than mine.

Two hours and yards of catgut later, we dusted the patched up peritoneal surface with sulphanilamide and pushed the entire mass back into the abdomen. When I had sutured muscle layers and skin everything looked tidy but I had a nasty feeling of sweeping undesirable things under the carpet. The extensive damage, all that contamination—peritonitis was inevitable.

'He's alive, anyway, Triss,' I said as we began to wash the instruments. 'We'll put him on to sulphapyridine and keep our fingers crossed.' There were still no antibiotics at that time but the new drug was a big advance.

The door opened and Helen came in. 'You've been a long time, Jim.' She walked over to the table and looked down at the sleeping cat. 'What a poor skinny little thing. He's all bones.'

'You should have seen him when he came in.' Tristan switched off the steriliser and screwed shut the valve on the anaesthetic machine. 'He looks a lot better now.'

She stroked the little animal for a moment. 'Is he badly injured?'

'I'm afraid so, Helen,' I said. 'We've done our best for him but I honestly don't think he has much chance.'

'What a shame. And he's pretty, too. Four white feet and all those unusual colours.' With her finger she traced the faint bands of auburn and copper-gold among the grey and black.

Tristan laughed. 'Yes, I think that chap has a ginger Tom somewhere in his ancestry.'

Helen smiled, too, but absently, and I noticed a broody look about her. She hurried out to the stock room and returned with an empty box.

'Yes . . . yes . . .' she said thoughtfully. 'I can make a bed in this box for him and he'll sleep in our room, Jim.'

'He will?'

'Yes, he must be warm, mustn't he?'

'Of course.'

Later, in the darkness of our bed-sitter, I looked from my pillow at a cosy scene. Sam in his basket on one side of the flickering fire and the cat cushioned and blanketed in his box on the other.

As I floated off into sleep it was good to know that my patient was so comfortable, but I wondered if he would be alive in the morning. . . .

I knew he was alive at 7.30 a.m. because my wife was already up and talking to him. I trailed across the room in my pyjamas and the cat and I looked at each other. I rubbed him under the chin and he opened his mouth in a rusty miaow. But he didn't try to move.

'Helen,' I said. 'This little thing is tied together inside with catgut. He'll have to live on fluids for a week and even then he probably won't make it. If he stays up here you'll be spooning milk into him umpteen times a day.'

'Okay, okay.' She had that broody look again.

It wasn't only milk she spooned into him over the next few days. Beef essence, strained broth and a succession of sophisticated baby foods found their way down his throat at regular intervals. One lunch time I found Helen kneeling by the box.

'We shall call him Oscar,' she said.

'You mean we're keeping him?'

'Yes.'

I am fond of cats but we already had a dog in our cramped quarters and I could see difficulties. Still I decided to let it go.

'Why Oscar?'

'I don't know.' Helen tipped a few drops of chop gravy on to the little red tongue and watched intently as he swallowed.

One of the things I like about women is their mystery, the unfathomable part of them, and I didn't press the matter further. But I was pleased at the way things were going. I had been giving the sulphapyridine every six hours and taking the temperature night and morning, expecting all the time to encounter the roaring fever, the vomiting and the tense abdomen of peritonitis. But it never happened.

It was as though Oscar's animal instinct told him he had to

move as little as possible because he lay absolutely still day after day and looked up at us—and purred.

His purr became part of our lives and when he eventually left his bed, sauntered through to our kitchen and began to sample Sam's dinner of meat and biscuit it was a moment of triumph. And I didn't spoil it by wondering if he was ready for solid food; I felt he knew.

From then on it was sheer joy to watch the furry scarecrow fill out and grow strong, and as he ate and ate and the flesh spread over his bones the true beauty of his coat showed in the glossy medley of auburn, black and gold. We had a handsome cat on our hands.

Once Oscar had fully recovered, Tristan was a regular visitor.

He probably felt, and rightly, that he, more than I, had saved Oscar's life in the first place and he used to play with him for long periods. His favourite ploy was to push his leg round the corner of the table and withdraw it repeatedly just as the cat pawed at it.

Oscar was justifiably irritated by this teasing but showed his character by lying in wait for Tristan one night and biting him smartly in the ankle before he could start his tricks.

From my own point of view Oscar added many things to our menage. Sam was delighted with him and the two soon became firm friends, Helen adored him and each evening I thought afresh that a nice cat washing his face by the hearth gave extra comfort to a room.

Oscar had been established as one of the family for several weeks when I came in from a late call to find Helen waiting for me with a stricken face.

'What's happened?' I asked.

'It's Oscar—he's gone!'

'Gone? What do you mean?'

'Oh, Jim, I think he's run away.'

I stared at her. 'He wouldn't do that. He often goes down to the garden at night. Are you sure he isn't there?'

'Absolutely. I've searched right into the yard. I've even had a walk round the town. And remember.' Her chin quivered. 'He . . . he ran away from somewhere before.'

I looked at my watch. 'Ten o'clock. Yes, that is strange. He shouldn't be out at this time.'

As I spoke the front door bell jangled. I galloped down the

stairs and as I rounded the corner in the passage I could see Mrs Heslington, the vicar's wife, through the glass. I threw open the door. She was holding Oscar in her arms.

'I believe this is your cat, Mr Herriot,' she said.

'It is indeed, Mrs Heslington. Where did you find him?'

She smiled. 'Well it was rather odd. We were having a meeting of the Mothers' Union at the church house and we noticed the cat sitting there in the room.'

'Just sitting . . . ?'

'Yes, as though he were listening to what we were saying and enjoying it all. It was unusual. When the meeting ended I thought I'd better bring him along to you.'

'I'm most grateful, Mrs Heslington.' I snatched Oscar and tucked him under my arm. 'My wife is distraught—she thought he was lost.'

It was a little mystery. Why should he suddenly take off like that? But since he showed no change in his manner over the ensuing week we put it out of our minds.

Then one evening a man brought in a dog for a distemper inoculation and left the front door open. When I went up to our flat I found that Oscar had disappeared again. This time Helen and I scoured the market place and side alleys in vain and when we returned at half past nine we were both despondent. It was nearly eleven and we were thinking of bed when the door bell rang.

It was Oscar again, this time resting on the ample stomach of Jack Newbould. Jack was leaning against a doorpost and the fresh country air drifting in from the dark street was richly intermingled with beer fumes.

Jack was a gardener at one of the big houses. He hiccuped gently and gave me a huge benevolent smile. 'Brought your cat, Mr Herriot.'

'Gosh, thanks, Jack!' I said, scooping up Oscar gratefully. 'Where the devil did you find him?'

'Well, s'matter o' fact, 'e sort of found me.'

'What do you mean?'

Jack closed his eyes for a few moments before articulating carefully. 'Thish is a big night, tha knows, Mr Herriot. Darts championship. Lots of t'lads round at t'Dog and Gun—lotsh and lotsh of 'em. Big gatherin'.'

'And our cat was there?'

'Aye, he were there, all right. Sittin' among t'lads. Shpent t'whole evenin' with us.'

'Just sat there, eh?'

'That 'e did.' Jack giggled reminiscently. 'By gaw 'e enjoyed isself. Ah gave 'im a drop o' best bitter out of me own glass and once or twice ah thought 'e was goin' to have a go at chuckin' a dart. He's some cat.' He laughed again.

As I bore Oscar upstairs I was deep in thought. What was going on here? These sudden desertions were upsetting Helen and I felt they could get on my nerves in time.

I didn't have long to wait till the next one. Three nights later he was missing again. This time Helen and I didn't bother to search—we just waited.

He was back earlier than usual. I heard the door bell at nine o'clock. It was the elderly Miss Simpson peering through the glass. And she wasn't holding Oscar—he was prowling on the mat waiting to come in.

Miss Simpson watched with interest as the cat stalked inside and made for the stairs. 'Ah, good, I'm so glad he's come home safely. I knew he was your cat and I've been intrigued by his behaviour all evening.'

'Where . . . may I ask?'

'Oh, at the Women's Institute. He came in shortly after we started and stayed there till the end.'

'Really? What exactly was your programme, Miss Simpson?'

'Well, there was a bit of committee stuff, then a short talk with lantern slides by Mr Walters from the water company and we finished with a cake-making competition.'

'Yes . . . yes . . . and what did Oscar do?'

She laughed. 'Mixed with the company, apparently enjoyed the slides and showed great interest in the cakes.'

'I see. And you didn't bring him home?'

'No, he made his own way here. As you know, I have to pass your house and I merely rang your bell to make sure you knew he had arrived.'

'I'm obliged to you, Miss Simpson. We were a little worried.'

I mounted the stairs in record time. Helen was sitting with the cat on her knee and she looked up as I burst in.

'I know about Oscar now,' I said.

'Know what?'

'Why he goes on these nightly outings. He's not running away —he's visiting.'

'Visiting?'

'Yes,' I said. 'Don't you see? He likes getting around, he loves people, especially in groups, and he's interested in what they do. He's a natural mixer.'

Helen looked down at the attractive mound of fur curled on her lap. 'Of course . . . that's it . . . he's a socialite!'

'Exactly, a high stepper!'

'A cat-about-town!'

It all afforded us some innocent laughter and Oscar sat up and looked at us with evident pleasure, adding his own throbbing purr to the merriment. But for Helen and me there was a lot of relief behind it; ever since our cat had started his excursions there had been the gnawing fear that we would lose him, and now we felt secure.

From that night our delight in him increased. There was endless joy in watching this facet of his character unfolding. He did the social round meticulously, taking in most of the activities of the town. He became a familiar figure at whist drives, jumble sales, school concerts and scout bazaars. Most of the time he was made welcome, but was twice ejected from meetings of the Rural District Council who did not seem to relish the idea of a cat sitting in on their deliberations.

At first I was apprehensive about his making his way through the streets but I watched him one or twice and saw that he looked both ways before tripping daintily across. Clearly he had excellent traffic sense and this made me feel that his original injury had not been caused by a car.

Taking it all in all, Helen and I felt that it was a kind stroke of fortune wihch had brought Oscar to us. He was a warm and cherished part of our home life. He added to our happiness.

When the blow fell it was totally unexpected.

I was finishing the evening surgery. I looked round the door and saw only a man and two little boys.

'Next, please,' I said.

The man stood up. He had no animal with him. He was middle-aged, with the rough weathered face of a farm worker. He twirled a cloth cap nervously in his hands.

'Mr Herriot?' he said.

'Yes, what can I do for you?'

He swallowed and looked me straight in the eyes. 'Ah think you've got ma cat.'

'What?'

'Ah lost ma cat a bit since.' He cleared his throat. 'We used to live at Missdon but ah got a job as ploughman to Mr Horne of Wederly. It was after we moved to Wederly that t'cat went missin'. Ah reckon he was tryin' to find 'is way back to his old home.'

'Wederly? That's on the other side of Brawton—over thirty miles away.'

'Aye, ah knaw, but cats is funny things.'

'But what makes you think I've got him?'

He twisted the cap around a bit more. 'There's a cousin o' mine lives in Darrowby and ah heard tell from 'im about this cat that goes around to meetin's. I 'ad to come. We've been huntin' everywhere.'

'Tell me,' I said. 'This cat you lost. What did he look like?'

'Grey and black and sort o' gingery. Right bonny 'e was. And 'e was allus goin' out to gatherin's.'

A cold hand clutched at my heart. 'You'd better come upstairs. Bring the boys with you.'

Helen was putting some coal on the fire of the bed-sitter.

'Helen,' I said. 'This is Mr—er—I'm sorry, I don't know your name.'

'Gibbons, Sep Gibbons. They called me Septimus because ah was the seventh in family and it looks like ah'm goin' t'same way 'cause we've got six already. These are our two youngest.' The two boys, obvious twins of about eight, looked up at us solemnly.

I wished my heart would stop hammering. 'Mr Gibbons thinks Oscar is his. He lost his cat some time ago.'

My wife put down her little shovel. 'Oh . . . oh . . . I see.' She stood very still, for a moment then smiled faintly. 'Do sit down. Oscar's in the kitchen, I'll bring him through.'

She went out and reappeared with the cat in her arms. She hadn't got through the door before the little boys gave tongue.

'Tiger!' they cried. 'Oh, Tiger, Tiger!'

The man's face seemed lit from within. He walked quickly across the floor and ran his big work-roughened hand along the fur.

'Hullo, awd lad,' he said, and turned to me with a radiant smile. 'It's 'im, Mr Herriot. It's 'im awright, and don't 'e look well!'

'You call him Tiger, eh?' I said.

'Aye,' he replied happily. 'It's them gingery stripes. The kids called 'im that. They were broken hearted when we lost 'im.'

As the two little boys rolled on the floor our Oscar rolled with them, pawing playfully, purring with delight.

Sep Gibbons sat down again. 'That's the way 'e allus went on wi' the family. They used to play with 'im for hours. By gaw we did miss 'im. He were a right favourite.'

I looked at the broken nails on the edge of the cap, at the decent, honest, uncomplicated Yorkshire face so like the many I had grown to like and respect. Farm men like him got thirty shillings a week in those days and it was reflected in the thread-bare jacket, the cracked, shiny boots and the obvious hand-me-downs of the boys.

But all three were scrubbed and tidy, the man's face like a red beacon, the children's knees gleaming and their hair carefully slicked across their foreheads. They looked like nice people to me. I didn't know what to say.

Helen said it for me. 'Well, Mr Gibbons.' Her tone had an unnatural brightness. 'You'd better take him.'

The man hesitated. 'Now then, are ye sure, Missis Herriot?'

'Yes . . . yes, I'm sure. He was your cat first.'

'Aye, but some folks 'ud say finders keepers or summat like that. Ah didn't come 'ere to demand 'im back or owt of t'sort.'

'I know you didn't, Mr Gibbons, but you've had him all those years and you've searched for him so hard. We couldn't possibly keep him from you.'

He nodded quickly. 'Well, that's right good of ye.' He paused for a moment, his face serious, then he stooped and picked Oscar up. 'We'll have to be off if we're goin' to catch the eight o'clock bus.'

Helen reached forward, cupped the cat's head in her hands and looked at him steadily for a few seconds. Then she patted the boys' heads. 'You'll take good care of him, won't you?'

'Aye, missis, thank ye, we will that.' The two small faces looked up at her and smiled.

'I'll see you down the stairs, Mr Gibbons,' I said.

On the descent I tickled the furry cheek resting on the man's shoulder and heard for the last time the rich purring. On the front door step we shook hands and they set off down the street. As they rounded the corner of Trengate they stopped and waved, and I waved back at the man, the two children and the cat's head looking back at me over the shoulder.

It was my habit at that time in my life to mount the stairs two or three at a time but on this occasion I trailed upwards like an old man, slightly breathless, throat tight, eyes prickling.

I cursed myself for a sentimental fool but as I reached our door I found a flash of consolation. Helen had taken it remarkably well. She had nursed that cat and grown deeply attached to him, and I'd have thought an unforeseen calamity like this would have upset her terribly. But no, she had behaved calmly and rationally. You never knew with women, but I was thankful.

It was up to me to do as well. I adjusted my features into the semblance of a cheerful smile and marched into the room.

Helen had pulled a chair close to the table and was slumped face down against the wood. One arm cradled her head while the other was stretched in front of her as her body shook with an utterly abandoned weeping.

I had never seen her like this and I was appalled. I tried to say something comforting but nothing stemmed the flow of racking sobs.

Feeling helpless and inadequate I could only sit close to her and stroke the back of her head. Maybe I could have said something if I hadn't felt just about as bad myself.

You get over these things in time. After all, we told ourselves, it wasn't as though Oscar had died or got lost again—he had gone to a good family who would look after him. In fact he had really gone home.

And of course, we still had our much-loved Sam, although he didn't help in the early stages by sniffing disconsolately where Oscar's bed used to lie then collapsing on the rug with a long lugubrious sigh.

There was one other thing, too. I had a little notion forming in my mind, an idea which I would spring on Helen when the time was right. It was about a month after that shattering night and we were coming out of the cinema at Brawton at the end of our half day. I looked at my watch.

'Only eight o'clock,' I said. 'How about going to see Oscar?'

Helen looked at me in surprise. 'You mean—drive on to Wederly?'

'Yes, it's only about five miles.'

A smile crept slowly across her face. 'That would be lovely. But do you think they would mind?'

'The Gibbons? No, I'm sure they wouldn't. Let's go.'

Wederly was a big village and the ploughman's cottage was at the far end a few yards beyond the Methodist chapel. I pushed open the garden gate and we walked down the path.

A busy-looking little woman answered my knock. She was drying her hands on a striped towel.

'Mrs Gibbons?' I said.

'Aye, that's me.'

'I'm James Herriot—and this is my wife.'

Her eyes widened uncomprehendingly. Clearly the name meant nothing to her.

'We had your cat for a while,' I added.

Suddenly she grinned and waved her towel at us. 'Oh aye, ah remember now. Sep told me about you. Come in, come in!'

The big kitchen-living room was a tableau of life with six children and thirty shillings a week. Battered furniture, rows of much-mended washing on a pulley, black cooking range and a general air of chaos.

Sep got up from his place by the fire, put down his newspaper, took off a pair of steel-rimmed spectacles and shook hands.

He waved Helen to a sagging armchair. 'Well, it's right nice to see you. Ah've often spoke of ye to t'missis.'

His wife hung up her towel. 'Yes, and I'm glad to meet ye both. I'll get some tea in a minnit.'

She laughed and dragged a bucket of muddy water into a corner. 'I've been washin' football jerseys. Them lads just handed them to me tonight—as if I haven't enough to do.'

As she ran the water into the kettle I peeped surreptitiously around me and I noticed Helen doing the same. But we searched in vain. There was no sign of a cat. Surely he couldn't have run away again? With a growing feeling of dismay I realised that my little scheme could backfire devastatingly.

It wasn't until the tea had been made and poured that I dared to raise the subject.

'How—' I asked diffidently. 'How is—er—Tiger?'

'Oh, he's grand,' the little woman replied briskly. She glanced up at the clock on the mantelpiece. 'He should be back any time now, then you'll be able to see 'im.'

As she spoke, Sep raised a finger. 'Ah think ah can hear 'im now.'

He walked over and opened the door and our Oscar strode in with all his old grace and majesty. He took one look at Helen and leaped on to her lap. With a cry of delight she put down her cup and stroked the beautiful fur as the cat arched himself against her hand and the familiar purr echoed round the room.

'He knows me,' she murmured. 'He knows me.'

Sep nodded and smiled. 'He does that. You were good to 'im. He'll never forget ye, and we won't either, will we mother?'

'No, we won't, Mrs Herriot,' his wife said as she applied butter to a slice of gingerbread. 'That was a kind thing ye did for us and I 'ope you'll come and see us all whenever you're near.'

'Well, thank you,' I said. 'We'd love to—we're often in Brawton.'

I went over and tickled Oscar's chin, then I turned again to Mrs Gibbons. 'By the way, it's after nine o'clock. Where has he been till now?'

She poised her butter knife and looked into space.

'Let's see, now,' she said. 'It's Thursday, isn't it? Ah yes, it's 'is night for the Yoga class."

CHAPTER

48

I knew it was the end of the chapter when I slammed the carriage door behind me and squeezed into a seat between a fat WAAF and a sleeping corporal.

I suppose I was an entirely typical discharged serviceman. They had taken away my blue uniform and fitted me with a 'demob suit', a ghastly garment of stiff brown serge with purple stripes which made me look like an old-time gangster, but they had allowed me to retain my R.A.F. shirt and tie and the shiny boots which were like old friends.

My few belongings, including Black's *Veterinary Dictionary*, lay in the rack above in a small cardboard suitcase of a type very popular among the lower ranks of the services. They were all I possessed and I could have done with a coat because it was cold in the train and a long journey stretched between Eastchurch and Darrowby.

It took an age to chug and jolt as far as London then there was a lengthy wait before I boarded the train for the north. It was about midnight when we set off, and for seven hours I sat there in the freezing darkness, feet numb, teeth chattering.

The last lap was by bus and it was the same rattling little vehicle that had carried me to my first job those years ago. The driver was the same too, and the time between seemed to melt away as the fells began to rise again from the blue distance in the early light and I saw the familiar farmhouses, the walls creeping up the grassy slopes, the fringe of trees by the river's edge.

It was mid morning when we rumbled into the market place and I read 'Darrowby Co-operative Society' above the shop on the far side. The sun was high, warming the tiles of the fretted line of roofs with their swelling green background of hills. I got out and the bus went on its way, leaving me standing by my case.

And it was just the same as before. The sweet air, the silence and the cobbled square deserted except for the old men sitting around the clock tower. One of them looked up at me.

'Now then, Mr Herriot,' he said quietly as though he had seen me only yesterday.

Before me Trengate curved away till it disappeared round the grocer's shop on the corner. Most of the quiet street with the church at its foot was beyond my view and it was a long time since I had been down there, but with my eyes closed I could see Skeldale House with the ivy climbing over the old brick walls to the little rooms under the eaves.

That was where I would have to make another start; where I would find out how much I had forgotten, whether I was fit to be an animal doctor again. But I wouldn't go along there yet, not just yet. . . .

A lot had happened since that first day when I arrived in Darrowby in search of a job but it came to me suddenly that my circumstances hadn't changed much. All I had possessed then was an old case and the suit I stood in and it was about the same now. Except for one great and wonderful thing. I had Helen and Jimmy.

That made all the difference. I had no money, not even a house to call my own, but any roof that covered my wife and son was personal and special. Sam would be with them, too, waiting for me. They were outside the town and it was a fair walk from here, but I looked down at the blunt toes of my boots sticking from the purple striped trousers. The R.A.F. hadn't only taught me to fly, they had taught me to march, and a few miles didn't bother me.

I took a fresh grip on my cardboard case, turned towards the exit from the square and set off, left-right, left-right, left-right on the road for home.

THE LORD GOD
MADE THEM ALL

TO ZOE
latest beautiful grandchild

Chapter
1

When the gate fell on top of me I knew I was really back home.

My mind drifted effortlessly back to the days before my spell in the R.A.F., and I recalled the last time I had visited the Ripleys. It was to "nip some calves," as Mr. Ripley said over the phone, or more correctly to emasculate them by means of the Burdizzo bloodless castrator, and with his summons I realised that a large part of my morning had gone.

It was always something of a safari to visit Anson Hall, because the old house lay at the end of a ridged and rutted track that twisted across the fields through no fewer than seven gates.

Gates are one of the curses of a country vet's life and in the Yorkshire Dales, before the coming of cattle grids, we suffered more than most. We were resigned to opening two or three on many farms but seven was a bit much. And at the Ripleys' it wasn't just the number but the character.

The first one, which led off the narrow road, was reasonably normal—an ancient thing of rusty iron—but when unlatched it, it did at least swing round, groaning on its hinges. It was the only one that swung; the others were of wood and of the type known in the Dales as "shoulder gates." I could see how they got their name as I hoisted each one up, balanced the top spar on my shoulder and dragged it round. These had no hinges but were tied at one end with binder twine, top and bottom.

Even with an ordinary gate there is a fair amount of work involved. You have to stop the car, get out, open the gate, drive through, stop the car again, dismount and close the thing behind you. But the road to Anson Hall was hard labour. The gates deteriorated progressively as I approached the farm, and I was puffing with my efforts as I bumped and rattled my way up to number seven.

This was the last and the most formidable—a malignant entity with a personality of its own. Over decades it had been patched and repaired with so many old timbers that probably none of the original structure remained. But it was dangerous.

I got out of the car and advanced a few steps. We were old foes, this gate and I, and we faced each other for some moments in the silence. We had fought several brisk rounds in the past and there was no doubt the gate was ahead on points.

The difficulty was that, apart from its wobbly, loosely nailed eccentricity, it had only one string hinge, halfway down. This enabled it to pivot on its frail axis with deadly effect.

With the utmost care I approached the right-hand side and began to unfasten the binder twine. The string, I noted bitterly, like all the others was neatly tied in a bow, and as it fell clear I grabbed hastily at the top spar. But I was too late. Like a live thing the bottom rail swung in and rapped me cruelly on the shins, and as I tried to correct the balance the top bashed my chest.

It was the same as all the other times. As I hauled it round an inch at a time, the gate buffeted me high and low. I was no match for it.

It was no help to see Mr. Ripley watching me benevolently from the farmhouse doorway. While I wrestled the gate open, contented puffs rose from the farmer's pipe and he did not stir from his position until I had hobbled over the last stretch of grass and stood before him.

"Now then, Mr. Herriot, you've come to nip me a few calves?" A smile of unaffected friendship creased the stubbled cheeks. Mr.

Ripley shaved once a week—on market day—considering, with some logic, that since only his wife and his cattle saw him on the other six days there was no point in scraping away at his face every morning with a razor.

I bent and massaged my bruised ankles. "Mr. Ripley, that gate! It's a menace! Do you remember that last time I was here you promised me faithfully you'd have it mended? In fact you said you'd get a new one—it's about time, isn't it?"

"Aye, you're right, young man," Mr. Ripley said, nodding his head in profound agreement. "Ah did say that, but tha knaws, it's one o' them little jobs which never seem to get done." He chuckled ruefully, but his expression altered to concern when I wound up my trouser leg and revealed a long abrasion on my shin.

"Eee, that's a shame; that's settled it. There'll be a new gate on there by next week. Ah'll guarantee it."

"But Mr. Ripley, that's exactly what you said last time when you saw the blood running down my knee. Those were your very words. You said you'd guarantee it."

"Aye, I knaw, I knaw." The farmer tamped down the tobacco with his thumb and got his pipe going again to his satisfaction. "Me missus is allus on to me about me bad memory, but don't worry, Mr. Herriot, I've had me lesson today. I'm right sorry about your leg, and that gate'll never bother ye again. Ah guarantee it."

"Okay, okay," I said and limped over to the car for the Burdizzo. "Where are the calves, anyway?"

Mr. Ripley crossed the farmyard unhurriedly and opened the half door on a loose box. "They're in there."

For a moment I stood transfixed as a row of huge, shaggy heads regarded me impassively over the timbers, then I extended a trembling finger. "Do you mean those?"

The farmer nodded happily. "Aye, them's them."

I went forward and looked into the box. There were eight strapping yearlings in there, some of them returning my stare with mild interest, others cavorting and kicking up their heels among the straw. I turned to the farmer. "You've done it again, haven't you?"

"Eh?"

"You asked me to come and nip some calves. Those aren't calves, they're bulls! And it was the same last time. Remember those monsters you had in the same box? I nearly ruptured myself closing the nippers, and you said you'd get them done at three months old in future. In fact you said you'd guarantee it."

The farmer nodded solemnly in agreement. He always agreed one hundred percent with everything I said. "That's correct, Mr. Herriot. That's what ah said."

"But these animals are at least a year old!"

Mr. Ripley shrugged and gave me a world-weary smile. "Aye, well, time gets on, doesn't it? Fairly races by."

I returned to the car for the local anaesthetic. "All right," I grunted as I filled the syringe. "If you can catch them I'll see what I can do." The farmer lifted a rope halter from a hook on the wall and approached one of the big beasts, murmuring encouragingly. He snared the nose with surprising ease, dropping the loops over nose and horn with perfect timing as the animal tried to plunge past him. Then he passed the rope through a ring on the wall and pulled it tight.

"There y'are, Mr. Herriot. That wasn't much trouble was it?"

I didn't say anything. I was the one who was going to have the trouble. I was working at the wrong end, nicely in range of the hooves which would surely start flying if my patients didn't appreciate having a needle stuck into their testicles.

Anyway, it had to be done. One by one I infiltrated the scrotal area with the local, taking the blows on my arms and legs as they came. Then I started the actual process of castration, the bloodless crushing of the spermatic cord without breaking the skin. There was no doubt this was a big advance on the old method of incising the scrotum with a knife and in little calves it was a trifling business lasting only a few seconds.

[4]

But it was altogether different with these vast creatures. It was necessary to open the arms of the Burdizzo beyond right angles to grip the great fleshy scrotum, and then they had to be closed again. That was when the fun started.

Thanks to my injection the beast could feel little or nothing, but as I squeezed desperately it seemed that I was attempting the impossible. However, it is amazing what the human frame can accomplish when pushed to the utmost, and as the sweat trickled down my nose and I gasped and strained, the metal arms inched closer until the jaws finally clicked together.

I always nipped each side twice, and I took a rest before repeating the process lower down the cord. When I had done the same with the other testicle I flopped back against the wall, panting and trying not to think of the other seven beasts still to do.

It was a long, long time before I got to the last one and I was wrestling away, pop-eyed and open-mouthed, when the idea came to me.

I straightened up and came along the side of the animal. "Mr. Ripley," I said breathlessly, "why don't you have a go?"

"Eh?" The farmer had been watching me with equanimity, blowing out slow clouds of blue smoke, but it was plain that I had jolted him out of his composure. "What d'ye mean?"

"Well, this is the last one, and I want you to understand what I've been talking about. I'd like to see you close those nippers."

He thought the matter over for a moment or two. "Aye, but who's goin' to hold t'beast?"

"That's all right," I said. "We'll tie him up short to the ring and I'll set everything up for you, then we'll see how you get on."

He looked a little doubtful but I was determined to make my point and ushered him gently to the rear end of the animal. I enclosed the scrotum in the Burdizzo and placed Mr. Ripley's fingers round the handles.

"Right," I said. "Off you go."

The farmer took a long breath, braced himself and began to exert pressure on the metal arms. Nothing happened.

[5]

I stood there for several minutes as his face turned red, then purple, his eyes protruded even further than mine and the veins on his forehead stood out in livid ridges. Finally he gave a groan and dropped to his knees.

"Nay, lad, nay, it's no good, I can't do it."

He got to his feet slowly and mopped his brow.

"But Mr. Ripley." I put a hand on his shoulder and smiled kindly at him. "You expect me to do it."

He nodded dumbly.

"Ah well, never mind," I said. "You understand now what I've been talking about. This is an easy little job made difficult by leaving it until the beasts are as big as this. If you'd called me out when they were calves of three months, I'd have been on and off your place in a few minutes, wouldn't I?"

"Aye, you would, Mr. Herriot, you're right. I've been daft, and I'll see it doesn't happen again."

I felt really clever. I don't often have moments of inspiration, but the conviction swelled in me that one of them had come to me today. I had finally got through to Mr. Ripley.

The feeling of exhilaration gave me added strength and I finished the job effortlessly. As I walked to the car I positively glowed, and my self-satisfaction deepened when the farmer bent to the window as I started the engine.

"Well, thank ye, Mr. Herriot," he said. "You've taught me summat this mornin. Next time ye come I'll have a nice new gate for ye and I'll never ask ye to nip big beasts like that again. Ah guarantee it."

All that had happened a long time ago, before the R.A.F., and I was now in the process of reinserting myself into civilian life, tasting the old things I had almost forgotten. But at the moment when the phone rang I was tasting something very near to my heart—Helen's cooking.

It was Sunday lunchtime, when the traditional roast beef and Yorkshire pudding were served. My wife had just dropped a slab of the pudding on my plate and was pouring gravy over it, a rich, brown flood with the soul of the meat in it and an aroma to dream of. I was starving, after a typical country vet's Sunday morning of rushing round the farms and I was thinking, as I often did, that if I had some foreign gourmet to impress with the choicest sample of our British food, then this is what I would give him.

A great chunk of Yorkshire pud and gravy was the expedient of the thrifty farmers to fill their families' stomachs before the real meal started—"Them as eats most puddin' gets most meat," was the wily encouragement—but it was heaven. And as I chewed my first forkful I was happy in the knowledge that when I had cleared my plate Helen would fill it again with the beef itself and with potatoes, peas and runner beans gathered from our garden that morning.

The shrilling phone cut cruelly into my reverie, but I told myself that nothing was going to spoil this meal. The most urgent job in veterinary practice could wait until I had finished.

But my hand shook as I lifted the receiver, and a mixture of anxiety and disbelief flowed through me as I heard the voice at the other end. It was Mr. Ripley. Oh please, no, not that long, long trek to Anson Hall on a Sunday.

The farmer's voice thundered in my ear. He was one of the many who still thought you had to bawl lustily to cover the miles between.

"Is that vitnery?"

"Yes, Herriot speaking."

"Oh, you're back from t'war, then?"

"Yes, that's right."

"Well, ah want ye out here right away. One of me cows is right bad."

"What's the trouble? Is it urgent?"

"Aye, it is! I think she's maybe broke 'er leg!"

I held the ear piece away from me. Mr. Ripley had increased his volume, and my head was beginning to ring. "What makes you think that?" I asked, suddenly dry-mouthed.

"Well, she's on three legs," the farmer blasted back at me. "And t'other's sort of hangin', like."

Oh God, that sounded horribly significant. I looked sadly across the room at my loaded plate. "All right, Mr. Ripley, I'll be along."

"You'll come straight away, won't ye? Right now?" The voice was an importunate roar.

"Yes, I'll come straight away." I put down the receiver, rubbed my ear and turned to my wife.

Helen looked up from the table with the stricken face of a woman who can visualise her Yorkshire pudding sagging into lifeless ruin. "Oh surely you don't have to go this minute?"

"I'm sorry, Helen, this is one of those things I can't leave." I could picture only too easily the injured animal plunging around in her agony, perhaps compounding the fracture. "And the man sounds desperate. I've just got to go."

My wife's lips trembled. "All right, I'll put it in the oven till you come back."

As I left I saw her carrying the plate away. We both knew it was the end. No Yorkshire pud could survive a visit to Anson Hall.

I increased my speed as I drove through Darrowby. The cobbled market place, sleeping in the sunshine, breathed its Sunday peace and emptiness with all the inhabitants of the little town eating busily behind closed doors. Out in the country the dry stone walls flashed by as I kept my foot on the boards, and when I finally arrived at the beginning of the farm track I had a sense of shock.

It was the first time I had been there since I had left the service, and I suppose I had been expecting to find something different. But the old iron gate was just the same, except that it was even more rusty than before. With a growing feeling of doom I fought my way through the other gates, untying the strings and shouldering the top spars round till finally I came to number seven.

This last and most terrible of the gates was still there, and unchanged. It couldn't be true, I told myself as I almost tiptoed towards it. All sorts of things had happened to me since I had last seen it. I had been away in a different world of marching and drilling and learning navigation and finally flying an aeroplane, while this rickety structure stood there unheeding.

I eyed it closely. The loose-nailed wobbly timbers were as before, as was the single string hinge—probably the same piece of string. It was unbelievable. And then I noticed something different. Mr. Ripley, apparently worried lest his livestock might rub against and damage the ancient bastion, had festooned the thing with barbed wire.

Maybe it had mellowed with time. It couldn't be as vicious as before. Gingerly I loosened the bottom string on the right-hand side, then with infinite care I untied the bow at the top. I was just thinking that it was going to be easy when the binder twine fell away and the gate swung with all its old venom on the left-hand string.

It got me on the chest first, then whacked against my legs, and this time the steel barbs bit through my trousers. Frantically I tried to throw the thing away from me, but it pounded me high and low and when I leaned back to protect my chest, my legs slid from under me and I fell on my back. And as my shoulders hit the track, the gate, with a soft woody crunch, fell on top of me.

I had been nearly underneath this gate several times in the past and had got clear at the last moment, but this time it had really happened. I tried to wriggle out, but the barbed wire had my clothing in its iron grip. I was trapped.

I craned desperately over the timbers. The farm was only fifty yards away, but there was not a soul in sight. And that was a funny thing. Where was the anxious farmer? I had expected to find him pacing up and down the yard, wringing his hands, but the place seemed deserted.

I dallied with the idea of shouting for help, but that would have been just too absurd. There was nothing else for it. I seized the top rail in both hands and pushed upwards, trying to close my ears to the tearing sounds from my garments, then, very slowly, I eased my way to safety.

I left the gate lying where it was. Normally I meticulously close all gates behind me but there were no cattle in the fields and anyway, I had had enough of this one.

I rapped sharply at the farmhouse door and Mrs. Ripley answered.

"Now then, Mr. Herriot, it's grand weather," she said. Her carefree smile reminded me of her husband's as she wiped at a dinner plate and adjusted the apron around her ample midriff.

"Yes . . . yes . . . it is. I've called to see your cow. Is your husband in?"

She shook her head. "Nay, 'e hasn't got back from t'Fox and Hounds yet."

"What!" I stared at her. "That's the pub at Diverton, isn't it? I thought he had an urgent case for me to see."

"Aye, well, he had to go across there to ring ye up. We haven't no telephone here, ye know." Her smile widened.

"But—but that was nearly an hour since. He should have been back here long ago."

"That's right," she said, nodding with perfect understanding. "But he'll 'ave met some of his pals up there. They all get into t'Fox and Hounds on a Sunday mornin'."

I churned my hair around. "Mrs. Ripley, I've left my meal lying on the table so that I could get here immediately!"

"Oh, we've 'ad ours," she replied, as though the words would be a comfort to me. And she didn't have to tell me. The rich scent drifting from the kitchen was unmistakably roast beef, and there was no doubt at all it would have been preceded by Yorkshire pudding.

I didn't say anything for a few moments, then I took a deep breath. "Well, maybe I can see the cow. Where is she, please?"

Mrs. Ripley pointed to a box at the far end of the yard.

"She's in there." As I set off across the cobbles she called after me. "You can be lookin' at her till 'e gets back. He won't be many minutes."

I flinched as though a lash had fallen across my shoulders.

Those were dreadful words. "Not many minutes" was a common phrase in Yorkshire and could mean anything up to two hours.

I opened the half-door and looked into the box at the cow. She was very lame, but when I approached her she hopped around in the straw, dotting the injured limb on the ground.

Well, she hadn't a broken leg. She couldn't take her weight on it, but there was none of the typical dangling of the limb. I felt a surge of relief. In a big animal a fracture usually meant the humane killer because no number of plaster bandages could take the strain. The trouble seemed to be in her foot but I couldn't catch her to find out. I'd have to wait for Mr. Ripley.

I went out into the afternoon sunshine and gazed over the gently rising fields to the church tower of Diverton pushing from the trees. There was no sign of the farmer and I walked wearily beyond the buildings onto the grass to await his coming.

I looked back at the house, and even through my exasperation I felt a sense of peace. Like many of the older farms, Anson Hall had once been a noble manor. Hundreds of years ago some person of title had built his dwelling in a beautiful place. The roof looked ready to fall in and one of the tall chimney stacks leaned drunkenly to one side, but the mullioned windows, the graceful arched doorway and the stately proportions of the building were a delight, with the pastures beyond stretching towards the green fells.

And that garden wall. In its former glory the sun-warmed stones would have enclosed a cropped lawn with bright flowers, but now there were only nettles. Those nettles fascinated me; a waist-high jungle filling every inch of space between wall and house. Farmers are notoriously bad gardeners but Mr. Ripley was in a class by himself.

My reverie was interrupted by a cry from the lady of the house. "He's comin', Mr. Herriot. I've just spotted 'im through the window." She came round to the front and pointed towards Diverton.

Her husband was indeed on his way, a black dot moving unhurriedly down through the fields and we watched him together for about fifteen minutes until at last he squeezed himself through a gap in a wall and came up to us, the smoke from his pipe rising around his ears.

I went straight into the attack. "Mr. Ripley, I've been waiting a long time! You asked me to come straight away!"

"Aye, ah knaw, ah knaw, but I couldn't very well ask to use t'phone without havin' a pint, could I?" He put his head on one side and beamed at me, secure in his unanswerable logic.

I was about to speak when he went on. "And then Dick Henderson bought me one, so I had to buy 'im one back, and then I was just leavin' when Bobby Talbot started on about them pigs he got from me last week."

His wife chipped in with bright curiosity. "Eee, that Bobby Talbot! Was he there this mornin', too? He's never away from t'pub, that feller. I don't know how his missus puts up with it."

"Aye, Bobby was there, all right. He allus is." Mr. Ripley smiled gently, knocked his pipe out against his heel and began to refill it. "And ah'll tell you who else ah saw—Dan Thompson. Haven't seen 'im since his operation. By gaw, it has fleeced him —he's lost a bit o' ground. Looks as though a few pints would do 'im good."

"Dan, eh?" Mrs. Ripley said eagerly. "That's good news, any road. From what I heard they thought he'd never come out of t'hospital."

"Excuse me," I broke in.

"Nay, nay, that was just talk," Mr. Ripley continued. "It was nobbut a stone in t'kidney. Dan'll be all right. He was tellin' me . . ."

I held up a hand. "Mr. Ripley, can I please see this cow? I haven't had my lunch yet. My wife put it back in the oven when you phoned."

"Oh, I 'ad mine afore I went up there." He gave me a reassuring smile and his wife nodded and laughed to put my mind fully at rest.

"Well, that's splendid," I said frigidly. "I'm glad to hear that."

[12]

But I could see that they took me at my word. The sarcasm was lost on them.

In the loose box Mr. Ripley haltered the cow and I lifted the foot. Cradling it on my knee I scraped away the caked muck with a hoof knife and there, glinting dully as the sunshine slanted in at the door, was the cause of the trouble. I seized the metal stud with forceps, dragged it from the foot and held it up.

The farmer blinked at it for a few seconds, then his shoulders began to shake gently. "One of me own hobnails. Heh, heh, heh. Well, that's a rum un. Ah must've knocked it out on t'cobbles; they're right slippery over there. Once or twice I've nearly gone arse over tip. I was sayin' to t'missus just t'other day . . ."

"I really must get on, Mr. Ripley," I interposed. "Remember, I still haven't had my lunch. I'll just slip out to the car for an antitetanus injection for the cow."

I gave her the shot, dropped the syringe into my pocket and was on my way across the yard when the farmer called after me.

"Have ye got your nippers with ye, Mr. Herriot?"

"Nippers . . .?" I halted and looked back at him. I couldn't believe this. "Well, yes, I have, but surely you don't want to start castrating calves now?"

The farmer flicked an ancient brass lighter and applied a long sheet of flame to the bowl of his pipe. "There's nobbut one, Mr. Herriot. Won't take a minute."

Ah, well, I thought, as I opened the boot and fished out the Burdizzo from its resting place on my calving overall. It didn't really matter now. My Yorkshire pudding was a write-off, a dried-up husk by now, and the beef and those gorgeous fresh vegetables would be almost cremated. All was lost, and nipping a calf wasn't going to make any difference.

As I turned back, a pair of double doors at the end of the yard burst open and an enormous black animal galloped out and stood looking around him warily in the bright sunshine, pawing the ground and swishing his tail bad-temperedly. I stared at the spreading horns, the great hump of muscle on the shoulder and

[13]

the coldly glittering eyes. It only needed a blast on a trumpet and sand instead of cobbles and I was in the Plaza de Toros in Madrid.

"Is that the calf?" I asked.

The farmer nodded cheerfully. "Aye, that's 'im. I thowt I'd better run 'im over to the cow house so we could tie 'im up by the neck."

A wave of rage swept over me and for a moment I thought I was going to start shouting at the man, then, strangely, I felt only a great weariness.

I walked over to him, put my face close to his and spoke quietly. "Mr. Ripley, it's a long time since we met, and you've had plenty of opportunities to keep the promise you made me then. Remember? About getting your calves nipped when they were little and about replacing that gate? Now look at that great bull and see what your gate has done to my clothes."

The farmer gazed with genuine concern at the snags and tears in my trousers and reached out to touch a gaping rent in my sleeve.

"Eee, I'm right sorry about that." He glanced at the bull. "And I reckon 'e is a bit big."

I didn't say anything and after a few moments the farmer threw up his head and looked me in the eye, a picture of resolution.

"Aye, it's not right," he said. "But ah'll tell ye summat. Just nip this 'un today, and I'll see nowt of this ever happens again."

I wagged a finger at him. "But you've said that before. Do you really mean it this time?"

He nodded vigorously. "Ah'll guarantee it."

Strangely, the familiar hollow promise did not irk me as I might have expected. Perhaps it was because I'd been away from Yorkshire so long, seeing a world changing faster than I sometimes liked, but this homely sign of immutability tickled me. I chuckled. And then I began to laugh. "A-ha," I bubbled, "a-ha-ha-ha!" Soon Mrs. Ripley got caught up with it. "Hee!" she agreed. "Hee-hee! Hee-hee!" And Mr. Ripley took his pipe from his mouth with great deliberation and said, "Heh. Heh-heh. Heh-

[14]

heh-heh." And the three of us stood there, bawling away a Sunday afternoon together.

Just then the bull snorted derisively.

"Aye, it's true," Mr. Ripley stammered through his laughter, wiping his eyes. "If ah was in your place, I wouldn't be laughing either."

Chapter
2

"Oooh . . . ooh-hoo-hooo!" The broken-hearted sobbing jerked me into full wakefulness. It was 1 A.M., and after the familiar jangling of the bedside phone I expected the gruff voice of a farmer with a calving cow. Instead, there was this terrible sound.

"Who is this?" I asked a little breathlessly. "What on earth is the trouble?"

I heard a gulping at the other end and then a man's voice pleading between sobs, "It's Humphrey Cobb. For God's sake, come out and see Myrtle. I think she's dyin'."

"Myrtle?"

"Aye, me poor little dog. She's in a 'ell of a state! Oooh-hooo!"

The receiver trembled in my grasp. "What is she doing?"

"Oh, pantin' and gaspin'. I think it's nearly all over with 'er. Come quick!"

"Where do you live?"

"Cedar House. End of Hill Street."

"I know it. I'll be there very soon."

"Oh, thank ye, thank ye. Myrtle hasn't got long. Hurry, hurry!"

I leaped from the bed and rushed at my clothes, draped over a chair against the wall. In my haste, in the darkness, I got both feet down one leg of my working corduroys and crashed full length on the floor.

Helen was used to nocturnal calls and often she only half

awoke. For my part, I always tried to avoid disturbing her by dressing without switching on the light, using the glow from the night light we kept burning on the landing for young Jimmy.

However, the system broke down this time. The thud of my falling body brought her into a sitting position.

"What is it, Jim? What's happening?"

I struggled to my feet. "It's all right, Helen, I just tripped over." I snatched my shirt from the chair back.

"But what are you dashing about for?"

"Desperately urgent case. I have to hurry."

"All right, Jim, but you won't get there any sooner by going on like this. Just calm down."

My wife was right, of course. I have always envied those vets who can stay relaxed under pressure. But I wasn't made that way.

I galloped down the stairs and through the long back garden to the garage. Cedar House was only a mile away and I didn't have much time to think about the case, but by the time I arrived I had pretty well decided that an acute dyspnoea like this would probably be caused by a heart attack or some sudden allergy.

In answer to my ring the porch light flashed on, and Humphrey Cobb stood before me. He was a little round man in his sixties, and his humpty-dumpty appearance was accentuated by his gleaming bald head.

"Oh, Mr. Herriot, come in, come in," he cried brokenly as the tears streamed down his cheeks. "Thank ye for gettin' out of your bed to help me poor little Myrtle."

As he spoke, the blast of whisky fumes almost made my head spin and I noticed that as he preceded me across the hall he staggered slightly.

My patient was lying in a basket by the side of an Aga cooker in a large, well-appointed kitchen. I felt a warm surge when I saw that she was a beagle like my own dog, Sam. I knelt down and looked at her closely. Her mouth was open and her tongue lolled, but she did not seem to be in acute distress. In fact, as I patted her head her tail flapped against the blanket.

[17]

A heart-rending wail sounded in my ear. "What d'ye make of her, Mr. Herriot? It's her heart, isn't it? Oh, Myrtle, Myrtle!" The little man crouched over his pet, and the tears flowed unchecked.

"You know, Mr. Cobb," I said. "She doesn't seem all that bad to me, so don't upset yourself too much. Just give me a chance to examine her."

I placed my stethoscope over the ribs and listened to the steady thudding of a superbly strong heart. The temperature was normal, and I was palpating the abdomen when Mr. Cobb broke in again.

"The trouble is," he gasped, "I neglect this poor little animal."

"What do you mean?"

"Well, ah've been all day at Catterick at the races, gamblin' and drinkin', with never a thought for me dog."

"You left her alone all that time in the house?"

"Nay, nay, t'missus has been with her."

"Well, then." I felt I was getting out of my depth. "She would feed Myrtle and let her out in the garden?"

"Oh aye," he said, wringing his hands. "But I shouldn't leave 'er. She thinks such a lot about me."

As he spoke, I could feel one side of my face tingling with heat. My problem was suddenly solved.

"You've got her too near the Aga," I said. "She's panting because she's uncomfortably hot."

He looked at me doubtfully. "We just shifted 'er basket today. We've been gettin' some new tiles put down on the floor."

"Right," I said. "Shift it back again and she'll be fine."

"But Mr. Herriot." His lips began to tremble again. "It's more than that. She's sufferin'. Look at her eyes."

Myrtle had the lovely big liquid eyes of her breed and she knew how to use them. Many people think the spaniel is number one when it comes to looking soulful, but I personally plump for the beagle. And Myrtle was an expert.

"Oh, I shouldn't worry about that, Mr. Cobb," I said. "Believe me, she'll be all right."

[18]

He still seemed unhappy. "But aren't ye going to do something?"

It was one of the great questions in veterinary practice. If you didn't "do something," they were not satisfied. And in this case, Mr. Cobb was in greater need of treatment than his pet. Still, I wasn't going to stick a needle into Myrtle just to please him so I produced a vitamin tablet from my bag and pushed it over the back of the little animal's tongue.

"There you are," I said. "I'm sure that will do her good." And after all, I thought, I wasn't a complete charlatan—it wouldn't do her any harm.

Mr. Cobb relaxed visibly. "Eee, that's champion. You've set me mind at rest." He led the way into a luxurious drawing room and tacked unsteadily towards a cocktail cabinet. "You'll 'ave a drink before you go?"

"No, really, thanks," I said. "I'd rather not, if you don't mind."

"Well, I'll 'ave a drop. Just to steady me nerves. I was that upset." He tipped a lavish measure of whisky into a glass and waved me to a chair.

My bed was calling me, but I sat down and watched as he drank. He told me that he was a retired bookmaker from the West Riding and that he had come to Darrowby only a month ago. Although no longer directly connected with horse racing, he still loved the sport and never missed a meeting in the north of England.

"I allus get a taxi to take me and I have a right good day." His face was radiant as he recalled the happy times, then for a moment his cheeks quivered and his woebegone expression returned. "But I neglect me dog. I leave her at home."

"Oh nonsense," I said. "I've seen you out in the fields with Myrtle. You give her plenty of exercise, don't you?"

"Oh aye, lots of walks every day."

"Well, then she really has a good life. This is just a silly little notion you've got."

He beamed at me and sloshed out another few fingers of

whisky. "Eee, you're a good lad. Come on, you'll just have one before you go."

"Oh, all right, just a small one, then."

As we drank he became more and more benign until he was gazing at me with something like devotion.

"James Herriot," he slurred. "I suppose it'll be Jim, eh?"

"Well, yes."

"I'll call you Jim, then, and you can call me Humphrey."

"Okay, Humphrey," I said, and swallowed the last of my whisky. "But I really must go now."

Out in the street he put a hand on my arm and his face became serious again. "Thank ye, Jim. Myrtle was right bad tonight and I'm grateful."

Driving away, I realised that I had failed to convince him that there was nothing wrong with his dog. He was sure I had saved her life. It had been an unusual visit and as my 2 A.M. whisky burned in my stomach I decided that Humphrey Cobb was a very funny little man. But I liked him.

After that night I saw him quite frequently, exercising Myrtle in the fields. With his almost spherical build he seemed to bounce over the grass, but his manner was always self-contained and rational, except that he kept thanking me for pulling his dog back from the jaws of death.

Then quite suddenly I was back at the beginning again. It was shortly after midnight and as I lifted the bedside phone, I could hear the distraught weeping before the receiver touched my ear.

"Oooh . . . oooh . . . Jim, Jim. Myrtle's in a terrible bad way. Will ye come?"

"What . . . what is it this time?"

"She's twitchin'."

"Twitching?"

"Aye, twitchin' summat terrible. Oh, come on, Jim, lad, don't keep me waiting. I'm worried to death. I'm sure she's got distemper." He broke down again.

[20]

My head began to reel. "She can't have distemper, Humphrey. Not in a flash, like that."

"I'm beggin' you, Jim," he went on as though he hadn't heard. "Be a pal. Come and see Myrtle."

"All right," I said wearily. "I'll be there in a few minutes."

"Oh, you're a good lad, Jim, you're a good lad. . . ." The voice trailed away as I replaced the phone.

I dressed at normal speed with none of the panic of the first time. It sounded like a repetition, but why after midnight again? On my way to Cedar House I decided it must be another false alarm—but you never knew.

The same dizzying wave of whisky fumes enveloped me in the porch. Humphrey, sniffling and moaning, fell against me once or twice as he ushered me into the kitchen. He pointed to the basket in the corner.

"There she is," he said, wiping his eyes. "I've just got back from Ripon and found 'er like this."

"Racing again, eh?"

"Aye, gamblin' on them 'osses and drinkin' and leavin' me poor dog pinin' at home. I'm a rotter, Jim, that's what I am."

"Rubbish, Humphrey! I've told you before. You're not doing her any harm by having a day out. Anyway, how about this twitching? She looks all right now."

"Yes, she's stopped doing it, but when I came in her back leg was goin' like this." He made a jerking movement with his hand.

I groaned inwardly. "But she could have been scratching or flicking away a fly."

"Nay, there's summat more than that. I can tell she's sufferin'. Just look at them eyes."

I could see what he meant. Myrtle's beagle eyes were pools of emotion, and it was easy to read melting reproach in their depths.

With a feeling of futility I examined her. I knew what I would find—nothing. But when I tried to explain to the little man that his pet was normal, he wouldn't have it.

"Oh, you'll give her one of them wonderful tablets," he pleaded. "It cured her last time."

I felt I had to pacify him, so Myrtle received another installment of vitamins.

Humphrey was immensely relieved and weaved his way to the drawing room and the whisky bottle.

"I need a little pick-me-up after that shock," he said. "You'll 'ave one, too, won't you, Jim, lad?"

This pantomime was enacted frequently over the next few months, always after race meetings and always between midnight and 1 A.M. I had ample opportunity to analyse the situation, and I came to a fairly obvious conclusion.

Most of the time Humphrey was a normal conscientious pet owner, but after a large intake of alcohol his affectionate feelings degenerated into glutinous sentimentality and guilt. I invariably went out when he called me because I knew that he would be deeply distressed if I refused. I was treating Humphrey, not Myrtle.

It amused me that not once did he accept my protestations that my visit was unnecessary. Each time he was sure that my magic tablets had saved his dog's life.

Mind you, I did not discount the possibility that Myrtle was deliberately working on him with those eyes. The canine mind is quite capable of disapproval. I took my own dog almost everywhere with me, but if I left him at home to take Helen to the cinema he would lie under our bed, sulking, and, when he emerged, would studiously ignore us for an hour or two.

I quailed when Humphrey told me he had decided to have Myrtle mated because I knew that the ensuing pregnancy would be laden with harassment for me.

That was how it turned out. The little man flew into a series of alcoholic panics, all of them unfounded, and he discovered imaginary symptoms in Myrtle at regular intervals throughout the nine weeks.

[22]

I was vastly relieved when she gave birth to five healthy pups. Now, I thought, I would get some peace. The fact was that I was just about tired of Humphrey's nocturnal nonsense. I have always made a point of never refusing to turn out at night, but Humphrey had stretched this principle to breaking point. One of these times he would have to be told.

The crunch came when the pups were a few weeks old. I had had a terrible day, starting with a prolapsed uterus in a cow at 5 A.M. and progressing through hours of road slogging, missed meals and a late-night wrestle with ministry forms, some of which I suspected I had filled up wrongly.

My clerical incompetence has always infuriated me and when I crawled, dog-tired, into bed, my mind was still buzzing with frustration. I lay for a long time, trying to put those forms away from me, and it was well after midnight when I fell asleep.

I have always had a silly fancy that our practice knew when I desperately wanted a full night's sleep. It knew and gleefully stepped in. When the phone exploded in my ear, I wasn't really surprised.

As I stretched a weary hand to the receiver, the luminous dial of the alarm clock read 1:15 A.M.

"Hello," I grunted.

"Oooh . . . oooh . . . oooh!" The reply was only too familiar.

I clenched my teeth. This was just what I needed. "Humphrey! What is it this time?"

"Oh, Jim, Myrtle's really dyin', I know she is. Come quick, lad, come quick!"

"Dying?" I took a couple of rasping breaths. "How do you make that out?"

"Well . . . she's stretched out on 'er side, tremblin'."

"Anything else?"

"Aye, t'missus said Myrtle's been lookin' worried and walkin' stiff when she let her out in the garden this afternoon. I'm not long back from Redcar, ye see."

"So you've been to the races, eh?"

"That's right . . . neglectin' me dog. I'm a scamp, nothin' but a scamp."

I closed my eyes in the darkness. There was no end to Humphrey's imaginary symptoms. Trembling, this time, looking worried, walking stiff. We'd had panting and twitching and head nodding and ear shaking—what would it be next?

But enough was enough. "Look, Humphrey," I said. "There's nothing wrong with your dog. I've told you again and again . . ."

"Oh, Jim, lad, don't be long. Oooh-hooo!"

"I'm not coming, Humphrey."

"Nay, nay, don't say that! She's goin' fast, I tell ye!"

"I really mean it. It's just wasting my time and your money, so go to bed. Myrtle will be fine."

As I lay quivering between the sheets, I realised that refusing to go out was an exhausting business. There was no doubt in my mind that it would have taken less out of me to get up and attend another charade at Cedar House than to say no for the first time in my life. But this couldn't go on. I had to make a stand.

I was still tormented by remorse when I fell into an uneasy slumber, and it is a good thing that the subconscious mind works on during sleep because with the alarm clock reading 2:30 A.M. I came suddenly wide awake.

"My God!" I cried, staring at the dark ceiling. "Myrtle's got eclampsia!"

I scrambled from the bed and began to throw on my clothes. I must have made some commotion because I heard Helen's sleepy voice.

"What is it? What's the matter?"

"Humphrey Cobb!" I gasped, tying a shoe lace.

"Humphrey . . . but you said there was never any hurry . . ."

"There is th is time. His dog's dying." I glared again at the clock. "In fact, she could be dead now." I lifted my tie, then hurled it back on the chair. "Damn it! I don't need that!" I fled from the room.

Down the long garden and into the car with my brain spelling out the concise case history which Humphrey had given me. Small bitch nursing five puppies, signs of anxiety and stiff gait this afternoon, and now prostrate and trembling. Classical puerperal eclampsia. Rapidly fatal without treatment. And it was nearly an hour and a half since he had phoned. I couldn't bear to think about it.

Humphrey was still up. He had obviously been consoling himself with the bottle because he could barely stand.

"You've come, Jim, lad," he mumbled, blinking at me.

"Yes, how is she?"

"Just t'same . . ."

Clutching my calcium and my intravenous syringe, I rushed past him into the kitchen.

Myrtle's sleek body was extended in a tetanic spasm. She was gasping for breath, quivering violently, and bubbles of saliva dripped from her mouth. Those eyes had lost their softness and were fixed in a frantic stare. She looked terrible, but she was alive . . . she was alive.

I lifted the squealing pups onto a rug nearby and quickly clipped and swabbed the area over the radial vein. I inserted the needle into the blood vessel and began to depress the plunger with infinite care and very slowly. Calcium was the cure for this condition but a quick blast would surely kill the patient.

I took several minutes to empty the syringe, then sat back on my heels and watched. Some of these cases needed narcotics as well as calcium, and I had nembutal and morphine ready to hand. But as the time passed, Myrtle's breathing slowed down and the rigid muscles began to relax. When she started to swallow her saliva and look round at me, I knew she would live.

I was waiting for the last tremors to disappear from her limbs

[25]

when I felt a tap on my shoulder. Humphrey was standing there with the whisky bottle in his hand.

"You'll 'ave one, won't you, Jim?"

I didn't need much persuading. The knowledge that I had almost been responsible for Myrtle's death had thrown me into a mild degree of shock.

My hand was still shaking as I raised the glass, and I had barely taken the first sip when the little animal got up from the basket and walked over to inspect her pups. Some eclampsias were slow to respond but others were spectacularly quick, and I was grateful for the sake of my nervous system that this was one of the quick ones.

In fact the recovery was almost uncanny because, after sniffing her family over, Myrtle walked across the table to greet me. Her eyes brimmed with friendliness and her tail waved high in the true beagle fashion.

I was stroking her ears when Humphrey broke into a throaty giggle. "You know, Jim, I've learned summat tonight." His voice was a slow drawl but he was still in possession of his wits.

"What's that, Humphrey?"

"I've learned . . . hee-hee-hee . . . I've learned what a silly feller I've been all these months."

"How do you mean?"

He raised a forefinger and wagged it sagely. "Well, you've allus been tellin' me that I got you out of your bed for nothin' and I was imaginin' things when I thought me dog was ill."

"Yes," I said. "That's right."

"And I never believed you, did I? I wouldn't be told. Well, now I know you were right all the time. I've been nobbut a fool, and I'm right sorry for botherin' you all those nights."

"Oh, I shouldn't worry about that, Humphrey."

"Aye, but it's not right." He waved a hand towards his bright-faced, tail-wagging little dog. "Just look at her. Anybody can see there was never anythin' wrong with Myrtle tonight."

Chapter
3

The high moorland road was unfenced, and my car wheels ran easily from the strip of tarmac onto the turf, cropped to a velvet closeness by the sheep. I stopped the engine, got out and looked around me.

The road cut cleanly through the grass and heather before dipping into the valley beyond. This was one of the good places where I could see into two dales, the one I had left and the one in front. The whole land was spread beneath me; the soft fields in the valley floors, the grazing cattle, the rivers pebbled at their edges in places, thickly fringed with trees at others.

The brilliant green of the walled pastures pushed up the sides of the fells until the heather and the harsh moor grass began, and only the endless pattern of walls was left, climbing to the mottled summits, disappearing over the bare ridges that marked the beginning of the wild country.

I leaned back against the car and the wind blew the cold sweet air around me. I had been back in civilian life only a few weeks, and during my time in R.A.F. blue I had thought constantly of Yorkshire, but I had forgotten how beautiful it was. Just thinking from afar could not evoke the peace, the solitude, the sense of the nearness of the wild that makes the Dales thrilling and comforting at the same time. Among the crowds of men and the drabness and stale air of the towns, my imagination could not sufficiently conjure up a place where I could be quite alone on the wide green roof of England where every breath was filled with the grass scent.

I had had a disturbing morning. Everywhere I had gone I was reminded that I had come back to a world of change, and I did not like change. One old farmer saying, "It's all t'needle now, Mr. Herriot," as I injected his cow had made me look down almost with surprise at the syringe in my hand, realising suddenly that this was what I was doing most of the time now.

I knew what he meant. Only a few years ago I would more likely have "drenched" his cow. Grabbed it by the nose and poured a pint of medicine down its throat.

We still carried a special drenching bottle around with us—an empty wine bottle because it had no shoulders and allowed the liquid to run more easily. Often we would mix the medicine with black treacle from the barrel that stood in the corner of most cow byres.

All this was disappearing, and the farmer's remark about "all t'needle" brought it home to me once more that things were never going to be the same again.

A revolution had begun in agriculture and in veterinary practice. Farming had become more scientific, and concepts cherished for generations were being abandoned, while in the veterinary world the first rivulets of the flood of new advances were being felt.

Previously undreamed-of surgical procedures were being carried out, the sulpha drugs were going full blast and, most exciting of all, the war, with its urgent need for better treatment of wounds, had given a tremendous impetus to the development of Sir Alexander Fleming's discovery of penicillin. This, the first of the antibiotics, was not yet in the hands of the profession except in the form of intramammary tubes for the treatment of mastitis, but it was the advance guard of the therapeutic army that was to sweep our old treatments into oblivion.

There were signs, too, that the small farmer was on the way out. These men, some with only six cows, a few pigs and poultry, still made up most of our practice and they were the truly rich characters, but they were beginning to wonder if they could make a living on this scale, and one or two had sold out to the bigger men. In our practice now, in the eighties, there are virtually no small farmers left. I can think of only a handful — old men doggedly doing the things they have always done for the sole reason that they have always done it. They are the last remnants of the men I cherished, living by the ancient values, speaking the old Yorkshire dialect that television and radio have swamped.

I took a last long breath and got into my car. The uncomfortable feeling of change was still with me but I looked through the window at the great fells thrusting their bald summits into the clouds, tier upon tier of them, timeless, indestructible, towering over the glories beneath, and I felt better immediately. The Dales had not changed at all.

I did one more call, then drove back to Skeldale House to see if there were any more visits before lunch.

All was new here, too. My partner, Siegfried, had married and was living a few miles outside Darrowby, and Helen and I with our little son, Jimmy, were installed in the practice headquarters. When I got out of the car I gazed up at the ivy climbing over the mellow brick to the little rooms that looked out from under the tiles to the hills. Helen and I had started our married life in those rooms but now we had the run of the whole house. It was too big for us, of course, but we were happy to be there because we both loved the old place, with its spaciousness and its Georgian elegance.

The house looked much the same as when I had first seen it those years ago. The only difference was that they had taken the iron railings away for scrap metal during the war, and our plates were now hanging on the wall.

Helen and I slept in the big room which I had occupied in my bachelor days, and Jimmy was in the dressing room where Siegfried's student brother, Tristan, used to rest his head. Tristan, alas, had left us. When the war ended, he was Captain Farnon of the Royal Army veterinary corps. He married and joined the Ministry of Agriculture as an infertility investigation officer. He left a sad gap in our lives, but fortunately we still saw him and his wife regularly.

I opened the front door and in the passage, the fragrance of *pulv aromat* was strong. It was the aromatic powder we mixed with our medicaments, and it had an excitement for me. It always seemed to be hanging about the house. It was the smell of our trade.

Halfway along the passage I passed the doorway to the long high-walled garden and turned into the dispensary. This was a room whose significance was already on the wane. The rows of beautifully shaped glass bottles with their Latin titles engraved on them looked down at me—*spiritus Aetheris Nitrosi, Liquor Ammonii Acetatis Fortis, Potassii Nitras, Sodii Salicylas*. Noble names. My head was stuffed with hundreds of them, their properties, actions and uses, and their dosage in horse, ox, sheep, pig, dog and cat. But soon I would have to forget them all and concern myself only with how much of the latest antibiotic or steroid to administer.

Some years were to pass before the steroids arrived on the scene, but they, too, would bring another little revolution in their wake.

As I left the dispensary I almost bumped into Siegfried. He was storming along the passage and he grabbed my arm in an agitated manner.

"Ah, James, just the man I was looking for! I've had the most ghastly time this morning. I knocked the exhaust off my car going up that bloody awful track to High Liston, and now I'm without transport. They've sent for a new exhaust, but until it arrives and they get it fitted I'm stuck. It's maddening!"

"That's all right, Siegfried. I'll do your calls."

"No, no, James, it's kind of you, but don't you see, this sort of thing is going to happen again and again. That's what I wanted to talk to you about. We need a spare car."

[30]

"A spare?"

"That's right. Doesn't have to be a Rolls Royce. Just something to fall back upon at a time like this. As a matter of fact, I rang Hammond at the garage to bring round something suitable for us to look at. I think I can hear him outside now."

My partner was always one for instant action, and I followed him to the front door. Mr. Hammond was there with the vehicle for our inspection. It was a 1933 Morris Oxford, and Siegfried trotted down the steps towards it.

"A hundred pounds, you said, eh, Mr. Hammond?" He walked around the car a couple of times, picking pieces of rust from the black paintwork, opening the doors and peering at the upholstery. "Ah, well, it's seen better days, but the appearance doesn't matter as long as it goes all right."

"It's a sound little job, Mr. Farnon," the garage proprietor said. "Re-bored two thousand miles ago and don't use hardly any oil. New battery and a good bit o' tread on the tyres." He adjusted the spectacles on his long nose, drew his thin frame upright and adopted a businesslike expression.

"Mmmm." Siegfried shook the rear bumper with his foot, and the old springs groaned. "How about the brakes? Important in this hilly country."

"They're champion, Mr. Farnon. First-rate."

My colleague nodded slowly. "Good, good. You don't mind if I drive her round the block, do you?"

"Nay, nay, of course not," Mr. Hammond replied. "Give 'er any trial you like." He was a man who prided himself on his imperturbability, and he dropped confidently into the passenger seat as Siegfried took the wheel.

"Hop in the back, James!" my partner cried. I opened the rear door and took my place behind Mr. Hammond in the musty interior.

Siegfried took off abruptly with a roaring and creaking from the old vehicle, and despite the garage man's outward calm I saw the back of his shirt collar rise a couple of inches above his blue serge jacket as we shot along Trengate.

The collar subsided a little when Siegfried slowed down at the church to make a left turn but reappeared spasmodically as we negotiated a series of sharp and narrow bends at top speed.

When we reached the long straight lane that runs parallel to Trengate Mr. Hammond appeared to relax, but when Siegfried put his foot on the boards and sent the birds squawking from the overhanging branches as he thundered beneath them, I saw the collar again.

When we reached the end of the lane, Siegfried came almost to a halt as he turned left.

"I think we'll test the brakes, Mr. Hammond," he said cheerfully and hurled the car suddenly along the home straight for Trengate. He really meant to carry out a thorough test. The roar of the ancient engine rose to a scream, and as the street approached with frightening rapidity the collar reappeared, then the shirt.

When Siegfried stood on the brakes, the car slewed violently to the right, and as we catapulted crabwise into Trengate, Mr. Hammond's head was jammed against the roof and his entire shirt back was exposed. When we came to a halt, he slid slowly back into his seat, and the jacket took over again. At no time had he spoken or, apart from his up-and-down movements, shown any emotion.

At the front door of the surgery we got out, and my colleague rubbed his chin doubtfully. "She does pull a little to the right on braking, Mr. Hammond. I think we'd need to have that rectified. Or perhaps you have another vehicle available?"

The garage man did not answer for a few moments. His spectacles were askew, and he was very pale. "Aye . . . aye . . ." he said shakily. "I 'ave another little job over there. It might suit you."

"Capital!" Siegfried rubbed his hands. "Perhaps you'd bring it along after lunch, and we can have a spin round to try it."

Mr. Hammond's eyes widened, and he swallowed a few times.

"Right . . . right, Mr. Farnon. But I'm goin' to be busy this afternoon. I'll send one of me men."

We bade him goodbye and went back into the house. Walking along the passage, my partner put an arm across my shoulders. "Well, James, another step towards increasing the efficiency of the practice. Anyway," he smiled and whistled a few cheerful bars, "I rather enjoy these little interludes."

Suddenly I began to feel good. So many things were new and different, but the Dales hadn't changed, and Siegfried hadn't changed either.

Chapter
4

"A voyage to Russia!" I stared at John Crooks.

Siegfried and I worked alone in the practice during the immediate postwar years, and this book is about that period. In 1951 John Crooks came to us as assistant and three years later left to set up his own practice in Beverley. Before he departed he paid us the charming compliment of "filling" a bottle with the air from Skeldale House, to be released in his new surgery with the object of transferring some of our atmosphere. Sometime in the future I shall write about John's spell in Darrowby, but at the moment I should like to jump forward in time to 1961 in order to interpolate some extracts from the journal I kept of my Russian adventure.

John was behind it. Although he no longer worked for us, he came back often as a friend and he had been describing some of his experiences in exporting animals from Hull. He often sailed with these animals as veterinary attendant, but it was the Russian thing that caught my imagination.

"That must have been very interesting," I said.

John smiled. "Oh yes, fascinating. I've been out there several times now and it's the real Russia, with the lid off, not a tour of the showplaces they want you to see. You get a glimpse of the country through the eyes of a seaman, and you meet the ordinary Russians, the commercial people, the workers."

"Sounds great!"

"And you get paid for it, too," John went on. "That makes it even better."

I sighed. "You're a lucky beggar. And these jobs come up pretty regularly?"

"Yes, they do." He looked at me closely, and I suppose my expression must have been wistful. "Would you like to have a go sometime?"

"Do you mean it?"

"Of course," he said. "Just say the word and you can sail on the next one. That'll be sometime around the end of October."

I thumped my fist into my palm. "Book me in, John. It's really kind of you. Country vetting is fine but sometimes I feel I'm sliding into a rut. A trip to Russia is just what I need."

"Well, that's grand." John stood up and prepared to leave. "I'll let you know the details later, but I believe you'll be sailing with a cargo of valuable sheep—breeding animals. The insurance company is bound to insist on veterinary supervision."

For a few weeks I went around in a fever of anticipation, but there were many people who didn't share my enthusiasm.

One cowman cocked an eye at me. "Ah wouldn't go there for a bloody big clock," he said. "One wrong word and you'll find yourself in t'nick for a long, long time."

He had a definite point. East-West relations were at one of their lowest ebbs at that time and I grew used to my clients making it clear that Russia was one place they would avoid. In fact, when I told Colonel Smallwood about it when I was tuberculin-testing his cattle a few days before I left, he raised his eyebrows and gave me a cold stare.

"Nice to have known you," he murmured.

But I have seafarers' blood in my veins going back several generations, and I felt only happy expectation.

October 28, 1961

The first day has come and gone. When I walked onto the

quayside at Hull, I saw our ship right in front of me. She is Danish, the *Iris Clausen* of 300 tons, and my first sensation is of mild shock that she is so small. I had cherished a mental picture of a substantial vessel for such a voyage.

When I first saw her at the dockside, only the bows and a portion of deck were visible. This part looked tiny, and a high superstructure obscured what I surmised must be the greater part of the ship. I walked along past this superstructure and experienced a moment of disquiet. I found that the ship ends right there. There just isn't any more.

To my untutored eyes, the *Iris Clausen* looked like a toy oil tanker, and it was difficult to imagine her crossing an ocean or weathering a storm.

The cargo of sheep had just been loaded and the decks were littered with straw. When I went into the little mess room I saw the captain, who was called Rasmussen, sitting at the head of the table around which were grouped representatives of the export company and two Russian veterinary surgeons who had been inspecting the sheep.

The table itself was heavily laden with a wonderful variety of Danish open sandwiches, beer, whisky, schnapps and other drinks, and with mountains of forms which everybody was furiously signing.

One of the Russians, a bespectacled little man, apparently realised who I was, because he came up and with a smile said, "Veterinary surgeon," and shook my hand warmly. His colleague, tall and gaunt, was painstakingly going through the forms and saying nothing.

The chief man from the export people informed me that not only am I to be the medical attendant to the 383 pedigree Romney Marsh and Lincoln sheep we are carrying, but I have also to deal with the Russians at our port of destination, Klaipeda. I have to bring back five acceptance forms signed by the Russians and myself, otherwise the company will not get paid.

"How much are the sheep worth?" I asked.

The export man's mouth twitched up at one corner. "Twenty thousand pounds."

My stomach lurched. It was a fortune. This was a responsibility I hadn't foreseen.

When the crowd had cleared, Captain Rasmussen and I were left alone in the room. He introduced himself charmingly and I was immediately attracted by his gentle manner. He is smallish, silver-haired and speaks excellent English.

He waved me to the chair by his side. "Sit down, Mr. Herriot, and let us talk."

We spoke about our families, then about the job in hand.

"This is a motor ship," said the captain. "Built for the sole purpose of transporting animals. There are two decks below with pens for the sheep. Perhaps you would like to see your charges?"

As we left the mess room I noticed that the captain was limping slightly. He smiled as he saw me looking down at his feet.

"Yes, I broke my ankle a few months ago. Fell down the steps from the bridge to my cabin during a storm. Silly of me."

I wondered if I would be doing any falling about over the next week or so. We walked around the sheep. Beautiful animals, all of them, and they were very comfortable, well bedded in straw and with lots of sweet hay to eat. The ventilation was just right and the atmosphere pleasantly warm.

When I left the captain, I was agreeably surprised at the first sight of my cabin. No doubt those on passenger liners are more sumptuous, but there is a bunk with spotless sheets and pillows, a desk, armchair and sofa, a wash basin, fitted wardrobe, two cupboards and a lot of drawers. The whole place is done out in shining light oak. I am very impressed with my temporary home.

I opened my suitcase. Only a tiny part of it was taken up by my personal effects; the rest was filled with the things I thought I might need. My black P.V.C. working coat, bottles of calcium, antibiotics and steroids, scalpel, scissors, suture materials, bandages, cotton wool and syringes.

I looked down thoughtfully at the limited array. Would I find it too meagre or would I not need any of it? The following days would tell me.

We took on the pilot at 8 P.M., and at 9 P.M. I heard some activity outside my window. I looked out and saw two of the crew winching up the anchor.

I went up on deck to watch our departure. The night was very dark, and the dockside was deserted. A cat scurried through the light thrown by a single street lamp but nothing else stirred. Then our siren gave a loud blast and I could see we were moving very slowly away from the quay. We glided through the narrow outlet of the dock, then began to head quite swiftly towards the mouth of the Humber, two miles away.

As I stood on the deck I could see several other ships sailing out on the evening tide, some quite close, cleaving through the water abreast of us only a few hundred yards away, a graceful and thrilling sight.

Away behind, the lights of Hull receded rapidly, and I was looking at their faint glitter beyond the stretch of dark water when I felt a touch on my arm.

It was a young sailor, and he grinned cheerfully as I turned round. "Doctor," he said. "You show me how to feed the sheeps?"

I must have looked puzzled because his grin widened as he explained. "Many times I sail with cattles and pigs but never with sheeps."

I understood and motioned him to lead on. Like all the crew, he was a Dane, big, fair-haired, typically Nordic, and I followed his broad back down to the animals' pens. He listened intently as I gave him the information about feeding and watering, especially about how much concentrates to give. I was particularly pleased to see that as well as the fine-quality hay, there was an abundance of a top-class brand of sheep nuts in big paper sacks.

While he got on with his work, I looked around at the animals which would be under my care. Most of them were Romney Marsh, and as the engines throbbed and the deck vibrated under my feet I marvelled again at their attractiveness. They had great woolly heads like teddy bears, and their eyes, soft and incurious, looked back at me as they lay in the straw or nibbled at their food.

Before coming down here to my cabin, I had an irresistible urge to return to the upper deck and look around. I have sea captains among my uncles and a great grandfather who was a ship's pilot and the sea has always had a pull for me. In the darkness I walked around the deck. This wasn't easy because there is only a narrow strip, twenty-five yards long, on either side.

The moon had come out, casting a cold white brilliance on the water of the river estuary. Far on the starboard side, a long row of lights glimmers—probably Grimsby. On the port side, about three hundred yards away, a ship sped silently through the night, keeping pace exactly with us. I watched her for a long time, but her position never varied and she was still there when I came down.

My cabin is now a place of shakes and shudders, of indefinable bumps, rattles and groans. As I write, I know for sure that we are now well out to sea because I am very aware of the rolling of the ship.

I have had an experimental lie in my bunk, and this is where the rolling is most noticeable. From side to side it goes, side to side, over and over again. At one time there was some talk of Helen coming with me on this trip, and I smile to myself at the thought. This wouldn't suit her at all—she soon becomes queasy sitting in the back of a car. But to me the gentle motion is like the rocking of a cradle. I know I shall sleep well.

Chapter
5

"Hello! Hello!" I bellowed.

"Hello! Hello!" little Jimmy piped just behind me.

I turned and looked at my son. He was four years old now and had been coming on my rounds with me for over a year. It was clear that he considered himself a veteran of the farmyards, an old hand versed in all aspects of agricultural lore.

This shouting was a common habit of mine. When a vet arrived on a farm, it was often surprisingly difficult to find the farmer. He might be a dot on a tractor half a mile across the fields; on rare occasions he might be in the house, but I always hoped to find him among the buildings, and I relied on a few brisk shouts to locate him.

Certain farms in our practice were for no apparent reason distinctive in that you could never find anybody around. The house door would be locked, and we would scour the barns, cow-houses and fold yards while our cries echoed back at us from the unheeding walls. Siegfried and I used to call them the "no-finding" places and they were responsible for a lot of wasted time.

Jimmy had caught on to the problem quite early, and there was no doubt he enjoyed the opportunity to exercise his lungs a bit. I watched him now as he strutted importantly over the cobbles, giving tongue every few seconds. He was also making an unnecessary amount of noise by clattering on the rough stones with his new boots.

Those boots were his pride, the final recognition of his status as veterinary assistant. When I first began to take him round with me, his initial reaction was the simple joy of a child at being able to see animals of all kinds, particularly the young ones—the lambs, foals, piglets, calves—and the thrill of discovery when he came upon a huddle of kittens in the straw or found a bitch with pups in a loose box.

Before long, however, he began to enlarge his horizons. He wanted to get into the action. The contents of my car boot were soon as familiar to him as his toy box at home, and he delighted in handing out the tins of stomach powder, the electuaries and red blisters, the white lotion and the still-revered long cartons of Universal Cattle Medicine. Finally he began to forestall me by rushing back to the car for the calcium and flutter valve as soon as he saw a recumbent cow. He had become a diagnostician as well.

I think the thing he enjoyed most was accompanying me on an evening call, if Helen would allow him to postpone his bedtime. He was in heaven driving into the country in the darkness, training my torch on a cow's teat while I stitched it.

The farmers were kind, as they always are with young people. Even the most uncommunicative would grunt, "Ah see you've got t'apprentice with ye," as we got out of the car.

But those farmers had something Jimmy coveted: their big hob-nailed boots. He had a great admiration for farmers in general; strong hardy men who spent their lives in the open and who pushed fearlessly among plunging packs of cattle and slapped the rumps of massive cart horses. I could see he was deeply impressed as he watched them—quite often small and stringy—mounting granary steps with twelve or sixteen stone stacks on their shoulders, or hanging on effortlessly to the noses of huge bullocks, their boots slithering over the floor, a laconic cigarette hanging from their lips.

It was those boots that got under Jimmy's skin most of all. Sturdy and unyielding, they seemed to symbolise for him the character of the men who wore them.

Matters came to a head one day when we were conversing in the car. Or, rather, my son was doing the conversing in the form of a barrage of questions which I did my best to fend off while trying to think about my cases. These questions went on pretty well nonstop every day, and they followed a well-tried formula.

"What is the fastest train—the Blue Peter or the Flying Scotsman?"

"Well now . . . I really don't know. I should say the Blue Peter."

Then, getting into deeper water, "Is a giant train faster than a phantom racing car?"

"That's a difficult one. Let's see, now . . . maybe the phantom racer."

Jimmy changed his tack suddenly. "That was a big man at the last farm wasn't he?"

"He certainly was."

"Was he bigger than Mr. Robinson?"

We were launching into his favourite "big man" game, and I knew how it would end, but I played my part. "Oh yes, he was."

"Was he bigger than Mr. Leeming?"

"Certainly."

"Was he bigger than Mr. Kirkley?"

"Without a doubt."

Jimmy gave me a sidelong glance, and I knew he was about to play his two trump cards. "Was he bigger than the gas man?"

The towering gentleman who came to read the gas meters at Skeldale House had always fascinated my son, and I had to think very carefully about my reply.

"Well, you know, I really think he was."

"Ah, but . . ." The corner of Jimmy's mouth twitched up craftily. "Was he bigger than Mr. Thackray?"

That was the killer punch. Nobody was bigger than Mr. Thackray, who looked down on the other inhabitants of Darrowby from six feet seven inches.

I shrugged my shoulders in defeat. "No, I have to admit it. He wasn't as big as Mr. Thackray."

Jimmy smiled and nodded, well satisfied, then he began to hum a little tune, drumming his fingers on the dashboard at the same time. Soon I could see he was having trouble. He couldn't remember how it went. Patience was not his strong point, and as he tried and stopped again and again, it was plain that he was rapidly becoming exasperated.

Finally, as we drove down a steep hill into a village and another abortive session of tum-te-tum-te-tum came to an abrupt halt, he rounded on me aggressively.

"You know," he exploded, "I'm getting just about fed up of this!"

"I'm sorry to hear that, old lad." I thought for a moment. "I think it's *Lilliburlero* you're trying to get." I gave a swift rendering.

"Yes, that's it!" He slapped his knee and bawled out the melody at the top of his voice several times in triumph. This put him in such high good humour that he broached something that must have been on his mind for some time.

"Daddy," he said. "Can I have some boots?"

"Boots? But you've got some already, haven't you?" I pointed down at the little Wellingtons in which Helen always rigged him before he set out for the farms.

He gazed at his feet sadly before replying. "Yes, I know, but I want proper boots like the farmers."

This was a facer. I didn't know what to say. "But, Jim, little boys like you don't have boots like that. Maybe when you're bigger . . ."

"Oh, I want them now," he moaned in anguished tones. "I want proper boots."

At first I thought it was a passing whim, but he kept up his

[43]

campaign for several days, reinforcing it with disgusted looks as Helen drew on the Wellingtons each morning and a listless slouching to convey the message that his footwear was entirely unsuitable for a man like him.

Finally Helen and I talked it over one night after he had gone to bed.

"They surely don't have farm boots his size, do they?" I asked.

Helen shook her head. "I wouldn't have thought so, but I'll look around in any case."

And it seemed that Jimmy wasn't the only little boy to have this idea because within a week my wife returned, flushed with success and bearing the smallest pair of farm boots I had ever seen.

I couldn't help laughing. They were so tiny, yet so perfect—thick hob-nailed soles, chunky uppers and a long row of lace-holes with metal loops at the top.

Jimmy didn't laugh when he saw them. He handled them almost with awe and once he had got them on, his demeanour changed. He was naturally square-set and jaunty, but to see him striding round a farmyard in corduroy leggings and those boots you would think he owned the place. He clumped and stamped, held himself very upright and his cries of "Hello! Hello!" took on a new authority.

He was never what I would call naughty—certainly never destructive or cruel—but he had that bit of devil which I suppose all boys need to have. He liked to assert himself, and, perhaps unconsciously, he liked to tease me. If I said, "Don't touch that," he would keep clear of the object in question but later would give it the merest brush with his finger, which could not be construed as disobedience but nevertheless served to establish his influence in the household.

Also, he was not above taking advantage of me in awkward situations. There was one afternoon when Mr. Garrett brought his sheepdog in. The animal was very lame and as I hoisted him onto the table in the consulting room, a small head appeared for a moment at the window that overlooked the sunlit garden.

I didn't mind that. Jimmy often watched me dealing with our small animal patients, and I half expected him to come into the room for a closer look.

It is often difficult to locate the source of a dog's lameness, but in this case I found it immediately. When I gently squeezed the outside pad on his left foot he winced, and a tiny bead of serum appeared on the black surface.

"He's got something in there, Mr. Garrett," I said. "Probably a thorn. I'll have to give him a shot of local anaesthetic and open up his pad."

It was when I was filling the syringe that a knee came into view at the corner of the window. I felt a pang of annoyance. Jimmy surely couldn't be climbing up the wistaria. It was dangerous, and I had expressly forbidden it. The branches of the beautiful creeper curled all over the back of the house, and though they were as thick as a man's leg near ground level, they became quite slender as they made their way up past the bathroom window to the tiles of the roof.

No, I decided that I was mistaken and began to infiltrate the pad. These modern anaesthetics worked very quickly and within a minute or two I could squeeze the area quite hard without causing pain.

I reached for the scalpel. "Hold his leg up and keep it as steady as you can," I said.

Mr. Garrett nodded and pursed his lips. He was a serious-faced man at any time and obviously deeply concerned about his dog. His eyes narrowed in apprehension as I poised my knife over the telltale drop of moisture.

For me it was an absorbing moment. If I could find and remove this foreign body, the dog would be instantly rid of his pain. I had dealt with many of these cases in the past, and they were so easy, so satisfying.

With the point of my blade I made a careful nick in the tough tissue of the pad, and at that moment a shadow crossed the window. I glanced up. It was Jimmy, all right, this time at the other side, just his head grinning through the glass from halfway up.

The little blighter *was* on the wistaria, but there was nothing I could do about it then, except to give him a quick glare. I cut a little deeper and squeezed, but still nothing showed in the wound. I didn't want to make a big hole, but it was clear that I had to make a cruciate incision to see further down. I was drawing the scalpel across at right angles to my first cut when, from the corner of my eye, I spotted two feet dangling just below the top of the window. I tried to concentrate on my job but the feet swung and kicked repeatedly, obviously for my benefit. At last they disappeared, which could only mean that their owner was ascending to the dangerous regions. I dug down a little deeper and swabbed with cotton wool.

Ah yes, I could see something now, but it was very deep, probably the tip of a thorn which had broken off well below the surface. I felt the thrill of the hunter as I reached for forceps, and just then the head showed itself again, upside down this time.

My God, he was hanging by his feet from the branches, and the face was positively leering. In deference to my client, I had been trying to ignore the by-play from outside, but this was too much. I leaped at the glass and shook my fist violently. My fury must have startled the performer, because the face vanished instantly and I could hear faint sounds of feet scrambling upwards.

That was not much comfort, either. Those top branches might not support a boy's weight. I forced myself back to my task.

"Sorry, Mr. Garrett," I said. "Will you hold the leg up again, please?"

He replied with a thin smile, and I pushed my forceps into the depths. They grated on something hard. I gripped, pulled gently and—oh, lovely, lovely—out came the pointed, glistening head of a thorn. I had done it.

It was one of the tiny triumphs that lighten vet's lives and I was beaming at my client and patting his dog's head when I heard the crack from above. It was followed by a long howl of terror, then a small form hurtled past the window and thudded with horrid force into the garden.

I threw down the forceps and shot out of the room, along the passage and through the side door into the garden. Jimmy was already sitting up among the wallflowers, and I was too relieved to be angry.

"Have you hurt yourself?" I gasped, and he shook his head.

I lifted him to his feet and he seemed to be able to stand all right. I felt him over carefully. There appeared to be no damage.

I led him back into the house. "Go along and see Mummy," I said and returned to the consulting room.

I must have been deathly pale when I entered because Mr. Garrett looked startled. "Is he all right?" he asked.

"Yes, yes, I think so. But I do apologise for rushing out like that. It was really too bad of me to . . ."

Mr. Garrett laid his hand on my shoulder. "Say no more, Mr. Herriot, I have children of my own." And then he spoke the words that have become engraven on my heart. "You need nerves of steel to be a parent."

Later at tea I watched my son demolishing a poached egg on toast, then he started to slap plum jam on a slice of bread. Thank heaven he was no worse for his fall, but still I had to remonstrate with him.

"Look, young man," I said. "That was a very naughty thing you did out there. I've told you again and again not to climb the wistaria."

Jimmy bit into his bread and jam and regarded me impassively. I have a big streak of old hen in my nature and down through the years, even to this day, he and later my daughter, Rosie, have recognised this and developed a disconcerting habit of making irreverent clucking noises at my over-fussiness. At this moment

I could see that whatever I was going to say he wasn't going to take too seriously.

"If you're going to behave like this," I went on, "I'm not going to take you round the farms with me. I'll just have to find another little boy to help me with my cases."

His chewing slowed down, and I looked for some reaction in this morsel of humanity who was later to become a far better veterinary surgeon than I could ever be, in fact, to quote thirty years later a dry Scottish colleague who had been through college with me and didn't mince words, "A helluva improvement on his old man."

Jimmy dropped the bread on his plate. "Another little boy?" he enquired.

"That's right. I can't have naughty boys with me. I'll have to find somebody else."

Jimmy thought this over for a minute or so, then he shrugged and appeared to accept the situation philosophically. He started again on the bread and jam.

Then in a flash his *sang froid* evaporated. He stopped in mid-chew and looked up at me in wide-eyed alarm.

His voice came out in a high quaver. "Would he have my boots?"

Chapter
6

"By gaw, it's Doctor Fu Manchu!"

The farmer dropped the buttered scone onto his plate and stared, horror-struck, through the kitchen window.

I was drinking a cup of tea with him and I almost choked in mid-sip as I followed his gaze.

Beyond the glass an enormous Oriental was standing. Slit eyes regarded us menacingly from a pock-marked face whose left cheek was hideously scarred from ear to chin, but the most arresting feature was the one-sided mustachio, black and greasy, with its single end dangling several inches from the upper lip. A robe of exotic colouring flowed from the man's shoulders and his hands, held across his body, were tucked deeply into the sleeves.

The farmer's wife screamed and jumped from the table, but I sat transfixed. I couldn't believe this apparition, framed as it was against the buildings and pastures of a Yorkshire farm.

The wife's rising screams were bordering on hysteria when suddenly she stopped and advanced slowly to the window. As she came close the big man's mouth relaxed into a friendly leer, then he withdrew a hand from the sleeve and waggled the fingers at her in Oliver Hardy fashion.

"It's Igor!" she gasped and swung round on her husband. "And that's me good house coat he's got on. You rotten devil, you put him up to this!"

The farmer rolled about in his chair, laughing helplessly. He couldn't have asked for a better response to his little joke.

Igor was one of a batch of prisoners of war who had recently arrived to work on the farm. There were hundreds of these men employed on the land at the end of the war and it was a happy arrangement all round. The farmers had a windfall in the shape of abundant labour, and the prisoners were content to spend their pre-repatriation time in the open air with ample farm meals to sustain them in a world of food rationing. I personally had a respite from one of my constant problems—the lack of help in my job. I found now that there were always willing hands to assist me in the rough-and-tumble of large-animal practice.

The prisoners were, of course, mainly German, but there were a number of Italians and, strangely, Russians. It baffled me at first when I saw hundreds of men who looked like Chinese in German uniforms disembarking at Darrowby railway station. I learned later that they were Mongolian Russians who had been pressed into fighting for the Germans and later were captured by the British. Igor was one of these.

I know of farming families who to this day spend their holidays at the homes of the Germans and Italians whom they befriended at this time.

I was still laughing after the Igor incident and the farmer was still receiving a tongue lashing from his wife when I climbed into my car and consulted the list of calls.

"Preston, Scarth Lodge, lame cow," I read. It was twenty minutes' drive away and, as always, I idly turned over the possibilities in my mind. Probably foul, maybe pus in the foot, which would entail some hacking with my hoof knife. Or it could be a strain. I'd soon see.

Hal Preston was bringing my patient in from the field as I arrived, and I didn't even have to get out of the car to make my diagnosis. It was one which gave me no joy.

The cow was hobbling slowly, her right hind foot barely touching the ground. The limb was shortened and carried underneath

[50]

the body, while a bulge in the pelvic region showed where the great trochanter of the femur pushed against the skin. Upward displacement. Absolutely typical.

"Just happened this mornin'," the farmer said. "She was as right as rain last night. Ah can't think . . ."

"Say no more, Mr. Preston," I said. "I know what it is. She's got a dislocated hip."

"Is that serious?"

"Yes, it is. You see, it takes tremendous force to pull the head of the displaced bone back into its socket. Even in a dog it is a difficult job, but in cattle it's sometimes impossible."

The farmer looked glum. "That's a beggar. This is a right good cow, smashin' milker. What 'appens if you can't get it back?"

"I'm afraid she'd always be a bit of a cripple," I replied. "Dogs usually form a very good false joint, but it's different with a cow. In fact, many farmers decide to slaughter the animal."

"Oh, 'ell, I don't want that!" Hal Preston rubbed his chin vigorously. "We'll have to have a go."

"Good, that's what I want." I turned towards my car. "I'm going back to the surgery for the chloroform muzzle, and, in the meantime, will you go round your neighbours and get a few strong chaps? We'll need all the manpower we can find."

The farmer looked round the rolling green miles with not another dwelling in sight. "Me neighbours are a long way away, but I don't need 'em today. Look 'ere."

He led the way into the farm kitchen where the savoury aroma of roast bacon was heavy in the air. Four burly Germans were seated at the table. In front of each lay a plate mounded high with potatoes, cabbage, bacon and sausage.

"They've sent me these fellers to help with haytime," Mr. Preston explained. "I reckon they look pretty useful."

"They do indeed." I smiled at the men and waved my hand in greeting. They jumped to their feet and bowed. "Right," I said to the farmer, "you can be having your dinners while I'm gone. I'll be back in about half an hour."

When I returned, we led the cow to a patch of soft grass. Her progress was painfully slow as she trailed her almost useless hind leg.

I buckled the muzzle to her head and dribbled the chloroform onto the sponge. As she inhaled the strange vapour her eyes widened in surprise, then she stumbled forward and sank to the turf.

I slipped a round stake into the animal's groin and stationed the two biggest men at either end of it, then I fastened a rope above the fetlock and gave the other end to Mr. Preston and the remaining two Germans.

The stage was set. I crouched over the pelvis and placed both hands on the bulging head of the femur. Would it stay obstinately still or would I feel it riding up the side of the acetabulum on the way to its proper home?

Anyway, this was the moment, and I took a deep breath. "Pull!" I shouted, and the three men on the rope hauled away, while the brown corded arms on each side of me took the strain on the stake.

No doubt an unedifying spectacle, this tug of war with the sleeping animal in the middle. Not much science in evidence, but country practice is often like that.

However, I had no time for theorising—all my mind was concentrated on that jutting bone under my hands. "Pull!" I yelled again, and fresh grunts of effort came back in reply.

I clenched my teeth. The thing wasn't moving. I couldn't believe it could resist the terrific traction, but it was like a rock.

Then, when the feeling of defeat was rising, I felt a stirring beneath my fingers. It all happened in seconds after that—the lifting of the femoral head as I pushed frantically at it and the loud click as it flopped into its socket. We had won.

I waved my arms in delight. "All right, let go!" I crawled to the cow's head and whipped off the muzzle.

We heaved her onto her chest, and she lay there, blinking and shaking her head as consciousness returned. I could hardly wait

[52]

for what is one of the most rewarding moments in veterinary practice, and it came when the cow rose to her feet and strolled over the grass without the trace of a limp. The five faces, sweating in the hot sunshine, watched in happy amazement, and though I had seen it all before, I felt the warm flush of triumph that is always new.

I handed cigarettes round the prisoners, and before I left I drew on my scanty store of German.

"*Danke schoen!*" I said fervently, and I really meant it.

"*Bitte! Bitte!*" they cried, all smiles. They had enjoyed the whole thing, and I had the feeling that this would be one of the tales they would tell when they returned to their homes.

A few days later, Siegfried and I alighted at Village Farm, Harford. We had come together because we had been told that our patient, a Red Poll bullock, was of an uncooperative disposition, and we thought that a combined operation was indicated.

The farmer led us to the fold yard where about twenty cattle were eating turnips. "That's the one," he said, pointing to an enormously fat beast, "and that's the thing I was tellin' ye about." He indicated a growth as big as a football dangling from the animal's belly.

Siegfried gave him a hard look. "Really, Mr. Harrison, you should have called us out to this long ago. Why did you let it get so big?"

The farmer took off his hat and scratched his balding head ruminatively. "Aye, well, you know how it is. Ah kept meanin' to give you a ring, but it slipped me mind and time went on."

"It's a hell of a size now," Siegfried grunted.

"Ah know, ah know. I allus had the hope that it might drop off because he's a right wild sod. You can't do much with 'im."

"All right, then." Siegfried shrugged. "Bring a halter, and we'll drive him into that box over there."

The farmer left, and my partner turned to me. "You know, James, that tumour isn't as fearsome as it looks. It's beautifully

[53]

pedunculated, and if we can get a shot of local into that narrow neck we can ligate it and have it off in no time."

The farmer returned with the halter, and he was accompanied by a dark little man in denims.

"This is Luigi," he said. "Italian prisoner. Don't speak no English, but 'e's very handy at all sorts o' jobs."

I could imagine Luigi being handy. He was short in stature, but his wide spread of shoulder and muscular arms suggested great strength.

We said hello, and the Italian returned our greetings with an inclination of his head and a grave smile. He carried an aura of dignity and self-assurance.

After a bit of galloping round the fold yard, we managed to get our patient into the box, but we soon realised that our troubles were only beginning.

Red Polls are big cattle, and an ill-natured one can be a problem. This fat creature had a mean look in his eyes, and all our attempts to halter him were unavailing. He either whipped away from the rope or shook his head threateningly at us. Once, as he thundered past me I got my fingers into his nose, but he brushed me off like a fly and lashed out with a hind leg, catching me a glancing blow on the thigh.

"He's like an elephant," I gasped. "God only knows how we're going to catch him."

The sedative injections for such animals and the metal crushes to restrain them were still years in the future, and Siegfried and I were looking gloomily at the bullock when Luigi stepped forward.

He held up a hand and loosed off a burst of Italian at us. None of us could understand him, but we took his point as he ushered us back against the wall with great ceremony. Plainly he was going to do something, but what?

He advanced stealthily on the bullock, then with a lightning movement he seized one of the ears in both hands. The animal took off immediately but without its previous abandon. Luigi was screwing the ear round on its long axis, and it seemed to act as a brake because the beast slowed to a halt and stood there, head on one side, glancing almost plaintively up at the little man.

I was reminded irresistibly of pictures of Billy Bunter being held by a Greyfriars prefect, and I almost expected the bullock to cry, "Ouch! Yaroo! Leggo my ear!"

But I didn't have much time for musing because Luigi, in full command of the situation, jerked his head towards the hanging tumour.

Siegfried and I leaped forward. We had never seen anybody catch a beast by the ear before, but we weren't going to discuss it. This was our chance.

I cradled the growth in my hands while Siegfried injected the local into the neck. As the needle entered the skin the hairy leg twitched, and under ordinary circumstances we would have been kicked out of the box, but Luigi took another half-turn on the ear and rapped out a colourful reprimand. The animal subsided immediately and stood motionless as we worked.

Siegfried applied a strong ligature and severed the neck of the growth bloodlessly with an ecraseur. The tumour thudded onto the straw. The operation was over.

Luigi released the ear and received our congratulations with a half-smile and a gracious nod of his head. He really was a man of enormous presence.

Now, more than thirty years later, Siegfried and I still talk about him. We have both tried to catch large cattle by the ears without the slightest success; so was Luigi just an amateur with wrists of steel or was he a farmer, and do they do it that way in Italy after a lifetime of practice? We still don't know.

One still summer evening I was returning from a call when I heard the sound of singing. It was a rich, swelling chorus of many voices, and it seemed to come from nowhere. I stopped the car

[55]

and wound down the window. The fells rose around me, their summits glinting in the last sunshine, but the only living creatures were the cattle and sheep grazing on the walled slopes.

Then I saw Knowle Manor perched on a plateau high above, and I remembered that hundreds of Russian prisoners were billeted there.

These men were singing the songs of their homeland, but the sound drifting from the windows of the big house was not that of a casual party. There was a vast, drilled choir up there, deep voices blending in thrilling harmonies that hung and lingered on the soft air.

I sat entranced for a long time, till the light faded and the chill of nightfall made me close my window and drive away.

Years later I read that these Russians went home to death or captivity, and whenever I thought of their fate, I remembered that summer evening and the beautiful music they made in the peace of the Yorkshire hills.

Chapter
7

October 29, 1961

"Breakfast, Mr. Herriot."

I heard the mess boy's call and his knock on my cabin door. It was the first of many during this day. "Lunch, Mr. Herriot." "Dinner, Mr. Herriot." "Coffee time, Mr. Herriot." He is a fresh-faced lad of seventeen and takes care I don't miss anything.

I hurried to the mess room. To my surprise I found it was empty, but there was a large pot of coffee on the table, along with a stack of rye bread and a remarkable selection of cold meats and fish. I counted nine different platters on the table.

Well, it was an unusual breakfast but I was hungry, so I started operations immediately. The coffee was delicious, and I was happily washing down wonderful raw herring and onion, smoked ham and a particularly toothsome meat loaf when the mess boy appeared and smilingly deposited two fried eggs and bacon in front of me.

I was surprised but undeterred, and as I started my fresh attack with the ship heaving and pitching, I thanked providence that I had never known sea-sickness.

I was soon joined by two of the ship's officers, the mate, a tubby little man also called Rasmussen, and the engineer, Hansen, very dark with a humorous face.

Neither of them spoke much English, but we managed to

converse on various subjects including football pools which, when they had the chance, they both filled up assiduously without success.

After breakfast I went down to inspect my animals. The general picture was a happy one, but I noticed a sheep limping as it walked to its hay. I examined the feet and found a small area of footrot. I had been told that the Russian vets were meticulous in their examination, but they had missed that one. I directed a long jet of Terramycin aerosol at the affected spot; I was confident that a few more similar treatments would put that right before we reached Klaipeda.

Another animal blinked painfully at me as I passed its pen, and I found that its eyes were weeping and inflamed. It was the only one so affected, and I felt that it had probably picked up some irritant material on the journey to Hull. I squeezed some chloramphenicol eye ointment across the eyeballs and decided to do the same at midday and in the evening.

I finished my tour with the comforting thought that so far my stock of drugs was adequate.

Before lunch the captain asked me to drink a glass of lager with him in his cabin. He himself, despite being a man of natural refinement, drank straight from the bottle; later today I found that this was the approved method among the ship's officers, but he gave me a glass.

I sat down at the end of the table and poured the lager, and at that moment the ship gave a tremendous roll. My chair went over; I literally flew through the air, shot across the floor on my side and finished up underneath a desk in the corner. My glass was shattered, and a pool of the precious Carlsberg Special spread across the floor.

The captain leaped anxiously to my assistance. "Oh, Mr. Herriot, I hope you do not hurt yourself!" As I have said, his English is very good but occasionally little inaccuracies creep in.

"No, I'm fine," I replied, laughing. I got up and started on another bottle, but this time I kept my knees jammed against the legs of the table. I am beginning to learn.

After this little contretemps we went down to lunch, passing on the way the cook's galley. This was about the size of a large cupboard and was crammed with pans, stove, ovens and food. I wondered how anybody could possibly produce proper meals in that tiny place, and it occurred to me that perhaps that was the reason for the lavish breakfast. The other meals would probably be makeshift, and I mentally resigned myself to the fact that I would have to put up with a primitive diet during the voyage.

When we had gathered round the table in the little mess room, the first course arrived. It was an exquisite asparagus soup in which floated meat balls and large stalks of asparagus. This was followed by what the captain described as "boneless birds"— tender veal steaks wrapped around strips of bacon, parsley and spices, with anchovies draped across them. We finished off with a sago pudding thickly sprinkled with cinnamon and with peaches nestling on its bosom. As I sipped my coffee and nibbled delicious Danish cheese, I felt I might have been eating at the Ritz.

The cook, Nielsen by name, a large smiling man in a white apron, pushed his head round the door at the end of the meal, and I called out to him that his food was wonderful. He looked intensely gratified but also surprised because the other ship's officers seem to take it all for granted.

His smile grew wider, and he nodded his head rapidly. "Thank you, thank you, thank you." He stared at me as though he had been looking for me all his life. I have a feeling that I have made a friend there.

After lunch, back down to t'ween decks and lower hold, to give them their proper names, for another look at the sheep, but on the way I had to stop for a few minutes on the upper deck to take gulping breaths of the unbelievably fresh air that swept over the heaving miles of water. Walking around is difficult because I find it almost impossible to stand upright with the constant movement of the ship.

Down below I studied the animals carefully. There was something on my mind. Right at the beginning I had heard the odd cough, and I hadn't paid much attention because all sheep cough occasionally, but since we sailed, it had become more frequent and had a rasping quality that was only too familiar.

As I walked around I heard it again, and this time I traced it to the affected sheep. I climbed into the pen—all Lincolns—and began to stir them around, and after a few seconds there was a regular chorus of coughs. I knew now; they had husk.

I took a few temperatures, leaning back against the swaying wall to read the thermometer, but there was clearly no secondary infection; it was a straightforward parasitic bronchitis, and with my pitiful little stock of drugs in the suitcase upstairs there was nothing I could do about it.

Of course, as I sit here writing in my cabin, I realise it is only a mild attack and since they are off the pasture, in top condition, and with an abundant supply of good food, they will certainly throw it off in time. But for all that, I don't like it. The vets in Hull didn't spot it but those in Klaipeda probably will, and I want to present a batch of healthy animals to them.

Later, I had a most interesting hour with the captain on the bridge. He showed me how the radar and other gadgets worked and pointed out our position on the chart. We are off the coast of Holland but out of sight of land.

I was intrigued by the mariner's view of a map. The sea is a complicated mass of lines, words and figures, while the land is a white blank.

At 6:30 P.M. I began again on what I had thought was to be my frugal living. Mountains of roast chicken with a piquant stuffing I had never tasted before, surrounded by thin layers of cucumber done up with sugar and vinegar. Fruit followed, and, of course, there was the ever-present array of herring in tomato, salami, salt beef, pork, smoked ham, bacon and endless kinds of

Danish sliced sausages and cheeses. I haven't mentioned the two most popular things among the Danes themselves—the liver paste and trays of dripping.

The ship's officers seem to love these two items, especially the dripping which they spread on rye bread and eat at the end of the meal.

After dinner we settled down to a two-hour session of smoking and swopping yarns over the schnapps and beer. I gather that this is a regular custom in the evenings. The seamen are very interesting with their tales of many countries and peoples and the often startling adventures they have had on their travels.

Chapter
8

"It was Hemingway who said that, wasn't it?"

Norman Beaumont shook his head. "No, Scott Fitzgerald."

I didn't argue because Norman usually knew. In fact, it was one of the attractive things about him.

I enjoyed having veterinary students seeing practice with us. They helped with fetching and carrying, they opened gates and they were company on our lonely rounds. In return, they absorbed a lot of knowledge from us in our discussions in the car, and it was priceless experience for them to be involved in the practical side of their education.

Since the war, however, my relationships with these young men had undergone a distinct change. I found I was learning from them just about as much as they were learning from me.

The reason, of course, was that veterinary teaching had taken a leap forward. The authorities seemed to have suddenly discovered that we weren't just horse doctors and that the vast new field of small-animal work was opening up dramatically. Advanced surgical procedures were being carried out on farm animals, too, and the students had the great advantage of being able to see such things done in the new veterinary schools with their modern clinics and operating theatres.

New specialist textbooks were being written that made my own thumbed volumes with everything related to the horse seem like museum pieces. I was still a young man, but all the bursting knowledge I had nurtured so proudly was becoming irrelevant. Quittor, fistulous withers, poll evil, bog spavin, stringhalt—they didn't seem to matter much anymore.

Norman Beaumont was in his final year and was a deep well of information at which I drank greedily. But apart from the veterinary side we had a common love of books and reading.

When we weren't talking shop the conversation was usually on literary lines, and Norman's companionship lightened my days and made the journeys between farms seem short.

He was immensely likable, with a personality that was formal and dignified beyond his twenty-two years and which was only just saved from pomposity by a gentle humour. He was a solid citizen in the making if ever I saw one, and this impression was strengthened by his slightly pear-shaped physique and the fact that he was determinedly trying to cultivate a pipe.

He was having a little trouble with the pipe, but I felt sure he would win through. I could see him plainly twenty years from now, definitely tubby, sitting around the fireside with his wife and children, puffing at that pipe which he had finally subjugated; an upright, dependable family man with a prosperous practice.

As the dry stone walls rolled past the car windows, I got back onto the topic of the new operations.

"And you say they are actually doing Caesarians on cows in the college clinics?"

"Good Lord, yes." Norman made an expansive gesture and applied a match to his pipe. "Doing them like hot cakes, it's a regular thing." His words would have carried more weight if he had been able to blow a puff of smoke out after them, but he had filled the bowl too tightly and, despite a fierce sucking which hollowed his cheeks and ballooned his eyeballs, he couldn't manage a draw.

"Gosh, you don't know how lucky you are," I said. "The number of hours I've slaved on byre floors calving cows. Sawing up calves with embryotomy wire, knocking my guts out trying to bring heads round or reach feet. I think I must have shortened my life. And if only I'd known how, I could have saved myself the trouble with a nice straightforward operation. What sort of a job is it, anyway?"

The student gave me a superior smile. "Nothing much to it, really." He relit his pipe, tamped the tobacco down and winced as he burned his finger. He shook his hand vigorously for a moment, then turned towards me. "They never seem to have any trouble. Takes about an hour, and no hard labour."

"Sounds marvellous." I shook my head wistfully. "I'm beginning to think I was born too soon. I suppose it's the same with ewes?"

"Oh yes, yes, indeed," Norman murmured airily. "Ewes, cows, sows—they're in and out of the place every day. No problem at all. Nearly as easy as bitch spays."

"Ah, well, you young lads are lucky. It's so much easier to tackle these jobs when you've seen a lot of them done."

"True, true." The student spread his hands. "But, of course, most bovine parturitions don't need a Caesarian, and I'm always glad to have a calving for my case book."

I nodded in agreement. Norman's case book was something to see; a heavily bound volume with every scrap of interesting material meticulously entered under headings in red ink. The examiners always wanted to see these books, and this one would be worth a few extra marks to Norman in his finals.

It was August Bank Holiday Sunday, and Darrowby market place had been bustling all day with holiday makers and coach parties. Each time we passed through I looked at the laughing throngs with a tiny twinge of envy. Not many people seemed to work on Sundays.

I dropped the student at his digs in late afternoon and went back to Skeldale House for tea. I had just finished when Helen got up to answer the phone.

"It's Mr. Bushell of Sycamore House," she said. "He has a cow calving."

"Oh damn. I thought we'd have Sunday evening to ourselves." I put down my cup. "Tell him I'll be right out, Helen, will you?" I smiled as she put down the receiver. "One thing, Norman will be pleased. He was just saying he wanted something for his case book."

I was right. The young man rubbed his hands in glee when I called for him, and he was in excellent humour as we drove to the farm.

"I was reading some poetry when you rang the bell," he said. "I like poetry. You can always find something to apply to your life. How about now, when I'm expecting something interesting. 'Hope springs eternal in the human breast.' "

"Alexander Pope, *Essay on Man,*" I grunted. I wasn't feeling so enthusiastic as Norman. You never knew what was ahead on these occasions.

"Jolly good." The young man laughed. "You aren't easy to catch out."

We drove through the farm gateway into the yard.

"You've made me think with your poetry," I said. "It keeps buzzing in my head. 'Abandon hope all ye who enter here.' "

"Dante, of course, *The Inferno.* But don't be so pessimistic." He patted me on the shoulder as I put on my Wellingtons.

The farmer led us into the byre, and in a stall opposite the window a small cow looked up at us anxiously from her straw bed. Above her head, her name, Bella, was chalked on a board.

"She isn't very big, Mr. Bushell," I said.

"Eh?" he looked at me enquiringly, and I remembered that he was hard of hearing.

"She's a bit small," I shouted.

The farmer shrugged. "Aye, she allus was a poor doer. Had a rough time with her first calvin', but she milked well enough after it."

I looked thoughtfully at the cow as I stripped off my shirt and soaped my arms. I didn't like the look of that narrow pelvis, and

I breathed the silent prayer of all vets that there might be a tiny calf inside.

The farmer poked at the light roan hairs of the rump with his foot and shouted at the animal to make her rise.

"She won't budge, Mr. Herriot," he said. "She's been painin' all day. Ah doubt she's about buggered."

I didn't like the sound of that either. There was always something far wrong when a cow strained for a long time without result. And the little animal did look utterly spent. Her head hung down and her eyelids drooped wearily.

Ah well, if she wouldn't get up, I had to get down. With my bare chest in contact with the ground, the thought occurred that cobbles didn't get any softer with the passage of the years. But when I slid my hand into the vagina, I forgot about my discomfort. The pelvic opening was villainously narrow, and beyond was something that froze my blood: two enormous hooves and, resting on their cloven surfaces, a huge expanse of muzzle with twitching nostrils. I didn't have to feel anymore, but with an extra effort I strained forward a few inches, and my fingers explored a bulging brow squeezing into the small space like a cork in a bottle. As I withdrew my hand, the rough surface of the calf's tongue flicked briefly against my palm.

I sat back on my heels and looked up at the farmer. "There's an elephant in there, Mr. Bushell."

"Eh?"

I raised my voice. "A tremendous calf, and no room for it to come out."

"Can't ye cut it away?"

"Afraid not. The calf's alive and, anyway, there's nothing to get at. No room to work."

"Well, that's a beggar," Mr. Bushell said. "She's a good little milker. Ah don't want to send 'er to the butcher."

Neither did I. I hated the very thought of it, but a great light was breaking beyond a new horizon. It was a moment of decision, of history. I turned to the student.

"This is it, Norman! The ideal indication for a Caesar. What a good job I've got you with me. You can keep me right."

I was slightly breathless with excitement, and I hardly noticed the flicker of anxiety in the young man's eyes.

I got to my feet and seized the farmer's arm. "Mr. Bushell, I'd like to do a Caesarian operation on your cow."

"A what?"

"A Caesarian. Open her up and remove the calf surgically."

"Tek it out o' the side, d'ye mean? Like they do wi' women?"

"That's right."

"Well that's a rum' un." The farmer's eyebrows went up. "I never knew you could do that wi' cows."

"Oh, we can now," I said airily. "Things have moved on a bit in the last few years."

He rubbed a hand slowly across his mouth. "Well, ah don't know. I reckon she'd die if you made a bloody great 'ole in her like that. Maybe she'd be better goin' for slaughter. I'd get a few quid for her and I allus think fust loss is best."

I could see my big moment slipping away from me. "But she's only a thin little thing. She wouldn't be worth much for meat, and with a bit of luck we might get a live calf out of her."

I was going against one of my steadfast rules—never to talk a farmer into doing something—but I was seized by a kind of madness. Mr. Bushell looked at me for a long time, then, without changing expression, he nodded.

"Awright, what do you want?"

"Two buckets of warm water, soap, towels," I replied. "And I'll bring some instruments into the house to boil, if I may."

When the farmer had departed, I thumped Norman on the shoulder. "This is just right. Plenty of light, a live calf to aim for and it's just as well poor Mr. Bushell doesn't hear too well. If we keep our voices down, I'll be able to ask you things as we go along."

Norman didn't say anything. I told him to set up some straw bales for our equipment and had him scatter loose straw around the cow while I boiled the instruments in a pan in the farm kitchen.

Soon all was ready—syringes, suture materials, scalpels, scissors, local anaesthetic and cotton wool laid in a row on a clean towel draped over one of the bales. I added some antiseptic to the water and addressed the farmer.

"We'll roll her over and you can hold the head down, Mr. Bushell. I think she's too tired to move much."

Norman and I pushed at the shoulder, and Bella flopped on her side without resistance. The farmer put his knee against her neck, and the long area of the left flank was exposed for our attention.

I nudged the student. "Where do I make the incision?" I whispered.

Norman cleared his throat. "Well, er, it's about . . ." he pointed vaguely.

I nodded. "Around the rumenotomy site, eh? But a bit lower, I suppose." I began to clip away the hair from a foot-long strip. It would need a big opening for that calf to come through. Then I quickly infiltrated the area with local.

We do these jobs under a local anaesthetic and in most cases the cow lies quietly on her side or even stands during the operation. The animal can't feel anything, of course, but I have a few extra grey hairs round my ears that owe their presence to the occasional wild cow suddenly rearing up halfway through and taking off with me in desperate pursuit, trying to keep her internal organs from flopping on the ground.

But that was all in the future. On this first occasion I had no such fears. I cut through skin, muscle layers and peritoneum, and was confronted by a protruding pink and white mass of tissue.

I poked at it with my finger. There was something hard inside. Could it be the calf?

"What's that?" I hissed.

"Eh?" Norman, kneeling by my side, jumped convulsively. "What do you mean?"

"That thing. Is it the rumen or the uterus? It's pretty low down, it could be the uterus."

The student swallowed a couple of times. "Yes . . . yes . . . that's the uterus all right."

"Good." I smiled in relief and made a bold incision. A great gout of impacted grass welled out, followed by a burst of gas and an outflow of dirty brown fluid.

"Oh, Christ!" I gasped. "It's the rumen. Look at all that bloody mess!" I groaned aloud as the filthy tide surged away down and out of sight into the abdominal cavity. "What the hell are you playing at, Norman?"

I could feel the young man's body trembling against mine.

"Don't just sit there!" I shouted. "Thread me one of those needles. Quick! Quick!"

Norman bounded to his feet, rushed over to the bale and returned with a trailing length of catgut extended in shaking fingers. Wordlessly, dry-mouthed, I stitched the gash I had made in the wrong organ. Then the two of us made frantic attempts to swab away the escaped rumenal contents with cotton wool and antiseptic, but much of it had run away beyond our reach. The contamination must be massive.

When we had done what we could, I sat back and looked at the student. My voice was a hoarse growl. "I thought you knew all about these operations."

He looked at me with frightened eyes. "They do quite a few of them at the clinic."

I glared back at him. "How many Caesarians have you seen?"

"Well . . . er . . . one, actually."

"One! To hear you speak I thought you were an expert! And, anyway, even if you'd seen only one, you should know a little bit about it."

"The thing is . . ." Norman shuffled his knees around on the cobbles. "You see . . . I was right at the back of the class."

[69]

I worked up a sarcastic snarl. "Oh, I understand. So you couldn't see very well?"

"That's about it." The young man hung his head.

"Well, you're a stupid young fool!" I said in a vicious whisper. "Dishing out your confident instructions when you know damn all. You realise you've killed this good cow. With all that contamination, she'll certainly develop peritonitis and die. All we can hope for now is to get the calf out alive." With an effort I turned my gaze from his stricken face. "Anyway, let's get on with it."

Apart from my first shouts of panic, the entire interchange had been carried out *pianissimo*, and Mr. Bushell kept shooting enquiring glances at us.

I gave him what I hoped was a reassuring smile and returned to the attack. Getting the calf out alive was easy to say, but it soon dawned on me that getting the calf out in any way whatsoever was going to be a mammoth task. Plunging my arm deep below what I now knew was the rumen, I encountered a smooth and mighty organ lying on the abdominal floor. It contained an enormous bulk with the hardness and immobility of a sack of coal.

I felt my way along the surface and came upon the unmistakable contours of a hock pushing against the slippery wall. That was the calf, all right, but it was far, far away.

I withdrew my arm and started on Norman again. "From your position at the back of the class," I enquired bitingly, "did you happen to notice what they did next?"

"Next? Ah, yes." He licked his lips, and I could see beads of sweat on his brow. "You are supposed to exteriorise the uterus."

"Exteriorise it? Bring it up to the wound, you mean?"

"That's right."

"Good God!" I said. "King Kong couldn't lift up that bloody uterus. In fact I can't move it an inch. Have a feel."

The student, who was stripped and soaped like myself, introduced his arm and for a few moments I watched his eyes pop and his face redden. Then he withdrew and nodded sheepishly. "You're right. It won't move."

"Only one thing to do." I picked up a scalpel. "I'll have to cut into the uterus and grab that hock. There's nothing else to get hold of."

It was very nasty, fiddling about away out of sight down in the dark unknown, my arm buried to the shoulder in the cow, my tongue hanging out with anxiety. I was terrified I might slash into something vital but, in fact, it was my own fingers that I cut, several times, before I was able to draw the scalpel edge across the bulge made by the hock. A second later I had my hand round the hairy leg. Now I was getting somewhere.

Gingerly, I enlarged the incision, inch by inch. I hoped fervently I had made it big enough, but working blind is a terrible thing, and it was difficult to be sure.

At any rate, I couldn't wait to deliver that calf. I laid aside my knife, seized the leg and tried to lift it, and immediately I knew that another little nightmare lay ahead. The thing was a tremendous weight and it was going to take great strength to bring it up into the light of day. Nowadays when I do a Caesar, I take care to have a big strong farm lad stripped off, ready to help me with this lifting job, but today I had only Norman.

"Come on," I panted. "Give me a hand."

We reached down together and began to pull. I managed to repel the hock and bring the foot round, and that gave us greater purchase, but it was still agonisingly laborious to raise the mass to the level of the skin incision.

Teeth clenched, grunting with effort, we hauled upwards till at last I was able to grasp the other hind leg. Even then, with a foot apiece in our hands, nothing wanted to move. It was just like doing a tough calving except it was through the side. And as we lay back, panting and sweating, pulling with every vestige of our strength, I had the sudden wave of illumination which comes to all members of our profession at times. I wished with all my heart and soul that I had never started this ghastly job. If only I had followed Mr. Bushell's suggestion to send the cow for slaughter I would now be driving peacefully on my rounds. Instead, here

I was, killing myself. And even worse than my physical torment was the piercing knowledge that I hadn't the slightest idea what was going to happen next.

But the calf was gradually coming through. The tail appeared, then an unbelievably massive rib cage and finally with a rush, the shoulders and head.

Norman and I sat down with a bump, the calf rolling over our knees. And like a gleam of light in the darkness, I saw that he was snorting and shaking his head.

"By gaw, he's a big 'un!" exclaimed the farmer. "And wick, too."

I nodded. "Yes, he's huge. One of the biggest I've ever seen." I felt between the hind legs. "A bull, as I thought. He'd never have come out the proper way."

My attention was whisked back to the cow. Where was the uterus? It had vanished. Again I started my frantic groping inside. My hand became entangled with yards of placenta. Oh hell, that wouldn't do any good floating around among the guts. I pulled it out and dropped it on the floor, but I still couldn't find the uterus. For a palpitating moment I wondered what would happen if I never did locate it, then my fingers came upon the ragged edge of my incision.

I pulled as much as possible of the organ up to the light, and I noticed with sinking disquiet that my original opening had been enlarged by the passage of that enormous calf and there was a long tear disappearing out of sight towards the cervix.

"Sutures." I held my hand out, and Norman gave me a fresh needle. "Hold the lips of the wound," I said and began to stitch.

I worked as quickly as I could and was doing fine until the tear ran out of sight. The rest was a kind of martyrdom. Norman hung on grimly while I stabbed around at the invisible tissue far below. At times I pricked the young man's fingers, at others my own. And to my dismay, a further complication had arisen.

The calf was now on its feet, blundering unsteadily around. The speed with which newly born animals get onto their legs has always fascinated me, but at this moment it was an unmitigated nuisance.

The calf, looking for the udder with that instinct which nobody can explain, kept pushing his nose at the cow's flank and at times toppling headfirst into the gaping hole in her side.

"Reckon 'e wants back in again," Mr. Bushell said with a grin. "By 'eck, he is a wick 'un."

"Wick" is Yorkshire for lively, and the word was never more aptly applied. As I worked, eyes half-closed, jaws rigid, I had to keep nudging the wet muzzle away with my elbow, but as fast as I pushed him back the calf charged in again, and with sick resignation I saw that every time he nosed his way into the cavity, he brought particles of straw and dirt from the floor and spread them over the abdominal contents.

"Look at that," I moaned. "As if there wasn't enough muck in there."

Norman didn't reply. His mouth was hanging open and the sweat ran down his blood-streaked face as he grappled with that unseen wound. And in his fixed stare I seemed to read a growing doubt as to his wisdom in deciding to be a veterinary surgeon.

I would rather not go into any more details. The memory is too painful. Sufficient to say that, after an eternity, I got as far down the uterine tear as I could, then we cleared away a lot of rubbish from the cow's abdomen and covered everything with antiseptic dusting powder. I stitched up the muscle and skin layers, with the calf trying all the time to get in on the act, and at last the thing was finished.

Norman and I got to our feet very slowly, like two old, old men. It took me a long time to straighten my back, and I saw the young man rubbing tenderly at his lumbar region. Then, since we were both plastered with caked blood and filth, we began the slow process of scrubbing and scraping ourselves clean.

Mr. Bushell left his position by the head and looked at the row of skin stitches. "Nice neat job," he said. "And a grand calf, too."

Yes, that was something. The little creature had dried off now, and he was a beauty, his body swaying on unsteady legs, his wide-set eyes filled with gentle curiosity. But that "neat job" hid things I didn't dare think about.

Antibiotics were still not in general use, but, in any case, I knew there was no hope for the cow. More as a gesture than anything else, I left the farmer some sulpha powders to give her three times a day. Then I got off the farm as quickly as I could.

We drove away in silence. I rounded a couple of corners, then stopped the car under a tree and sank my head against the steering wheel.

"Oh hell," I groaned. "What a bloody balls-up."

Norman replied only with a long sigh and I continued, "Did you ever see such a performance? All that straw and dirt and rumenal muck in among that poor cow's bowels. Do you know what I was thinking about towards the end? I was remembering the story of that human surgeon of olden times who left his hat inside his patient. It was as bad as that."

"I know." The student spoke in a strangled undertone. "And it was all my fault."

"Oh no, it wasn't," I replied. "I made a right bollocks of the whole thing all by myself, and I tried to blame you because I got in a panic. I shouted and nagged at you and I owe you an apology."

"Oh no, no . . ."

"Yes, I do. I am supposed to be a qualified veterinary surgeon, and I did nearly everything wrong." I groaned again. "And on top of it all, I behaved like an absolute swine towards you, and I'm sorry."

"You didn't really, you didn't . . . I . . ."

"Anyway, Norman," I broke in. "I'm going to thank you now. You were a tremendous help to me. You worked like a Trojan and I'd have got nowhere at all without you. Let's go and have a pint."

With the early-evening sunshine filtering into the bar parlour of the village inn, we dropped into a quiet corner and pulled deeply at our beer glasses. We were both hot and weary and there didn't seem to be anything more to say.

It was Norman who broke the silence. "Do you think that cow has any chance?"

I examined the cuts and punctures on my fingers for a moment. "No, Norman. Peritonitis is inevitable, and I'm pretty sure I've left a good-sized hole in her uterus." I shuddered and slapped my brow at the memory.

I was sure I would never see Bella alive again, but first thing next morning a morbid curiosity made me lift the phone to find out if she had survived so far.

The "buzz-buzz" at the other end seemed to last a long time before Mr. Bushell answered.

"Oh, it's Mr. Herriot. Cow's up and eatin'." He didn't sound surprised.

It was several seconds before I was able to absorb his words.

"Doesn't she look a bit dull or uncomfortable?" I asked huskily.

"Nay, nay, she's bright as a cricket. Finished off a rackful of hay, and I got a couple o' gallons of milk from 'er."

As in a dream I heard his next question. "When'll you take them stitches out?"

"Stitches . . . Oh yes." I gave myself a shake. "In a fortnight, Mr. Bushell, in a fortnight."

After the horrors of the first visit, I was glad Norman was with me when I removed the sutures. There was no swelling round the wound, and Bella chewed her cud happily as I snipped away. In a pen nearby the calf gambolled and kicked his feet in the air.

I couldn't help asking, "Has she shown any symptoms at all, Mr. Bushell?"

"Nay." The farmer shook his head slowly. "She's been neither up nor down. You wouldn't know owt had happened to 'er."

That was the way it was at my first Caesarian. Over the years Bella went on to have eight more calves normally and unaided, a miracle which I can still hardly believe.

But Norman and I were not to know that. All we felt then was an elation all the sweeter for being unexpected.

As we drove away I looked at the young man's smiling face. "Well, Norman," I said. "That's veterinary practice for you. You get a lot of nasty shocks, but some lovely surprises, too. I've often heard of the wonderful resistance of the bovine peritoneum, and thank heavens it's true."

"The whole thing's marvellous, isn't it?" he murmured dreamily. "I can't describe the way I feel. My head seems to be full of quotations like 'Where there is life there's hope.' "

"Yes, indeed," I said. "John Gay, isn't it—*The Sick Man and the Angel.*"

Norman clapped his hands. "Oh, well done."

"Let's see." I thought for a moment. "How about 'But t'was a famous victory.' "

"Excellent," replied the young man. "Southey, *The Battle of Blenheim.*"

I nodded. "Quite correct."

"Here's a good one," the student said. " 'Out of this nettle, danger, we pluck this flower, safety.' "

"Splendid, splendid," I replied. "Shakespeare, *Henry Fifth.*"

"No, *Henry Fourth.*"

I opened my mouth to argue, but Norman held up a confident hand. "It's no good, I'm right. And this time I *do* know what I'm talking about."

Chapter
9

October 30, 1961

At 6:30 A.M. this morning we reached the Kiel Canal. There is a little town at the western end and a big lock gate. We had to wait for about half an hour to get through the lock, and during this time we took aboard a German policeman and a Dutch pilot. The policeman's job was to see that we did not pollute the canal by throwing out the manure and soiled bedding from the ship. He was very smart in a black leather coat with gold buttons and a neat blue uniform with two pips on the shoulder, and we spent a pleasant time chatting. He shamed me, as so many foreigners do, by speaking quite good English.

After passing through the lock gate it was a delight to be gliding along in still water for a change, and I stood out on the strip of deck, watching the many types of vessels that use the canal. There were several German warships, and the young sailors with their little caps on the side of their heads waved cheerily to me as they passed.

The countryside was flat with much farmland and woods, looking very pretty with their autumn tints. We passed many villages with attractive houses, most of which had long, steeply sloping roofs and dormer windows.

After about six hours we arrived at the eastern end of the canal. Here a German immigration official came aboard and stamped my passport. He also put a stamp on my name in the ship's articles, since this morning I was officially signed on as a member of the ship's company. It was odd to see the list of Danish names and then "James Herriot, Supercargo." I felt strangely uplifted. Me, a supercargo!

The sheep looked quite happy this morning, though there is still that nagging cough among the Lincolns. The one with the eye irritation is almost normal now, but the lame sheep has not improved; in fact, it has deteriorated slightly and is running a high temperature, so I have got it in a pen on its own and have given it a shot of penicillin as well as the antibiotic spray. Obviously the infection was deeper than I thought.

The sailor who is my constant helper is the same one who spoke to me on the first evening. His name is Raun and he is a flaxen-haired young husky with great shoulders and a flattened-nosed boxer's face, but when he smiles he radiates charm. He is warm-natured and an animal lover. When we had installed the lame sheep in its pen he knelt down, put his arms round the woolly neck and gave it a long hug. I have noticed him doing this with the other sheep, particularly the massive Romney Marsh rams. As I have said, they are like huge teddy bears, and Raun seems to find them irresistible. Anyway, I am delighted they have chosen such a man to be my assistant.

At the east end the canal widened out into the Baltic. I could see the town of Kiel just round the corner, and there was a tremendous amount of shipping. We passed an imposing memorial to the Germans killed in the First World War, and there were a few deserted sandy beaches with summer houses around them.

As we headed out into the sea I found a hidden corner of the deck and did a bit of hopping about and running on the spot. I must try to make a habit of this because the only exercise I get is clambering up and down the ladders to the hold, and I will have to work off Nielsen's abundant fare somehow.

I have decided that I will make a final inspection of the animals each night at ten o'clock and go round them with Raun to hold

[78]

any I want to examine more closely. Tonight I was told that Raun was steering but that if I went up on the bridge he would soon be relieved.

The ship was pitching wildly as I staggered out onto the upper deck. This, I thought, was the real thing as I felt my way along in the inky blackness, drenched with sea spray, the boards heaving and slippery under my feet, my hands grabbing at anything to hold me upright.

I stumbled onto the bridge and found myself in a decidedly eerie atmosphere. The bridge is an entirely different place at night —absolutely dark—and I had to stand there for a long time before I could pick out the lonely figure at the wheel. That is a quiet job if ever there was one.

When Raun came down with me, I gave the ewe with the eye trouble what ought to be its final application of ointment and injected the lame sheep again. The animals that tried to stand were swaying and tumbling around, but they didn't seem any the worse. However, I wondered what they would be like in the morning because Raun told me he had heard the captain say there was a real storm blowing up.

"No matter," the big sailor said cheerfully. "You come and have a beer with me."

"Okay, thanks," I replied, and we went together to the crew's mess room. We sat down, he gave me a "Camels" cigarette and as we talked I looked around at the other members of the crew. Strangely, though the officers were dark, these were all of a type; thick yellow hair, fine physiques, tremendous men. All of them were cheerful and polite.

Raun told me about himself in his limited English. He is twenty-eight, has been at sea for fourteen years and is married, with two young children. He never stopped smiling, except at the end when he leaned across the table and tapped me on the chest.

"Doctor, on my last voyage we take two hundred cattles from Dublin to Lübeck. When we get to Lübeck, five cattles dead."

I whistled. "That's nasty. Didn't they have a vet with them?"

"No, no." His battered face was very serious. "No doctor for the cattles. Is good that you are here for the sheeps."

It made me think. Maybe I really was going to earn my keep.

I thanked him, said goodnight to everybody and made my way back to my quarters. Just outside my cabin is a door that opens onto a small platform on the stern of the ship. I like to go out there for a lungful of the good air before going to bed. Tonight, in the roaring wind, I could see only the creamy wash from the ship's propellors disappearing into the surrounding blackness. Above, there were a million stars, and I could pick out the plough and the pole star plainly. I didn't have to be an expert navigator to find our course. We are heading dead east.

I am finding it difficult to write my log tonight because the cabin keeps tilting steeply. I feel the captain is going to be right about the storm.

Chapter
10

To any conscientious veterinary surgeon, killing a patient is a terrible thought. I am not talking about euthanasia which is so often merciful, but of inadvertently killing when attempting to cure.

This has probably happened to many of us, and I think it happened to me. I can never be sure, but the memory still haunts me.

It all started when a young representative from a pharmaceutical company called at the surgery and started to talk about a wonderful new treatment for foul of the foot in cattle.

This condition was a headache in those early days. Judging by its name, it had been going on for centuries, and it happened when the interdigital space between the cleats of the cloven-footed bovine was invaded by the organism *Fusiformis necrophorus*, usually through some small wound or abrasion.

This resulted in the actual death of an area of tissue in the region along with swelling of the foot and extreme lameness. A good cow could lose condition at an alarming rate due simply to the pain. The medieval-sounding name came from the fact that the dead tissue gave off a particularly offensive smell.

The treatment we used to employ ranged from the tedious to the heroic. Cow's hind feet were never meant to be lifted up, and I was always relieved when it was a forefoot that was affected.

With hind feet, even applying antiseptics was a chore. If that didn't work, we bandaged on pads of cotton wool impregnated with caustics like copper sulphate, and a very popular treatment among the farmers was dressing the area with Stockholm tar and salt—a messy and unpleasant business with the feet whistling round the head of the operator.

So I couldn't believe it when the representative told me that an injection of M & B 693 into the vein would rapidly clear up the condition.

I actually laughed at the young man. "I know you chaps have to make a living, but this sounds like one of your tallest stories."

"It works, I tell you," he said. "It has been well tested, and I promise you it really does the trick."

"And you don't have to touch the foot at all?"

"No, only for diagnosis. Then you can forget about it."

"How long does it take to have an effect?"

"Just a few days. And I give you my word, the cow is sometimes much better within twenty-four hours."

It sounded like a beautiful dream. "Okay," I said. "Send some on. We'll give it a try."

He made a note on his pad, then looked up. "There's just one thing. This drug is very irritant. You must be sure you don't get it subcutaneous, or it could cause an abscess."

As he walked out of the door, I wondered if this really meant the end of one of our most disagreeable tasks. I had already had occasion to be thankful for the beneficent M & B tablets. They had wrought some minor miracles in our practice. But I found it hard to believe that an intravenous injection could cure a necrotic condition of the foot.

When the stuff arrived, I had the same trouble convincing the farmers. "What are you doin', injectin' the neck? You should be puttin' it into t'bloody foot." Or, "Is that all you're goin' to do? Aren't you goin' to give me summat to put on t'foot?" These were typical remarks, and my answers were halting because I had the same reservations as the stock owners.

[82]

But oh, how magically everybody's attitude changed because it was just as the young man said. Very often within a single day the beast was walking sound, the swelling had gone down, the pain had vanished. It was like witchcraft.

It was a giant step forward and I was at the height of my euphoria when I saw Robert Maxwell's cow. The reddened swollen foot, the agonised hopping, the stinking discharge—it was all there.

The fact is that it was so bad that I was delighted; I had found that the worst cases, with the acute lameness and the interdigital tissues pouting from toe or heel, were the ones that recovered quickest.

"We'll have some work on with this 'un," the farmer grunted. He was in his late forties, a dynamic little man and one of the bright farmers of the district. He was always to the fore in farmers' discussion groups, always eager to learn and teach.

"Not a bit of it, Mr. Maxwell," I said airily. "There's a new injection for this now. No foot dressing—that's gone for good."

"Well, that would be a blessin', anyway. It's savage amusement, hangin' onto cows' feet." He bent over the leg and looked down. "Where exactly do ye inject this new stuff, then?"

"In the neck."

"In the neck!"

I grinned. I never seemed to get tired of the reaction. "That's right. Into the jugular vein."

"Well, there's summat new every day now." Robert Maxwell shrugged and smiled, but he accepted it. The intelligent farmers like him were the ones who didn't argue. It was always the thickheads who knew everything.

"Just hold the nose," I said. "That's right, pull the head a little way round. Fine." I raised the jugular with my finger, and it stood out like a hosepipe as I slipped the needle into it. The M & B solution ran into the blood stream in about two minutes, and I pulled the needle out.

"Well, that's it," I said with a trace of smugness.

[83]

"Nothing else?"

"Not a thing. Forget about it. That cow will be sound in a few days."

"Well, I don't know." Robert Maxwell looked at me with a half-smile. "You young fellers keep surprising me. I've been in farmin' all me life, but you do things I've never dreamed of."

I saw him at a farmers' meeting about a week later.

"How's that cow?" I asked.

"Just like you said. Sound as a bell o' brass. That stuff shifts foul, all right, there's no doubt about it; it's like magic."

I was just expanding when his expression changed. "But there's a heck of a swelling on 'er neck."

"You mean, where I injected her?"

"Yes."

My happy feeling evaporated. I didn't like the sound of that. My first thought was that I must have got some of the solution under the skin, but I seemed to remember the blood still gushing from the needle when I pulled it out.

"That's funny," I said. "I can't see any reason for that."

Robert Maxwell shook his head. "I can't, either. I did that cow over with fly spray right after you left. Could some of that have got in your needle wound?"

"No . . . surely not. I've never heard of such a thing. I'd better have a look at her tomorrow."

I made it one of my first calls the next morning. The farmer had not been exaggerating. There was a marked swelling on the neck, but it was not confined to the injection site. It ran right along the course of the jugular. The vein itself had a solid, corded feel, and there was oedema around the swollen area.

"She's got phlebitis," I said. "The vein has somehow got infected through my injection."

"How would that happen?"

"I just don't know. I'm pretty sure none of the solution escaped, and my needle was clean."

The farmer peered closely at the cow's neck. "It's not like an abscess, is it?"

"No," I replied. "There's no abscess."

"And what's that long, hard lump goin' up to the jaw?"

"That's a thrombus."

"A what?"

"A thrombus. A big clot in the vein." I wasn't enjoying this little pathological lecture, considering that I had been responsible for the whole thing myself.

Robert Maxwell gave me a searching look. "Well, what's going to happen? What do we do?"

"Usually, collateral circulation develops within a few weeks. That is, other veins take over the job. And, in the meantime, I'll put her onto a course of mixed sulphonamide powders."

"Aye, well, she doesn't seem bothered," the farmer said.

That was one gleam of light. The cow had been looking round at us contentedly as we spoke, and now I saw her pulling a little hay from her rack.

"No . . . no . . . She doesn't look concerned at all. I'm sorry this has happened, but it should just be a question of time before she's right."

He scratched the root of the animal's tail for a moment. "Would bathin' with hot water do any good?"

I shook my head vigorously. "Please don't touch that place at all. It would be dangerous if that clot broke down."

I left the powders and drove away, but I had that nasty feeling I always have when I know I have boobed. I gripped the wheel and swore under my breath. What had I done wrong? The sterilised disposable needles and syringes which we take for granted now were unknown then, but Siegfried and I always boiled our hypodermics and carried them in cases where they were always immersed in surgical spirit. We could hardly do more. Had the farmer's fly spray done something? Hard to believe.

In any case, I comforted myself with the thought that the cow didn't look ill. These cases recovered in time. But the unpalatable fact remained. That animal had had a simple case of foul until James Herriot MRCVS took a hand, and now she had jugular phlebitis.

Helen had just put my breakfast in front of me on the following morning when the phone rang. It was Robert Maxwell.

"That cow's dead," he said.

I stared stupidly at the wall in front of me for several seconds before I could speak. "Dead . . . ?"

"Aye, found 'er laid in her stall this mornin'. Just as though she'd dropped down."

"Mr. Maxwell . . . I . . . er." I had to clear my throat more than once. "I'm terribly sorry. I never expected this."

"What's happened, then?" The farmer's voice was strangely matter-of-fact.

"There's only one explanation," I said. "Embolism."

"What's that?"

"It's when a piece of the clot breaks off and gets into the circulation. When an embolus reaches the heart, it usually means death."

"I see. That would do it, then."

I swallowed. "Let me say again, Mr. Maxwell, I'm very sorry."

"Ah, well . . ." There was a pause. "These things happen in farmin'. I just thought I'd let you know. Good mornin'."

I felt sick as I put the phone down, and the feeling persisted as I sat at the breakfast table, staring at my plate.

"Aren't you going to eat, Jim?" Helen asked.

I looked down sadly at the nice slice of home-fed ham. "Sorry, Helen, it's no good. I can't tackle it."

"Oh, come on." My wife smiled and pushed the plate nearer to me. "I know you worry about your work, but I've never known it to put you off your food."

I shrugged miserably. "But this is different. I've never killed a cow before."

Of course, I didn't know this for sure—I never will know—but

[86]

the thing stayed with me for a long time. I am a great believer in Napoleon's dictum, "Throw off your worries when you throw off your clothes," and I had never known the meaning of insomnia, but for many nights, turgid jugular veins and floating emboli brought me gasping to wakefulness.

As time passed I continued to wonder at the farmer's attitude on the phone. Most people would have been furious at a disaster like this, and it would have been natural enough if Robert Maxwell had blasted me at great length. But he hadn't been rude, hadn't even tried to blame me.

Of course, there was always the possibility that he might be going to sue me. He was a nice man, but, after all, he had suffered a financial loss, and it would not take a legal genius to make out a good case that I was the villain.

But the solicitor's letter never arrived. In fact, I did not hear a word from the farmer for nearly a month, and since I had been a regular visitor on his place, I concluded that he had changed his veterinary surgeon. Well, I had lost the practice of a good client, and that was not a pleasant thought, either.

Then one afternoon the phone rang, and it was Robert Maxwell again, speaking in the same quiet voice. "I want you to come and look at one of me cows, Mr. Herriot. There's somethin' amiss with her."

A wave of relief went through me. Not a mention of the other thing, just a call for assistance as if nothing had happened. There were a lot of charitable farmers in the Dales, and this man was one of them. I just hoped I could make it up to him in some way.

What I wanted was a case I could cure quickly and, if possible, in a spectacular manner. I had a lot of ground to make up on this farm.

Robert Maxwell received me with his usual quiet courtesy.

"That was a good rain last night, Mr. Herriot. The grass was gettin' right parched." It was as though my last unhappy visit had never occurred.

The cow was a big Friesian, and when I saw her my hopes of

a cheap triumph vanished in an instant. She was standing, arch-backed and gaunt, staring at the wall in front of her. One thing I hate to see is a cow staring at the wall. As we approached she showed no interest, and I made a spot diagnosis. This was traumatic reticulitis. She had swallowed a wire. I would have to operate on her, and after my last experience in this byre the idea did not appeal.

Yet, when I began to examine her, I realised that things were not adding up. The rumen was working well, seething and bubbling under my stethoscope, and when I pinched her withers she did not grunt—just swivelled an anxiety-ridden eye in my direction before turning her attention to the wall again.

"She's a bit thin," I said.

"Aye, she is." Robert Maxwell dug his hands into his pockets and surveyed the animal gloomily. "And I don't know why. She's had nobbut the best of stuff to eat, but she's lost condition fast over the last few days."

Pulse, respiration and temperature were normal. This was a funny one.

"At first I thought she had colic," the farmer went on. "She kept tryin' to kick at her belly."

"Kicking at her belly?" Something was stirring at the back of my mind. Yes, that was often a symptom of nephritis. And as if to clinch my decision, the animal cocked her tail and sent a jet of bloody urine into the channel. I looked at the pool behind her. There were flecks of pus among the blood, and though I knew her trouble now, it did not make me happy.

I turned to the farmer. "It's her kidneys, Mr. Maxwell."

"Her kidneys? What's the matter wi' them?"

"Well, they're inflamed. They've become infected in some way. It's called pyelonephritis. Probably the bladder is affected, too."

The farmer blew out his cheeks. "Is it serious?"

How I wished I could give him, of all people, a light answer, but there was no doubt that this was a usually fatal condition. I had a feeling of doom.

"I'm afraid so," I replied. "It is very serious."

"I had a feelin' there was somethin' far wrong. Can you do owt for her?"

"Yes," I said. "I would like to try her with some mixed sulphonamides."

He glanced at me quickly. That was what I had used for the phlebitis.

"It really is the best thing," I went on hurriedly. "Cows like this used to be hopeless to treat, but since the sulpha drugs came on the scene, we do have a chance."

He gave me one of his long, calm looks. "All right, then, we'd better get started."

"I'll keep an eye on her," I said as I handed over the powders.

And I did keep an eye on her. I was in the Maxwell byre every day. I desperately wanted that cow to live. But after four days there was no improvement; in fact, she was slowly sinking.

I was steeped in gloom as I stood by the farmer's side and looked at the animal's jutting ribs and pelvic bones. She was thinner than ever, and still she passed that blood-stained urine.

I could not bear the thought that another tragedy was going to follow so soon after the first one, but the certainty was growing in my mind that death was imminent.

"The sulphonamides are keeping her alive," I said, "but we need something stronger."

"Is there anythin' stronger?"

"Yes, penicillin."

Penicillin. The marvellous new drug, the first of the antibiotics, but as yet the veterinary profession had no injectable form. All we had were the tiny tubes, each containing 300 mg in an oily base, for the treatment of mastitis. The nozzle of the tube was inserted into the teat canal and the contents squeezed up into the udder. It was a magical improvement on any previous mastitis treatment, but at that stage of my career I had never injected an antibiotic into an animal hypodermically.

I am not usually inventive but I had a sudden idea. I went out to my car, found a box of twelve mastitis tubes and tried the nozzle in the base of a record hypodermic needle. It fitted perfectly.

I am no scientific theorist so I didn't know whether I was doing the right thing or not, but I plunged the needle into the cow's rump and squeezed tube after tube into the depths of the muscle until the box was empty. Would the penicillin be absorbed in that form? I didn't know. But there was comfort in the knowledge that at least it was in there. It was a spark of hope.

I kept this up for three days and on the third I knew I was doing some good.

"Look!" I said to Robert Maxwell. "Her back isn't arched now. She seems to have relaxed."

The farmer nodded. "You're right. She isn't as tucked up as she was."

The sight of the cow standing there peacefully, looking around her and occasionally pulling a mouthful of hay from her rack, was like a blast of trumpets to me. The pain in the kidneys was plainly subsiding, and the farmer had said that the urine was not as dark as it had been.

I seemed to go mad after that. With the scent of victory in my nostrils, I pumped my little tubes into the animal day after day. I didn't know the correct dose for a bovine—nobody did at that time—so I just whacked them in, willy-nilly, sometimes more, sometimes less, and all the time the improvement continued steadily.

There came the happy day when I was quite certain that the battle was won. As I worked on the cow, she straddled her legs and sent out a cascade of crystal-clear urine. I stepped back, and as if for the first time I contemplated the change in my patient. The gaunt frame of that first day was padded with flesh, and the cow's coat shone with the gloss of health. She had returned to normal just as quickly as she had fallen away. It was remarkable.

I threw down the empty box. "Well, Mr. Maxwell, I think we can say she's about right. I'll give her another treatment tomorrow, and that will be the end."

"You're comin' back tomorrow, then?"

"Yes, for the last time."

The farmer's face grew grave, and he stepped closer to me. "All right, then, I 'ave a complaint to make about you."

Oh God, at last he was going to tackle me about that phlebitis. And what a terrible moment to pick, just when I was flushed with success. Human nature could be very strange, and if he had decided to give me hell after all this time, there was nothing I could do about it. I would just have to take it.

"Oh, yes?" I replied shakily. "And what is that?"

He leaned forward and tapped my chest with his forefinger. His face was transfigured, heavy with menace. "D'ye think I've got nothin' better to do than sweep up after you every day?"

"Sweep up . . . what . . ." I stared at him stupidly.

He waved an arm over the byre floor. "Just look at all this dang mess! I've got to clear it away!"

I looked down at the scattering of empty penicillin tubes, the paper pamphlets which always went with them and the discarded box. Totally unheeding, I had hurled them far and wide as I worked.

"Gosh, I'm sorry," I muttered. "I didn't realise . . ."

I was interrupted by a great burst of laughter from the farmer.

"Nay, I'm just havin' ye on, lad. Of course you didn't realise. You were ower busy curin' me cow." He thumped me on the shoulder, and I knew it was his way of saying thanks.

That was my first experience of injecting an antibiotic, and even though the method was bizarre, I learned something from it. But I learned more on that farm about the way to live than I did about veterinary science. Over the following thirty years I knew him, the farmer never alluded to that disaster which he could so easily have laid at my door.

During that period there have been occasions when I have suffered misfortunes due to the shortcomings of others, when I have found people at fault and at my mercy if I wished to make trouble for them. At these times I had a standard of conduct to follow. I tried to behave like Robert Maxwell.

Chapter 11

"You know, Jim," said Tristan, pulling thoughtfully at his Woodbine, "I often wonder if there is any other household where the mark of a lady's favour is expressed in goat shit."

In quiet moments I often thought about the old bachelor days in Skeldale House, and it was at one of these times that I recalled Tristan's observation. I could remember looking up at him from the day book in surprise. "Well, isn't that funny? I've just been thinking the same thing. It certainly is rather an odd business."

We had just come through from the dining room, and my memory of the breakfast table was very clear. Mrs. Hall always placed our letters next to our plates, and there, at Siegfried's place, dominating the scene like an emblem of triumph, stood the tin of goat droppings from Miss Grantley.

We all knew what it was, despite its wrapping of brown paper, because Miss Grantley always used the same container, an empty cocoa tin about six inches high. Either she collected them from friends or she was very fond of cocoa.

One indisputable thing was that she was very fond of goats. In fact, they seemed almost to rule her existence, which was strange because the care of goats was an unlikely hobby for a blond beauty who could have stepped effortlessly into the film world.

Another odd thing about Miss Grantley was that she had never married. Each time I had been at her house I had marvelled that anybody like her was able to keep the men away. She would be about thirty, with a nicely rounded figure and elegant legs and sometimes when I looked at the fine contours of her face, I wondered whether that rather firm jaw might have frightened prospective suitors. But no, she was cheerful and charming; I decided that she just didn't want to get married. She had a lovely home and obviously plenty of money. She appeared to be perfectly happy.

There was no doubt at all that the goat droppings were a mark of favour. Miss Grantley took her stock keeping very seriously and insisted on regular laboratory examination of faeces samples for internal parasites or any other abnormality that might be found.

These samples were always addressed personally to Mr. Siegfried Farnon and I had attached no importance to this until one morning, a few days after I had pleased her immensely by removing an embedded piece of chaff from one of her Billies' eyes, the familiar tin appeared by my breakfast plate and I read, "James Herriot Esq., MRCVS," on the label.

That was when I realised it was an accolade, a gesture of approval. In ancient days the feudal knights would carry a glove at their saddle bow or a scarf on their lance point as a symbol of their lady's esteem, but with Miss Grantley it was goat droppings.

On the occasion when I got mine, Siegfried's face showed the slightest flicker of surprise and I suppose I might have shown a trace of smugness, but he needn't have worried. Within a week or two the tin reappeared at his end of the table.

And after all, it was the natural thing, because if sheer male attractiveness entered into this situation, there was no doubt that Siegfried was out in front by a street. Tristan pursued the local girls enthusiastically and with considerable success; I had no reason to complain about my share of female company, but Siegfried was in a different class. He seemed to drive women mad.

He didn't have to chase them; they chased him. I hadn't known him long before I realised that the tales I had heard about the irresistible appeal of tall, lean-faced men were true. And when you added his natural charm and commanding personality, it was inevitable that the goat droppings would land regularly by his plate.

In fact, that is how it was for a long time even though Tristan and I paid almost as many visits to Miss Grantley's goats as Siegfried. As I said, she seemed to be quite rich because she called us out to the slightest ailment and was as good a client as some of our big farmers.

However, when I heard her voice on the telephone one morning, I knew that this time it wasn't for something trivial. She sounded agitated.

"Mr. Herriot, Tina has caught her shoulder on a nail and torn herself rather badly. I do hope you can come out immediately."

"Yes, as it happens, I can. There is nothing urgent at the moment. I'll leave right away."

A mild glow of satisfaction rippled through me. This would be just another stitching job and I liked stitching. It was easy and always impressed the client. I would be on happier ground there than when Miss Grantley was quizzing me about goat diseases. They had taught me practically nothing about goats at college, and though I had tried to catch up by snatches of reading here and there, I realised uncomfortably that I was no expert.

I was leaving the room when Tristan levered himself slowly from the depths of the armchair where he spent a lot of his time. Since breakfast I had been aware of his presence only by the rustle of the *Daily Mirror* under a cloud of Woodbine smoke.

He yawned and stretched. "Miss Grantley's, eh? Think I'll come with you. Just feel like a ride out."

I smiled. "Okay, come on, then." He was always good company.

Miss Grantley met us in a tight-fitting pale-blue boiler suit of some silky material which did nothing to diminish her attractions.

"Oh, thank you so much for coming," she said. "Please follow me."

Following her was rewarding. In fact, on entering the goat

house Tristan failed to see the step and fell onto his knees. Miss Grantley glanced at him briefly before hurrying to a pen at the far end.

"There she is," she said and put a hand over her eyes. "I can't bear to look."

Tina was a fine white Saanen, but her beauty was ravaged by a huge laceration that had pulled the skin down from her shoulder in a long V, exposing the naked smoothness of the supraspinatus and infraspinatus muscles. The bony spine of the scapula gleamed white through the blood.

It was a mess, but I had to stop myself rubbing my hands. It was all superficial, and I could put it right and look very good in the process. Already I could see myself inserting the last stitch and pointing to the now almost-invisible wound. "There, now, that looks a lot better, doesn't it?" Miss Grantley would be in raptures.

"Yes . . . yes . . ." I murmured in my most professional manner as I probed the damaged area. "It's nasty, really nasty."

Miss Grantley clasped her hands together. "But do you think you can save her?"

"Oh, yes." I nodded weightily. "It will be a big stitching job and take rather a long time, but I feel sure she will pull through."

"Oh, thank heaven." She gave a long sigh of relief. "I'll fetch some hot water."

Soon I was ready for action. My needles, cotton wool, scissors, suture materials and forceps laid out on a clean towel, Tristan holding Tina's head, Miss Grantley hovering anxiously, ready to help.

I cleaned the whole area thoroughly, sprinkled dusting powder with a liberal hand, then began to stitch. Miss Grantley was soon in action, passing me the scissors to clip each suture. It was a nice smooth start, but it was a very large wound and this was going to take some time. I searched my mind for light conversation.

Tristan chipped in, apparently thinking the same thing. "Wonderful animal, the goat," he said lightly.

"Ah, yes." Miss Grantley looked across at him with a bright smile. "I do agree."

"When you think about it, they are probably the earliest of the domestic animals," he went on. "It always thrills me to realise that there is ample evidence of domestication of goats in prehistoric times. There are cave paintings of goats and later, ancient books from all over the world mention their existence. They have been part of the world of man since recorded time. It is a fascinating thought."

From my squatting position I looked up at him in surprise. In my relationship with Tristan I had discovered several things which fascinated him, but goats were not one of them.

"And another thing," he went on. "They have such a marvellous metabolism. They will consume food other animals won't look at, and they will produce abundant milk from that food."

"Yes, indeed," breathed Miss Grantley.

Tristan laughed. "They're such characters, too. Tough and hardy under all climatic conditions, absolutely fearless and ready to tackle any other animal, no matter how large. And, of course, it is a known fact that they can eat with impunity many poisonous plants which would kill most creatures in a very short time."

"Oh, they *are* amazing." Miss Grantley gazed at my friend and passed the scissors to me without turning her head.

I felt I ought to make some contribution. "Goats certainly are extremely . . ." I began.

"But really, you know," Tristan was in full flow again, "I think that the thing which appeals to me most about them is their affectionate nature. They are friendly and sociable, and I feel that that is why people become so deeply attached to them."

Miss Grantley nodded gravely. "How true, how true."

My colleague stretched out a hand and fingered the hay in the animal's rack. "I see you feed them properly. There's all sorts of rough stuff in here—thistles and bits of shrubs and coarse plants.

Obviously you know that goats prefer such things to grass. No wonder your animals are so healthy."

"Oh thank you." She blushed faintly. "Of course I give them concentrates, too."

"Whole grain, I hope?"

"Oh yes, always."

"Good, good. Keeps up the pH of the rumen. You know, you can get hypertrophy of the rumenal walls and inhibition of cellulose-digesting bacteria with a low pH?"

"Well, no . . . I didn't really understand it in those terms." She was staring at him as if he were a prophet.

"Ah, no matter," Tristan said airily. "You are doing all the right things, and that is the important point."

"Can I have the scissors, please?" I grunted. I was beginning to feel cramped in my bent-over position and also a little piqued at the growing impression that Miss Grantley had forgotten all about me.

But I stitched on doggedly, one-half of my mind watching thankfully as the skin gradually covered the denuded area, the other listening in amazement as Tristan pontificated on the construction of goat houses, their dimensions, ventilation and relative humidity.

A long time later Miss Grantley hardly noticed as I inserted the last suture and straightened up wearily. "Well, now, that looks better, doesn't it?" I said, but there wasn't the expected impact because Tristan and my client were deeply involved in a discussion of the relative merits of the different breeds of goats.

"Are you really in favour of the Toggenburg and Anglo-Nubian?" she asked.

"Oh yes." Tristan inclined his head judicially. "Excellent animals, both of them."

Miss Grantley suddenly became aware that I had finished. "Oh, thank you so much," she said absently. "You have taken such pains. I am most grateful. Now you must both come in for a cup of coffee."

As we balanced our cups on our knees in the elegant sitting room, Tristan carried on, unabated. He dealt in depth with reproductive problems, obstetrics and the feeding of weaned kids, and he was well into a little treatise on anaesthesia for dehorning when Miss Grantley turned towards me. She was clearly still under his spell but no doubt felt that it would be only polite to bring me into the conversation.

"Mr. Herriot, one thing worries me. I share a pasture with the farmer next door, and very often my goats are grazing with his ewes and lambs. Now, I have heard that his sheep are troubled with coccidiosis. Is there any chance that my goats could contract it from them?"

I took a long pull at my coffee cup to give myself time to think. "Well . . . er . . . I would say . . ."

My friend broke in again effortlessly. "Most unlikely. It seems that most types of coccidiosis are specific to their individual hosts. I don't think you need worry on that account."

"Thank you." Miss Grantley addressed me again, as though deciding to give me a last chance. "And how about worms, Mr. Herriot? Can my goats become infected with worms from the sheep?"

"Ah now, let's see . . ." My cup rattled in the saucer, and I could feel a light perspiration breaking out on my brow. "The thing is . . ."

"Quite so," murmured Tristan, gliding once more to my aid. "As Mr. Herriot was about to say, helminthiasis is a different proposition. There is a very real danger of infection, since the common nematodes are the same in both species. You must always worm regularly, and if I can give you a brief programme . . ."

I sank deeper in my chair and let him get on with it, only half hearing erudite remarks about the latest anthelmintics and their actions on trichostrongyles, haemonchus and ostertagia.

It came to an end at last, and we went out to the car. "I'll come back in ten days to remove the stitches," I said as Miss Grantley showed us off the premises. It struck me that it was just about the only sensible thing I had said.

I drove a few hundred yards along the road, then I stopped the car.

"Since when have you been a goat lover?" I demanded bitterly. "And where the hell did you get all that high-powered stuff you were preaching back there?"

Tristan giggled, then threw back his head and laughed immoderately. "Sorry, Jim," he said when he had recovered. "I have exams coming up in a few weeks, as you know, and I heard that one of the examiners is really goat-orientated. Last night I boned up on every bit of goat literature I could find. Uncanny how I had the opportunity to trot it all out so soon after."

Ah, well, that made sense. Tristan had the kind of brain that absorbed information like a sponge. I could believe that he would have to read those chapters only once, and they would be his for good. In my student days I often had to go over a thing about six times before it sank in.

"I see," I said. "You'd better let me see those things you read last night. I didn't realise I was so ignorant."

There was an interesting little sequel about a week later. Siegfried and I were going in to breakfast when my partner stopped in mid-stride and stared at the table. The familiar brown-wrapped cocoa tin was there, but it was at his brother's place. Slowly he walked over and examined the label. I had a look, too, and there was no mistake. It read, "Mr. Tristan Farnon."

Siegfried said nothing but sat down at the head of the table. Very soon the young man himself joined us, examined the tin with interest and started on his meal.

Not a word was spoken and the three of us sat in silence, but over everything the undeniable fact hung heavy in the room. Tristan, for the moment, at least, was top man.

Chapter 12

October 31, 1961

Getting into bed last night wasn't easy. With every passing minute the ship's movements became more violent, and I fell down several times while undressing.

Once in the bunk I was thrown from side to side, not in the gentle roll of the other nights but with an unpleasant jarring bump. I turned onto my stomach, braced arms and legs against the wood and after about half an hour I managed to fall asleep.

Around two o'clock in the morning I was jerked from a troubled slumber into a world gone mad. I was being tossed about like a rubber ball, the wind howled, driving rain spattered against the cabin window and a frightful din rose from all over the ship. The banging and clattering were deafening. I could hear the pans in the galley flying around against the walls, a loose iron door clanged repeatedly on its hinges and from everywhere came a medley of undefined rattles and groans.

I switched on the light and looked out on a scene of chaos. My money, keys, pipe and tobacco were rolling about on the floor; the desk drawers were shooting out to their full extent, then slamming back again; the chair and my suitcase were sliding from one side to another.

Reeling about in the pandemonium, falling down repeatedly, I did my best to clear up the mess. Then I got back into bed. But

I couldn't stand the thumping of the drawers against the chair so I got out again, jammed the chair against the drawers and my suitcase between chair and bunk, and clambered wearily up again. But though this cured most of the local noise, the uproar outside was unabated, and I got very little sleep after that.

At dawn a cheerless sight greeted me as I looked out of my window. All around was an empty waste of grey water tossed up into mighty green- and white-topped waves that broke up into clouds of spray as the wind caught them. It gave me an uncomfortable thrill to see our little ship climb up one monstrous wave after another and then drop into a series of deep watery valleys beyond. The Baltic was really playing up.

My first thought was for the sheep, but I heard the knock on my door and the familiar voice of the mess boy. "Breakfast, Mr. Herriot."

I hurried to the mess room. I would have a quick bite and then collect Raun. The captain was seated alone at the table when I entered.

"Good morning, Mr. Herriot," he said and gave me a long appraising stare, which I couldn't quite understand.

I sat down and waited. I was impatient to get down to the hold, and I wished the breakfast would arrive. On top of that I was distinctly peckish, and I jabbed busily at the smoked ham, herring and salt beef. The captain watched me with narrowed eyes all the time.

After a few minutes the mess boy appeared. His face was as green as grass, and he averted his eyes from the piled plateful of sausages, scrambled eggs and fried potatoes.

I grabbed a piece of rye bread and fell upon the savoury mound without delay. I was hacking at a sausage when the captain spoke again.

"Are you feeling all right, Mr. Herriot?"

I looked up in surprise and replied with my mouth full, "Mm, yes, fine, thanks, a bit tired, maybe. I didn't get much sleep last night."

"But you are hungry, yes?"

"I am, yes, I certainly am. All that bouncing around seems to have stimulated my appetite."

"This is most unusual," the captain said in his precise way. "We have just come through a force-nine gale, and I was sure you would be seasick this morning. You are a very good sailor."

I laughed. "Well, thank you. I don't suppose there's anything very clever about that. I'm just made that way. Motion of any kind has never troubled me."

"Yes, yes . . ." The captain nodded gravely. "Still, it is remarkable. Didn't you notice Peter's face?"

"Peter?"

"Yes, the mess boy. All mess boys are called Peter, by the way, no matter what their real name is. He is feeling very ill; in fact, he is always ill in bad weather."

"Oh, poor lad. It *was* pretty rough last night, wasn't it?"

"Yes, Mr. Herriot, and I might say that we were sailing with the wind behind us. If we have to come back in weather like that with the wind against us, then heaven help us. It will be much worse."

"Really? I didn't know that. I . . ."

Raun's face, poking round the door, cut me off in mid-sentence.

"Doctor, come queek. The sheeps . . . the sheeps are bad!"

I bolted the last of the sausage and followed him to the hold as quickly as the heaving of the ship would allow me.

"Look, Doctor!" The big Dane pointed excitedly at one of the Romney Marsh rams.

The sheep was standing with some difficulty, legs straddled wide. It was panting violently, its mouth gaped and a bubbling saliva poured from its lips. The normally docile eyes were wide and charged with terror as the animal fought for breath.

All the euphoria I had felt since boarding the *Iris Clausen* evaporated as I rushed feverishly around the pens. A lot of the other sheep were behaving in exactly the same way, and I realised with a sense of shock that I wasn't on a pleasure cruise after all.

I suppressed a rising panic as I examined the animals. They all looked as though they were going to die, and I had a strong conviction that those unknown Russians waiting at the other end were not going to be amused when the expert veterinary attendant presented them with a heap of carcasses. A fine start it would be to my first venture at sea.

But as I went round the pens again, I began to calm down. None of the sheep looked happy, but it was only the biggest that were affected in this way—all the rams and one or two of the larger ewes, about a dozen in all. So, though it might be a tragedy, it wasn't going to be total disaster. With Raun hanging onto the necks, I took the temperatures. They were all around 107.

I leaned back against the wooden rail and tried to rationalise my thoughts. This was stress—a classical example. It must be; up in my case I had a few bottles of the new wonder drug, cortisone, and one of its indications was just this.

I was up to my cabin and down again quicker than I thought was possible and in the pockets of my working coat the precious bottles bumped against each other. The brand name was Predsolan; it was one of the first of the steroid products and though I had used it for arthritic and inflammatory conditions, I had never tried it in a case like this.

It wasn't only the ship's pitching that made my hand shake and wobble as I drew the liquid into my syringe. The supply was very limited, and heaven only knew how many more sheep would go down. I rationed the injections to 3 c.c. per sheep, and as I went round the stricken animals, my spirits sank lower. Only three of them could stand; the others were slumped on their chests, necks craning forward, eyes starting from their heads, their flanks heaving uncontrollably.

As I worked, Raun stroked the woolly heads and muttered endearments in Danish. It was the first time I had seen him look unhappy, and I knew how he felt. I hadn't been seasick, but I was sick now with apprehension.

[104]

These beautiful pedigree animals. And it was the rams, the most valuable of all, which were struck down. I could only wait now, but I was convinced that the whole business was hopeless. I realised that I couldn't bear to stand there watching them any longer, and I hurried up the iron ladders to the top deck, which was running with water and slanting at crazy angles. It was clearly no place for me, and I went up to the bridge.

The captain, as always, greeted me courteously, and when I told him about the sheep he looked thoughtful. Then he smiled.

"I know they are in good hands, Mr. Herriot. Do not be upset. I am sure you will cure them."

I couldn't share his optimism, and, in any case, I was pretty certain he was only trying to cheer me up. To take my mind off my troubles he again showed me our position on the chart and began to talk of maritime things.

"We are out of the sea lanes now," he said. He waved a hand round the desolation on all sides. "You see no ships now, and I think you see no ships all day."

As we talked we looked out through the glass at the bows of the ship, dipping into each gulf, then climbing up the green mountain on the other side. This was the best position to appreciate the size of those mighty waves, and a part of me never stopped being surprised as our tiny vessel fought her way up again and again.

The captain fell silent for a few minutes and gazed impassively at the endless stretch of sea beyond the glass.

"I tell you again, Mr. Herriot, we are running before the wind now, and if it is like this on our return journey, we are in big trouble." He turned and smiled. "You see, once we are unloaded, we must come back straightaway. A ship is doing no good lying in harbour."

All the time I was hanging on grimly to a rail, and it fascinated me to see the mate stroll casually onto the bridge, pipe in mouth, hands in pockets, and begin to move around effortlessly. At times his body seemed to be at an angle of forty-five degrees to the ground. I have noticed that all the crew are wonderfully adept at this, but for me it is frankly very dangerous to walk anywhere at all without support.

After two hours I had to give in to my gnawing anxiety. It would be too soon to expect any improvement in my patients, but at least I could check to see that they were no worse.

I struggled, a foot at a time, back to my cabin to get my gear, and on the way I passed the galley. The cell-like room was a chaos of tumbled pans and plates, and the walls were almost entirely covered with soup which Nielsen, the cook, was wiping away with a cloth. When he saw me, he nodded and smiled as he worked. He didn't seem in the least put out; this was probably a common occurrence for him.

Down those iron ladders again; they really are uncomfortable when the world is whirling and wet. I rushed straight to the pen that held the first ram, and for a moment I was sure I had gone to the wrong place, because a large woolly head was regarding me placidly over the rails. A few strands of hay hung from the mouth, then the jaws began to move in a contented chew.

I was standing there, bewildered, when from the deep straw in the pen the massive figure of Raun rose like a golden-maned genie and began to wave his arms about.

"Look, Doctor, look!" His boxer's face vibrated in every feature as he gestured at the ram, then at the other patients in the hold.

I moved among them like a man in a dream. They were all normal. Not just improved, but right back to where they were before the trouble started, and all within two hours.

Over my veterinary career, I have learned about new things in various odd places, and I learned about cortisone in the bowels of a little cattle ship on the way to Russia.

And it was sweet, made sweeter by the ecstatic response of Raun to the little miracle. He vaulted over the rails from pen to pen, hugging the sheep as though they were dogs, and laughing nonstop.

"Is wonderful, Doctor, is wonderful! So queek—they dying,

now they live. So queek, how you do it?" He stared at me with undisguised admiration.

Just then, I felt a pang of envy for Danish vets. I have had my black moments in practice, but I have also pulled off the occasional spectacular cure without seeing anything like this reaction from the Yorkshiremen. But then, maybe Danish farmers don't leap about with joy, either. After all, Raun is a sailor.

Anyway, I was filled with the exhilaration every veterinary surgeon knows when the curtain of despair is unexpectedly lifted. The pre-lunch beer with the captain tasted like nectar, and lunch itself in the swaying mess room was a celebration.

Somehow, the wonder man in the galley had conjured up a glorious vegetable soup with pieces of sausage and dumpling floating around in it. This was followed by "Fregadillas," which were delicious and, I was told, are made from chopped pork and veal rolled into balls bound together with egg and highly spiced.

As I write, I am conscious that my journal is in danger of degenerating into a kind of Cattle Boat Cook Book, but how Nielsen manages to produce this kind of food in a cubbyhole and in stormy weather is a constant source of wonder to me. I am going to find it difficult to resist making references to his artistry.

He has a habit of poking his head round the door halfway through every meal. He looks only at me, the one who recognises him as a culinary genius, and when I put my fingers to my lips and close my eyes, his sweating face beams with delight. He thinks I am wonderful.

My cabin is almost opposite the galley, and between meals he experiments on me constantly with his own special tidbits. I admit I am a willing subject.

The bad weather continued throughout the day, and, as the captain had prophesied, we did not see another ship at any time. I kept a close eye on the sheep and a few more showed the beginnings of the stress symptoms, but I was on them immediately with my Predsolan and crushed the trouble before it became alarming.

Tonight, the ritual after-dinner session with the schnapps and lager was particularly pleasant. The ship's officers are such likable men. They showed me pictures of their families and of the places they have visited, and the conversation never flagged. At the end, the captain raised a finger and looked at me smilingly. "Would you like to telephone your wife?"

I laughed. "You're joking, aren't you?"

"No, no, it is quite simple."

He took me up to the bridge, and within a few minutes I was talking to Helen and daughter Rosie in the darkness. With a sense of unreality, I heard their voices giving me the news of home, of Jimmy at the university, of the latest football scores. It put the final touch on a rewarding day.

I have made a close inspection of the sheep before I came to my cabin, because tomorrow we will be in Klaipeda and I will have to hand them over, then. They look fine. No more stress; the lame animal has recovered, as has the one with the discharging eyes. There is just that cough among the Lincolns, and it is a worry. What will those Russians make of it? I know that it is just a touch of parasitic bronchitis, that it is getting better all the time and that it will soon be gone completely. But will I be able to explain that to the Russian vets? I will soon know.

Chapter
13

The farm man moved between the cows and took hold of my patient's tail, and when I saw his haircut, I knew immediately that Josh Anderson had been on the job again. It was a Sunday morning and everything fitted into place. I really didn't have to ask.

"Were you in the Hare and Pheasant last night?" I enquired carelessly as I inserted my thermometer.

He ran a hand ruefully over his head. "Aye, bugger it, ah was. Ye can see straight off, can't ye? T'missus has been playin' 'ell with me ever since."

"I suppose Josh had had one too many, eh?"

"Aye, he had. I should've known better, pickin' a Saturday night. It's me own fault."

Josh Anderson was one of the local barbers. He liked his job, but he also liked his beer. In fact he was devoted to it, even to the extent of taking his scissors and clippers to the pub with him every night. For the price of a pint, he would give anybody a quick trim in the gents' lavatory.

Habitués of the Hare and Pheasant were never surprised to find one of the customers sitting impassively on the toilet seat with Josh snip-snipping round his head. With beer at sixpence a pint it was good value, but Josh's clients knew they were taking a chance. If the barber's intake had been moderate, they would escape relatively unscathed because the standard of hair styling in the Darrowby district was not very fastidious, but if he had imbibed beyond a certain point, terrible things could happen.

Josh had not as yet been known to cut off anybody's ear, but if you strolled around the town on Sundays and Mondays, you were liable to come across some very strange coiffures.

I looked again at the farm man's head. From my experience, I judged that Josh had been around the ten-pint mark when he did that one. The right sideburn had been trimmed off meticulously just below eye level, while the left was nonexistent. The upper hair seemed to have been delved into at random, leaving bare patches in some parts and long dangling wisps in others. I couldn't see the back, but I had no doubt it would be interesting, too. There could be a pigtail or anything lurking behind there.

Yes, I decided, definitely a ten-pinter. After twelve to fourteen pints, Josh was inclined to cast away all caution and simply run over his victim's head with the clippers, leaving a tuft in front. The classical convict's crop necessitated wearing a cap, well pulled down at all times, for several weeks thereafter.

I always played safe, and when my hair needed cutting, I went to Josh's shop where he operated in a state of strict sobriety.

I was sitting there a few days later, waiting my turn with my dog, Sam, under my seat, and as I watched the barber at work, the wonder of human nature seemed to glow with a particular radiance. There was a burly man in the chair, and his red face, reflected in the mirror above the enveloping white sheet, was contorted every few seconds with spasms of pain. Because the simple fact was that Josh didn't cut hair, he pulled it out.

He did this not only because his equipment was antiquated and needed sharpening, but because he had perfected a certain flick of the wrist with his hand clippers which wrenched the hairs from their follicles at the end of each stroke. He had never got round to buying electric clippers, but with his distinctive technique I doubt whether it would have made any difference.

One wonder was that anybody went to Josh for a haircut

because there was another barber in the town. My own opinion was that it was because everybody liked him.

Sitting there in his shop I looked at him as he worked. He was a tiny man in his fifties with a bald head that made a mockery of the rows of hair restorer on his shelves, and on his face rested the gentle smile which never seemed to leave him. That smile and the big, curiously unworldly eyes gave him an unusual attraction.

And then there was his obvious love of his fellow men. As his client rose from the chair, patently relieved that his ordeal was over, Josh fussed around him, brushing him down, patting his back and chattering gaily. You could see that he hadn't been just cutting this man's hair, he had been enjoying a happy social occasion.

Next to the big farmer, Josh looked smaller than ever, a minute husk of humanity, and I marvelled as I had often done at how he managed to accommodate all that beer.

Of course, foreigners are often astonished at the Englishman's ability to consume vast quantities of ale. Even now, after forty years in Yorkshire, I cannot compete. Maybe it is my Glasgow upbringing, but after two or three pints, discomfort sets in. The remarkable thing is that, throughout the years, I can hardly recall seeing a Yorkshireman drunk. Their natural reserve relaxes and they become progressively jovial as the long cascade goes down their throats, but they seldom fall about or do anything silly.

Josh, for instance. He would swallow around eight pints every night of the week, except Saturday when he stepped up his intake to between ten and fourteen, yet he never looked much different. His professional skill suffered, but that was all.

He was turning to me now. "Well, Mr. Herriot, it's good to see you again." He warmed me with his smile and those wide eyes with their almost mystic depths caressed me as he ushered me to the chair. "Are you very well?"

"I'm fine, thank you, Mr. Anderson," I replied. "And how are you?"

"Nicely, sir, nicely." He began to tuck the sheet under my chin, then laughed delightedly as my little beagle trotted in under the folds.

"Hullo, Sam, you're there as usual, I see." He bent and stroked the sleek ears. "By gum, Mr. Herriot, he's a faithful friend. Never lets you out of 'is sight if he can help it."

"That's right," I said. "And I don't like to go anywhere without him." I screwed round in my chair. "By the way, didn't I see you with a dog the other day?"

Josh paused, scissors in hand. "You did an' all. A little bitch. A stray—got 'er from the Cat and Dog Home at York. Now that our kids have all left home, t'missus and I fancied gettin' a dog, and we think the world of her. I tell ye, she's a grand 'un."

"What breed is she?"

"Eee, now you're askin'. Nobbut a mongrel, I reckon. I can't see any pedigree about her, but money wouldn't buy 'er."

I was about to agree with him when he held up a hand. "Hang on a minute and I'll bring 'er down."

He lived above the shop, and his feet clumped on the stairs as he returned with a little bitch in his arms. "There you are, Mr. Herriot. What d'you think of that?" He stood her on the floor for my inspection.

I looked at the little animal. She was a light grey in colour, with very long crinkled hair. In fact, at a quick glance she looked like a miniature Wensleydale sheep. Definitely a hound of baffling lineage, but the panting mouth and swishing tail bore witness to her good nature.

"I like her," I said. "I think you've picked a winner there."

"That's what we think." He stooped and fondled his new pet, and I noticed that he kept picking up the long hairs and rubbing them gently between finger and thumb again and again. It looked a little odd, then it occurred to me that that was what he was used to doing with his human customers. "We've called her Venus," he said.

"Venus?"

"Aye, because she's so beautiful." His tone was very serious.

"Ah yes," I said. "I see."

He washed his hands, took up his scissors again and grasped a few strands of my hair. Again, I saw that he went through the same procedure of rubbing the hairs between his fingers before cutting them.

I couldn't understand why he did this, but my mind was too preoccupied to give the matter much thought. I was steeling myself. Still, it wasn't too bad with the scissors—just an uncomfortable tug as the blunt edges came together.

It was when he reached for the clippers that I gripped the arms of the chair as though I were at the dentist. It was all right as long as he was running the things up the back of my neck; it was that jerk at the end, plucking the last tuft from its roots, that set my face grimacing at me in the mirror. Once or twice an involuntary "Ooh!" or "Aah!" escaped me, but Josh gave no sign of having heard.

I remembered that for years I had sat in that shop listening to the half-stifled cries of pain from the customers, but at no time had the barber shown any reaction.

The thing was that, though he was the least arrogant or conceited of men, he did consider himself a gifted hairdresser. Even now, as he gave me a final combing, I could see the pride shining from his face. Head on one side, he patted my hair repeatedly, circling the chair and viewing me from all angles, making a finicky snip here and there before holding up the hand mirror for my inspection.

"All right, Mr. Herriot?" he enquired with the quiet satisfaction that comes from a job well done.

"Lovely, Mr. Anderson, just fine." Relief added warmth to my voice.

He bowed slightly, well pleased. "Aye, you know, it's easy enough to cut hair off. The secret is knowin' what to leave on."

I had heard him say it a hundred times before, but I laughed dutifully as he whisked his brush over the back of my coat.

[113]

My hair used to grow pretty fast in those days, but I didn't have time to pay another visit to the barber before he arrived on my front doorstep. I was having tea at the time and I trotted to the door in answer to the insistent ringing of the bell.

He was carrying Venus in his arms but she was a vastly different creature from the placid little animal I had seen in his shop. She was bubbling saliva from her mouth, retching and pawing frantically at her face.

Josh looked distraught. "She's chokin', Mr. Herriot. Look at 'er! She'll die if you don't do summat quick!"

"Wait a minute, Mr. Anderson. Tell me what's happened. Has she swallowed something?"

"Aye, she's 'ad a chicken bone."

"A chicken bone! Don't you know you should never give a dog chicken bones?"

"Aye, ah know, ah know, everybody knows that, but we'd had a bird for our dinner and she pinched the frame out of the dustbin, the little beggar. She had a good crunch at it afore I spotted 'er, and now she's goin' to choke!" He glared at me, lips quivering. He was on the verge of tears.

"Now just calm down," I said. "I don't think Venus is choking. By the way she's pawing, I should say there's something stuck in her mouth."

I grabbed the little animal's jaws with finger and thumb and forced them apart. And I saw with a surge of relief the sight familiar to all vets—a long spicule of bone jammed tightly between the back molars and forming a bar across the roof of the mouth.

As I say, it is a common occurrence in practice and a happy one because it is harmless and easily relieved by a flick of the forceps. Recovery is instantaneous, skill minimal and the kudos most warming. I loved it.

I put my hand on the barber's shoulder. "You can stop worrying, Mr. Anderson, it's just a bone stuck in her teeth. Come through to the consulting room and I'll have it out in a jiffy."

I could see the man relaxing as we walked along the passage to the back of the house. "Oh, thank God for that, Mr. Herriot. I thought she'd had it, honest, I did. And we've grown right fond of the little thing. I couldn't bear to lose 'er."

I gave a light laugh, put the dog on the table and reached for a strong pair of forceps. "No question of that, I assure you. This won't take a minute."

Jimmy, aged five, had left his tea and trailed after us. He watched with mild interest as I poised the instrument. Even at his age, he had seen this sort of thing many a time and it wasn't very exciting. But you never knew in veterinary practice; it was worth hanging around because funny things could happen. He put his hands in his pockets and rocked back and forth on his heels, whistling softly as he watched me.

Usually it is simply a matter of opening the mouth, clamping the forceps on the bone and removing it. But Venus recoiled from the gleaming metal and so did the barber. The terror in the dog's eyes was reproduced fourfold in those of its owner.

I tried to be soothing. "This is nothing, Mr. Anderson. I'm not going to hurt her in the least, but you'll just have to hold her head firmly for a moment."

The little man took a deep breath, grasped the dog's neck, screwed his eyes tight shut and turned his head as far away as he could.

"Now, little Venus," I cooed, "I'm going to make you better."

Venus clearly didn't believe me. She struggled violently, pawing at my hand, to the accompaniment of strange moaning sounds from her owner. When I did get the forceps into her mouth, she locked her front teeth on the instrument and hung on fiercely. And as I began to grapple with her, Mr. Anderson could stand it no longer and let go.

The little dog leaped to the floor and resumed her inner battle there while Jimmy watched appreciatively.

I looked at the barber more in sorrow than in anger. This was just not his thing. He was manually ham-fisted, as his hairdressing proved, and he seemed quite incapable of holding a wriggling dog.

"Let's have another go," I said cheerfully. "We'll try it on the floor this time. Maybe she's frightened of the table. It's a trifling little job, really."

The little man, lips tight, eyes like slits, bent and extended trembling hands towards his dog, but each time he touched her she slithered away from him until, with a great shuddering sigh, he flopped facedown on the tiles. Jimmy giggled. Things were looking up.

I helped the barber to his feet. "I tell you what, Mr. Anderson, I'll give her a short-acting anaesthetic. That will cut out all this fighting and struggling."

Josh's face paled. "An anaesthetic? Put her to sleep, you mean?" Anxiety flickered in his eyes. "Will she be all right?"

"Of course, of course. Just leave her to me and come back for her in about an hour. She'll be able to walk, then." I began to steer him through the door into the passage.

"Are you sure?" He glanced back pitifully at his pet. "We're doing the right thing?"

"Without a doubt. We'll only upset her if we go on this way."

"Very well, then, I'll go along to me brother's for an hour."

"Splendid." I waited till I heard the front door close behind him, then quickly made up a dose of pentothal.

Dogs do not put on such a tough front when their owners are not present and I scooped Venus easily from the floor onto the table. But her jaws were still clamped tight and her front feet at the ready. She wasn't going to stand for any more messing with her mouth.

"Okay, old girl, have it your own way," I said. I gripped her leg above the elbow and clipped an area from the raised radial vein. In those days, Siegfried or myself were often left to anaesthetise dogs without assistance. It is wonderful what you can do when you have to.

Venus didn't seem to care what I was about as long as I kept away from her face. I slid the needle into the vein, depressed the plunger and within seconds her fighting pose relaxed, her head dropped and her whole body sagged onto the table. I rolled her over. She was fast asleep.

"No trouble now, Jimmy, lad," I said. I pushed the teeth apart effortlessly with finger and thumb, gripped the bone with the forceps and lifted it from the mouth. "Nothing left in there—lovely. All done."

I dropped the piece of chicken bone into the waste bin. "Yes, that's how to do it, my boy. No undignified scrambling. That's the professional way."

My son nodded briefly. Events had gone dull again. He had been hoping for great things when Mr. Anderson draped himself along the surgery floor, but this was tame stuff. He had stopped smiling.

My own satisfied smile, too, had become a little fixed. I was watching Venus carefully, and she wasn't breathing. I tried to ignore the lurch in my stomach, because I have always been a nervous anaesthetist and am not very proud of it. Even now, when I come upon one of my younger colleagues operating, I have a nasty habit of placing my hand on the patient's chest wall over the heart and standing wide-eyed and rigid for a few seconds. I know the young surgeons hate to have me spreading alarm and despondency, and one day I am going to be told to get out in sharp terms, but I can't help it.

As I watched Venus, I told myself as always that there was no danger. She had received the correct dose and anyway, you often did get this period of apnoea with pentothal. Everything was normal, but just the same I wished to God she would start breathing.

The heart was still going all right. I depressed the ribs a few times—nothing. I touched the unseeing eyeball—no corneal reflex. I began to rap my fingers on the table and stare closely at the little animal, and I could see that Jimmy was watching me just as keenly. His deep interest in veterinary practice was built upon a fascination for animals, farmers and the open air, but it was

[117]

given extra colour by something else; he never knew when his father might do something funny or something funny might happen to him.

The unpredictable mishaps of the daily round were all good for a laugh and my son, with his unerring instinct, had a feeling that something of the sort was going to happen now.

His hunch was proved right when I suddenly lifted Venus from the table, shook her vainly a few times above my head, then set off at full gallop along the passage. I could hear the eager shuffle of the little slippers just behind me.

I threw open the side door and shot into the back garden. I halted at the narrow part—no, there wasn't enough room there —and continued my headlong rush till I reached the big lawn.

Here I dropped the little dog onto the grass and fell down on my knees by her side in an attitude of prayer. I waited and watched as my heart hammered, but those ribs were not moving and the eyes stared sightlessly ahead.

Oh, this just couldn't happen! I seized Venus by a hind leg in either hand and began to whirl her round and round my head. Sometimes higher, sometimes lower, but attaining a remarkable speed as I put all my strength into the swing. This method of resuscitation seems to have gone out of fashion now, but it was very much in vogue then. It certainly met with the full approval of my son. He laughed so much that he fell down and sprawled on the grass.

When I stopped and glared at the still immobile ribs, he cried, "Again, Daddy, again." And he didn't have to wait more than a few seconds before Daddy was in full action once more, with Venus swooping through the air like a bird on the wing.

It exceeded all Jimmy's expectations. He probably had wondered about leaving his jam sandwiches to see the old man perform, but how gloriously he had been rewarded. To this day the whole thing is so vivid: my tension and misery lest my patient should die for no reason at all; and, in the background, the helpless, high-pitched laughter of my son.

I don't know how many times I stopped, dropped the inert form on the grass, then recommenced my whirling, but at last, at one of the intervals, the chest wall gave a heave and the eyes blinked.

With a gasp of relief I collapsed facedown on the cool turf, peering through the green blades as the breathing became regular and Venus began to lick her lips and look around her.

I dared not get up immediately because the old brick walls of the garden were still dancing around me and I am sure I would have fallen.

Jimmy was disappointed. "Aren't you going to do any more, Daddy?"

"No, son, no." I sat up and dragged Venus onto my lap. "It's all over now."

"Well, that was funny. Why did you do it?"

"To make the dog breathe."

"Do you always do that to make them breathe?"

"No, thank heaven, not often." I got slowly to my feet and carried the little animal back to the consulting room.

By the time Josh Anderson arrived, his pet was looking almost normal.

"She's still a little unsteady from the anaesthetic," I said. "But that won't last long."

"Eee, isn't that grand! And that nasty bone, is it . . . ?"

"All gone, Mr. Anderson."

He shrank back as I opened the mouth. "You see?" I said. "Not a thing."

He smiled happily. "Did ye have any bother with her?"

Well, my parents brought me up to be honest rather than clever, and the whole story almost bubbled out of me. But why should I worry this sensitive little man? To tell him that his dog had been almost dead for a considerable time would not cheer him, nor would it bolster his faith in me.

I swallowed. "Not a bit, Mr. Anderson. A quite uneventful

operation." The whitest of lies, but it nearly choked me, and the aftertaste of guilt was strong.

"Wonderful, wonderful. I am grateful, Mr. Herriot." He bent over the dog, and again I noticed the strange rolling of the strands of hair between his fingers.

"Have ye been floatin' through the air, Venus?" he murmured absently.

The back of my neck prickled. "What . . . what makes you say that?"

He turned his eyes up to me, those eyes with their unworldly depths. "Well . . . I reckon she'd think she was floatin' while she was asleep. Just a funny feeling I had."

"Ah, yes, well, er . . . right." I had a very funny feeling myself. "You'd better take her home now and keep her quiet for the rest of the day."

I was very thoughtful as I finished my tea. Floating . . . floating.

A fortnight later I was again seated in Josh's barber's chair, bracing myself for the ordeal. To my alarm he started straight in with the dread clippers. Usually he began with the scissors and worked up gradually, but he was throwing me in at the deep end this time.

In an attempt to alleviate the pain, I began to chatter with an edge of hysteria in my voice.

"How is—ouch—Venus going on?"

"Oh fine, fine." Josh smiled at me tenderly in the mirror. "She was neither up nor down after that job."

"Well—ooh, aah—I really didn't expect any trouble. As I said, it was—ow—just a trifling thing."

The barber whipped out another tuft with that inimitable flick of his. "The thing is, Mr. Herriot, it's grand to 'ave faith in your vet. I knew our little pet was in good 'ands."

"Well, thank you very much, Mr. Anderson, it's—aaah—very nice to hear that." I was gratified, but that guilt feeling was still there.

[120]

I got tired of trying to speak while watching my twitching features in the mirror, so I tried to concentrate on something else. It is a trick I adopt at the dentist's and it doesn't work very well, but as the little man tugged away, I thought as hard as I could about my garden at Skeldale House.

The lawns really did want mowing, and there were all those weeds to get at when I had a minute to spare. I had got round to considering whether it was time to put some fertiliser on my outdoor tomatoes when Josh laid down the clippers and lifted his scissors.

I sighed and relaxed. The next part was only mildly uncomfortable, and, who knew, he might have had the scissors sharpened since last time. My mind was wandering over the fascinating subject of tomatoes when the barber's voice pulled me back to reality.

"Mr. Herriot." He was twiddling away at a wisp of my hair with his fingers. "I like gardening, too."

I almost jumped from the chair. "That's remarkable. I was just thinking about my garden."

"Aye, ah know." There was a faraway look in his eyes as he rolled and rolled with finger and thumb. "It comes through the hair, ye know."

"Eh?"

"Your thoughts. They come through to me."

"What!"

"Yes, just think about it. Them hairs go right down into your head, and they catch summat from your brain and send it up to me."

"Oh, really, you're kidding me." I gave a loud laugh that nevertheless had a hollow ring.

Josh shook his head. "I'm not jokin' nor jestin', Mr. Herriot. I've been at this game for nearly forty years, and it keeps happenin' to me. You'd be flabbergasted if I told ye some of the thoughts that's come up. Couldn't repeat 'em, I tell ye."

I slumped lower in my white sheet. Absolute rubbish and nonsense, of course, but I made a firm resolve never to think of Venus's anaesthetic during a haircut.

Chapter
14

November 1, 1961

When I awoke this morning everything was wonderfully still. It was a blessed relief because last night was as the others, and I was thrown about in my bunk like a rag doll.

I went up on deck and found we were anchored in the mouth of a river or inlet. A few hundred yards away I could see the Russian port of Klaipeda.

I couldn't believe the calm — only a gentle swell rocked the ship—but half a mile back, the great sea waves still dashed themselves against the entrance to the harbour.

Up on the bridge I found the captain, pale and unshaven. He told me he had had a terrible job bringing the ship between the concrete walls at the entrance to the harbour. He had signalled repeatedly for a pilot but none had come, and finally he was forced to bring the ship in himself. Doing this, in the dark, in unfamiliar waters and during a storm, must have been a great strain.

He said we were waiting now for a pilot to take us through the great concrete breakwaters to a berth at the quayside. At length one arrived, a little stubbly-chinned man of about thirty-five, in a very Russian-looking overcoat a couple of sizes too big for him and a large peaked cap.

He was very nervous as he guided us in. He kept hopping about the bridge, peering here and there, and then dashing to have a look over the ship's side. I was astonished to hear that he gave his commands in English and it was strange to hear him cry, "Starrboard," and the big Dane at the wheel reply, "Starrboard," then, "Meedsheeps," followed by the answering call, "Meedsheeps."

Up in the bows, the mate and a sailor were gazing down into the water and signalling back to the bridge—apparently testing the depth and looking for obstructions.

To my untutored eyes it seemed that the captain brought the ship in himself. He was as always, calm and self-contained, and as we approached another ship or part of the breakwater, he would say, "Perhaps a little astern, Mr. Pilot," or, "Port side, perhaps, Mr. Pilot," in a quiet voice while the little man rushed about the bridge in a panic.

On either side of the estuary, the banks were thickly clothed in pine trees, and further ahead I could see tenement buildings, and then the cranes and quays of the port.

Once we had been moored by the quayside, I looked eagerly ashore, almost into the eyes of a young Russian soldier. There were two of them standing by the gangway of the *Iris Clausen,* and at least two guarding each of the other ships in the port.

They all had automatic guns slung on their backs and were wearing long, greenish coats, crinkly, Wellington-type boots and furry hats turned up at the front and sides.

Leaning over the rail of our little ship, I was only a few yards away from my soldier. I raised my hand and gave him a wave.

"Good morning," I cried cheerfully.

His expression never changed. He looked back at me with a completely impassive, dead countenance.

I moved along the rail and tried his colleague. "Hello," I called, waving again.

The response was exactly the same. A blank, unsmiling stare.

Just then it started to rain, and they both reached back and pulled hoods over their heads.

I felt it was not a happy start, and I looked past them at a sight that was not much more cheering: a network of railway lines with wagons; a forest of huge cranes; and, around the perimeter, tall watch towers, each with its armed soldier looking down at us. Beyond the port itself rose an assortment of dilapidated houses.

Klaipeda is, of course, the old Lithuanian port of Memel, and I have previously read that when the Russians took over, a proportion of the native population was deported and replaced by Russians. I am unable to ascertain the extent of this, and since Klaipeda is now part of the Soviet Union, I shall refer to all the people I meet as Russians.

Very soon a large number of officials came aboard, and I was relieved to find that they were cheerful and smiling. There was much shaking of hands and loud laughter and everybody addressed me as Doktor in a guttural tone with the accent on the second syllable. Most of them were from the customs and immigration authorities, and among them were several young women, one of whom spoke very good English. In fact, nearly all of them seemed to be able to get along in English; the other language in which they conversed with the captain was German.

The exception in this merry company was a tall, lugubrious sanitary inspector, wearing breeches and a cowboy hat. I had to go down into the hold with him, where he looked around him sadly but said nothing.

Immediately afterwards, a little fat woman beckoned to me to accompany her to where the animals' food was kept. There were several tons of this surplus, and it was all to be left for the Russians, free of charge. But it seemed that they suspected some catch in this because, to my astonishment, the little woman began to slash open the bags of super-quality sheep nuts and the bales of sweet hay. She pushed her hand into the centre of each bag and bale and dropped some of the contents into a series of polythene bags. Apparently these samples had to go to a laboratory to be examined before they would accept the food.

I went back up to the captain's room, where the officials were still signing forms and smoking and drinking. They had been joined by the chief of "Saufratt," which deals with all the incoming and outgoing cargoes, and like the others, he was polite, friendly and ready to roar with laughter at the slightest excuse.

I was interested in the dress of these men who are obviously important people. They all wore smartly cut dark suits, and some had greenish gabardine macintoshes, but the materials of their clothes looked cheap and shoddy. Still, they were trim and neatly turned out, but the whole effect was spoiled by the fact that every man sported an abominable off-white tweedy cloth cap pulled right down to his ears. This was clearly the fashion in these parts, but to me the result was truly ghastly.

However they were very pleasant, and I found their conversation fascinating. I was struck forcefully by their tremendous willingness to work and their desire to learn. They told me that most of them had begun as factory workers but had studied at night and in every available moment to rise to their present positions.

Of course all the time I was anxiously awaiting the veterinary examination of the sheep. The veterinary surgeon turned out to be a little fat woman very like the one who had inspected the food. Unlike the officials she could not speak a word of English, but she marched up to me, tapped her chest and said, "Doktor." As we shook hands as colleagues she burst into an infectious, bubbling laugh.

She had a helper with her, a big, tough-looking chap in blue dungarees and we all went down to the hold together. I was intrigued by her method of examining the sheep. The man penned five animals in a corner while she opened a little bag and took out a whole bunch of thermometers. These were strange-looking flat things with centigrade markings and attached to each was a piece of string with a clip on the end.

She methodically dipped each nozzle in a jar of vaseline before inserting it in the rectum and clipping the string to the wool. Then she stood looking at her watch for what seemed an age. Finally, she removed the thermometers and took the readings.

After that she had another five caught up, and again we had the lengthy wait and the reading before moving to another pen.

The realisation burst on me with a sense of shock that these were two-minute thermometers, unlike our half-minute ones, and also that she was going to examine ten sheep in every pen. This was going to take an awfully long time.

Gallantly holding her jar of vaseline, I tried to alleviate the boredom by making conversation. It was difficult since neither of us spoke a word of the other's language, but I managed to get over to her that most of the sheep were of the Romney Marsh breed. This appeared to delight her because thereafter, when she pushed the thermometer up a sheep's rectum, she would cry, "Rromnee Marrsh!" and laugh happily, then on to the next one and again the thrust of the thermometer and the joyous, "Rromnee Marrsh!"

It lightened the proceedings to a certain extent, but after an hour and a half we had covered only one side of the 'tween decks hold—about a quarter of the sheep—and I quailed at the thought of another four and a half hours of this.

But there was no doubt she was a pleasant little woman. She was dressed in a cheap-looking, navy-blue raincoat and the kind of velour hat you see in jumble sales in England, and her chubby face never stopped smiling.

The only time she looked serious was when she heard a cough from one of the Lincolns. It was the moment I had been dreading, and she turned to me questioningly.

"Ah-ah, ah-ha, ah-ha," she said in a fair imitation of the parasitic bark and raised her eyebrows.

I shrugged my shoulders. What could I do? How could I explain?

The animal's temperature was normal and she appeared reassured, but some time later another sheep coughed.

"Ah-ah, ah-ha, ah-ha?" she asked, and again I shrugged and gave a noncommittal smile.

About halfway through, we were joined by another vet, obviously the little woman's superior. He was very well dressed in dark overcoat and black trilby hat, and his handsome, high-cheek-boned, Asiatic face radiated charm as he shook my hand and thumped me on the back.

"Salaam aleikum," he said, somewhat to my surprise.

He, too, spoke no English, and when he heard the cough he swung round on me.

"Ah-ah, ah-ha, ah-ha?" he enquired.

I spread my hands and shook my head, and he laughed suddenly. He seemed a happy-go-lucky fellow and was clearly in a hurry to be off. He waved goodbye to his colleague, shook my hand warmly and smiled, then he strode from the hold.

I was still baffled by the oriental greeting and turned to the little woman. *"Salaam aleikum?"*

"Irkutsk, Tartar," she replied.

I realised that he came from the other end of this vast country, and, to let her know I understood, I pulled the corners of my eyes outwards.

She burst into a high-pitched giggle. She did love to laugh.

But the strain of hanging around with the pot of vaseline was beginning to tell. I tried to get rid of the tension by saying things like, "Look, this is driving me right up the bloody wall," at which she would give me a nod and a sweet, uncomprehending smile, but at last I could stand it no longer. I gave her back the vaseline and fled to the sanctuary of my cabin. I heard later that it took her five hours to get round the sheep.

The unloading berth is occupied by another ship, the *Ubbergen,* which is discharging a cargo of cattle and taking on a lot of little cob-like horses, so we cannot start our unloading until she moves. My immediate ambition was to get ashore, but the customs and immigration people had taken our passports, and until they came back nobody could leave the ship.

When the passports were returned I looked around for a companion, because John Crooks had warned me not to go ashore alone. The mate and engineer would not budge as they were worried about relations between Denmark and Russia, following a verbal attack on the Scandinavian countries by Khrushchev which they had heard on the radio in the Danish news. In fact, as I went around, it soon became obvious that none of the ship's company had any intention of going ashore.

It was the captain, gentlemanly as always, who stepped in. He could see that I was disappointed and said that, if I gave him a few minutes to wash and change, he would come with me.

As I waited on the deck the daylight faded rapidly to dusk, and lights began to appear in the tenements beyond the port. They all seemed like forty-watt bulbs, and the general effect was dreary in the extreme.

By the time the captain was ready, it was quite dark. I had been strongly advised by the man from Saufratt to visit the seamans' club called Interklub and I decided to do this and leave the exploration of the town until tomorrow.

We went down the gangway, showed our passports to the soldiers and I took my first step onto Russian soil. I said, "Interklub?" and the soldiers pointed vaguely along the railway lines into the distance. They still preserved the deadpan look I had seen in the morning, and it struck me that they were just about the only unsmiling Russians I had met all day. I wondered why they acted so very differently.

There were floodlights shining down from the cranes, and we began to pick our way along by their light. But it was slow going. We were in a maze of sheds, cranes and wagons, and the quayside seemed to stretch indefinitely ahead.

I soon became impatient. "Look," I said to the captain. "The town's just over there." I pointed to the high fence that surrounded the harbour. "Surely there's a gate of some kind here."

The captain shook his head. "I think not. There will be a gate house somewhere along at the end. We must go through there."

Now, I believe I am fundamentally a fairly solid citizen, but every now and then I do something daft. This was one of those times. I decided to look for a shortcut.

I groped my way into the darkness behind a row of wagons, and I was studying the dim silhouette of the fence when suddenly an enormous dog shot out at me from the gloom. It was of an Alsatian type, and it came at me with a terrifying baying sound. I caught a glimpse of a snarling mouth and white teeth, but I didn't wait to make a closer examination. I took off at great speed, but after a few yards I tripped over a railway line and fell flat on my face.

At that moment I was sure it was all over with me. I am not going to suggest that my past life flashed before my eyes, but in that second or two I did have a vivid impression of the incongruity of my situation. I, James Herriot, Yorkshire Dales veterinary surgeon and dog lover, meeting my end by being torn to pieces by a dog behind a railway wagon on a dark night in Russia.

I was waiting for the first crunch when I heard the animal twang to a stop at the end of its chain, and as I looked back, I could see it fighting to get at me, the great teeth, gleaming in the floodlights, about six inches from my leg.

I scrabbled along on my stomach to where the captain was waiting. That usually calm man was visibly shaken, and he helped me up, gripped my arm and hurried me along the road we had first taken.

As I struggled to regain my breath, I felt I had learned my first lesson. Do not go nosing about in dark places in Russia. Keep to the proper path.

When we came to the gate house, I had to smile to myself. My nerves were still vibrating after my encounter with that creature back there, but when I saw the groups of soldiers around the brightly lit room and more soldiers behind a sliding window carrying out an interminable, hard-eyed scrutiny of our passports and ourselves, the absurdity of my idea of a shortcut was forced on me. Before passing through, I took a last glance at the long stretch of quayside behind us, and I wondered how many more four-legged killers were lurking in the shadows under the fence.

Once in the street, we asked a young fellow in the inevitable light cloth cap about Interklub, and he politely marched us to the door before shaking hands and leaving us.

Inside we found a very comfortable, even mildly luxurious club. Russian time is two hours ahead of ours so most of the activities had ceased for the night, but nevertheless the little man in charge was effusive in his welcome.

The captain spoke to him in German and told him who we were, and he kept bowing and smiling as though we were his long-lost brothers.

He insisted on taking us on a tour of the establishment and ushered us into each room with a deferential, "Please, please"—a common and much-used word among the people I have met here.

There were a little cinema, dance hall, bar, and a billiard room where some young German sailors were knocking balls about. We saw several cosy lounges, in one of which a large radio was giving a commentary of Tottenham Hotspur in the European Cup.

Our guide led us into a library and reading room where there were newspapers in all languages, and I hastened to the English section, hoping to catch up with some of the latest news. However, I found only a pile of the *Daily Worker,* and the most recent was a fortnight old. I was moodily reading about the long-past England v. Wales football match when the little man bustled up, all smiles, and began to load me with a huge quantity of books and pamphlets, all in English.

These books were all beautifully produced, and one of them, *Khrushchev in the U.S.A.,* would be very expensive to buy in England. I was also presented with a roll of cine film of the same visit and a little badge which I must keep for Rosie.

We left on a wave of cordiality, and as I came out into the night and looked at the gaunt tenements nearby, it struck me how sharply they contrasted with that club.

Tonight, as I complete my journal, two thoughts are uppermost in my mind. First, my bed will keep still for a change, and second, it has been an eventful day.

Chapter
15

"This is Amber," Sister Rose said. "The one I wanted you to examine."

I looked at the pale, almost honey-coloured shading of the hair on the dog's ears and flanks. "I can see why you've given her that name. I bet she'd really glow in the sunshine."

The nurse laughed. "Yes, funnily enough it was sunny when I first saw her, and the name just jumped into my mind." She gave me a sideways glance. "I'm good at names, as you know."

"Oh yes, without a doubt," I said, smiling. It was a little joke between us. Sister Rose had to be good at christening the endless stream of unwanted animals passing through the little dog sanctuary that lay behind her house and which she ran and maintained by organising small shows and jumble sales, and by spending her own money.

And she didn't only give her money, she gave her precious time, because as a nursing sister she led a full life of service to the human race. I often asked myself how she found the time to fight for the animals, too. It was a mystery to me, but I admired her.

"Where did this one come from?" I asked.

Sister Rose shrugged. "Oh, found wandering in the streets of Hebbleton. Nobody knows her, and there have been no enquiries to the police. Obviously abandoned."

I felt the old tightening of anger in my throat. "How could they do this to such a beautiful dog? Just turn it away to fend for itself."

"Oh, people like that have some astonishing reasons. In this case I think it's because Amber has a little skin disease. Perhaps it frightened them."

"They could at least have taken her to a vet," I grunted as I opened the door of the pen.

I noticed some bare patches around the toes, and as I knelt and examined the feet, Amber nuzzled my cheek and wagged her tail. I looked up at her, at the flopping ears, the pronounced jowls and the trusting eyes that had been betrayed.

"It's a hound's face," I said. "But how about the rest of her? What breed would you call her?"

Sister Rose laughed. "Oh, she's a puzzle. I get a lot of practice at guessing, but this one beats me. I wondered if a fox hound had got astray and mated with something like a Labrador or Dalmatian, but I don't know."

I didn't know, either. The body, dappled with patches of brown, black and white, was the wrong shape for a hound. She had very large feet, a long thin tail in constant motion and everywhere on her coat the delicate sheen of gold.

"Well," I said. "Whatever she is, she's a bonny one, and good-natured, too."

"Oh, yes, she's a darling. We'll have no difficulty in finding a home for her. She's the perfect pet. How old do you think she is?"

I smiled. "You can never tell for sure, but she's got a juvenile look about her." I opened the mouth and looked at the rows of untainted teeth. "I'd say nine or ten months. She's just a big pup."

"That's what I thought. She'll be really large when she reaches full size."

As if to prove the sister's words, the young bitch reared up and planted her forefeet on my chest. I looked again at the laughing mouth and those eyes. "Amber," I said. "I really like you."

"Oh, I'm so glad," Sister Rose said. "We must get this skin

trouble cleared up as quickly as possible, and then I can start finding her a home. It's just a bit of eczema, isn't it?"

"Probably . . . probably . . . I see there's some bareness around the eyes and cheeks, too." Skin diseases in dogs, as in humans, are tricky things, often baffling in origin and difficult to cure. I fingered the hairless areas. I didn't like the combination of feet and face, but the skin was dry and sound. Maybe it was nothing much. I banished to the back of my mind a spectre that appeared for a brief instant. I didn't want to think of that, and I had no intention of worrying Sister Rose. She had enough on her mind.

"Yes, probably eczema," I said briskly. "Rub this ointment well into the parts, night and morning." I handed over the box of zinc oxide and lanolin. A bit old-fashioned, maybe, but it had served me well for a few years and ought to do the trick, in combination with the nurse's good feeding.

When two weeks passed without news of Amber, I was relieved. I was happy, too, at the thought that she would now be in a good home among people who appreciated her.

I was brought back to reality with a bump when Sister Rose phoned one morning.

"Mr. Herriot, those bare patches aren't any better. In fact, they're spreading."

"Spreading? Where?"

"Up her legs and on the face."

The spectre leaped up, mouthing and gesticulating. Oh, not that, please. "I'll come right out, Sister," I said, and on my way to the car I picked up the microscope.

Amber greeted me as she had before, with dancing eyes and lashing tail, but I felt sick when I saw the ragged denudation of the face and the naked skin staring at me on the legs.

I got hold of the young animal and held her close, sniffing at the hairless areas.

Sister Rose looked at me in surprise. "What are you doing?"

"Trying to detect a mousy smell."

"Mousy smell? And is it there?"

"Yes."

"And what does that mean?"

"Mange."

"Oh, dear." The nurse put a hand to her mouth. "That's rather nasty, isn't it." Then she put her shoulders back in a characteristic gesture. "Well, I've had experience of mange before, and I can tackle it. I've always been able to clear it up with sulphur baths, but there's such a danger of infection to the other dogs. It really is a worry."

I put Amber down and stood up, feeling suddenly weary. "Yes, but you're thinking of sarcoptic mange, Sister. I'm afraid this is something rather worse."

"Worse? In what way?"

"Well, the whole look of the thing suggests demodectic mange."

She nodded. "I've heard of that—and it's more serious?"

"Yes. . . ." I might as well bite the bullet. "Very often incurable."

"Goodness me, I had no idea. She wasn't scratching much, so I didn't worry."

"Yes, that's just it," I said wryly. "Dogs scratch almost nonstop with sarcoptic mange and we can cure it, but they often show only mild discomfort with demodectic, which usually defeats us."

The spectre was very large in my mind now, and I use the word literally because this skin disease had haunted me ever since I had qualified. I had seen many fine dogs put to sleep after the most prolonged attempts to treat them.

I lifted the microscope from the back of the car. "Anyway, I may be jumping the gun. I hope I am. This is the only way to find out."

There was a patch on Amber's left foreleg which I squeezed and scraped with a scalpel blade. I deposited the debris and serum on a glass slide, added a few drops of potassium hydroxide and put a cover-slip on top.

Sister Rose gave me a cup of coffee while I waited, then I rigged up the microscope in the light from the kitchen window and looked down the eyepiece. And there it was. My stomach tightened as I saw what I didn't want to see—the dread mite, demodex canis; the head, the thorax with its eight stumpy legs and the long, cigar-shaped body. And there wasn't just one. The whole microscopic field was teeming with them.

"Ah, well, that's it, Sister," I said. "There's no doubt about it. I'm very sorry."

The corners of her mouth drooped. "But . . . isn't there anything we can do?"

"Oh, yes, we can try. And we're going to try like anything because I've taken a fancy to Amber. Don't worry too much. I've cured a few demodex cases in my time, always by using the same stuff." I went to the car and fished around in the boot. "Here it is—Odylen." I held up the can in front of her. "I'll show you how to apply it."

It was difficult to rub the lotion into the affected patches as Amber wagged and licked, but I finished at last.

"Now do that every day," I said, "and let me know in about a week. Sometimes that Odylen really does work."

Sister Rose stuck out her jaw with the determination that had saved so many animals. "I assure you I'll do it most carefully. I'm sure we can succeed. It doesn't look so bad."

I didn't say anything, and she went on. "But how about my other dogs? Won't they become infected?"

I shook my head. "Another odd thing about demodex. It very rarely spreads to another animal. It is nothing like as contagious as the sarcops, so you have very little cause for worry in that way."

"That's something, anyway. But how on earth does a dog get the disease in the first place?"

"Mysterious again," I said. "The veterinary profession is pretty well convinced that all dogs have a certain number of demodex mites in their skins, but why they should cause mange in some and not in others has never been explained. Heredity has got something to do with it because it sometimes occurs in several dogs in the same litter. But it's a baffling business."

I left Sister Rose with her can of Odylen. Maybe this would be one of the exceptions to my experiences with this condition. I had to hope so.

I heard from the nurse within a week. She had been applying the Odylen religiously but the disease was spreading further up the legs.

I hurried out there, and my fears were confirmed when I saw Amber's face. It was disfigured by the increasing hairlessness, and when I thought of the beauty that had captivated me on my first visit, the sight was like a blow. Her tail-wagging cheerfulness was undiminished, and that seemed to make the whole thing worse.

I had to try something else, and in view of the fact that a secondary subcutaneous invasion of staphylococci was an impediment to recovery, I gave the dog an injection of staph toxoid. I also started her on a course of Fowler's solution of arsenic, which at that time was popular in the treatment of skin conditions.

When ten days passed I had begun to hope, and it was a bitter disappointment when Sister Rose telephoned just after breakfast.

Her voice trembled as she spoke. "Mr. Herriot, she really is deteriorating all the time. Nothing seems to do any good. I'm beginning to think that . . ."

I cut her off in mid-sentence. "All right, I'll be out there within an hour. Don't give up hope yet. These cases sometimes take months to recover."

I knew as I drove to the sanctuary that my words were only meant to comfort. They had no real substance. But I had tried to say something helpful because there was nothing Sister Rose hated more than putting a dog to sleep. Of all the hundreds of animals that had passed through her hands, I could remember only a handful that had defeated her. Very old dogs, in a hopeless plight with chronic kidney or heart conditions, or young ones with distemper. With all the others she had battled until they were fit to go to their new homes. And it wasn't only Sister Rose—I myself recoiled from the idea of doing such a thing to Amber. Something about that dog had taken hold of me.

When I arrived I still had no idea what I was going to do, and when I spoke I was half-surprised at the things I said.

"Sister, I've come to take Amber home with me. I'll be able to treat her myself every day, then. You've got enough to do, looking after your other dogs. I know you have done everything possible, but I'm going to take on this job myself."

"But . . . you are a busy man. How will you find the time?"

"I can treat her in the evenings and any other spare moments. This way I'll be able to check on her progress all the time. I'm determined to get her right."

And, driving back to the surgery, I was surprised at the depth of my feeling. Throughout my career I have often had this compulsive desire to cure an animal, but never stronger than with Amber. The young bitch was delighted to be in the car with me. Like everything else, she seemed to regard this as just another game, and she capered around, licking my ear, resting her paws on the dash and peering through the windscreen. I looked at her happy face, scarred by the disease and smeared with Odylen, and thumped my hand on the wheel. Demodectic mange was hell, but this was one case that was going to get better.

It was the beginning of a strangely vivid episode in my life, as fresh now as it was then, more than thirty years ago. We had no facilities for boarding dogs—very few vets had at that time—but I made up a comfortable billet for her in the old stable in the yard. I penned off one of the stalls with a sheet of plywood and put down a bed of straw. Despite its age, the stable was a substantial building and free from draughts. She would be snug in there.

I made sure of one thing. I kept Helen out of the whole business. I remembered how stricken she had been when we adopted Oscar the cat and then lost him to his rightful owner, and I knew she would soon grow too fond of this dog. But I had forgotten about myself.

Veterinary surgeons would never last in their profession if they became too involved with their patients because I knew from experience that most of my colleagues were just as sentimental over animals as the owners, but before I knew what was happening, I became involved with Amber.

I fed her myself, changed her bedding and carried out the treatment. I saw her as often as possible during the day, but when I think of her now, it is always night. It was late November, when darkness came in soon after four o'clock, and the last few visits were a dim-sighted fumbling in cow byres; when I came home, I always drove round to the yard at the back of Skeldale House and trained my headlights on the stable.

When I threw open the door, Amber was always there, waiting to welcome me, her forefeet resting on the plywood sheet, her long yellow ears gleaming in the bright beam. That is my picture of her to this day. Her temperament never altered, and her tail swished the straw unceasingly as I did all the uncomfortable things to her: rubbing the tender skin with the lotion, injecting her with the staph toxoid, taking further skin scrapings to check progress.

As the days and the weeks went by and I saw no improvement, I became a little desperate. I gave her sulphur baths, derris baths, although I had done no good with such things in the past, and I also began to go through all the proprietary things on the market. In veterinary practice every resistant disease spawns a multitude of quack "cures," and I lost count of the shampoos and washes I swilled over the young animal in the hope that there might be some magic element in them, despite my misgivings.

Those nightly sessions under the headlights became part of my life, and I think I might have gone on blindly for an indefinite period, until one very dark evening with the rain beating on the cobbles of the yard I seemed to see the young dog for the first time.

The condition had spread over the entire body, leaving only tufts and straggling wisps of hair. The long ears were golden no longer. They were almost bald, as was the rest of her face and head. Everywhere, her skin was thickened and wrinkled and had assumed a bluish tinge. And when I squeezed it, a slow ooze of pus and serum came up around my fingers.

I flopped back and sat down in the straw while Amber leaped around me, licking and wagging. Despite her terrible state, her nature was unchanged.

But this couldn't go on. I knew now that she and I had come to the end of the road. As I tried to think, I stroked her head, and her cheerful eyes were pathetic in the scarecrow face. My misery was compounded of various things. I had grown too fond of her, I had failed and she had nobody. Only Sister Rose and myself. And that was another thing. What was I going to tell that good lady after all my brave words?

It took me until the following lunchtime to summon the will to telephone her. In my effort to be matter-of-fact about the thing, I fear I was almost brusque.

"Sister," I said, "I'm afraid it's all over with Amber. I've tried everything, and she has got worse all the time. I do think it would be the kindest thing to put her to sleep."

Shock was evident in her voice. "But . . . it seems so awful. Just for a skin disease."

"I know, that's what everybody thinks. But this is a dreadful thing. In its worst form it can ruin an animal's life. Amber must be very uncomfortable now, and soon she is going to be in pain. We can't let her go on."

"Oh . . . well, I trust in your judgment, Mr. Herriot. I know you wouldn't do anything that wasn't necessary." There was a long pause, and I knew she was trying to control her voice. Then she spoke calmly. "I think I would like to come out and see her when I can get away from the hospital."

"Please, Sister," I said gently. "I'd much rather you didn't."

Again the pause, then, "Very well, Mr. Herriot. I leave everything to you."

I had an urgent visit immediately afterwards, and a rush of work

[140]

kept me going all afternoon. I never really stopped thinking about what I had to do later, but at least the other pressures stopped it from obsessing me. It was, as always, pitch-dark when I drove into the yard and opened the garage doors.

And it was like all the other times. Amber was there in the beam, paws on the plywood, body swinging with her wagging, mouth open and panting with delight, welcoming me.

I put the barbiturate and syringe into my pocket before climbing into the pen. For a long time I made a fuss of her, patting her and talking to her as she leaped up at me. Then I filled the syringe.

"Sit, girl," I said, and she flopped obediently onto her hindquarters. I gripped her right leg above the elbow to raise the radial vein. There was no need for clipping—all the hair had gone. Amber looked at me interestedly, wondering what new game this might be as I slipped the needle into the vein. I realised that there was no need to say the things I always said. "She won't know a thing." "This is just an overdose of anaesthetic." "It's an easy way out for her." There was no sorrowing owner to hear me. There were just the two of us.

And as I murmured, "Good girl, Amber, good lass," while she sank down on the straw, I had the conviction that if I *had* said those things, they would have been true. She didn't know a thing between her playfulness and oblivion, and it was indeed an easy way out from that prison which would soon become a torture chamber.

I stepped from the pen and switched off the car lights, and in the cold darkness the yard had never seemed so empty. After the weeks of struggle, the sense of loss and failure was overpowering, but at the end I was at least able to spare Amber the ultimate miseries: the internal abscesses and septicaemia that await a dog suffering from a progressive and incurable demodectic mange.

For a long time I carried a weight around with me, and I feel some of it now after all these years. Because the tragedy of Amber was that she was born too soon. At the present time we can cure

[141]

most cases of demodectic mange by a long course of organo-
phosphates and antibiotics, but neither of these things was available then when I needed them.

It is still a dread condition, but we have fought patiently with
our modern weapons and won most of the battles over the past
few years. I know several fine dogs in Darrowby who have survived, and when I see them in the streets, healthy and glossy-
coated, the picture of Amber comes back into my mind. It is
always dark, and she is always in the headlight's beam.

Chapter
16

"Just look at that," the farmer said.

"At what?" I was "cleansing" a cow (removing the afterbirth), and my arm was buried deep in the cow's uterus. I turned my head to see him pointing at the byre floor beneath my patient. I saw four white jets of milk spurting onto the concrete from the animal's udder.

He grinned. "That's a funny thing, isn't it?"

"It isn't, really," I said. "It's a reflex action caused by my hand twiddling the uterus about. This acts on a gland in the brain which causes the milk to flow. I often see cows letting their milk down like that when I'm cleansing them."

"Well, that's a rum 'un." The farmer laughed. "Any road, you'd better get finished quick or you'll have a few pints of milk to knock off your bill."

That was in 1947, the year of the great snow. I have never known snow like that before or since, and the odd thing was that it took such a long time to get started. Nothing happened in November and we had a green Christmas, but then it began to get colder and colder. All through January a north-east wind blew, apparently straight from the Arctic; usually after a few days of this sort of unbearable blast, snow would come and make things a bit warmer. But not in 1947.

Each day we thought it couldn't get any colder, but it did, and then, borne on the wind, very fine flakes began to appear over the last few days of the month. They were so small you could hardly see them, but they were the forerunners of the real thing. At the beginning of February, big, fat flakes started a steady, relentless descent on our countryside, and we knew, after all that buildup, that we were in for it.

For weeks and weeks the snow fell, sometimes in a gentle, almost lazy curtain that remorselessly obliterated the familiar landmarks, at others in fierce blizzards. In between, the frost took over and transformed the roads into glassy tracks of flattened snow over which we drove at fifteen miles an hour.

The long garden at Skeldale House disappeared under a white blanket. There was a single deep channel by the wall-side where I fought my way daily to my car in the yard at the top.

The yard itself had to be dug out every day and the opening of the big double doors into the yard was a back-breaking job. One day I found the doors were jammed immovably in high mounds of frozen snow. There was nothing I could do about it so they were left standing open for the rest of the winter.

To get to our cases we did a lot of walking since so many of the farm tracks were blocked wall to wall. On the very high country there were some farms we couldn't reach at all, and that was very sad because there was no doubt that many animals died for lack of veterinary help. It was around the middle of March when helicopters were dropping food on these isolated spots that Bert Kealey telephoned me.

He was one of those out of reach on a high moor that was bleak even in summertime, and I was surprised to hear his voice.

"I thought your phone wires would be down, Bert," I said.

"Naw, they've survived, God knows how." The young farmer's voice was cheerful, as always. He ran a small suckling herd on the high tops and was one of the many who scratched a living from the unfriendly soil.

"But ah'm in trouble," he went on. "Polly's just had a litter, and she hasn't a drop of milk."

[144]

"Oh dear, that's unfortunate," I said. Polly was the only pig on the Kealey farm.

"Aye, it's a beggar. Bad enough losin' the litter—there's twelve smashin' little pigs—but it's Tess I'm bothered about."

"Yes . . . yes . . ." I was thinking of Tess, too. She was Bert's eight-year-old daughter, and she had a thing about little pigs. She had persuaded her father to buy her an in-pig sow for her birthday so that she could have a litter of her own. I could remember Tess's excitement when she showed me her birthday gift a few days after its arrival.

"That's Polly Pig," she said, pointing to the sow nuzzling the straw in its pen. "She's mine. My dad gave her to me."

I leaned over the pen. "Yes, I know. You're a lucky girl. She looks a fine pig to me."

"Oh, she is, she is." The little girl's eyes shone with pleasure. "I feed her every day, and she lets me stroke her. She's nice."

"I bet she is. She looks nice."

"Yes, and do you know something else?" Tess's face grew serious, and her voice took on a conspiratorial tone. "She's going to have babies in March."

"Well, I never!" I said. "Is that so? You'll have a whole lot of little pink pigs to look after." I held my hands a few inches apart. "Just about this size."

She was so thrilled at the thought that she was lost for words. She just smiled happily, got hold of the wall of the pen and began to jump up and down.

All this came back to me as I listened to Bert Kealey's voice on the phone.

"Do you think she's got mastitis, Bert? Is the udder red and swollen? Is she off her food?"

"No, nowt like that. She's eatin' her head off, and her udder's not a bit inflamed."

"Well, then, it's a straight case of agalactia. She needs a shot of pituitrin, but how the heck is she going to get it? Your district's been cut off for weeks now."

It takes a lot to make a Yorkshire farmer admit that his farm is inaccessible because of the weather, but these were exceptional circumstances and Bert had to agree.

"I know," he said. "Ah've tried diggin' me road out, but it fills up as fast as I clear it. Anyway, top road's blocked for two miles, so I'm wastin' me time."

I thought for a moment. "Have you tried getting some cow's milk into the piglets? An egg mixed with a quart of milk and a teaspoonful of glucose isn't a bad milk substitute. I know you got some glucose for those scouring calves."

"I've tried 'em with that," Bert replied. "Put it in a Yorkshire puddin' tin and dipped their noses in it, but they wouldn't look at it. If only they could have a good suck at their mother and get summat into their bellies it would start them off, and then they'd maybe have a go at t'substitute."

He was right. There was nothing to compare with that first suck. And if they didn't get it, those tiny creatures with their empty stomachs could start dying at an alarming rate.

"Looks like they're all goin' to go down t'nick," Bert said. "Ah don't know what little Tess is goin' to say. She'll be heartbroken."

I tapped my fingers against the receiver. An idea was forming in my mind. "There's just one possibility," I said. "I know I can get to the top of Dennor Bank because the road is open to there. After that it's all flat going to your place. I could maybe get there on skis."

"Skis?"

"Yes, I've been doing a bit of that lately. But I've not tackled anywhere as far off as your farm. I can't be sure that I'll make it, but I'll try."

"By 'eck, I'd be very grateful if you would, Mr. Herriot. It's t'little lass ah'm thinkin' of."

"Same here, Bert. Anyway, I'll have a go. I'll leave now."

On the summit of Dennor Bank I manoeuvered my car as close as possible to the tall white walls the snow ploughs had thrown up, got out and buckled on my skis. I have to admit I was beginning to fancy myself a bit on skis, because one bonus of the long spell of snow and frost was that some nice little slopes had become available. With a few other enthusiasts I had been rushing out to the hillsides at every opportunity and I had found that gliding down again and again in the frosty air was one of the most exhilarating things I had ever known. I had bought a book on the subject and thought I was becoming quite skilful.

All I needed was the bottle of pituitrin and a syringe, and I put them in my pocket.

To get to the Kealey farm in normal conditions you drove a couple of miles along a very straight road, turned right and made for the high-lying village of Branderley. Bert's farm lay in an isolated position about halfway along this second road.

But today, although I had travelled this region a hundred times, I might have been in a strange country, somewhere I had never seen before. The stone walls had been deeply engulfed, so there were no fields, no roads, nothing but a yawning white expanse with the tops of telegraph poles sticking up here and there. It was uncanny.

Without skis there was no saying how far I might have sunk into the billowing drifts. I felt a twinge of misgiving, but I had promised to try. Anyway, I would be able to travel cross-country. It would be like cutting off two sides of a triangle, and I was pretty sure the farm lay in one of the hollows just below the dark skyline.

I am afraid this is not a glorious episode in my history. I had slithered amateurishly for about half a mile when the snow started again. It seemed to come from nowhere and was by no means a blizzard, just a white veil that cut me off completely from my surroundings. There was no point in going on because I had lost all sense of direction; the swirling screen of flakes was impenetrable. There is no disguising the fact that I was scared. As I stood stock-still in the cold with my eyes half-closed, I wondered what would happen to me if the snow didn't stop. In fact, I still wonder about that, because I could have blundered for miles in that empty wilderness without coming upon a house.

It is a question that will never be answered because the flurry stopped as suddenly as it had begun. My heart thumped as I stared around me, and the dark smudge of my car roof in the white distance was a sweet sight. I headed back to it with a speed worthy of an Olympic skier, and I am sure my eyes were popping as I kept them fixed on my link with home.

Relief flowed through me as I threw my skis into the back and started the engine, and I had left Dennor Bank behind and was well on the way to Darrowby before my pulse rate returned to normal.

"Bert," I said on the phone. "I'm terribly sorry but I just couldn't make it. I got caught by a snow shower and had to turn back."

"Well, ah'm glad ye did turn. I've been a bit worried since ye left. Fellers have got lost and died in the snow up here. I shouldn't have let you try."

He paused for a moment, then said wistfully, "If only there was some other way to make Polly let 'er milk down."

As he spoke, the picture flashed into my mind of that cow I was cleansing and the white jets striking the byre floor. And there were other memories—when I was doing uterine examinations on sows, the same thing had happened.

"Maybe there is a way," I blurted out.

"What d'ye mean?"

"Bert, have you ever had your hand inside a sow?"

"Eh?"

"Have you ever examined a sow internally?"

"You mean . . . in 'er pig bed?"

"Yes."

"Nay, nay, ah leave that to you chaps."

"Well, I want you to start now. Get some warm water and soap and . . ."

"Hey, hang on, Mr. Herriot. I'm sure there's no more pigs left in 'er."

"I don't suppose there are, Bert, but do as I say. Soap your arm well and use any household antiseptic you have. Then feel your way into the vagina till you come to the cervix. She's only just farrowed, so the cervix should still be open. Put a finger inside and waggle the pig bed around a bit."

"Oh, 'eck, I don't fancy this. What's it all about?"

"It often brings the milk down, that's what it's about, so get going."

I put down the phone and went through to have lunch. Helen kept glancing at me during the meal as I answered little Jimmy's questions in a preoccupied way. She knew something was on my mind, and I don't suppose she was surprised when I leaped to my feet at the sound of the phone ringing.

It was Bert. He sounded breathless but triumphant. "It worked, Mr. Herriot! I 'ad a good waggle round like you said, then I tried the udder. I could draw milk out of every tit and there wasn't a drop there before. It was like magic."

"Are the piglets feeding?"

"Not half! They were fightin' to get a drink before, but they're all laid quiet in a row, suckin' hard. It's lovely to see them."

"Well, that's great," I said. "But we haven't won yet. The piglets have had that vital first feed, but Polly will probably dry up again by tomorrow or even tonight. You'll have to get your hand in again."

"Oh, crumbs." A lot of the enthusiasm went out of Bert's voice. "I thought I'd finished wi' that."

The poor man did indeed have to perform his unusual task several times and, in fact, Polly never did come fully to her milk, but the piglets were kept going until they were able to drink the milk substitute from the tin. The litter was saved.

The great snow of 1947 was followed by the most glorious summer I can remember, but in late April in the high country, the white streaks still lay behind the walls, standing out against the green moorland like the ribs of a great beast. But the roads were clear, and my journey to see one of Bert Kealey's heifers had none of the drama of last time.

When I had finished my job, young Tess took me through to see her beloved Polly and family.

"They're pretty, aren't they?" she said as we looked into the pen at the twelve chunky little pigs playing around their mother.

"They certainly are, Tess," I replied. "Your first attempt at pig breeding has been a big success, but I really think you have to thank your father for it. He did a wonderful job."

Bert gave a wry smile, then screwed up his face at the memory. "Aye, maybe so, and I reckon it was worth it. Aye, well, it's wonderful what ye can do when you have to."

Chapter 17

"Are you all right, Helen?"

I looked round anxiously as my wife fidgeted in her seat. We were in the one- and-ninepennies in the La Scala cinema in Brawton, and I had a strong conviction that we had no right to be there.

I had voiced my doubts that morning. "I know it's our half-day, Helen, but with the baby due anytime, don't you think it would be safer to stay around Darrowby?"

"No, of course not." Helen laughed incredulously at the very idea of missing our outing. And I could see her point because it was an oasis of relaxation in our busy lives. For me it was an escape from the telephone and the mud and the Wellington boots, and for my wife it meant a rest from her own hard slog, plus the luxury of having meals cooked and served by somebody else.

"But, honestly," I said. "What if the thing comes on quickly? It's all right you laughing. We don't want our second child to be born in Smith's book shop or the back of a car."

The whole business had me worried. I wasn't as bad as when Jimmy was on his way. I was in the R.A.F. then, and I went into a sort of decline during which I lost two stones in weight, which wasn't all due to the hard training. People make jokes about this syndrome, but I didn't find it funny. There was something about having babies that really got through to me, and lately I had spent a lot of time flapping around watching Helen's every move, much to her amusement. I just couldn't be calm about the thing. There isn't much of the yogi in my make-up at any time, and over the last two days the tension had built up.

But Helen had been adamant this morning. She wasn't going to be done out of her half-day by such a trifle, and now here we were in the La Scala, with Humphrey Bogart competing vainly for my attention and my blood pressure rising steadily as my wife squirmed around and occasionally ran a thoughtful hand over her swollen abdomen.

As I scrutinised her keenly from the corner of my eye, she gave a convulsive jerk and her lips parted in a soft moan. An instant dew of perspiration had already sprung out all over me before she turned and whispered, "I think we'd better go now, Jim."

Stumbling over the outstretched legs in the darkness, I guided her up the sloping aisle, and such was my panic that I felt sure the crisis would be upon us before we reached the usherette standing at the back with her torch.

I was thankful to reach the street and see our little car standing only a few yards away. As we set off, I seemed to notice the rattles and bumping of the old springs for the first time. It was the only time in my life that I wished I had a Rolls Royce.

The twenty-five miles to Darrowby seemed to take an eternity. Helen sat very quiet by my side, occasionally closing her eyes and catching her breath, while my heart beat a tattoo against my ribs. When we reached our little town I turned the car to the right towards the market place.

Helen looked at me in surprise. "Where are you going?"

"Well, to Nurse Brown's, of course."

"Oh, don't be so silly. It's not time for that yet."

"But . . . how do you know?"

"I just know." Helen laughed. "I've had a baby before, don't you remember? Come on, let's go home."

Heavy with misgiving, I drove to Skeldale House, and as we mounted the stairs I marvelled at Helen's composure.

It was the same when we got into bed. She lay there, obviously not very comfortable but quite patient, and there was about her a calm acceptance of the inevitable which I could not share.

I suppose I kept dropping into what is termed a fitful slumber because it was 6 A.M. when she nudged my arm.

"Time to go, Jim." Her tone was very matter-of-fact.

I shot from the bed like a jack-in-the-box, threw on my clothes and shouted across the landing to Auntie Lucy who was staying with us for the occasion, "We're off!"

A faint reply came through the door. "All right, I'll see to Jimmy."

When I returned to our bedroom, Helen was dressing methodically.

"Get that suitcase out of the cupboard, Jim," she said.

I opened the cupboard door. "Suitcase?"

"Yes, that one. It's got my nighties and toilet things and baby clothes and everything I'll need. Go on, bring it out."

Suppressing a groan, I carried the case out and stood waiting. I had missed all this last time because of the war and had often regretted it, but at that moment I wasn't at all sure whether I wouldn't rather be elsewhere.

Outside, it was a glorious May morning, the air limpid with the new-day freshness that had soothed the irritation of many an early call, but it was all lost on me today as I drove across the empty market place.

We had only about half a mile to go, and I was pulling up outside Greenside Nursing Home within minutes. There was a touch of grandeur about the name, but, in fact, it was just the small dwelling house of Nurse Brown. Upstairs there were a couple of bedrooms which for many years had seen the arrival of the local children.

I knocked at the door and pushed it open. Nurse Brown gave me a quick smile, put her arm round Helen's shoulders and led her upstairs. I was left in the kitchen feeling strangely alone and helpless, but a voice cut in on my jumbled thoughts.

[153]

"Now then, Jim, it's a grand mornin'."

It was Cliff, Nurse Brown's husband. He was sitting in the corner of the kitchen eating his breakfast, and he spoke to me casually as though we had encountered each other in the street. He wore the broad grin that never seemed to leave his face, but I suppose I half expected that he would leap from the table, seize my hand and say, "There, there," or something of the sort.

However, he continued to work his way phlegmatically through the stack of bacon, eggs, sausages and tomatoes on his plate, and I realised that over the years he must have seen hundreds of quivering husbands standing in that kitchen. It was old stuff to Cliff.

"Yes, Cliff . . . yes. . . ." I replied. "I think it will turn out hot later."

He nodded absently and pushed his plate to one side to join an empty porridge bowl before turning his attention to bread and marmalade. Nurse Brown was a noted cook as well as a baby expert, and it was evident that she believed in ensuring that her husband, a very big man and a lorry driver for one of the local contractors, would not grow faint from hunger during the morning.

Watching him slapping on the marmalade, I cringed inwardly at the creaking sounds from the floorboards above. What was happening in that bedroom?

As he chewed, Cliff seemed to notice that I was perhaps one of the more distraught type of husbands because he turned his big, kind smile on me. He was and is one of the nicest men in our town, and he spoke gently.

"Don't worry, lad," he said. "It'll be right."

His words were mildly soothing, and I fled. In those days it was unheard of for the husband to be present at the birth, and though it is now the in thing to observe it all, I marvel at the fortitude of these young men. I know beyond all doubt that Herriot would be carried away unconscious at some time during the proceedings.

When Siegfried arrived at the surgery, he was very thoughtful.

"You'd better stick around, James. I'll get through the morning round on my own. Take it quietly, my boy. All will be well."

It was difficult to take it quietly. I found that expectant fathers really did pace the floor for long periods, and I varied this by trying to read the newspaper upside down.

It was around eleven o'clock when the long-awaited telephone call came. It was my doctor and good friend, Harry Allinson. Harry always spoke in a sort of cheerful shout, and his very presence in a sickroom was a tonic. This morning the booming voice was like the sweetest music.

"A sister for Jimmy!" His words were followed by a burst of laughter.

"Oh great, Harry. Thank you, thank you. That's marvellous news." I held the receiver against my chest for a few moments before putting it down. I walked with dragging steps to the sitting room and lay back in a chair until my nerves had stopped vibrating.

Then, on an impulse, I leaped to my feet. I believe I have said before that I am a fairly sensible man with a propensity for doing daft things, and I decided that I had to go round to the nursing home immediately.

At that time, a husband was not welcome straight after the birth. I knew it because I had gone to see Jimmy too soon and had not been well received. But still I went.

When I burst into her establishment, Nurse Brown's usual smile was absent. "You've done it again, haven't you?" she said with some asperity. "I told you with Jimmy that you should have given us time to get the baby washed, but it seems you took no notice."

I hung my head sheepishly, and she relented. "Oh, well, now you're here you might as well come upstairs."

Helen had the same tired, flushed look that I remembered before. I kissed her thankfully. We didn't say anything, just smiled at each other. Then I had a look in the cot by the bed.

Nurse Brown regarded me with tight lips and narrowed eyes as

I peered down. Last time I had been so aghast at Jimmy's appearance that I had mortally offended her by asking if there was anything wrong with him, and heaven help me, I felt the same now. I won't go into details but the new little girl's face was all squashed and red and bloated, and the sense of shock hit me as it had done before.

I looked up at the nurse, and it was only too clear that she was waiting for me to say something derogatory. Her normally laughing face was set in a threatening scowl. One wrong word from me and she would have kicked me on the shins—I was sure of that.

"Gorgeous," I said weakly. "Really gorgeous."

"All right." She had seen enough of me. "Out you go."

She ushered me downstairs, and as she opened the outside door, she fixed me with a piercing eye. That bright little woman could read me without effort. She spoke slowly and deliberately, as though addressing a person of limited intelligence.

"That . . . is . . . a . . . lovely . . . healthy . . . baby. . . ." she said and closed the door in my face.

And, bless her heart, her words helped me, because as I drove away, I knew she must be right. And now, all these years later, when I look at my handsome son and my beautiful daughter, I can hardly believe my own stupidity.

When I returned to the surgery, there was one visit waiting for me, high in the hills, and the journey up there was like a happy dream. My worry was over, and it seemed that all nature was rejoicing with me. It was the ninth of May, 1947, the beginning of the most perfect summer I can remember. The sun blazed; soft breezes swirled into the car, carrying their fragrance from the fells around; an elusive breath of the bluebells, primroses and violets scattered everywhere on the grass, flowing among the shadows of the trees.

After I had seen my patient, I took a walk on the high tops along a favourite path of beaten earth on the hill's edge, with Sam trotting at my heels.

I looked away over the rolling patchwork of the plain, sleeping in the sun's haze, and at the young bracken on the hillside, springing straight and green from last year's dead brown stalks. Everywhere new life was calling out its exultant message, and it was so apt with my new little daughter lying down there in Darrowby.

We had decided to call her Rosemary. It is such a pretty name and I still love it, but it didn't last long. It became Rosie at a very early stage and though I did make one or two ineffectual stands, it has remained so to this day. She is now Dr. Rosie in our community.

On that May day I caught myself just in time. It has always been my practice to recline in the sunshine on the springy bed of heather that clusters on these hillsides, and I was just settling down when I remembered I had other things to do today. I sped back to Skeldale House and began to telephone my glad news all over the country.

It was received rapturously by all, but it was Tristan who grasped the essentials of the situation.

"We've got to wet this baby's head, Jim," he said seriously.

I was ready for anything. "Of course, of course, when are you coming over?"

"I'll be there at seven," he replied crisply, and I knew he would be.

Tristan was concerned about the venue of the celebration. There were four of us in the sitting room at Skeldale House— Siegfried, Tristan, Alex Taylor and myself. Alex was my oldest friend—we started school together in Glasgow at the age of four —and when he came out of the army after five years in the western desert and Italy, he came to spend a few weeks with Helen and me in Darrowby. It wasn't long before he had fallen under the spell of country life, and now he was learning farming and estate agency with a view to starting a new career. It was good that he should be with me tonight.

Tristan's fingers drummed on the arm of his chair as he thought aloud. His expression was fixed and grave, his eyes vacant.

"We'd normally go to the Drovers but they've got that big party on tonight, so that's no good," he muttered. "We want a bit of peace and quiet. Let's see, now, there's the George and Dragon—Tetley's beer, splendid stuff, but I've known them a bit careless with their pipes and I've had the odd sour mouthful. And, of course, we have the Cross Keys. They pull a lovely pint of Cameron's, and the draught Guinness is excellent. And we mustn't forget the Hare and Pheasant—their bitter can rise to great heights, although the mild is ordinary." He paused for a moment. "We might do worse than the Lord Nelson—very reliable ale—and, of course, there's always . . ."

"Just a minute, Triss," I broke in. "I went round to Nurse Brown's this evening to see Helen, and Cliff asked if he could come with us. Don't you think it would be rather nice to go to his pub since the baby was born in his house?"

Tristan narrowed his eyes. "Which pub is that?"

"The Black Horse."

"Ah, yes, ye-es." Tristan looked at me thoughtfully and put his fingertips together. "Russell and Rangham's. A good little brewery, that. I've had some first-rate pints in the Black Horse, though I've noticed a slight loss of nuttiness under very warm conditions." He looked anxiously out of the window. "It's been a hot day today. Perhaps we'd . . ."

"Oh, for heaven's sake!" Siegfried leaped to his feet. "You sound like an analytical chemist. It's only beer you're talking about, after all."

Tristan looked at him in shocked silence, but Siegfried turned to me briskly. "I think that's a pleasant idea of yours, James. Let's go with Cliff to the Black Horse. It's a quiet little place."

And indeed, as we dropped to the chairs in the bar parlour, I felt we had chosen the ideal spot. The evening sunshine sent long golden shafts over the pitted oak tables and the high-backed settles where a few farm men sat with their glasses. There was nothing smart about this little inn, but the furniture which hadn't been changed for a hundred years gave it an air of tranquillity. It was just right.

Reg Wilkey, the diminutive landlord, welcomed us and charged our glasses from his tall white jug.

Siegfried raised his pint. "James, may I be the first to wish a long life, health and happiness to Rosemary."

"Thank you, Siegfried," I said, feeling suddenly very much among friends as the others said, "Here, here," and began to drink.

Cliff, his face wreathed in his eternal smile, lowered the level in his glass by half, then turned to the landlord. "It gets better, Reg," he said reverently. "It gets better."

As Reg bowed modestly, Cliff said, "Ye know, Jim, I've said for years that me two best friends are Mr. Russell and Mr. Rangham. I think the world of 'em."

Everybody laughed, and the stage was set for a happy celebration. With my anxieties over, I felt wonderful.

After a couple of pints, Siegfried patted me on the shoulder. "I'm off, James. Have a good time. Can't tell you how pleased I am."

I watched him go, and I didn't argue. He was right. There was a veterinary practice out there, and somebody had to watch the shop. And this was my night.

It was one of those cosy evenings when everything seemed perfect. Alex and I recalled our childhood in Glasgow, Tristan came up with some splendid memories of Skeldale House in the bachelor days and over everything, like a beneficent moon, hung the huge smile of Cliff Brown.

A great love of my fellow men mounted in me, and I kept buying drinks for the local people around us. Finally I grew tired of fumbling for money and handed my wallet to the landlord. It was stuffed with notes because I had made a special visit to the bank that afternoon.

"Here, Reg," I said. "Just keep taking the drinks out of that."

"Aye, right, Mr. Herriot," he replied without changing expression. "It'll mek it easier."

It did make it a lot easier. Men whom I hardly knew raised their glasses and toasted my new daughter repeatedly, and all I had to do was smile and raise mine in return.

When closing time was announced, it didn't seem possible that it was all coming to an end.

As the little pub emptied, I approached the landlord. "We can't go home yet, Reg."

He looked at me quizzically. "Well, ye know the law, Mr. Herriot."

"Yes, but this is a special night, isn't it?"

"Aye, it is, I suppose." He hesitated for a moment. "Tell ye what. I'll lock up, then we could go down and 'ave one or two in the cellar, just to finish off."

I put my arm round his shoulders. "Reg, what a delightful idea. Let's go down there."

We descended a few steps into the pub cellar, switched on the light and pulled the trapdoor closed after us. As we disposed ourselves among the barrels and crates, I looked around the company. Apart from the original four, we were now augmented by two young farmers, one of the local grocers and an official from the Darrowby Water Board. We were a warmly knit little group.

It was much easier down there. No need to bother the landlord with his jug. We just went to a barrel and turned the tap.

"Still plenty in the wallet, Reg?" I shouted.

"Aye, there's plenty 'ere, don't worry. Help yourselves."

We kept doing that, and the party never flagged. It must have been past midnight when we heard the thumping on the outside door. Reg listened for a few moments, then went upstairs. He returned soon but was preceded through the trapdoor by the long blue legs, tunic, cadaverous face and helmet of Police Constable Hubert Goole.

A silence fell on the merry gathering as the constable's melancholy gaze passed slowly over us.

[160]

"Drinkin' a bit late, aren't ye?" he enquired tonelessly.

"Ah, well." Tristan gave a gay little laugh. "It's a special occasion, you see, Mr. Goole. Mr. Herriot's wife gave birth to a daughter this morning."

"Oh, aye?" The Old Testament countenance looked down on my friend from its bony perch. "I don't remember Mr. Wilkey applyin' for an extended licence for tonight."

It was the nearest he could get to making a joke, because P. C. Goole never made jokes. He was known in the town as a stern and unbending man, one who went by the book. It was no good riding a bike at night without lights when P. C. Goole was around. He was particularly merciless on this offence. He sang in the church choir, his morals were impeccable, he was active in community work, he did everything right. It was strange that in his mid-fifties he was still an ordinary constable.

Tristan bounced back. "Ah, yes, ha-ha, very good. But, of course, this was a totally impromptu thing. Spur of the moment, you know."

"Ye can call it what ye like, but you're breakin' the law and you know it." The big man unbuttoned his breast pocket and flipped open his notebook. "I'll have to 'ave your names."

I was sitting on an upturned crate, and I gripped my knees tightly. What an end to the happy evening. Nothing much happened in the town, and this would make headlines in the *Darrowby and Houlton Times*. It would look great, with all my friends involved, too. And poor little Reg standing sheepishly in the background—he would really get it in the neck, and it was all my fault.

Tristan, however, was not beaten yet. "Mr. Goole," he said coldly, "I'm disappointed in you."

"Eh?"

"I said I'm disappointed. I'd have expected you to show a different attitude on an occasion like this."

The constable was unmoved. He poised his pencil. "I'm a policeman, Mr. Farnon, and I 'ave my duty to do. We might as

[161]

well start with your name." He wrote carefully, then looked up. "What's your address, now?"

"It seems to me," said Tristan, ignoring the question, "that you have forgotten all about little Julie."

"What about Julie?" The long face showed a certain animation for the first time. Tristan's mention of P. C. Goole's beloved Yorkshire terrier had found a tender spot.

"Well, as I recall," Tristan went on, "Mr. Herriot sat up for several hours during the night with Julie when she was having pups. In fact, if it hadn't been for him, you might have lost the pups and Julie, too. I know it's a few years ago, but I remember it distinctly."

"Now, then, that has got nowt to do with tonight. I've told ye, I have my duty to do." He turned to the official of the Water Board.

Tristan returned to the attack. "Yes, but surely you could have a drink with us on a night like this when Mr. Herriot has become a father for the second time. It's the same thing, in a way."

P. C. Goole paused, and his face softened. "Julie's still goin' strong."

"Yes, I know," I said. "Wonderful little thing for her age."

"And I still have one of them pups."

"Of course. You've had him in to see me a few times."

"Aye . . . aye . . ." P. C. Goole hitched up his tunic, delved in his trouser pocket and brought out a large watch. He studied it thoughtfully. "Well, I'm off duty about now. Suppose I could have a drink with ye. I'll just phone in to the office first."

"Oh, good!" Tristan moved quickly to the barrel and drew another pint.

When the constable returned from the phone, he raised the glass solemnly. "Here's wishin' t'little lass all the best," he said and took a long swallow.

"Thank you, Mr. Goole," I replied. "You're very kind."

He sat down on one of the lower steps, placed his helmet on a crate and had another deep drink. "Both well, I 'ope?"

"Yes, just grand. Have another."

It was surprising how soon he seemed to forget all about his notebook, and the party picked up again rapidly. The relief of the escape added greatly to the festivities, and joy reigned unrestrained.

"It's bloody 'ot down 'ere," P. C. Goole remarked after some time and removed his tunic. With this symbolic gesture, the last barrier went down.

And yet, over the next two hours, nobody got really plastered. Nobody, that is, except P. C. Goole. With the rest of us it was a case of laughter, reminiscing and an undoubted heightening of the senses, but the policeman passed through various phases on the road to a fairly profound inebriation.

The first was when he insisted on a Christian-name relationship, then he became almost tearfully affectionate as he rhapsodised on the wonders of birth, human and canine. The latest phase was more sinister. He was turning aggressive.

"You're 'avin' another, Jim." It was a statement rather than an enquiry as the tall, shirt-sleeved figure bent, swaying slightly, over the tap of the barrel, glass at the ready.

"No thanks, Hubert," I replied. "I've had enough."

He blinked at me owlishly. "You're not 'avin' another?"

"No, honestly, Hubert, I've had it. I started long before you."

He sent another pint frothing into his glass before continuing. "Then you're a bloody piker, Jim," he said. "And if there's one thing I can't shtand, if there's one thing I can't bloody well shtand, it's a bloody piker."

I tried an ingratiating smile. "I'm terribly sorry, Hubert, but I'm up to here, and, anyway, it's half-past two. I really think we ought to be going."

It seemed to be a general sentiment because the assembly all began to get to their feet.

"Goin'?" Hubert glared at me belligerently. "Whassa matter with you? The night's young yet." He slurped down another mouthful of beer indignantly. "You ask a feller to 'ave a drink with you, and next minute ye say we're goin'. Itsh not right."

"Now, now, Hubert," said little Reg Wilkey, sidling up to him, smiling and radiating the bonhomie that came from thirty years' practice at easing reluctant clients from his premises. "Be a good lad, now. We've all 'ad a grand time and it's been lovely seein' you, but everybody's settin' off 'ome. Now where's your jacket?"

The constable muttered and grumbled as we helped him into his tunic and balanced his helmet on his head but allowed us to lead him up the steps into the darkness of the pub. Outside, I installed him in the back of my car, with Tristan and Alex on either side. Cliff sat with me in front.

Before we left, the landlord passed my wallet through the window. It had slimmed down to the point of emaciation, and it occurred to me that my bank manager, who was always advising me in the kindest possible way to watch my overdraft, would be tossing uneasily in his bed if he knew.

I drove through the sleeping town and turned down the narrow street towards the market place. As we approached, I could see that the cobbled square was deserted except for two figures standing at the edge of the roadway under a street light. With a twinge of alarm I recognised Inspector Bowles and Sergeant Rostron, our two head policemen. They were standing, very erect and trim-looking, hands behind their back, glancing around them keenly. They looked as though they wouldn't miss any misdemeanours in their vicinity.

A sudden scream from the back seat almost sent me through a shop window. Hubert had seen them, too.

"It's that bugger Rostron!" he yelled. "I 'ate that bugger! He's 'ad it in for me for years, and I'm goin' to tell 'im what I think about 'im!"

There was a thrashing of arms in the back as he wound down the window and started his tirade at the top of his voice. "You bloody rotten . . . !"

For the second time that night an icy dread swept me that something awful was going to happen because of me.

"Quell him!" I shouted. "For God's sake, quell him!"

However, my friends in the rear had anticipated me. Hubert's cries were suddenly switched off as Tristan and Alex bundled him to the floor and fell on top of him. Tristan was actually sitting on his head when we came up to the two policemen, and only muffled sounds drifted from below.

As we passed, the inspector nodded and smiled, and the sergeant gave me a friendly salute. It was not difficult to read their minds as they docketed away another item of information. Mr. Herriot, returning from yet another night call. A dedicated vet, that young man.

With their colleague writhing on the floor behind me, I could not relax until we had turned off the square, out of sight and sound. Hubert, when allowed to get up, seemed to have lost a lot of his belligerence. In fact he was reaching the sleepy stage and when he arrived at his home, he walked quietly and fairly steadily up his garden path.

Back in Skeldale House, I went up to our bedroom. The big room with the double bed, wardrobe and dressing table was eerily empty without Helen.

I opened the door to the long, narrow apartment that had been the dressing room in the great days of the old house. It was where Tristan had slept when we were all bachelors together, but now it was Jimmy's room, and his bed stood in exactly the same place as my old friend's.

I looked down on my son as I had often looked down on Tristan in his slumbers. I used to marvel at Tristan's cherubic innocence, but even he could not compete with a sleeping child.

I gazed at little Jimmy, then glanced at the other end of the room where a cot stood to receive Rosie.

Soon, I thought, I would have two in here. I was becoming rich.

Chapter
18

November 2, 1961

We learned this morning that we would not start unloading the sheep until this evening as the *Ubbergen* was still occupying the berth, so this gave me plenty of opportunity to explore the town.

Shortly after breakfast an important person came aboard, the head director of "Inflot," which deals with the movement of all ships in the harbour.

He was a kindly-looking man of about fifty, with an attractive smile. He wore very thick glasses, and he told me that his weak eyesight had been caused by hours of studying at night. His English was very good.

Maybe it was because he was so pleasant that I was emboldened to broach the question of the school. Another reason, of course, was that I was somewhat puffed up by my own importance. When I was recently elected chairman of the Darrowby Parent-Teachers' Association, it gave my ego a definite boost, and when our headmaster expressed an interest in Russian education, he started an idea in my mind.

Anyway, whatever the cause, I was about to do another of my daft things.

"Do you think I could possibly see inside a Russian school?" I asked him.

The eyes behind the glasses stopped twinkling, and he gave me a long, thoughtful stare. After a few moments he nodded. "I think it will be all right if you ask permission when you get to the school. As it happens, my wife is a teacher, and if you go to Skola Number Two, you could ask for Madame Juowskaya."

I could hardly wait to get ashore, but again I couldn't find any volunteers to come with me. When I finally approached the captain, he probably felt like throwing me over the side. He was short of sleep after our stormy voyage and weary with his long negotiations with the officials but still he had the goodness to humour me.

He smiled and said, "Of course, Mr. Herriot." As he settled his peaked hat on his silvery head and pulled on a smart navy-blue coat, I thought how very distinguished he looked.

Down the gangway again, past the unsmiling soldiers and along the railway tracks towards the gate. But I just had to solve the mystery of the man-eating dog. As we passed the wagon of last night I caught the captain's arm.

"Just a minute," I said. "I want to have a peep behind here."

For a moment he lost his poise and his eyes widened. "Mr. Herriot, no! What are you doing?"

"It's all right." I smiled reassuringly. "I only want a quick look."

With the greatest care I edged my way behind the wagon, but the dog was gone. There was only an empty kennel. Then I noticed there was a kennel about every fifty yards and a chain attached by a ring to a wire that stretched along the entire length of the fence.

As I re-emerged, to the obvious relief of the captain, I saw in the distance groups of dogs being led towards us. We passed them on the way to the gate house; large, stringy creatures loping along on the end of their leads, looking neither to right nor left. They were of the Alsatian type but taller, and they certainly had a lean and hungry look.

[167]

I looked around at the soldiers by the water's edge and in the watch towers, and back again at the dogs. Best of luck, I thought, to anybody who tried to get in or out of here after dark.

As we walked along, loudspeakers blared at us from all directions. This has gone on all the time the ship has been in Klaipeda; it is not music, but talking. Talk, talk, talk, all day. I do not know if it is political indoctrination or news of Soviet achievements, but it goes on without stopping, and I am getting tired of it.

Once outside the harbour, we began to make our way through the streets. Klaipeda is a town of 100,000 inhabitants, and we headed for what we thought was the centre of the place.

The streets on the outskirts were simply packed-down earth, and this applied also to the footpaths. Great muddy puddles stood everywhere, and there were holes, sometimes three- or four-feet-deep, dug in the footpaths and apparently just left with the heap of soil beside them.

Apart from the tenements there were the old Lithuanian houses, and these were in a very poor state of repair, with the paint flaking and roof tiles loose or missing. Many of the houses had little balconies in front of the upper windows.

There were quite a few people about, picking their way over the reddish clay.

We walked until we reached the main street, Montes Street. This had a cobbled surface and proper pavements, and there were shops on either side.

The book shops seemed to sell only technical literature. There was a store full of bicycles, scooters and mopeds and a sports shop with roller skates — of a different type from ours—fencing foils and table-tennis sets in the window. One shop was apparently devoted entirely to chessmen and chessboards.

We saw what looked like one of our licenced grocers, with lots of tinned and bottled goods and bottles of wine on show, but the place that really intrigued me was the fish shop. Its window was filled with large imitation fish of all colours. These models were covered with dust and were enough to put one off fish for life.

Inside, I could see a high counter, with white enamel bowls filled with the real things.

A characteristic of all the shops was their general dinginess. The windows were all dirty and unwashed, and there was no attempt to display their wares attractively.

There was very little traffic—mainly commercial vehicles, with an occasional private car or taxi.

There were a lot of people in the town centre, most of the women in head scarves and undistinguished clothes. It occurred to me then that I had not seen a single smartly dressed woman since my arrival. In fact, women seemed to do a lot of the rough jobs. Back in the harbour, women, dressed in cloaks and hoods, operated some of the mighty cranes that served the ships. I noticed, too, on a building site a group of girls throwing bricks from one to another, as our bricklayers do. Their hands must have been hard and rough.

A column of youngsters marched by, led by a tall man, probably a teacher. They were laughing and singing and looked very like English children, except that many of the boys had peaked army-style caps and the little girls without exception wore long, brown woollen stockings of the sort girls used to wear in our country in my early schooldays. All the children looked healthy and happy.

I stopped a young man in the street and showed him the slip of paper with the name of the school written in Russian. Again there was the polite response. He went out of his way and led us to the door of the school.

It was a large, old-fashioned type of building set flush on the roadside, with no sign of a playground. It looked more like a big block of offices.

The man from Inflot had told me to ask permission, but there didn't seem to be anybody about, so I did my second daft thing of the trip: I just barged inside, followed dutifully by the captain.

Once through the door there was something I noticed immediately—the intense silence, unusual in a school. We were in a long passage, with walls hung with brightly coloured paintings of every conceivable sporting activity and of Russian feats of arms. These latter were done in a very romantic style: soldiers with bandaged foreheads, bayonets outstretched, handsome faces gazing fearlessly ahead. There was a glass case containing diplomas and certificates.

Many doors led off the passage, and I began to work my way along, knocking first, then trying the handle. They all seemed to be locked, and when I reached one near the end I had given up hope. I turned the handle without knocking, and it flew open.

I almost fell into a big room with a lot of startled women looking at me. They were all seated around a long table, and at the top was a big, impressive man with craggy features. He was staring at me harder than any of them.

I was obviously in the staff room, and I realised that I must have presented a strange sight. I had brought only my working clothes with me on the voyage and was clad in the black plastic macintosh I wore round the farms. This coat was frayed at cuffs and collar, and tattered by many horn thrusts. When horns tore off buttons and ripped pockets, I didn't like to pass it on to Helen to repair, because despite my efforts to keep it clean it carried the powerful odour of the farmyard deep in its seams. So I always did the sewing myself, using the thick, bright-blue nylon with which I stitched cows' wounds. This, with the ends of the coloured threads hanging loose, gave the garment an even more bizarre appearance.

They all continued to stare, but the man at the head of the table had clearly seen enough. He rose from his chair and hurried through a door at the far end. It didn't need a lot of intuition to know that he had gone to the telephone.

A realisation of my imprudence was dawning on me, but I swallowed a lump in my throat, gave what I hoped was a winning smile and said, "Madame Juowskaya?"

One of the women nodded; the others looked at her questioningly, and she turned deathly pale. She must have thought I was somebody sinister because she was undoubtedly frightened.

The captain could see it was time he took over. He stepped in front of me and addressed the company rapidly in German. He told them that I was chairman of the P.T.A. in Darrowby, but this information, not surprisingly, evoked no gasps of awe.

I stood there, the centre of all those female eyes. They were a very attractive lot of young women, for all the world like teachers in Britain except for one dark-skinned Mongolian miss, but it was easy to see that they were not similarly impressed with me.

The captain, a man of infinite resource, came to the rescue again and asked which one was the English teacher. The prettiest of them all came forward, and I was just about to speak to her when the door behind me burst open and two Russian army officers marched in.

They were massive men, very smart in their high-shouldered uniforms, epaulettes with stars, breeches and shiny high boots. They began to speak rapidly with the man who had returned to the top of the table, glaring over at me every few seconds. The man was wide-eyed, throwing his arms around, shaking his head, and I required no knowledge of Russian to divine that he was telling them that I had rushed in here from nowhere, he had no idea who the devil I was and he didn't like the look of me one little bit.

I do not wish to be over-dramatic, but I am convinced that if Captain Rasmussen had not been with me, I would have been hustled off to the local jail, but he stepped in once more with a flurry of explanations in German.

Another thing that saved me was that the little English teacher began to talk to me about the school. I sat down by her side at the table, and the officers moved close to me as we spoke together. All the time I was very conscious of their towering presence; they hung over me, looking me up and down, no doubt mystified at my eccentric apparel.

On an inspiration, I asked the English teacher her name. It was a real jawbreaker and I couldn't make much of it, but she said she was known as what sounded like "Kitty." She told me she was married, with a child of six.

She clapped her hands together. "Oh, I am so excited," she said. "I have taught English for so long, but I have never spoken to a real Englishman before. You must tell me if my pronunciation is very bad."

"I give you my word, you speak better English than I do," I replied. And with my thick Glaswegian, it was the literal truth. Kitty was delighted.

She told me that the director of the school had taken all the 1200 children away for the day on what was a regular visit to some local institution, where they saw a film show and listened to talks. This accounted for the silence. The big man at the head of the table was the deputy director.

As we swapped information, the other teachers pulled their chairs closer to us and listened with the greatest interest as Kitty passed everything on to them. Even the forbidding deputy director could not contain his curiosity and leaned across the table, elbows on the wood, watching me intently.

As the atmosphere grew more cordial, I was relieved to see the two officers move away and lean against the wall. Their previous hostile expressions were now merely impassive.

A hectic question-and-answer ensued, with Kitty relaying my words round the table.

"At what age do your children start school?" she asked.

When I replied, "At four or five years old," it caused general amazement.

"Ours do not start till seven or eight years old," she said, and I was similarly surprised.

The deputy director got quite heated on this point. He banged his hand on the table and declared that, according to the principles of education, it was impossible to teach children of five. What could they possibly learn? he wanted to know.

When I told him they learned simple sums and words to start with, he shook his head vigorously in disbelief.

All the teachers were astonished, too, to hear about the normal school hours in Britain. Kitty told me that younger Russian children go from 8:30 A.M. till 2:30 P.M., and the fifth and sixth formers go from 2:30 P.M. till 7 P.M. or 8 P.M. at night.

Their classes average about thirty in number, and they teach all the mathematical subjects, physics, chemistry, biology, geography and Russian history. The principal foreign language at that school is English, then German and Lithuanian. French or Latin is not taught.

I had to get in a question about sport. "Do you have games in your curriculum?"

Kitty raised her hands and laughed. "Many, many games. Volley ball is the most popular, but there is also swimming, hockey, skating, football, P.E. and gymnastics.

"Also," she went on, "we have many school clubs and outside activities. Do you have pioneers in your country?"

I presumed that this meant camping and hiking. I said yes, we did this, too, in our schools, and I launched into an explanation of the Duke of Edinburgh's Award Scheme. I struck an unexpected snag here because none of them had even heard of the Duke of Edinburgh.

I laughed. "Oh, surely you must know him. Our Queen's husband?"

Blank faces and shrugs all round.

"Edinbor? Edinbor?" Kitty queried.

"Yes, of course," I replied. "The capital of Scotland."

"But Dublin is the capital of Scotland," she said, so I decided to drop that topic.

Just about then, the army officers, seeing the teachers grouped around me, laughing and talking animatedly, apparently decided I was harmless and left the room. The atmosphere, which had thawed remarkably, became still more cordial, and the questioning went on at top speed.

"Do you teach religion?" I asked. Of course, I knew very well that they didn't, but I was interested to see what they would say.

Their reaction was pretty uniform—a kind of pitying amusement. One big dark girl, smiling sarcastically, put a question through Kitty.

"Do you teach about Darwin, too?"

I nodded. "Yes, we teach religion, and also about evolution and the scientific explanations of the beginnings of the world and of man."

This caused general puzzlement.

We discussed their attitude to religion, and I gathered that it is regarded as a private thing and people can go to church if they wish. It is not banned, nor is there any propaganda against it in the schools. The teachers seemed to be of the opinion that it would just quietly die out. There are three churches in Klaipeda, but in some towns of a similar size there are many more.

The teachers commiserated with me on the tremendous unemployment and poverty in Britain, and I got the impression that they thought I came from a land of starvation and soup kitchens. When I told them that British workers enjoyed a steady improvement in their living standards and that many of them owned cars, they looked at me with frank incredulity. Obviously they thought I was purveying capitalist propaganda.

And in one way, I couldn't blame them. I could see their eyes flickering over my ragged coat with the torn-down pockets and the buttons with their blue garlands. If this was a British professional man, what were the ordinary workers like?

"But your teachers do not have our standard of living," one of them declared.

I wondered if she had a point. These women were all beautifully dressed and clearly prosperous. I had the feeling that the teacher is a very prestigious person in Russia.

"What is the eleven-plus examination?" was the next question.

I tried to explain it as well as I could, but they really grilled me on this. The deputy director burst in, his deep-chested voice booming like an organ note amid the female chatter.

"There is absolutely no point in classing children according to ability as you describe!" He was clearly a man of immovable opinions.

I looked across at him. "Well, do you have all levels in one class?"

The answer came back through Kitty. "All Russian children are clever." This was said with complete conviction and quite seriously.

In the ensuing discussion, I gathered that a very high proportion of the pupils go on to universities and that further education in the form of night schools is very popular. In fact, many Russians obtain a complete education up to university standard by working in these night schools.

"How about school meals?" I asked.

"Oh, yes," Kitty replied. "All the children stay for meals." She mentioned the number of kopeks they paid each day, and it worked out to about one shilling per meal.

"For this," Kitty went on, "they get a glass of tea, bread and sausage."

This did not sound as substantial as the food in English schools.

A volley of Russian from the deputy director was translated as an attack on the private school system in Britain. In the course of my reply I mentioned that the private schools were called public schools, which made them all look blank. The big man kept hammering home his point that only the children of the rich got a proper education in Britain, but when I pointed out that through university grants everybody in our country could receive a full education no matter what their financial position, he narrowed his eyes suspiciously. I don't think he believed me.

However, the party was really going with a bang, with lots of laughter, banter and give-and-take. It was a pity in one way that the children were away, but on the other hand I should never have had this priceless opportunity of a long discussion with all the teachers.

I was enjoying it so much that I could have stayed all day, but I saw the captain glancing anxiously at his watch and knew he was worried about getting back to the ship. Poor chap, he must be praying that he never has to sail with another veterinary attendant like me.

We took our leave in the friendliest spirit, with laughter and handshakes all round. Little Kitty was particularly nice.

"Oh, I am so thrilled. I will always remember meeting a real live Englishman," she said as we parted.

The deputy director also revealed an unexpected vein of massive charm as he led us out formally to the main door. His powerful features relaxed into a pleasant smile as he shook hands, bowed and waved us off down the street.

As we left the school, I saw some of the children coming back. They were all boys about twelve years old, and many had a greenish, military-style uniform and peaked cap. I saw one with a stripe on his arm. Whether this was a school uniform or whether they were members of a cadet corps, I do not know.

Back at the ship, trouble awaited me. A woman—who, I was told, was a farm commissar—had been asking to see me.

She was huge, well over six feet and broad in proportion, and as she towered over me, two hard eyes in a rough-hewn countenance regarded me coldly from under a black beret. She obviously meant business.

She spoke no English but came to the point straightaway.

"Ah-ha, ah-ha, ah-ha!" The other Russians had simulated the sheep's cough very closely, but this, rumbling from deep in her mighty rib-cage, was the best effort yet.

I tried my shrug and vacant smile, but they didn't work with this one. She seized my arm in steel claws and propelled me effortlessly towards the hold.

Down there among the sheep, she pointed an accusing finger at the Lincolns and went through the coughing routine again and again, while I replied with a series of reassuring grins that became more and more exhausting.

She produced a thermometer, and I wondered if she were a vet. If so, I greatly preferred her chubby little colleague of the morning. She needed no assistance to hold the sheep but jammed a great knee against each animal, trapping them against the wall as though they were puppy dogs. All the readings were normal, and she grew more and more impatient.

As she charged around the pens, she made frequent contact with me. I am a fairly solidly built man of around five feet ten, but she never even noticed as I bounced off her, and the thought occurred to me that if we both donned boxing gloves and got into a ring together, I would be lucky to last a three-minute round.

Finally she produced a tiny Russian-English dictionary and tried me out with various incomprehensible words. The nearest she came to the root of the matter was "broncheetees," but by then she had lapsed into a discontented muttering. I had the feeling that she was no longer aware of my presence, so I took my opportunity and made a bolt for my cabin.

I was almost there when Nielsen's head poked out from his cooking cell.

"You miss your lunch, Mr. Herriot. You have tough time, you look tired. Wait there." He held up a hand. "I make you something."

I stood in the doorway as he laid out a slice of rye bread and began to chop onto it tiny pieces of raw steak. He slashed away like lightning, his huge knife glinting with expert movements. Then he began to whittle away at a raw onion till the meat was covered with the fragments, then followed this by cracking an egg onto the top of the pile. He finished by dusting the whole mound with salt and black pepper before holding the final result proudly in my direction.

"Beef tartare!" His voice had a triumphant ring. "You eat, Mr. Herriot. You feel better!"

I shrank back a pace. How could I possibly eat this concoction? Raw meat, uncooked egg—it was unthinkable. I was desperately scouring my mind for some excuse to decline when I looked up again at Nielsen's beaming face. He was my friend, this unsung genius of the galley, and he was trying to succour me in my time of need. I would undoubtedly be ill later, but I couldn't say no.

It took courage, but I thanked him, seized the heaped slice of bread and bit resolutely into it. I thought if I held my breath throughout I wouldn't taste anything, but there was too much of it, and as I exhaled I got the full flavour. It was delicious.

The cook's expression became more and more ecstatic as he saw the growing wonder in my face. Then, as I chewed steadily, he must have noticed a fleeting doubt, a moment of disbelief in my eyes because he rested a hand anxiously on my shoulder.

"A leetle more pepper, maybe?"

I swallowed and regarded him for a moment. "Well . . . yes, possibly . . . just a touch."

He plied the grater, and as I started again on the delicacy, he began to pour me a glass of lager, his face a picture of delight.

I was sorry when I came to the end of the beef tartare, but the strong Carlsberg was just right to wash it down. Nielsen's taste was impeccable, as always.

It was dark—about 8 P.M.—when the *Ubbergen* moved out. Our ship took its place, and the discharging of the cargo commenced. Wagons drew up on the railway lines alongside the ship, a great crane lowered a gangway and my poor little sheep were driven up the ramps.

I had literally lived with them for six days, and even though I knew that as pedigree breeding animals they would get the best of treatment, it tugged at my heart to see them go. Those beautiful Romney Marsh with their teddy bear heads trotting under the glaring lights and disappearing into the black interiors of the wagons—I didn't like it at all. They had come from the green fields of Kent, and as the doors closed behind them, I wondered where they were going.

A throng of black-capped Russian workers swarmed on the quayside, wheeling the wagons from the darkness into the light thrown by the cranes. They all looked frail, dark and washed-out in contrast with the strapping Danes on the ship. My faithful helper, Raun, was in the thick of the action, all six feet four of him, his mop of golden hair flapping as he ushered the animals along the ramp.

Another striking figure was Jumbo, the youngest seaman on the ship. Apparently the youngest member of the crew is always called Jumbo, pronounced "Yoombo," and this chap is just about the bonniest lad I have ever seen. Seventeen years old, immensely tall and with massive shoulders, yet he has an angelic face, with large blue eyes and thick yellow hair growing down over his ears.

His job was the unloading of the surplus fodder, and I marvelled at the effortless way he roped and hoisted the heavy bags and bales onto the hook which swung down again and again from the crane on the quay. I cannot help thinking of the Vikings when I see these men. If they are typical, the Danes are a wonderful people.

Finally, at about midnight, the last sheep had trotted from sight and the last bale of hay and bag of nuts had been lifted out. The man in charge of the Russian workers waved up at me as I looked down from the rail of the ship.

"Doktor, goodbye," he cried and went off into the night.

I walked around the empty holds, feeling a sense of loss; then I went up to the captain's cabin to await a representative from Saufratt to sign my acceptance forms.

He came at about 2 A.M., and that is 4 A.M. Russian time. He was a young chap of about twenty-five and had been hard at it all day, checking the sheep and supervising the unloading. He was exhausted, white-faced and grimy, and I noticed that his nails were bitten right back. But he was no fool. He could speak and write English very well, and he had the authority to sign for £20,000 worth of sheep.

On the first form he wrote, "About twenty percent of Lincoln sheeps have cough." Gently I pointed out that it should be "sheep," and though he was so tired that he could hardly keep his eyes open, he launched into an interrogation as to why the singular should be the same as the plural and wanted to know all the other English words which had this peculiarity. It was another symptom of the passion for learning that I had found repeatedly in Klaipeda.

He was followed by the customs and immigration people who cleared our passports; then the Inflot representatives came aboard and presented their bills to the captain—so many rubles for pilot, berthing and so forth.

The captain gave them hell in his gentlemanly way and said they charged far too much, but they only shrugged their shoulders and laughed heartily.

The very last Russian to come aboard was the pilot, a different one this time.

His face was grave as he spoke to the captain. "There is big storm blowing out beyond the estuary—force six–eight and getting worse. I advise you to pull away from the berth and anchor in the harbour till morning." He wagged a finger as he made his final admonition. "It will not be so good out there for you to-night."

The captain paced up and down the cabin, trying to make up his mind. He badly wanted to be off, but dare he risk the storm?

At last he said, "I think you are right, Mr. Pilot. We had better stay here tonight."

Leaving the cabin, I bumped into the mate. He had overheard the conversation, and he looked at me ruefully.

"I tell you this, Mr. Herriot, I have heard this before. We will leave tonight. Captain Rasmussen, he is not afraid of storms. Prepare yourself."

Sitting here over my log, I am very sleepy and my bunk looks very inviting. Still and peaceful, it beckons to me. It has been a long, long day.

Chapter
19

"This is Biggins 'ere."

I gripped the telephone tightly and dug the nails of my other hand into my palm. Mr. Biggins's vacillations always tried me sorely. He regarded calling out the vet as a final desperate measure, and it was always sheer torture for him to make up his mind to take it. On top of that he was extremely pig-headed about taking my advice if I did manage to fight my way onto his farm, and I knew beyond doubt that I had never ever managed to please him.

He had made me suffer during my pre-R.A.F. days, and now, with the war well over, he was still there, a bit older and a bit more pig-headed.

"What's the trouble, Mr. Biggins?"

"Well . . . I 'ave a heifer badly."

"Right, I'll have a look at her this morning."

"Haud on, just a minute." Mr. Biggins was still not sure if he wanted me out there, even though he had got as far as lifting the phone. "Are you sure she needs seein'?"

"Well, I don't know. What is she doing?"

There was a long pause. "Just laid out, like."

"Laid out?" I said. "That sounds rather serious to me. I'll be along as soon as possible."

"Now then, now then, she 'asn't allus been laid out."

"Well, how long, then?"

"Just this last couple o' days."

"You mean she just dropped down?"

"Nay, nay, nay." His voice took on an edge of exasperation at my thick-headedness. "She's been off her grub for a week, and now she's gone down."

I took a long breath. "So she's been ill for a week, and now she's collapsed and you've decided to call me?"

"Aye, that's right. She were pretty bright about t'head till she went off 'er legs."

"Right, Mr. Biggins, I'll be with you very soon."

"Ah, but . . . but . . . are ye sure there's any need . . . ?"

I put down the receiver. I knew from hard experience that this conversation could go on for a long time. I also knew that I was probably visiting a hopeless case, but if I got there immediately I might be able to do something.

I was on the farm within ten minutes, and Mr. Biggins met me with his typical attitude—hands in pockets, shoulders hunched, eyes regarding me suspiciously from under a thick fringe of greying eyebrows.

"Ye're ower late," he grunted.

I stopped with one foot out of the car. "You mean she's dead?"

"Nay, but just about. Ye're too late to do owt about it now."

I gritted my teeth. This animal had been ill for a week, I had arrived ten minutes after being summoned, but the farmer's tone was unequivocal; if it died it would be my fault. I had come ower late.

"Ah, well," I said, trying to relax. "If she's dying there's nothing I can do." I began to get back into the car.

Mr. Biggins lowered his head and kicked at a cobblestone with a massive boot. "Are ye not going to look at 'er while you're 'ere?"

"I thought you said it was too late."

"Aye . . . aye . . . but you're the vitnery."

"Right, if that's what you want." I climbed out again. "Where is she?"

He hesitated. "Will ye charge me extra?"

"No, I won't. I've made the journey to your farm, and if I can't do anything more, that's all you'll pay for."

It was a sadly familiar sight. The skinny young beast lying in a dark corner of the fold yard. Eyes sunken and glazed and moving every few seconds with the slow nystagmus of approaching death. Temperature was 99°F.

"Yes, you're right, Mr. Biggins," I said. "She's dying." I put my thermometer away and began to leave.

The farmer was a picture of gloom, with his head sunk deep in his shoulders as he looked down at the beast. Then he glanced at me quickly. "Where are ye goin'?"

I looked back in surprise. "I'm going on my round. I'm truly sorry about your heifer, Mr. Biggins, but she's beyond human aid."

"So you're just goin' to walk away without doin' owt?" He gave me a truculent stare.

"But she's dying. You said so yourself."

"Aye, but you're t'vet, not me. And I've allus heard that where there's life there's hope."

"Not in this case, I assure you. She could go any minute."

He continued to stare down at the animal. "Look, she's breathin', isn't she? Aren't you goin' to give her a chance?"

"Well . . . if you like, I can try giving her a stimulant injection into her vein."

"It's not what ah like. You're t'one that's supposed to know."

"Very well, I'll have a go." I trailed out to the car for the injection.

The heifer, in a deep coma, knew nothing as I slipped the needle into the jugular vein. As I depressed the plunger, Mr. Biggins gave tongue again.

"Expensive things, them injections. How much is this goin' to cost me, then?"

"I honestly don't know." My brain was beginning to reel.

[183]

"You'll know awright when you get t'pen in your 'and to send me that big bill, won't ye?"

I didn't answer. As the last drop of fluid trickled into the vein the heifer extended her fore limbs, stared sightlessly ahead for a second, then stopped breathing. I watched her for a few moments and put my hand over her heart. "I'm afraid she's dead, Mr. Biggins."

He bent quickly. "Have ye killed 'er?"

"No, no, of course not. She was just ready to go."

The farmer rubbed his chin. "It wasn't much of a bloody stimulant, was it?"

I had no answer to that one and began to put my syringe away. I was conscious of an increasing desire to get off this farm as quickly as possible.

I was on the way to the car when Mr. Biggins caught at my arm.

"Well, what was t'matter with 'er?"

"I don't know."

"You don't know? Well, you've wasted ma money with that injection. Vets are supposed to know, aren't they?"

"Yes, Mr. Biggins, they are. But in this case I could only say that the animal was dying. You would need a postmortem examination to find out the cause of death."

The farmer began to pluck excitedly at his coat. "Well, this is a funny carry-on. I 'ave a dead beast here, and nobody knows what killed her. Could be anything, couldn't it?"

"Well . . . I suppose so."

"Could be anthrax!"

"Oh no, Mr. Biggins. Anthrax is very sudden, and you say this heifer was ill for over a week."

"Nay, nay, not right ill. Just a bit off it, then she went down like a shot at t'end. That was sudden enough!"

"Oh, but . . ."

"And Fred Bramley along t'road had a beast wi' anthrax last month, didn't he?"

[184]

"Yes, that's right. There was a positive case there—first around here for several years. But that was in a cow he found dead."

"Ah don't care!" Mr. Biggins stuck his jaw out. "The *Darrowby and Houlton Times* was on about it, and they said that all sudden deaths should be examined for anthrax because it was right dangerous and fatal to people. I want ma heifer examined!"

"Okay," I replied wearily. "If you say so. As it happens, I have my microscope with me."

"Microscope? That sounds a costly job. How much will that be?"

"That's all right, the Ministry pays me," I said and began to walk towards the house.

Mr. Biggins nodded with glum satisfaction, then raised his eyebrows. "Where you goin' now?"

"Into the house. I've got to use your phone to report to the Ministry. I can't do anything till I get permission. I'll pay for the call." I added the last few words because he was beginning to look worried.

He stood by me as I spoke to the Ministry clerk. He fidgeted impatiently when I asked him for his full name, the proper name of the farm, the breed of the heifer.

"Didn't know ah'd have to go through all this," he mumbled.

I went out and produced my postmortem knife from the car boot. It was a large and dangerous carving knife that I used only on dead animals.

Mr. Biggins's eyes widened at the sight of it. "By gaw, I don't like the look of that bloody great knife. What are you goin' to do with that?"

"Just take a bit of blood." I bent and made a nick at the root of the heifer's tail and smeared a film of blood onto a glass slide. I took this, along with the microscope, into the farmhouse kitchen.

"Now what do you want?" Mr. Biggins asked sourly.

I looked around. "I want the use of the sink, the fire and that table by the window."

The sink was full of dirty dishes which the farmer removed with groans of protest, while I fixed the blood film by drawing it through the flames in the hearth. Then I moved to the sink and poured methylene blue over the slide. In the process, a small blue pool formed in the white sink bottom, and the colouration stayed there after I had swilled the slide with cold water from the tap.

"Look at the bloody mess you've made!" Mr. Biggins exclaimed. "You've stained t'sink. The missus'll play 'ell when she gets home this afternoon."

I forced a smile. "Don't worry, that isn't a stain. It will come off quite easily." But I could see he didn't believe me.

I dried the slide off at the fire, rigged up the microscope on the table and peered through the eyepiece. As I expected, I found only the usual pattern of red and white corpuscles. Not an anthrax bacillus in sight.

"Well, there's nothing there," I said. "You can call the knacker man quite safely."

Mr. Biggins blew out his cheeks and made a long-suffering gesture with one hand. "All that bloody fuss for nothin'," he sighed.

As I drove away I felt, not for the first time, that you just couldn't win with Mr. Biggins, and a month later the conviction was strengthened when he came into the surgery one market day.

"One of me cows has wooden tongue," he announced. "I want some iodine to paint on."

Siegfried looked up from the day book where he was checking the visits. "Oh, you're a bit out of date, Mr. Biggins," he said, smiling. "We've got far better medicine than that now."

The farmer took up his usual stance, head down, glowering under his eyebrows. "I don't care about your new medicine. Ah want the stuff I've allus used."

"But Mr. Biggins." Siegfried was at his most reasonable. "Painting the tongue with iodine went out years ago. Since then we've used intravenous injections of sodium iodide, which was much better, but now even that has been replaced by sulphanila-mide."

"Big words, Mr. Farnon, big fancy words," grunted the farmer. "But ah know what's best for me cow, so are you goin' to give me the iodine or not?"

"No, I am not," Siegfried replied, the smile fading from his face. "I wouldn't be a competent veterinary surgeon if I prescribed something as totally outdated as that." He turned to me. "James, would you slip through to the stockroom and bring a pound packet of the sulphanilamide?"

Mr. Biggins was protesting as I hurried from the office. In the stockroom the sulphanilamide packets stood in rows, some pounds, others half-pounds, but there were plenty of them because at that time this drug bulked very large in our veterinary life. It was such a striking improvement on our old remedies. It was useful in many kinds of bacterial diseases, it was an excellent dusting powder for wounds and, of course, as Siegfried had said, it cleared up actinobacillosis, or wooden tongue, quite rapidly.

The packets were square and wrapped in white paper tied down with string. I grabbed one from the shelf and returned at a trot, listening to the two voices echoing along the passage.

The argument was still raging when I came back to the office, and I could see that Siegfried's patience was running out. He seized the packet from me and began to write the instructions on the label.

"You give three tablespoonsful in a pint of water to start with, then . . ."

"But ah tell you ah don't want . . ."

". . . you follow with one tablespoonful three times daily . . ."

". . . got no faith in them new things . . ."

". . . and after you've used the packet, let us know, and we'll give you another supply if necessary."

The farmer glared at my partner. "That stuff'll do no good."

"Mr. Biggins," Siegfried said with ominous calm. "It will cure your cow."

"It won't!"

"It will!"

"It won't!"

Siegfried brought his hand down on the desk with a thud. Clearly he had had enough. "Take this, and if it doesn't do the trick I won't charge you, all right?"

Mr. Biggins narrowed his eyes, but I could see that the idea of something for nothing had an irresistible appeal. Slowly he stretched out his hand and took the sulphanilamide.

"Splendid!" Siegfried jumped up and patted the farmer's shoulder. "Now, you get in touch with us when you've used it. I bet you anything your cow will soon be much better."

It would be about ten days after this interview that Siegfried and I were out together castrating colts, and on the way back to the surgery we had to pass through Mr. Biggins's village.

Siegfried slowed down when he saw the farmhouse. It was square-faced and massive, and the front garden showed only the sprouting heads of potato plants. Mr. Biggins did not believe in wasting money on ornamentation.

"Tell you what, James," my partner murmured. "We'll just drop in there. We haven't heard from our old friend about the sulphanilamide. Doesn't want to lose face, I suspect." He laughed softly. "We'll be able to rub it in a bit."

He turned the wheel and drove round to the yard at the back of the house. Outside the kitchen door Siegfried raised his hand to knock, then he gripped my arm. "Look at that, James!" he said in an urgent whisper.

He pointed to the kitchen window, and there on the sill was our square white packet, virgin and unopened, the string binding undisturbed.

My partner clenched his fist. "The cussed old blighter! He won't try it — out of sheer spite."

At that moment the farmer opened the door and Siegfried

greeted him cheerfully. "Ah, good morning to you, Mr. Biggins. We were just passing and thought we'd check on how your cow was progressing."

The eyes under the shaggy brows registered sudden alarm, but my partner held up a reassuring hand. "No charge, I give you my word. This is just for our own interest."

"But . . . but . . . I've got me slippers on. Was just havin' a cup o' tea. There's no need for ye to . . . "

But Siegfried was already striding towards the cow byre. The patient was easy to pick out. Her skin was stretched tightly over the jutting ribs and pelvic bones, saliva drooled from her lips and a long swelling bulged from under her jaw. She was a scarecrow among her sleek neighbours.

Siegfried moved quickly to her head, seized the nose and pulled it towards him. With his other hand he prised open the mouth and fingered the tongue.

"Feel that, James," he said softly.

I ran my hand over the knobbly hard surface which for centuries has given actinobacillosis its evocative name. "This is awful. It's a wonder she can eat at all." I sniffed at my fingers. "And there's iodine here."

Siegfried nodded. "Yes, he's been to the chemist despite what I said."

At that moment the byre door burst open and Mr. Biggins hurried in, panting slightly.

My partner looked at him sadly along the cow's back. "Well, it seems you were right. Our medicine hasn't done a bit of good. I can't understand it." He rubbed his chin. "And your poor cow is a mess, I'm afraid. Almost starving to death. I do apologise."

The farmer's face was a study. "Aye, well . . . that's right . . . she's done no good . . . I reckon she'll . . ."

Siegfried broke in. "Look here," he said. "I feel responsible for this. My medicine has failed, so it's up to me to get her right." He strode from between the cows. "I have an injection in the car which I think will do the trick. Excuse me for a moment."

"Now, then, wait a minute . . . I don't know . . ." But the farmer's words went unheeded as my colleague hurried out to the yard.

He was back very quickly, holding a bottle that I couldn't recognise. He held it up and began to fill a 20 c.c. syringe, watching the rising level intently and whistling tunelessly under his breath.

"Hold the tail, will you, James?" he said and poised the needle over the cow's rump. With his hand still held high, he looked across at Mr. Biggins. "This is an excellent injection, but it's a good job you've been using our medicine."

"Why's that?"

"Well, on its own it could have serious effects on the animal."

"You mean . . . could kill 'er?"

"Just possible," Siegfried murmured. "But you've nothing to worry about. She's had the sulphanilamide." He was about to plunge the needle in when the farmer gave tongue.

"Hey, hey, haud on. Don't do that!"

"What is it, Mr. Biggins? Something wrong?"

"Nay, nay, but there's maybe been a bit of a misunderstandin'." Conflicting emotions chased across the farmer's face. "Ye see, it's like this—ah don't think she's been gettin' enough of your stuff."

Siegfried lowered his arm. "You mean you've been underdosing? I wrote the instructions on the packet if you remember."

"That's right. But ah must have got a bit mixed up."

"Oh, that doesn't matter. As long as you put her back to full dosage, all will be well." Siegfried inserted the needle and, ignoring Mr. Biggins's yelp of alarm, he injected the full contents.

As he put the syringe back in its case, he sighed with satisfaction. "Well, I'm sure that will put everything right. But remember, you must start again with the full three tablespoonsful and continue till you've finished the packet. The cow is in such a state that I'm pretty sure you'll need a further supply, but you'll let us know about that, eh?"

[190]

As we drove away I stared at my colleague. "What the devil was that injection?"

"Oh, mixed vitamins. It'll help the poor thing's condition, but it had nothing to do with the wooden tongue. Just part of my plan." He smiled gleefully. "Now he's *got* to use the sulphanilamide. It will be interesting to see what happens."

It was indeed interesting. Within a week Mr. Biggins was back in the surgery, looking sheepish.

"Can I have some more o' that stuff?" he muttered.

"By all means." Siegfried extended his arm in an expansive gesture. "As much as you like." He leaned on the desk. "I suppose the cow is looking better?"

"Aye."

"Stopped slavering?"

"Aye."

"Putting on flesh, is she?"

"Aye, aye, she is." Mr. Biggins lowered his head as though he didn't want to answer any more questions. Siegfried gave him another packet.

Through the surgery window we watched him cross the street, and my partner thumped me on the shoulder. "Well, James. That was a little victory. At last we've managed to beat Mr. Biggins."

I laughed, too, because it was very sweet, but when I look back over the years, I realise it was the only time we did beat him.

Chapter
20

There is nothing very exciting about tuberculin testing, and I was quite pleased when George Forsyth, the insurance agent, came into the byre and started to make conversation.

I was doing the annual test on the little farm of the Hudson brothers. Clem, the elder, about forty years old, was painstakingly writing the numbers in the book, while Dick, a few years younger, was rubbing the inner surfaces of the ears to find the tattoo marks.

As I clipped, measured and injected, I listened to George's observations on the weather, the latest cricket scores and the price of pigs. He was leaning against a wall, taking leisurely pulls at a cigarette as though he had all the time in the world, but I had a fair idea he had come along for something more than idle talk.

After a few minutes he got round to the point.

"You know, Clem," he said, "you fellows should be properly insured."

Clem carefully rounded off a figure in the book. "What are ye talkin' about? We've got the car insured and we're covered for fire and lightnin'. That's enough, isn't it?"

"Enough!" George was shocked. "That's nothing. You should both have life policies, for a start."

"Nay, nay." Clem shook his head. "Don't believe in all that. In fact, I don't believe in insurance at all except what we've got to have."

Dick raised his head from the front of the cow. "And ah don't believe in it either. You're wastin' your time, George."

"Honestly," the agent said, "you two are living in the past. Don't you think it would be a good thing for your dependants to have a nice sum of money in the event of your deaths?"

"Not goin' to die for a long time yet," Clem grunted, moving along to the next cow.

"How the heck do you know that?"

"All the Hudsons is long-lived," Dick said. "They nearly have to shoot some of 'em. Our old dad's over eighty, and he's fightin' fit. He passed the farm over to us, but 'e could be workin' now if he wanted."

George tiptoed daintily to one side in his patent leather shoes as a cow raised her tail dangerously in his direction. "You don't seem to get the point, but I won't press the matter. However," he raised a finger, "you should certainly have sickness policies."

Both the brothers had a good laugh at this.

"Sickness?" Clem said, a pitying smile creasing his craggy features. "Neither of us 'ave ever ailed a thing in our lives. Never even had a cold. We 'aven't missed a day's work since we started on this place."

"But how do you know that's going to continue?" the agent replied weakly. "As you get older, you'll be more liable to illness."

"Oh, leave off, George." Dick pushed his way out from between two cows. "We've told you—we don't believe in insurance, and that's all about it. And we're not goin' to chuck our money away on any of your fancy policies."

George narrowed his eyes. This was a challenge, and I could see he was going to rise to it.

"I tell you what . . ." he began, but I had got to the end of the byre.

"Where do we go now?" I asked.

Clem pointed across the yard. "Few heifers in a box over there."

These were big, rough beasts, and I pressed back against the wall as they careered around in the straw. The brothers had made a few ineffectual throws with a rope halter when I noticed George's head appearing over the box door.

"I tell you what," he repeated, and I was reminded of the old couplet, "There's no guy got endurance/like the guy who sells insurance." "How about an accident policy? Both of you ought to have one."

Clem managed to snare one of the galloping animals and leaned back on the rope. "Accident? Fiddlesticks! We've never 'ad a accident."

"Aha! That's the very reason why you should start protecting yourselves. The fact that nothing has happened to you makes it more probable that something is waiting round the corner. It's simple mathematics."

"There's nowt simple about it," Dick said. "Just because we've never had a accident doesn't mean that . . ." His words were cut off as the haltered beast went violently into reverse and its bony rump thudded into his midriff, crushing him with brutal force against the rough stones of the wall.

He sank down in the straw, completely winded, and sat motionless, holding his middle.

"Look at that!" George cried. "Just what I've been talking about! Yours is a dangerous trade. Anything could happen."

"Aye, well, 'e's all right," Clem said doubtfully as his brother eased himself to his feet.

George's eyes had the fanatical gleam of an insurance man who suddenly finds fate on his side. "Yes, yes, maybe he is all right this time, but he might have had an internal injury, mightn't he? Could have been off work for ages, and then where would you be? You'd have to pay for extra labour, wouldn't you? And with a nice little policy from me, you'd have the money to do it."

The musical sound of the word "money" appeared to stir something in Clem. He gave the agent a sidelong glance. "How much?"

George became brisk and businesslike. "Now, then, I have just the thing for you here." He pulled a sheaf of policies from his inside pocket. "For a premium of ten pounds per annum, you would receive twenty pounds a week in the case of incapacitating injuries. There are other benefits, of course; look here."

Clem put on a pair of steel-rimmed spectacles and perused the document while Dick looked over his shoulder. I could hear mutterings.

"Twenty pun a week . . . lot o' money . . . not bad."

Twenty pounds was indeed a tidy sum in 1948 when the average weekly wage for a qualified veterinary assistant was around ten pounds.

Finally Clem looked up. "Reckon we might 'ave a go at that. Twenty pun a week would come in right handy."

"Splendid, splendid." George produced a silver pencil. "Just sign here, both of you. Thank you very much."

He paused for a moment. "And of course there's young Herbert who works for you."

"Aye, he's down t'fields," Dick said. "What about 'im?"

"Well, you ought to have him covered, too."

"But he's nobbut a lad."

"Okay." George spread his hands. "He goes in cheaper. Five pounds a year. Same benefits."

The brothers' resistance seemed to have crumbled. "Awright, s'pose we might as well. We'll do 'im, too."

George tripped off to his car, whistling merrily, and we got on with the test.

It was about three weeks later that I met Clem in Darrowby market place. He was sauntering along, looking in the shop windows, and he was wearing a smart dark suit, obviously not his working clothes. It was late afternoon when he would normally have been bringing in his cows for milking, and I wondered at his presence in the town until he turned round and I saw that his arm was in a sling.

"What on earth have you been doing, Clem?" I asked.

He looked down at the bulky white cast. "Broke me arm.

Slipped up on the cow-house floor. And would you believe it?" His eyes widened. "It was nubbut three days after I'd signed that insurance form. Ah'm gettin' twenty pun a week, and the doctor reckons it'll be another nine weeks afore I can start work. That'll be more than two hundred quid I'll have collected. All right, eh?"

"It certainly is. What a blessing you took George Forsyth's advice. But you'll be paying for somebody to help you?"

"Nay, nay, we're managin' grand as it is." He walked away, chuckling.

Clem's injury had healed by the time I had to visit the Hudson farm again to "cleanse" a cow. Clem brought me a bucket of hot water, and I was soaping my arms when Dick came in. I should say he hobbled in, because he was on crutches.

I stared at him, and an eerie sense of the workings of fate stirred in my mind. "Broken leg?"

"Aye," Dick replied laconically. "Did it as easy as owt. Tryin' to catch an awd ewe on top pasture and upskittled meself in a rabbit hole."

"You'll be out of action for a while, then?"

"Aye, plaster's got to stay on for fourteen weeks. It's a bloody nuisance, but all them twenty quids is very nice. Good job we signed that paper."

I didn't see him until he came into the surgery one market day to pay his veterinary bill. He had shed his cast but was still limping slightly.

"How is the leg, Dick?" I asked as I wrote in the receipt book.

He grimaced. "Nobbut middlin'. Aches like 'ell sometimes, but I think it's gettin' stronger."

"Ah, well." I handed him the receipted account. "You'll just have to take things a bit easier till you're back to normal."

"Can't do that," he said, shaking his head. "We're short-handed as it is. Young Herbert's had a accident."

"What!"

"Aye, stuck a hay fork into 'is foot and got blood poisonin'. He's well enough in 'imself, but Doctor says it'll be a long time afore he can walk about."

In fact, it was ten weeks before Herbert returned to work, but as Clem confided to me over a beer when I encountered him one night in the Drovers' Arms, the two hundred pounds they collected from the insurance company had been something of a consolation.

"Remarkable thing," I said. "George Forsyth must have been sent from heaven that morning. His company has been a tremendous help to you."

Clem showed no enthusiasm but stared gloomily into his glass. "But ah'll tell tha summat. They're funny fellers, them insurance men. Would ye believe it, after all that talkin' they don't want us any more."

"Really? How's that?"

"Well, we got a letter from them sayin', 'We do not wish to renew your insurance.' What d'you make of that?"

"That sometimes happens, Clem," I said. Privately, I wasn't surprised. For an outlay of twenty-five pounds, the Hudsons had received more than seven hundred pounds within a few months. I could imagine any company beating a hasty retreat.

"Any road," he continued, "we got another lot to take us on at t'end of the year. We've shifted all our business to them— farm, car and t'lot."

"And another accident policy, I suppose?"

Clem tipped up his glass and took a long swallow. "Oh, aye." Then he turned to me with an injured expression. "But they've made us pay an extra pound each."

It was some months later, shortly after the new company had shouldered the burden of the Hudsons' insurance, that Dick fell into the bowels of the tractor. He could have been seriously injured but sustained only a fracture of the thumb, which kept him off work for eight weeks.

He told me about it himself when he had recovered and I was

having a cup of tea in the farmhouse. "Another one hundred sixty pounds into the kitty," he said philosophically, pushing a plateful of homemade scones towards me.

I must have looked bemused because he laughed. "And that's not all, Mr. Herriot. I had a accident with the car."

"No!"

"Aye, ah did. Ran into t'side of young Bessie Trenholm's car and smashed me radiator and lights."

"Well, that's almost unbelievable. And another claim, eh?"

Dick gave me a wry smile. "Well, now, I'll tell ye. There's a bit of a story there. It was Bessie's fault, all right—she came out of her farm gate with no warnin'—but ah'd only insured my car for third party, and I thought if it came to an argument wi' only my word against hers, I'd have no chance because she's a bonny young lass, is Bessie. So I decided not to claim, though ah did mention it to the agent."

"So nothing doing this time?"

Dick's smile widened. "That's what ah thought, but the agent came to see me a few days after and told me they'd made a mistake at his office. They'd insured me car comprehensive."

"Good Lord! So you collected again?"

"Aye, another one hundred fifty pounds. Not bad." Dick cut a piece from a wedge of Wensleydale cheese, and his expression grew serious. "There's only one thing we're worried about. The agent acted a bit queer-like when 'e gave us the money. Didn't seem ower pleased. We're just hopin' this company isn't goin' to give us t'push like the last one."

"Yes," I said. "I understand. That would be unfortunate."

"It would 'an all." Dick nodded gravely. "Clem and me's big believers in insurance."

Chapter
21

November 3, 1961

I crawled into my bunk at 3 A.M., and it seemed that I had hardly fallen asleep before I was awakened by the ship leaping and bucking like a wild thing. I looked out of my window at a vast stretch of wind-tossed ocean.

Away in the distance, the lights of Klaipeda glimmered and faded. So the mate had been right; our captain was not to be deterred by a bit of bad weather.

For the rest of the night I remembered painfully the warnings I had heard about coming home against the wind. On the way to Klaipeda, the main motion had been a sideways rolling, which I had countered by jamming knees and elbows against the sides of the bunk, but this was a violent fore-and-aft movement, and it was ten times worse. Over and over again I slid from one end of the bunk to the other, and there wasn't a thing I could do about it. From my weird changes of position, I could divine that the ship's bows were high in the air one moment and pointing right down the next.

Outside, the gale howled, spray dashed against the windows and the cabin furniture and my worldly goods flew around the place unchecked. I let them get on with it. Tidying up, I felt, would be a fruitless and dangerous business.

Being thrown about constantly and listening to the medley of bangs and clatterings from all over the ship gave me small chance of sleep, and when dawn came I peered out at a dismal scene.

I discovered then the reason for one of the new sounds I had heard during the night. Whereas the ship had slid down the sides of the huge waves with the wind behind it, it now fell, keel first, into each green chasm, and when this happened, there was a jarring crash as though we had hit a rock. It was like a diver doing a belly flop, and the effect was alarming.

It seemed that after this terrible night my friends on the ship had decided that I would be prostrate and helpless this morning, because instead of the mess boy calling me at 8 A.M., Nielsen himself knocked and spoke through the door.

"You stay in bed, Mr. Herriot. I bring you a little breakfast."

"No thanks," I replied. "Come in."

He opened the door and looked startled when he saw me trying to shave with my back jammed against one wall and my foot against another.

"You okay?" he asked disbelievingly.

I seized upon a momentary pause in the ship's pitching to scrape another inch of soap from my face. "Yes, fine. What did you say about breakfast?"

"Well . . . we have kippers, fried eggs and some nice smoked sausage."

"Sounds great. I'll be there in a few minutes."

He gave me a final incredulous glance and left.

When I entered the mess room, only the mate was present. He was working among the assorted foodstuffs, and he raised his eyebrows and paused, fork halfway to his mouth, when he saw me start enthusiastically on my piled plate.

"Mr. Herriot," he said solemnly, "you are the first landsman I have known who is not sick after last night."

It made me feel good. As I have said, there is nothing clever about not being sick, but it was nice to know I had something special in the way of stomachs.

It is interesting to note that the only time I felt strange was

[200]

when I struggled up to the deck for some fresh air and stood for some time looking out on the crazily swinging sea. After a while, as I hung onto a rail, I began to experience a sort of dizziness. It was a visual thing, brought on somehow by watching the constant lifting and falling of the world about me, but it wasn't pleasant and I went back to my cabin.

In fact, I have stayed in my bunk most of the day. It is the only safe place. Since my sheep have gone I have nothing to do and, in any case, it is dangerous for an inexperienced sailor like me to move about. I have had one or two frights through being suddenly catapulted off my feet, and the danger of breaking a limb or splitting my head on a sharp projection is very real.

So it looks as though my life for the next few days is going to consist of lying on my back, reading paperback books and eating. This is all very fine, but I am used to an active existence, and I feel that a very bloated Herriot is going to roll back to Darrowby.

One hazard is that the faithful Nielsen now has me at his mercy. The galley is only a few yards away, and he keeps opening my door and sliding in a crate of lager or a tray with a mug of coffee and bread and jam.

Sometimes it is a more substantial offering, as when he marched into my cabin this afternoon, his body adjusting miraculously to the shifting slope of the floor. In one hand he held a plate and in the other a jug. On the plate rested a ring of mashed potatoes, into which he poured hot fat containing bacon and onions.

He laughed eagerly. "This is beeg food of the poor in Denmark. Is called Hot Love."

He watched with deep satisfaction as I consumed this strange dish. I relished every morsel, though dieticians would frown on it. The same dieticians would be horrified if they knew that this was merely an interlude between a lunch of huge beefy things that looked like hamburgers followed by a chocolate soup with un-pronounceable rusks broken into it, and a dinner consisting of a creation of sauerkraut cooked in butter, milk and flour and mixed with potatoes. I say nothing of the usual array of cold dishes always at my disposal to allay any lingering hunger pangs. Yes, there is no doubt about it. I am going to get fat.

If I was on this ship long enough, I would probably finish up like Carl Rasmussen, the plump little mate. He is the champion eater of the ship. He ploughs impassively through the official meal, then starts on the cold stuff, of which he consumes a vast quantity before finishing with slice after slice of bread and dripping. The captain often looks at him with his gentle smile and pats his stomach wonderingly.

I am not going to say that he has the biggest appetite I have ever seen because I have come across some mighty troughers on the Dales farms, but he is undoubtedly in the top flight. I myself have a modest reputation in this field—Tristan often refers to me as "the big eater from Darrowby"—but I am not in Carl's class. He enthralls me.

Over the schnapps the captain told me that they had intended to go to Danzig on the way back, but the plan has been changed. We are going instead to the Polish port of Stettin. At least, those were their names when they were part of Germany, but they are now called Gdansk and Szczecin, although the ship's officers refer to them by their German names. We have to pick up 800 pigs to transport to Lübeck.

He hopes to arrive in Stettin (I think I'll stick to the old spelling) on Sunday and get the pigs to Lübeck by Monday, but everything depends on the weather, which is still foul. With this gale against us, we are managing to do only six knots.

As I scribble in my diary I keep sliding down to the cabin door, then I have to drag myself back to the other end and start again. It looks like another sleepless night.

Chapter
22

"I let my heart fall into careless hands." Little Rosie's voice piped in my ear as I guided my car over a stretch of rutted road. I had singing now to cheer the hours of driving.

I was on my way to dress a wound on a cow's back and it was nice to hear the singing. But it was beginning to dawn on me that something better still was happening. I was starting all over again with another child. When Jimmy went to school I missed his company in the car, but I did not realise that the whole thing was going to begin anew with Rosie.

The intense pleasure of showing them the farm animals and seeing their growing wonder at the things of the countryside, the childish chatter that never palled; the fun and the laughter that lightened my days—it all happened twice to me.

The singing had originated in the purchase of a radiogram. Music has always meant a lot to me and I owned a record player that gave me a lot of pleasure. Still, I felt I wanted something better, some means of reproducing more faithfully the sounds of my favourite orchestras, singers, instrumentalists.

Hi-fi outfits hadn't been heard of at that time, nor stereo, nor wrap-around sound, nor any of the other things that have revolutionised the world of listening. The best the music lover could do was to get a good radiogram.

After much agonising and reading of pamphlets and listening

to advice from many quarters, I narrowed my list down to three models and made my choice by having them brought round to Skeldale House and playing the opening of the "Beethoven Violin Concerto" on one after the other, again and again. I must have driven the two men from the electric shop nearly mad, but at the end there was no doubt left in my mind.

It had to be the Murphy, a handsome piece of furniture with a louvred front and graceful legs, and it bellowed out the full volume of the Philharmonia Orchestra without a trace of muzziness. I was enchanted with it, but there was one snag; it cost over ninety pounds, and that was an awful lot of money in 1950.

"Helen," I said when we had installed it in the sitting room, "we've got to look after this thing. The kids can put records on my old player, but we must keep them away from the Murphy."

Foolish words. The very next day as I came in the front door, the passage was echoing with *Yippee ay ooooh, yippee ay aaaay, ghost riders in the skyyy!* It was Bing Crosby's back-up choir, belting out the other side of the "Careless Hands" record, and the Murphy was giving it full value.

I peeped round the sitting-room door. "Ghost Riders" had come to an end, and with her chubby little hands Rosie removed the record, placed it in its cover and marched, pigtails swinging, to the record cabinet. She selected another disc and was halfway across the floor when I waylaid her.

"Which one is that?" I asked.

" 'The Little Gingerbread Man,' " she replied.

I looked at the label. It was, too, and how did she know, because I had a whole array of these children's records, and many of them looked exactly the same. The same colour, the same grouping of words, and Rosie, at the age of three, could not read.

She fitted the disc expertly on the turntable and set it going. I listened to "The Gingerbread Man" right through and watched as she picked out another record.

I looked over her shoulder. "What is it this time?"

" 'Tubby the Tuba.' "

And indeed it was. I had an hour to spare, and Rosie gave me a recital. We went through "Uncle Mac's Nursery Rhymes," "The Happy Prince," "Peter and the Wolf" and many of the immortal Bing, to whom I was and am devoted. I was intrigued to find that her favourite Crosby record was not "Please," or "How Deep Is the Ocean" or his other classics, but "Careless Hands." This one had something special for her.

At the end of the session, I decided that it was fruitless to try to keep Rosie and the Murphy apart. Whenever she was not out with me, she played with the radiogram. It was her toy.

It all turned out for the best, too, because she did my precious acquisition no harm, and when she came with me on my rounds, she sang the things she had played so often and which were word-perfect in her mind. And I really loved that singing. "Careless Hands" soon became my favourite, too.

There were three gates on the road to this farm, and we came bumping up to the first one now. The singing stopped abruptly. This was one of my daughter's big moments. When I drew up she jumped from the car, strutted proudly to the gate and opened it. She took this duty very seriously, and her small face was grave as I drove through. When she returned to take her place by my dog, Sam, on the passenger seat, I patted her knee.

"Thank you, sweetheart," I said. "You're such a big help to me all the time."

She didn't say anything but blushed and seemed to swell with importance. She knew I meant what I said, because opening gates is a chore.

We negotiated the other two gates in similar manner and drove into the farmyard. The farmer, Mr. Binns, had shut the cow up in a ramshackle pen with a passage that stretched from a dead end to the outside.

Looking into the pen, I saw with some apprehension that the animal was a Galloway—black and shaggy with a fringe of hair hanging over bad-tempered eyes. She lowered her head and switched her tail as she watched me.

[205]

"Couldn't you have got her tied up, Mr. Binns?" I asked.

The farmer shook his head. "Nay, I'm short o' room, and this 'un spends most of 'er time on the moors."

I could believe it. There was nothing domesticated about this animal. I looked down at my daughter. Usually I lifted her into hayracks or onto the tops of walls while I worked, but I didn't want her anywhere near the Galloway.

"It's no place for you in there, Rosie," I said. "Go and stand at the end of the passage, well out of the way."

We went into the pen, and the cow danced about and did her best to run up the wall. I was pleasantly surprised when the farmer managed to drop a halter over her head. He backed into a corner and held tightly to the shank.

I looked at him doubtfully. "Can you hold her?"

"I think so," Mr. Binns replied, a little breathlessly. "You'll find t'place at the end of her back, there."

It was a most unusual thing—a big discharging abscess near the root of the tail. And that tail was whipping perpetually from side to side—a sure sign of ill nature in a bovine.

Gently I passed my fingers over the swelling, and, like a natural reflex, the hind foot lashed out, catching me a glancing blow on the thigh. I had expected this, and I got on with my exploration.

"How long has she had this?"

The farmer dug his heels in and leaned back on the rope. "Oh, 'bout two months. It keeps bustin' and fillin' up over and over again. Every time I thought it'd be the last, but it looks like it's never goin' to get right. What's t'cause of it?"

"I don't know, Mr. Binns. She must have had a wound there at some time, and it's become infected. And, of course, being on the back, drainage is poor. There's a lot of dead tissue which I'll have to clear away before the thing heals."

I leaned from the pen. "Rosie, will you bring me my scissors, the cotton wool and that bottle of peroxide?"

The farmer watched wonderingly as the tiny figure trotted to the car and came back with the three things. "By gaw, t'little lass knows 'er way around."

"Oh, yes," I said, smiling. "I'm not saying she knows where everything is in the car, but she's an expert on the things I use regularly."

Rosie handed me my requirements as I reached over the door. Then she retreated to her place at the end of the passage.

I began my work on the abscess. Since the tissue was necrotic, the cow couldn't feel anything as I snipped and swabbed, but that didn't stop the hind leg from pistoning out every few seconds. Some animals cannot tolerate any kind of interference, and this was one of them.

I finished at last with a nice wide, clean area onto which I trickled the hydrogen peroxide. I had a lot of faith in this old remedy as a penetrative antiseptic when there was a lot of pus about, and I watched contentedly as it bubbled on the skin surface. The cow, however, did not seem to enjoy the sensation because she made a sudden leap into the air, tore the rope from the farmer's hands, brushed me to one side and made for the door.

The door was closed, but it was a flimsy thing, and she went straight through it with a splintering crash. As the hairy black monster shot into the passage I desperately willed her to turn left, but to my horror she went right and, after a wild scraping of her feet on the cobbles, began to thunder down towards the dead end where my little daughter was standing.

It was one of the worst moments of my life. As I dashed towards the broken door, I heard a small voice say, "Mama." There was no scream of terror, just that one quiet word. When I left the pen, Rosie was standing with her back against the end wall of the passage and the cow was stationary, looking at her from a distance of two feet.

The animal turned when she heard my footsteps, then whipped round in a tight circle and galloped past me into the yard.

I was shaking when I lifted Rosie into my arms. She could easily

[207]

have been killed, and a jumble of thoughts whirled in my brain. Why had she said, "Mama"? I had never heard her use the word before—she always called Helen "Mummy" or "Mum." Why had she been apparently unafraid? I didn't know the answers. All I felt was an overwhelming thankfulness. To this day I feel the same whenever I see that passage.

Driving away, I remembered that something very like this had happened when Jimmy was out with me. It was not so horrific because he had been playing in a passage with an open end leading into a field, and he was not trapped when the cow I was working on broke loose and hurtled towards him. I could see nothing, but I heard a piercing yell of *"Aaaagh!"* before I rounded the corner. To my intense relief, Jimmy was streaking across the field to where my car was standing and the cow was trotting away in another direction.

This reaction was typical because Jimmy was always the noisy one of the family. Under any form of stress he believed in making his feelings known in the form of loud cries. When Dr. Allinson came to give him his routine inoculations, he heralded the appearance of the syringe with yells of *"Ow! This is going to hurt! Ow! Ow!"* He had a kindred spirit in our good doctor, who bawled back at him, *"Aye. You're right, it is! Oooh! Aaah!"* But Jimmy really did scare our dentist because his propensity for noise appeared to carry on even under general anaesthesia. The long quavering wail he emitted as he went under the gas brought the poor man out in a sweat of anxiety.

Rosie solemnly opened the three gates on the way back, then she looked up at me expectantly. I knew what it was—she wanted to play one of her games. She loved being quizzed, just as Jimmy had loved to quiz me.

I took my cue and began. "Give me the names of six blue flowers."

She coloured quickly in satisfaction because, of course, she knew. "Field Scabious, Harebell, Forget-me-not, Bluebell, Speedwell, Meadow Cranesbill."

"Clever girl," I said. "Now, let's see—how about the names of six birds?"

Again the blush and the quick reply. "Magpie, Curlew, Thrush, Plover, Yellowhammer, Rook."

"Very good indeed. Now, name me six red flowers." And so it went on, day after day, with infinite variations. I only half realised at the time how lucky I was. I had a demanding, round-the-clock job, and yet I had the company of my children at the same time. So many men work so hard to keep the home going that they lose touch with the families who are at the heart of it, but it never happened to me.

Both Jimmy and Rosie, until they went to school, spent most of their time with me round the farms. With Rosie, as her school days approached, her attitude, always solicitous, became distinctly maternal. She really couldn't see how I was going to get by without her, and by the time she was five she was definitely worried.

"Daddy," she would say seriously, "how are you going to manage when I'm at school? All those gates to open and having to get everything out of the boot by yourself. It's going to be awful for you."

I used to try to reassure her, patting her head as she looked up at me in the car. "I know, Rosie, I know. I'm going to miss you, but I'll get along somehow."

Her response was always the same. A relieved smile, and then the comforting words, "But never mind, Daddy, I'll be with you every Saturday and Sunday. You'll be all right then."

I suppose it was a natural result of my children seeing veterinary practice from early childhood and witnessing my own pleasure in my work that they never thought of being anything else but veterinary surgeons.

There was no problem with Jimmy. He was a tough little fellow and well able to stand the buffets of our job, but somehow I couldn't bear the idea of my daughter being kicked and trodden on and knocked down and covered with muck. Practice was so much rougher in those days. There were no metal crushes to hold the big struggling beasts; there were still quite a number of farm horses around, and they were the ones that regularly put the vets in hospital with broken legs and ribs. Rosie made it very clear that she wanted country practice, and to me this seemed very much a life for a man. In short, I talked her out of it.

This really wasn't like me because I have never been a heavy father and have always believed that children should follow their inclinations. But as Rosie entered her teens, I dropped a long series of broad hints and perhaps played unfairly by showing her as many grisly, dirty jobs as possible. She finally decided to be a doctor on humans.

Now, when I see the high percentage of girls in the veterinary schools and observe the excellent work done by the two girl assistants in our own practice, I sometimes wonder if I did the right thing.

But Rosie is a happy and successful doctor, and, anyway, parents are never sure that they have done the right thing. They can only do what they think is right.

However, all that was far in the future as I drove home from Mr. Binns's with my three-year-old daughter by my side. She had started to sing again and was just finishing the first verse of her great favourite, *"Careless hands don't care when dreams slip through."*

Chapter
23

It was in 1950 that one of my heroes, George Bernard Shaw, broke his leg while pruning apple trees in his garden. By a coincidence I had been reading some of the prefaces that same week, revelling in the unique wit of the man and enjoying the feeling I always had with Shaw—that I was in contact with a mind whose horizons stretched far beyond those of the other literary figures of the day, and most other days.

I was shocked when I read about the calamity, and there was no doubt the national press shared my feelings. Banner headlines pushed grave affairs of state off the front pages, and for weeks bulletins were published for the benefit of an anxious public. It was right that this should be, and I agreed with all the phrases that rolled off the journalists' typewriters. "Literary genius . . ." "Inspired musical critic who sailed fearlessly against the tide of public opinion . . ." "Most revered playwright of our age . . ."

It was just about then that the Caslings' calf broke its leg, too, and I was called to set it. The Casling farm was one of a group of homesteads set high on the heathery Yorkshire moors. They were isolated places and often difficult to find. To reach some of them you had to descend into gloomy, garlic-smelling gills and climb up the other side; with others there was no proper road, just a clay path through the heather, and it came as a surprise to find farm buildings at the end of it.

Caslings' place didn't fall into either of these categories. It was perched on the moor top, with a fine disregard for the elements. The only concession was a clump of hardy trees that had been planted to the west of the farm to give shelter from the prevailing wind, and the way those trees bent uniformly towards the stones of house and barns was testimony to the fact that the wind hardly ever stopped blowing.

Mr. Casling and his two big sons slouched towards me as I got out of the car. The farmer was the sort of man you would expect to find in a place like this, his sixty-year-old face purpled and roughened by the weather, wide, bony shoulders pushing against the ragged material of his jacket. His sons, Alan and Harold, were in their thirties and resembled their father in almost every detail, even to the way they walked, hands deep in pockets, heads thrust forward, heavy boots trailing over the cobbles. Also, they didn't smile. They were good chaps, all of them, in fact, a nice family, but they weren't smilers.

"Now, Mr. Herriot." Mr. Casling peered at me under the frayed peak of his cap and came to the point without preamble. "Calf's in t'field."

"Oh, right," I said. "Could you bring me a bucket of water, please? Just about lukewarm."

At a nod from his father, Harold made wordlessly for the kitchen and returned within minutes with a much-dented receptacle.

I tested the water with a finger. "Just right. That's fine."

We set off through a gate with two stringy little sheepdogs slinking at our heels, and the wind met us with savage joy, swirling over the rolling bare miles of that high plateau, chill and threatening to the old and weak, fresh and sweet to the young and strong.

About a score of calves was running with their mothers on a long rectangle of green cut from the surrounding heather. It was easy to pick out my patient, although, when the herd took off at the sight of us, it was surprising how fast he could run with his dangling hind leg.

[212]

At a few barked commands from Mr. Casling, the dogs darted among the cattle, snapping at heels, baring their teeth at defiant horns till they had singled out cow and calf. They stood guard then till the young men rushed in and bore the little animal to the ground.

I felt the injured limb over with a tinge of regret. I was sure I could put him right, but I would have preferred a foreleg. Radius and ulna healed so beautifully. But in this case the crepitus was midway along the tibia, which was more tricky.

However, I was thankful it was not the femur. That would have been a problem, indeed.

My patient was expertly immobilised, held flat on the sparse turf by Harold at the head, Alan at the tail and their father in the middle. One of a country vet's difficulties is that he often has to do vital work on a patient that won't keep still, but those three pairs of huge hands held the shaggy creature as in a vice.

As I dipped my plaster bandages in the water and began to apply them to the fracture, I noticed that our heads were very close together. It was a very small calf—about a month old—and at times the three human faces were almost in contact. And yet nobody spoke.

Veterinary work passes blithely by when there is good conversation, and it is a positive delight when you are lucky enough to have one of those dry Yorkshire raconteurs among your helpers. At times I have had to lay down my scalpel and laugh my fill before I was able to continue. But here all was silence.

The wind whistled, and once I heard the plaintive cry of a curlew, but the group around that prostrate animal might have been Trappist monks. I began to feel embarrassed. It wasn't a difficult job; I didn't need a hundred percent concentration. With all my heart I wished somebody would say something.

Then, like a glorious flash of inspiration, I remembered the recent clamour in the newspapers. I could start things off, at least.

"Just like Bernard Shaw, eh?" I said with a light laugh.

The silence remained impenetrable, and for about half a minute it seemed that I was going to receive no reply.

Then Mr. Casling cleared his throat. " 'oo?" he enquired.

"Bernard Shaw, George Bernard Shaw, you know. He's broken his leg, too." I was trying not to gabble.

The silence descended again, and I had a strong feeling that I had better leave it that way. I got on with my job, dousing the white cast with water and smoothing it over while the plaster worked its way under my fingernails.

It was Harold who came in next. "Does 'e live about 'ere?"

"No . . . no . . . not really." I decided to put on one more layer of bandage, wishing fervently that I had never started this topic.

I was tipping the bandage from the tin when Alan chipped in. "Darrowby feller, is 'e?"

Things were becoming more difficult. "No," I replied airily. "I believe he spends most of his time in London."

"London!" The conversation, such as it was, had been carried on without any movement of the heads, but now the three faces jerked up towards me with undisguised astonishment and the three voices spoke as one.

After the initial shock had worn off the men looked down at the calf again, and I was hoping that the subject was dead when Mr. Casling muttered from the corner of his mouth. "He won't be in t'farmin' line, then?"

"Well, no . . . he writes plays." I didn't say anything about Shaw's intuitive recognition of Wagner as a great composer. I could see by the flitting side glances that I was in deep enough, already.

"We'll just give the plaster time to dry," I said. I sat back on the springy turf as the silence descended again.

After a few minutes I tapped a finger along the length of the white cast. It was as hard as stone. I got to my feet. "Right, you can let him go now."

The calf bounded up and trotted away with his mother as though nothing had happened to him. With the support of the

[214]

plaster his lameness was vastly diminished, and I smiled. It was always a nice sight.

"I'll take it off in a month," I said, but there was no further talk as we made our way over the field towards the gate.

Still, I knew very well what the remarks would be over the farmhouse dinner table. "Queer lad, that vitnery. Kept on about some friend of his in London broke his leg."

"Aye. Kept on just like the man knows us."

"Aye. Queer lad."

And my last feeling as I drove away was not just that all fame is relative but that I would take care in future not to start talking about somebody who doesn't live about 'ere.

Chapter
24

November 4, 1961

The weather was, if anything, worse this morning, and I spent a night very like the one before. I noticed at mealtimes that the tablecloth was soaking wet. I kept quiet because I assumed that somebody had spilled something, but when it stayed wet all day, I had to mention it.

The captain smiled at my query. "Ah, yes, Mr. Herriot, I should have told you. We have dipped it in water. It does not slide about the table so much." He looked at me ruefully. "When the cloth is wet, you can bet the weather is really bad.

I saw his point. The sliding cloth, the slopping soup and, indeed, the constant restlessness of everything on the table had been a problem for some time.

I cannot rid myself of the feeling that we have struck a rock every time the ship falls from the summit of the waves, and apparently it is a standing joke among the crew, because after one of these shattering belly flops during lunch, the plates and cutlery flew all over the room, and Hansen, the engineer, jumped to his feet and peered out of the porthole.

"Deed you see that beeg stone?" he cried, staring at me with a terrified expression. It was a little jest for my benefit.

Again I have spent another disgracefully lazy day, stretched on my bunk, reading. I would have loved to do a few exercises on my hidden corner on deck, but I dare not take the chance. Even my trip for my daily shower is fraught with danger. It is a communal shower and, so far as I know, the only one on this tiny vessel. It is just a few yards away down the passage past the crew's quarters, but it seemed a long way as I reeled along, armed with towel and soap.

On my way, I could see several of the big, flaxen-haired seamen lying on their bunks, and I am sure I did not imagine the hollow groans issuing from the doorways. Can it be that even these supermen are seasick . . . ?

I really have nothing more to write about today, but tomorrow we should be in Stettin, and with a bit of luck I might get ashore and see something of interest.

November 5, 1961

My wedding anniversary. Strange to be spending it in Poland.

This morning when I awoke, the world was still, and the sea and sky were not wheeling beyond my cabin windows. I realised that we must be in Stettin and heaved myself up in my bunk. I saw that we were moored to a frost-covered quay. It was very foggy, but I could see several men with rods fishing from the quayside.

There was a Polish soldier on guard, but he was not festooned with artillery like the Russians. Also, he smiled when I called out to him. We were lying in a quiet backwater of the main river, the Oder, and there were willow trees and rushes at the water's edge. I judged from the wooden sheds with pens that this was probably a special place for the loading of livestock.

The usual mob of officials descended on us. Representatives from customs, immigration and farms. Among them was a handsome young Polish army officer who insisted not only on seeing the passports, but on interviewing each of their owners too.

I tentatively approached the captain as he dealt with the throng in his cabin.

"I'd like to go ashore into the town," I said.

His expression was slightly harassed, and I couldn't help feeling that he would be glad to get rid of this pest from Yorkshire. He looked at me thoughtfully for a moment.

"I am too busy to go with you, Mr. Herriot, and we must leave here at 11 A.M."

"Well, that gives me two hours," I replied. My natural curiosity and my almost desperate desire for some exercise lent weight to my appeal.

"All right." He raised a finger. "But you will not be late?"

"No, I promise you."

He nodded and returned to his business, while I showed my pass to the soldier and set off for the town. Oh, it was lovely to be able to stride out in the frosty air, to feel my limbs moving after the days of immobility and Nielsen's insidious skills. The fog had lifted, and I could see, about two miles away, the roofs and spires of a sizable town.

First I passed a military barracks with gymnastic equipment outside it, then allotments with a few women digging in them. My immediate impression as I approached the town was of the tremendous devastation left from the R.A.F. raids in wartime. Everywhere there were ruins and empty spaces. Vast buildings, some with ornate statuary over the doors, stood roofless, with gaping windows.

During the first mile of my walk, I saw hardly any evidence of effort to repair these ravages. It was not until I reached the town centre that I came on modern blocks of flats with shops on their ground floors. I took great care to impress every turning on my mind—if I got lost, I couldn't ask my way back.

Right inside the town, I was able to gain a general impression of the place and people. Obviously they observed Sunday as a holiday, because there was nobody working in the port area, and most of the shops were closed. Notable exceptions were two hairdressers' salons side by side, designated "Damski" and "Meski" above their respective doors. A lady was having a manicure in the front window of "Damski."

[218]

The population was arrayed in its Sunday best, and it seemed to me remarkable that the well-dressed man in Poland wore what amounted almost to a uniform. Black beret with a small stalk projecting from the top, dark gabardine macintosh and navy-blue suit. Also, every single one had a scarf crossed under his coat. The women were much smarter than in Klaipeda.

There were little kiosks on every corner, and people were strolling up to buy their newspapers and cigarettes. These places also sold draught beer and, having been on an exclusive diet of bottled lager for some time, I watched with envy as one fellow downed a frothing pint. If I had possessed any Polish money, it would have been nice to emulate him.

Stettin has 350,000 inhabitants, and I was struck by the greater air of comfort and civilisation, compared with Klaipeda. The people looked altogether smoother and more urbane, and the town had a cheerful atmosphere despite the ever-present ruins.

Funny little single-decker tramcars ran through the streets, always in pairs, one joined to the other, and there were a lot of private cars and taxis.

Shops displayed attractive dresses and materials, but a huge picture of Lenin reminded me that I was still behind the iron curtain.

Groups of youths, well dressed and laughing among themselves, were sauntering around, and I watched one family getting off a tram: Mum very chic in a light, fluffy hat and brightly coloured coat, Dad in the unvarying black beret and mac, and two teenage sons in identically the same outfit.

As I passed over the main river bridge, I could see innumerable barges moored along the banks. I walked past many churches but saw only two elderly women going into them.

I was amused when a little man in a soft hat, breeches and riding boots came and asked me the way to somewhere in an unintelligible gibberish. He, too, it seemed was a stranger, but not, I warrant, as much a stranger as I.

It was now a glorious cold, sunny day and I was revelling in the activity after my incarceration, but I kept referring to my son Jimmy's pocket watch and, when I saw I had been away an hour, I had to turn back.

I reached the ship before 11 A.M. and found the Polish officials still in the captain's cabin. They had given the free booze and cigarettes a severe hammering and were exuding bonhomie when I came in.

They seemed very glad to see me and shouted for me to sit down with them with merry cries of "Doktor, please, Doktor, please." I thought it was the schnapps that made them so welcoming, but later the captain said they had been anxious in case I got lost and kept asking him, "Has the Englishman returned yet?"

But, he said, there was no doubt they had wrought havoc among the bottles, all except the young Polish officer, who had been very correct and after one drink politely declined any more.

I went down to the hold and had a look at the pigs. We have them for only twenty-four hours and nobody seems particularly concerned about them, but pigs are funny things—they often fight among themselves, and it occurred to me that if 800 of them started a free-for-all, it would be a problem.

However, Polish pigs are perhaps more placid than ours because I found them all lying asleep, snuggling up to each other in perfect harmony. During the day I heard an occasional squeal from the hold and dashed down there in some anxiety, but it always turned out to be an isolated squabble or flash of irritation, with none of the bleeding scars or torn ears I had seen so often in Yorkshire. On the whole, peace has reigned.

We have taken aboard a great load of potatoes to feed them till we reach Lübeck.

The crew do not like carrying pigs because of the smell, and there is no doubt the ship has an entirely different aroma now. This does not percolate as far as the cabins or mess room, but I am told that in the summer it is pretty bad and shipboard life is dominated by the ever-present atmosphere of pig.

After lunch I spent a fascinating afternoon on the deck as the ship made its way through the delta of the Oder, which spreads itself into a maze of huge lakes. This, I was told, is characteristic of the coastline in this region, right along through Estonia, Latvia and Lithuania. If ever a pilot were needed, it is here.

We sailed through the strangest and most desolate countryside I have ever seen—endless miles of flat marshlands with innumerable rush-lined inlets and pools, and occasional belts of trees. Clouds of wild ducks and geese provided the only signs of life, and the effect was inexpressibly wild and lonely despite the bright sunshine.

After about four hours the delta narrowed to a straight channel, and we came to the port of Swinemunde on the Baltic. This is a big naval base, and I saw a lot of Russian destroyers, torpedo boats and submarines.

At the entrance to the port we dropped the pilot and headed out to sea again. The gale had dropped, and the weather was now much better. It was very pleasant to stand out there in the stern, watching the land recede as the ship glided through calm water with hardly any rolling.

As far as my eye could reach, the coastline was thickly wooded, mainly with pine trees right down to the water's edge. There were some sandy beaches and cliffs, but no hills.

I stayed outside as we cruised along the East German coast, never out of sight of land, and maybe it was because my voyage was nearly over, but I didn't want to go below. I came inside only when the daylight was drowned in a magnificent sunset.

The ship's officers have been particularly charming today since it is my anniversary. They have shaken my hand warmly and bombarded me with lager. The captain asked anxiously if he should send a telegram to my wife but I explained that I had left a card with Rosie and I felt that a telegram might alarm Helen.

The cook, too, produced what I think must have been a banquet in my honour because it had a touch of England about it— a delectable soup of celery spinach and other vegetables, then roast pork with crackling, accompanied by roast ham, potatoes and red cabbage. Dessert was sago pudding, thickly sprinkled with cinnamon.

After dinner we had our usual and, sadly, my last session with the schnapps. The captain, red-eyed and tired after one and a half hours of sleep in the last twenty-four, still managed to be the perfect host.

November 6, 1961

The end of it all. From Lübeck to Hamburg by train, then by plane to Heathrow, London, before the last lap to Darrowby. I had much to think of on the way. I had been lucky enough to have a peep at mysterious places, a glimpse of a totally different world, but when I looked back on the last ten days, my warmest and most vivid memories were of the animals, the ship and the people aboard her.

The brave little *Iris Clausen* butting her way through the storms with the sheep safe inside her; the big, tough, yellow-haired crewmen, especially Raun and "Yoombo"; and of course, the ship's officers who had treated me so kindly. The captain who never seemed to lose his grace; Carl Rasmussen, the mate, tubby, balding and with the mighty appetite; Peter Hansen, the engineer, always ready with a joke; and, of course, my devoted Nielsen, who, I feel sure, has put half a stone of surplus flesh onto me.

I hope they have the same friendly memories of me. The captain, invariably courteous as he was, must have regarded me as an unmitigated nuisance at times, but Nielsen I know is going to miss me.

Chapter
25

"Was there no peace in a vet's life?" I wondered fretfully as I hurried my car along the road to Gilthorpe village. Eight o'clock on a Sunday evening and here I was, trailing off to visit a dog ten miles away which, according to Helen who had taken the message, had been ailing for more than a week.

I had worked all morning then spent an afternoon in the hills with the children and some of their friends, a long-standing weekly event during which we had managed to explore nearly every corner of the district over the years. Jimmy had set a brisk pace with his hardy young pals and I had had to carry Rosie on my shoulders up the steepest slopes. After tea there was the usual routine of baths, story reading and bed for the two of them, then I was ready to settle down with the Sunday papers and listen to the radio.

Yet here I was back on the treadmill, staring through the windscreen at the roads and the walls that I saw day in, day out. When I left Darrowby, the streets of the little town were empty in the gathering dusk and the houses had that tight-shut, comfortable look that raised images of armchairs and pipes and firesides, and now, as I saw the lights of the farms winking on the fell-sides, I could picture the stocksmen dozing contentedly with their feet up.

I had not passed a single car on the darkening road. There was nobody out but Herriot.

I was really sloshing around in my trough of self-pity when I drew up outside a row of greystone cottages at the far end of Gilthrope. Mrs. Cundall, Number Four, Chestnut Row, Helen had written on the slip of paper, and as I opened the gate and stepped through the tiny strip of garden, my mind was busy with half-formed ideas of what I was going to say.

My few years' experience in practice had taught me that it did no good at all to remonstrate with people for calling me out at unreasonable times. I knew perfectly well that my words never seemed to get through to them and that they would continue to do exactly as they had done before, but for all that I had to say something, if only to make me feel better.

No need to be rude or ill-mannered, just a firm statement of the position: that vets liked to relax on Sunday evenings just like other people; that we did not mind at all coming out for emergencies, but that we did object to having to visit animals that had been ill for a week.

I had my speech fairly well prepared when a little middle-aged woman opened the door.

"Good evening, Mrs. Cundall," I said, slightly tight-lipped.

"Oh, it's Mr. Herriot." She smiled shyly. "We've never met, but I've seen you walkin' round Darrowby on market days. Come inside."

The door opened straight into the little low-beamed living room, and my first glance took in the shabby furniture and some pictures framed in tarnished gilt when I noticed that the end of the room was partly curtained off.

Mrs. Cundall pulled the curtain aside. In a narrow bed a man was lying, a skeleton-thin man whose eyes looked up at me from hollows in a yellowed face.

"This is my husband, Ron," she said cheerfully, and the man smiled and raised a bony arm from the quilt in greeting.

"And here is your patient, Hermann," she went on, pointing to a little dachshund who sat by the side of the bed.

"Hermann?"

"Yes, we thought it was a good name for a German sausage dog." They both laughed.

"Of course," I said. "Excellent name. He looks like a Hermann."

The little animal gazed up at me, bright-eyed and welcoming. I bent down and stroked his head, and the pink tongue flickered over my fingers.

I ran my hand over the glossy skin. "He looks very healthy. What's the trouble?"

"Oh, he's fine in himself," Mrs. Cundall replied. "Eats well and everything, but over the last week he's been goin' funny on 'is legs. We weren't all that worried but tonight he sort of flopped down and couldn't get up again."

"I see. I noticed he didn't seem keen to rise when I patted his head." I put my hand under the little dog's body and gently lifted him onto his feet. "Come on, lad," I said. "Come on, Hermann, let's see you walk."

As I encouraged him he took a few hesitant steps, but his hind end swayed progressively, and he soon dropped into the sitting position again.

"It's his back, isn't it?" Mrs. Cundall said. "He's strong enough on 'is forelegs."

"That's ma trouble, too," Ron murmured in a soft husky voice, but he was smiling, and his wife laughed and patted the arm on the quilt.

I lifted the dog onto my knee. "Yes, the weakness is certainly in the back." I began to palpate the lumbar vertebrae, feeling my way along, watching for any sign of pain.

"Has he hurt 'imself?" Mrs. Cundall asked. "Has somebody hit 'im? We don't usually let him out alone, but sometimes he sneaks through the garden gate."

"There's always the possibility of an injury," I said. "But there are other causes." There were, indeed—a host of unpleasant possibilities. I did not like the look of this little dog at all. This syndrome was one of the things I hated to encounter in canine practice.

"Can you tell me what you really think?" she said. "I'd like to know."

"Well, an injury could cause haemorrhage or concussion or oedema—that's fluid—all affecting his spinal cord. He could even have a fractured vertebra, but I don't think so."

"And how about the other causes?"

"There's quite a lot. Tumours, bony growths, abscesses or discs can press on the cord."

"Discs?"

"Yes, little pads of cartilage and fibrous tissue between the vertebrae. In long-bodied dogs like Hermann, they sometimes protrude into the spinal canal. In fact, I think that is what is causing his symptoms."

Ron's husky voice came again from the bed. "And what's 'is prospects, Mr. Herriot?"

Oh, that was the question. Complete recovery or incurable paralysis. It could be anything. "Very difficult to say at this moment," I replied. "I'll give him an injection and some tablets, and we'll see how he goes over the next few days."

I injected an analgesic and some antibiotic, and counted out some salicylate tablets into a box. We had no steroids at that time. It was the best I could do.

"Now, then, Mr. Herriot." Mrs. Cundall smiled at me eagerly. "Ron has a bottle o' beer every night about this time. Would you like to join 'im?"

"Well . . . it's very kind of you, but I don't want to intrude . . ."

"Oh, you're not doing that. We're glad to see you."

She poured two glasses of brown ale, propped her husband up with pillows and sat down by the bed.

"We're from south Yorkshire, Mr. Herriot," she said.

I nodded. I had noticed the difference from the local accent.

"Aye, we came up here after Ron's accident, eight years ago."

"What was that?"

"I were a miner," Ron said. "Roof fell in on me. I got a broken back, crushed liver and a lot o' other internal injuries, but two of me mates were killed in the same fall, so ah'm lucky to be 'ere." He sipped his beer. "I've survived, but Doctor says I'll never walk no more."

"I'm terribly sorry."

"Nay, nay," the husky voice went on. "I count me blessings, and I've got a lot to be thankful for. Ah suffer very little, and I've got t'best wife in the world."

Mrs. Cundall laughed. "Oh, listen to 'im. But I'm right glad we came to Gilthorpe. We used to spend all our holidays in the Dales. We were great walkers, and it was lovely to get away from the smoke and the chimneys. The bedroom in our old house just looked out on a lot o' brick walls, but Ron has this big window right by 'im and he can see for miles."

"Yes, of course," I said. "This is a lovely situation." The village was perched on a high ridge on the fell-side, and that window would command a wide view of the green slopes running down to the river and climbing high to the wildness of the moor on the other side. This sight had beguiled me so often on my rounds, and the grassy paths climbing among the airy tops seemed to beckon to me. But they would beckon in vain to Ron Cundall.

"Gettin' Hermann was a good idea, too," he said. "Ah used to feel a bit lonely when t'missus went into Darrowby for shoppin', but the little feller's made all the difference. You're never alone when you've got a dog."

I smiled. "How right you are. What is his age now, by the way?"

"He's six," Ron replied. "Right in the prime o' life, aren't you, old lad?" He let his arm fall by the bedside, and his hand fondled the sleek ears.

"That seems to be his favourite place."

"Aye, it's a funny thing, but 'e allus sits there. T'missus is the one who has to take 'im for walks and feeds 'im, but he's very faithful to me. He has a basket over there but this is 'is place. I only have to reach down and he's there."

This was something that I had seen on many occasions with disabled people: that their pets stayed close by them as if conscious of their role of comforter and friend.

I finished my beer and got to my feet. Ron looked up at me. "Reckon I'll spin mine out a bit longer." He glanced at his half-full glass. "Ah used to shift about six pints some nights when I went out wi' the lads but you know, I enjoy this one bottle just as much. Strange how things turn out."

His wife bent over him, mock-scolding. "Yes, you've had to right your ways. You're a reformed character, aren't you?"

They both laughed as though it were a stock joke between them.

"Well, thank you for the drink, Mrs. Cundall. I'll look in to see Hermann on Tuesday." I moved towards the door.

As I left I waved to the man in the bed, and his wife put her hand on my arm. "We're very grateful to you for comin' out at this time on a Sunday night, Mr. Herriot. We felt awful about callin' you, but you understand it was only today that the little chap started going off his legs like that."

"Oh, of course, of course, please don't worry. I didn't mind in the least."

And as I drove through the darkness I knew that I didn't mind —now. My petty irritation had evaporated within two minutes of my entering that house, and I was left only with a feeling of humility. If that man back there had a lot to be thankful for, how about me? I had everything. I only wished I could dispel the foreboding I felt about his dog. There was a hint of doom about those symptoms of Hermann's, and yet I knew I just had to get him right. . . .

On Tuesday he looked much the same, possibly a little worse.

"I think I'd better take him back to the surgery for X-ray," I said to Mrs. Cundall. "He doesn't seem to be improving with the treatment."

In the car Hermann curled up happily on Rosie's knee, submitting with good grace to her petting.

I had no need to anaesthetise him or sedate him when I placed him on our newly acquired X-ray machine. Those hind quarters stayed still all by themselves—a lot too still for my liking.

I was no expert at interpreting X-ray pictures, but at least I could be sure there was no fracture of the vertebrae. Also, there was no sign of bony extoses, but I thought I could detect a narrowing of the space between a couple of the vertebrae, which would confirm my suspicions of a protrusion of a disc.

Laminectomy or fenestration had not even been heard of in those days, so I could do nothing more than continue with my treatment, and hope.

By the end of the week, hope had grown very dim. I had supplemented the salycilates with long-standing remedies like tincture of nux vomica and other ancient stimulant drugs, but when I saw Hermann on the Saturday he was unable to rise. I tweaked the toes of his hind limbs and was rewarded by a faint reflex movement, but with a sick certainty I knew that complete posterior paralysis was not far away.

A week later, I had the unhappy experience of seeing my prognosis confirmed in the most classical way. When I entered the door of the Cundalls' cottage, Hermann came to meet me, happy and welcoming in his front end but dragging his hind limbs helplessly behind him.

"Hello, Mr. Herriot." Mrs. Cundall gave me a wan smile and looked down at the little creature stretched frog-like on the carpet. "What d'you think of him now?"

I bent and tried the reflexes. Nothing. I shrugged my shoulders, unable to think of anything to say. I looked at the gaunt figure in the bed, the arm outstretched as always on the quilt.

"Good morning, Ron," I said as cheerfully as I could, but there

[229]

was no reply. The face was averted, looking out of the window. I walked over to the bed. Ron's eyes were staring fixedly at the glorious panorama of moor and fell, at the pebbles of the river, white in the early sunshine, at the criss-cross of the grey walls against the green. His face was expressionless. It was as though he did not know I was there.

I went back to his wife. I don't think I have ever felt more miserable.

"Is he annoyed with me?" I whispered.

"No, no, no, it's this." She held out a newspaper. "It's upset him something awful."

I looked at the printed page. There was a large picture at the top, a picture of a dachshund exactly like Hermann. This dog, too, was paralysed, but its hind end was supported by a little four-wheeled bogie. In the picture it appeared to be sporting with its mistress. In fact, it looked quite happy and normal, except for those wheels.

Ron seemed to hear the rustle of the paper because his head came round quickly. "What d'ye think of that, Mr. Herriot? D'ye agree with it?"

"Well . . . I don't really know, Ron. I don't like the look of it, but I suppose the lady in the picture thought it was the only thing to do."

"Aye, maybe." The husky voice trembled. "But ah don't want Hermann to finish up like that." The arm dropped by the side of the bed and his fingers felt around on the carpet, but the little dog was still splayed out near the door. "It's 'opeless now, Mr. Herriot, isn't it?"

"Well, it was a black lookout from the beginning," I said. "These cases are so difficult. I'm very sorry."

"Nay, I'm not blamin' you," he said. "You've done what ye could, same as the vet for that dog in the picture did what 'e could. But it was no good, was it? What do we do now—put 'im down?"

"No, Ron, forget about that just now. Sometimes paralysis

cases just recover on their own after many weeks. We must carry on. At this moment I honestly cannot say there is no hope."

I paused, then turned to Mrs. Cundall. "One of the problems is the dog's natural functions. You'll have to carry him out into the garden for that. If you gently squeeze each side of his abdomen, you'll encourage him to pass water. I'm sure you'll soon learn how to do that."

"Oh, of course, of course," she replied. "I'll do anything. As long as there's some hope."

"There is, I assure you, there is."

But on the way back to the surgery, the thought hammered in my brain. That hope was very slight. Spontaneous recovery did sometimes occur, but Hermann's condition was extreme. I repressed a groan as I thought of the nightmarish atmosphere that had begun to surround my dealings with the Cundalls. The paralysed man and the paralysed dog. And why did that picture have to appear in the paper just at this very time? Every veterinary surgeon knows the feeling that fate has loaded the scales against him, and it weighed on me, despite the bright sunshine spreading into the car.

However, I kept going back every few days. Sometimes I took a couple of bottles of brown ale along in the evening and drank them with Ron. He and his wife were always cheerful, but the little dog never showed the slightest sign of improvement. He still had to pull his useless hind limbs after him when he came to greet me, and, though he always returned to his station by his master's bed, nuzzling up into Ron's hand, I was beginning to resign myself to the certainty that one day that arm would come down from the quilt and Hermann would not be there.

It was on one of these visits that I noticed an unpleasant smell as I entered the house. There was something familiar about it.

I sniffed, and the Cundalls looked at each other guiltily. There was a silence, and then Ron spoke.

"It's some medicine ah've been givin' Hermann. Stinks like 'ell, but it's supposed to be good for dogs."

"Oh, yes?"

"Aye, well . . ." His fingers twitched uncomfortably on the bedclothes. "It was Bill Noakes put me onto it. He's an old mate o' mine—we used to work down t'pit together—and he came to visit me last weekend. Keeps a few whippets, does Bill. Knows a lot about dogs, and 'e sent me this stuff along for Hermann."

Mrs. Cundall went to the cupboard and sheepishly presented me with a plain bottle. I removed the cork, and as the horrid stench rose up to me, my memory became suddenly clear. Asafoetida, a common constitutent of quack medicines before the war and still lingering on the shelves of occasional chemist shops and in the medicine chests of people who liked to doctor their own animals.

I had never prescribed the stuff myself, but it was supposed to be beneficial in horses with colic and dogs with digestive troubles. My own feeling had always been that its popularity had been due solely to the assumption that anything which stank as badly as that must have some magical properties, but one thing I knew for sure was that it could not possibly do anything for Hermann.

I replaced the cork. "So you're giving him this, eh?"

Ron nodded. "Aye, three times a day. He doesn't like it much, but Bill Noakes has great faith in it. Cured hundreds o' dogs with it, 'e says." The deep-sunk eyes looked at me with a silent appeal.

"Well, fine, Ron," I said. "You carry on. Let's hope it does the trick."

I knew the asafoetida couldn't do any harm, and since my treatment had proved useless I was in no position to turn haughty. But my main concern was that these two nice people had been given a glimmer of hope, and I wasn't going to blot it out.

Mrs. Cundall smiled and Ron's expression relaxed. "That's grand, Mr. Herriot," he said. "Ah'm glad ye don't mind. I can dose the little feller myself. It's summat for me to do."

It was about a week after the commencement of the new treatment that I called in at the Cundall's as I was passing through Gilthorpe.

"How are you today, Ron?" I asked.

"Champion, Mr. Herriot, champion." He always said that, but today there was a new eagerness in his face. He reached down and lifted his dog onto the bed. "Look 'ere."

He pinched the little paw between his fingers, and there was a faint but definite retraction of the leg. I almost fell over in my haste to grab at the other foot. The result was the same.

"My God, Ron," I gasped. "The reflexes are coming back."

He laughed his soft, husky laugh. "Bill Noakes's stuff's working, isn't it?"

A gush of emotions, mainly professional shame and wounded pride, welled in me, but it was only for a moment. "Yes, Ron," I replied. "It's working. No doubt about it."

He stared up at me. "Then Hermann's going to be all right?"

"Well, it's early days yet, but that's the way it looks to me."

It was several weeks more before the little dachshund was back to normal, and, of course, it was a fairly typical case of spontaneous recovery, with nothing whatever to do with the asafoetida or, indeed, with my own efforts. Even now, thirty years later, when I treat these puzzling back conditions with steroids, broad-spectrum antibiotics and sometimes colloidal calcium, I wonder how many of them would have recovered without my aid. Quite a number, I imagine.

Sadly, despite the modern drugs, we still have our failures, and I always regard a successful termination with profound relief.

But that feeling of relief has never been stronger than it was with Hermann, and I can recall vividly my final call at the cottage in Gilthorpe. As it happened, it was around the same time as my first visit—eight o'clock in the evening—and when Mrs. Cundall ushered me in, the little dog bounded joyously up to me before returning to his post by the bed.

"Well, that's a lovely sight," I said. "He can gallop like a racehorse now."

Ron dropped his hand down and stroked the sleek head. "Aye, isn't it grand? By heck, it's been a worryin' time."

[233]

"Well, I'll be going." I gave Hermann a farewell pat. "I just looked in on my way home to make sure all was well. I don't need to come anymore now."

"Nay, nay," Ron said. "Don't rush off. You've time to have a bottle o' beer with me before ye go."

I sat down by the bed, and Mrs. Cundall gave us our glasses before pulling up a chair for herself. It was exactly like that first night. I poured my beer and looked at the two of them. Their faces glowed with friendliness, and I marvelled because my part in Hermann's salvation had been anything but heroic.

In their eyes everything I had done must have seemed bumbling and ineffectual, and, in fact, they must be convinced that all would have been lost if Ron's old chum from the coal face had not stepped in and effortlessly put things right.

At best, they could only regard me as an amiable fathead, and all the explanations and protestations in the world would not alter that. But though my ego had been bruised, I did not really care. I was witnessing a happy ending instead of a tragedy, and that was more important than petty self-justification. I made a mental resolve never to say anything that might spoil their picture of this triumph.

I was about to take my first sip when Mrs. Cundall spoke up. "This is your last visit, Mr. Herriot, and all's ended well. I think we ought to drink some sort o' toast."

"I agree," I said. I looked around for an inspiration, and on a far shelf my eye caught a glimpse of the asafoetida bottle. The memory of its stench lanced briefly at my nose, defying me to put my humbled resolution to the test. "I have just the right toast," I said, raising my glass. "Here's to Bill Noakes."

Chapter
26

The bull with the bowler hat.

That was one of the irreverent terms for Artificial Insemination when it first arrived on the postwar scene. Of course, A.I. was a wonderful advance. Up till the official licencing of bulls, the farmers had used any available male bovine to get their cows in calf. A cow had to produce a calf before it would give milk and it was milk that was the goal of the dairy farmers, but, unfortunately, the progeny of these "scrub" bulls were often low-grade and weakly.

But A.I. was a great improvement on licencing. To use a high-class, pedigree, proven bull to inseminate large numbers of cows for farmers who could never afford to own such an animal was and is a splendid idea.

Over the years I have seen countless thousands of superior young heifers, bullocks and bulls populate the farms of Britain, and I have rejoiced.

I am speaking theoretically. My own practical experience of Artificial Insemination was brief and unhappy.

When the thing first began, most practitioners thought they would be rushing about, doing a lot of insemination on their own account, and Siegfried and I could hardly wait to get started. We purchased an artificial vagina, which was a tube of hard, vulcanised rubber about eighteen inches long with a lining of latex.

There was a little tap on the tube, and warm water was run into this to simulate the temperature of a genuine bovine vagina. On one end of the A.V. was a latex cone secured by rubber bands, and this cone terminated in a glass tube in which the semen was collected.

Apart from its use in insemination, this instrument provided an excellent means of testing the farmers' own bulls for fertility. It was in this context that I had my first experience.

Wally Hartley had bought a young Ayrshire bull from one of the big dairy farmers, and he wanted the animal's fertility tested by the new method. He rang me to ask if I would do the job and I was elated at the chance to try out our new acquisition.

At the farm I filled the liner with water just nicely at blood heat and fastened on the cone and glass tube. I was ready and eager for action.

The required cow in oestrus was in a large loose box off the yard, and the farmer led the bull towards it.

"He's nobbut a little 'un," Mr. Hartley said, "but I wouldn't trust 'im. He's a cheeky young bugger. Never served a cow yet, but keen as mustard."

I eyed the bull. Certainly he wasn't large, but he had mean eyes and the sharp, curving horns of the typical Ayrshire. Anyway, this job shouldn't be much trouble. I had never seen it done but had flipped through a pamphlet on the subject, and it seemed simple enough.

All you did was wait till the bull started to mount, then you directed the protruded penis into the A.V. Apparently then, the bull, with surprising gullibility, thrust happily into the water-filled cylinder and ejaculated into the tube. I had been told repeatedly that there was nothing to it.

I went into the box. "Let him in, Wally," I said, and the farmer opened the half-door.

The bull trotted inside, and the cow, fastened by a halter to a ring on the wall, submitted calmly as he sniffed around her. He

[236]

seemed to like what he saw because he finally stationed himself behind her with eager anticipation.

This was the moment. Take up position on the right side of the bull, the pamphlet had said, and the rest would be easy.

With surprising speed the young animal threw his forelegs on the cow's rump and surged forward. I had to move quickly, and as the penis emerged from the sheath I grabbed it and poised the A.V. for action.

But I didn't get the chance. The bull dismounted immediately and swung round on me with an affronted glare. He looked me carefully up and down as though he didn't quite believe what he saw, and there was not an ounce of friendliness in his expression. Then he appeared to remember the rather pressing business on hand and turned his attention to the cow again.

He leaped up, I grabbed and once more he suspended his activities abruptly and brought his forefeet thudding to the ground. This time there was more than outraged dignity in his eyes; there was anger. He snorted, shook the needle-sharp horns in my direction and dragged a little straw along the floor with a hoof before fixing me with a long, appraising stare. He didn't have to speak; his message was unequivocal. Just try that once more, chum, and you've had it.

As his eyes lingered on me, everything seemed to become silent and motionless as though I were part of a picture—the cow standing patiently, the churned straw beneath the animals and, beyond them, the farmer out in the yard, leaning over the half-door, waiting for the next move.

I wasn't particularly looking forward to that next move. I felt a little breathless and my tongue pressed against the roof of my mouth.

At length the bull, with a final warning glance at me, decided to resume his business and reared up on the cow once more. I gulped, bent quickly and as his slim red organ shot forth, I grasped it and tried to bring the A.V. down on it.

[237]

This time the bull didn't mess about. He sprang away from the cow, put his head down and came at me like a bullet.

In that fleeting instant I realised what a fool I had been to stand with the animals between me and the door. Behind me was the dark corner of the box. I was trapped.

Fortunately, the A.V. was dangling from my right hand, and as the bull charged I was able to catch him an upward blow on the snout. If I had hit him on the top of the head, he would never have felt it, and one or both of those nasty horns would inevitably have started to explore my interior. But as it was, the hard rubber cylinder thumping against his nose brought him to a slithering halt, and while he was blinking and making up his mind about having a second go, I rained blows on him with a frenzy born of terror.

I have often wondered since that day if I am the only veterinary surgeon to have used an artificial vagina as a defensive weapon. It certainly was not built for the purpose because it soon began to disintegrate under my onslaught. First, the glass tube hurtled past the ear of the startled farmer who was watching, wide-eyed, from the doorway, then the cone spun away against the flank of the cow who had started to chew her cud placidly, oblivious of the drama being enacted by her side.

I alternated my swipes with thrusts and lunges worthy of a fencing master, but still I couldn't jockey my way out of that corner. However, although my puny cylinder couldn't hurt the bull, I obviously had him puzzled. His instinct told him that right about now he should be having a good time, and yet all he was getting were raps on the nose. While he weighed this incongruity, apart from a lot of weaving and prodding with his horns he made no sign of repeating his first headlong charge and seemed content to keep me penned in the few feet of space.

But I knew it was only a matter of time. He was out to get me, and I was wondering how it felt to receive a *cornada* when he took a step back and came in again full tilt, head down.

I met him with a back-handed slash and that was what saved

me, because the elastic holding the latex lining came off and the warm water from within fountained into the bull's eyes.

He stopped suddenly, and it was then I think he just decided to give up. In his experience of humans I was something new to him. I had taken intimate liberties with him in the pursuit of his lawful duty, I had belaboured him with a rubber instrument and finally squirted water in his face. He had plainly had enough of me.

During his pause for thought I dodged past him, threw open the door and escaped into the yard.

The farmer looked at me as I fought for breath. "By gaw, Mr. Herriot, it's a 'ell of a job, this A.I., isn't it?"

"Yes, Wally," I replied shakily. "It is, rather."

"Is it allus like that?"

"No, Wally, no. . . ." I looked sadly at my bedraggled A.V. "This is an exceptional case. I . . . I think we'd better get a specialist in to collect a sample from this bull."

The farmer rubbed his ear where the tube had clipped it in passing. "Awright, then, Mr. Herriot. You'll let me know when you're comin', I suppose. It'll be another bit of excitement to look forward to."

His words did nothing to ease the feeling of abject failure as I crept away from the farm. Vets were taking semen samples every day now with no trouble at all. What was the matter with me?

Back in the surgery I phoned the advisory service. Yes, they said, they would send out one of their sterility advisory officers. He would meet me on the farm at ten o'clock the next morning.

When I arrived there on the following day, the officer was already in the yard, and I thought there was something familiar about the back of the jaunty figure strolling over the cobbles and blowing out clouds of cigarette smoke. When he turned round I saw with a gush of relief that it was Tristan. I hadn't been looking forward to recounting my shameful performance to a stranger.

His broad grin was like a tonic. "Hello, Jim, how are things?"

"Fine," I replied. "Except for this semen collection. I know you're doing it all the time, but I had a shambolic experience yesterday."

"Really?" He pulled deeply at his Woodbine. "Tell me about it. Mr. Hartley's just on his way in from the fields."

We stepped inside the loose box, the scene of the previous day's debacle, and I began my tale.

I hadn't got far before Tristan's jaw dropped. "You mean you just let the bull in here on his own, without any restraint?"

"That's right."

"You daft bugger, Jim. You're lucky to be here. In the first place, this job should always be done out in the open, and secondly, the bull should always be held by a pole or a halter through the nose ring. I like to have two or three blokes helping me." He shot me an incredulous glance as he lit another Woodbine. "Anyway, go on."

As I proceeded with my story, his expression began to change. His mouth twitched, his chin trembled and little giggles burst from him. "Are you trying to tell me that you grabbed him by his old man?"

"Well . . . yes."

"Oh, dear, oh, dear!" Tristan leaned back against the wall and laughed immoderately for a long time. When he had recovered, he regarded me pityingly. "Jim, old lad, you are supposed to put your hand only on the sheath to do the directing."

I gave a wry smile. "Oh, I know that now. I had another read at the pamphlet last night and realised I had made a lot of mistakes."

"Well, never mind," he said. "Carry on with your story. You're beginning to interest me."

The next few minutes had a devastating effect on my colleague. As I described the bull's attack on me, he slumped, shouting, against the door, and by the time I had finished, he was hanging limply with his arms dangling over the woodwork. Tears coursed down his cheeks and feeble little moans issued from his mouth.

"You were . . . you were in that corner, fighting the bull off with the A.V. Clouting him over the nut with all that stuff . . . flying around." He reached for his handkerchief. "For God's sake, don't tell me any more, Jim. You'll do me an injury." He wiped his eyes and straightened up, but I could see that the whole thing had taken it out of him.

He turned unsteadily as he heard the farmer's footsteps in the yard. "Ah, good morning, Mr. Hartley," he said. "We can get started now."

Tristan was very businesslike as he directed operations. Yesterday's cow was still in oestrus, and within minutes she was tied to a gatepost in the yard with a man on either side. "That's to stop her swinging round when the bull mounts," he explained to me.

He turned to the farmer and handed him the A.V. "Will you fill this with warm water, please, and screw the stopper on tightly?"

The farmer trotted into the house, and as he returned, another of his men led out the bull. This time my antagonist of yesterday was securely held by a halter through his ring.

Tristan had certainly got everything arranged in an orderly fashion.

The farmer had said that the bull was keen as mustard, and his words were verified when the young animal took one look at the cow and started towards her, a picture of urgent lust. Tristan scarcely had time to get the A.V. into his hand before the bull was clambering eagerly aboard his quarry.

I had to admit that my young colleague was lightning-fast as he stooped, seized the sheath and sent the penis plunging into the A.V. So that was how it was done, I thought wistfully. So very easy.

My feeling of shame was building up when the bull pushed out his tongue and emitted a long-drawn, deafening bellow of rage. And he had scarcely entered the A.V. when he withdrew with a backward leap and began to caper around on the end of his halter, filling the air with disapproving bawls.

"What the hell . . ." Tristan stared at the animal in bewilderment. Then he poked his finger into the A.V. "Good God!" he cried. "The water in here is steaming hot!"

"Aye," Wally Hartley nodded, accepting the compliment. "The kettle had just come to the boil when I went into t'house."

Tristan clutched his brow and groaned. "Oh, bugger it!" he muttered to me. "I always check the temperature, but what with talking . . . Boiling water! No wonder the poor sod got out quick."

Meanwhile the animal had stopped his noise and was circling the cow, sniffing her over and regarding her with a mixture of disbelief and respect. "What a woman!" was clearly the dominant thought in his mind.

"Anyway, let's have another try." Tristan made for the farmhouse. "I'll fill the thing myself this time."

Soon the stage was set once more—Tristan standing at the ready, and the bull, apparently undeterred by his recent experience, patently eager to join battle yet again. By his attitude now, he looked as though, come hell or high water, he was going to serve that cow.

My impression was confirmed when he made a sudden rush at her. Tristan, slightly pop-eyed, managed to jam the A.V. over the penis as it hurtled past him. But then something went wrong. The bull, wild with frustration and distracted by those two-legged fools around him, lost his footing. In the next instant two images flashed before me. The bull went down, still flying forward, somehow got on his back and slid clean under the cow. In the same moment, I could see the A.V., jerked from Tristan's grasp and soaring high into the air. Mr. Hartley and I followed the glass container, open-mouthed, as it described a graceful parabola toward certain doom. Then our mouths clapped shut in disbelief as it landed harmlessly on a pile of straw at the other end of the yard.

The bull scrambled to his feet, and Tristan strolled unhurriedly towards the straw. The glass tube was still attached to the cylinder, and my friend held it up at eye level.

"Ah, yes," he murmured. "A nice three c.c. sample."

[242]

The farmer came puffing up. "You've got what you wanted, 'ave you?"

"Yes indeed," Tristan replied airily. "Exactly what I wanted."

The farmer shook his head admiringly. "By 'ell, it's wondrous how the veterinary business has advanced, isn't it?"

Tristan shrugged his shoulders. "Have to keep up with the times, Mr. Hartley. New science means new methods. I'll get my microscope from the car and examine the sample."

It didn't take long, and soon afterwards we were all having a cup of tea in the kitchen.

My colleague put down his cup and reached for a scone. "That's a fine fertile bull you have there, Mr. Hartley."

"Eee, that's champion." The farmer rubbed his hands. "I paid a fair bit o' brass for 'im, and it's grand to know he's up to scratch." He looked across at the young man with undisguised admiration. "You've done a grand job. I couldn't do what you did in a hundred years."

As I sipped my tea the thought occurred to me that, despite the passage of time, things hadn't changed. Like the glass tube landing on soft straw, Tristan always landed on his feet.

Chapter
27

I winced as Jack Scott's slender frame crashed against the cow's ribs, but Jack himself didn't seem unduly troubled. His eyes popped a little and his cap slid over one ear, but he took a fresh grip on the tail, braced his boots once more against the cobbles and prepared himself for further action.

I was trying to irrigate the cow's uterus with Lugol's iodine. This was the common postwar treatment for infertility in cattle caused by endometritis, but it involved the insertion of the long, metal Nielsen catheter through the uterine cervix, and this animal didn't seem to appreciate it. Every time I attempted to work the catheter through the cervical folds, she swung round violently, and since the farmer weighed only about eight stones, he was whirled repeatedly against the neighbouring cow.

But this time I had the feeling I was winning. The tube was sliding nicely into the uterus, and if only she would stand still for a few seconds, the job would be over.

"Hang on, Jack," I gasped as I began to pump in the Lugol's. As soon as the cow felt the fluid trickling in, she veered over again, and the farmer's mouth fell open as he was squashed between the big creatures. And when a hoof descended on his toes, a soft groan escaped him.

"Lovely, that's it." I withdrew the catheter and stepped back, thinking at the same time that this had been a singularly uncooperative patient.

Jack, however, didn't seem to share my view. Hobbling on his bruised foot, he went up to the front of the cow and put his arms round her neck.

"Ah, you're a grand awd lass," he murmured, resting his cheek against the craggy jaw.

I looked at him wonderingly. It was always like this with Jack. He had a deep affection for every creature, human and animal, on his farm, and, with an occasional exception such as the cow I had just treated, the feeling seemed to be returned.

When he had concluded his embrace, he pushed his way out and hopped over the dung channel. His face wore its usual smile. It was not the ruddy face of the typical farmer; in fact it was always pale and haggard, as though its owner hadn't slept for a few nights, and the deep wrinkles on the cheeks and forehead made Jack look older than his forty years. But the smile was radiant, like an inner light.

"Ah've one or two other jobs for ye, Mr. Herriot," he said. "First, I want you to give a bullock a shot. He's got a bit of a cough."

We walked across the yard with Jack's sheepdog, Rip, gambolling around his master in delight. Often these farm dogs were slinking, furtive little creatures, but Rip behaved like a happy pet.

The farmer bent and patted him. "Hello, feller, are you comin', too?" As the dog went into further transports, a little boy and girl, the two youngest of the Scott family, trotted along with us.

"Dad, where are ye goin'?" "Dad, what are ye doin'?" They cried. There were usually children mixed up with the visits on this farm, getting in between the cows' legs, often hindering the work, but it never worried Jack.

The bullock was lying in deep straw in a loose box. He was a huge animal and obviously not very ill because he was placidly chewing his cud as we entered.

[245]

"There's nowt much wrong with 'im," Jack said. "Maybe just a bit o' cold. But I've heard 'im cough a few times, and I reckon he'd be better with an injection."

The temperature was slightly elevated, and I filled a syringe with a penicillin suspension, which the veterinary profession had recently acquired. I leaned over, gave the hairy rump the usual quick thump with my hand and plunged the needle in.

On any other farm, an animal of this size could have been something of a problem to inject, perhaps involving a chase round the box, but this one did not even rise to his feet. Nobody was restraining him in any way, but he continued to chew, merely looking round with mild interest as I drove the needle deep into his muscle.

"Champion. Good lad, good lad." Jack scratched the hairy poll for a few minutes before we left. "There's some lambs ah want you to look at," he said and led me into a Nissen hut. "I've never seen owt like them."

There were a number of ewes and lambs in the hut, but it was not difficult to see what the farmer meant. Several of the lambs were wobbling on their hind legs as they walked, and two could take only a few faltering steps before collapsing on their sides.

Jack turned to me. "What's the matter wi' them, Mr. Herriot?"

"They've got swayback," I replied.

"Swayback? What's that?"

"Well, it's a copper deficiency. Causes degeneration of the brain, which makes them weak on their hindquarters. That's the typical form, but sometimes they become paralysed or take fits. It's a funny disease."

"That's strange," the farmer said. "Them ewes have had copper licks to go at all the time."

"I'm afraid that's not enough. If you get many cases, you ought to inject the ewes with copper halfway through pregnancy to prevent it for next time."

He sighed. "Ah, well, now we know what it is, you'll be able to put these lambs right."

"Sorry, Jack," I replied. "There's no cure. Only prevention."

"Well, that's a beggar." The farmer tipped back his cap. "What's goin' to happen to this lot, then?"

"Well, the ones that are just wobbly have a good chance of making fat lambs, but I haven't much hope for those two." I pointed to the pair lying on their sides. "They are already partially paralysed. I honestly think the kindest thing would be . . ."

That was when the smile left Jack's face. It always did at the merest suggestion of putting an animal down. It is a country vet's duty to advise his clients when treatment is obviously unprofitable. He must always have the farmer's commercial interest in mind.

This system worked on most places, but not at Jack Scott's. Tell him to get rid of a cow that had lost a couple of quarters with mastitis, and the curtain would come down over that smiling face. He had various animals on the farm that could not possibly be making him any money, but they were his friends and he was happy to see them pottering about.

He dug his hands deep in his pockets and looked down at the prostrate lambs. "Are they sufferin', Mr. Herriot?"

"No, Jack, no. It doesn't seem to be a painful disease."

"Awright, I'll keep them two. If they can't suck, I'll feed 'em meself. Ah like to give things a chance."

He didn't have to tell me. He gave everything a chance. No farmer likes to have the extra work of lamb feeding, especially when the little creatures are abnormal, but I knew it was no use arguing with Jack. It was his way.

Out in the yard again, he leaned against the half-door of a loose box. "Any road, I'll have to remember to do them ewes with copper next time."

As he spoke, an enormous head poked over the door. This was

the bull box, and the great Shorthorn inside clearly wished to pay his respects.

He began to lick the back of Jack's neck, and as the rasping tongue repeatedly knocked his cap over his eyes, the farmer remonstrated gently. "Give over, George, ye daft thing. What d'you think you're doin'?" But he reached back and tickled the animal's chin at the same time.

The expression on George's face made him look more like a dog than a bull. Goofy-eyed and anxious to please, he licked and nuzzled faster than ever, despite the farmer's protests. On many farms a bull that size would be a potential killer, but George was just another of Jack's pets.

As lambing time was left behind and the summer wore on, I was glad to see that Jack's dedication had paid off. The two semi-paralysed lambs were surviving and doing well. They still flopped down after a few steps, but they were able to nibble the fast-growing grass and the demyelination of their brains had mercifully not progressed.

It was in October, when the trees around the Scott farm were bursting into a blaze of warm colour, that Jack hailed me as I drove past his gate.

"Will ye stop for a minute and see Rip?" His face was anxious.

"Why, is he ill?"

"Naw, naw, just lame, but I can't mek it out."

I didn't have to go far to find Rip—he was never far from his master—and I experienced a shock of surprise when I saw him because his right foreleg was trailing uselessly.

"What's happened to him?" I asked.

"He was roundin' up t'cows when one of 'em lashed out and got him on the chest. He's been gettin' lamer ever since. The funny thing is, ah can't find a thing wrong with his leg. It's a mystery."

Rip wagged vigorously as I felt my way up his leg from foot to shoulder. There was no pain in the limb, no wound or injury, but he winced as I passed my hand over his first rib. Diagnosis was not difficult.

"It's radial paralysis," I said.

"Radial . . . what's that?"

"The radial nerve passes over the first rib, and the kick must have damaged rib and nerve. This has put the extensor muscles out of action so that he can't bring his leg forward."

"Well, that's a rum 'un." The farmer passed a hand over the shaggy head and down the fine white markings of the cheeks. "Will he get better?"

"It's usually a long job," I replied. "Nervous tissue is slow to regenerate, and it could take weeks or months. Treatment doesn't seem to make much difference."

The farmer nodded. "Awright, we'll just have to wait. There's one thing"—and again the bright smile flooded his face—"he can still get round them cows, lame or not. It 'ud break 'is heart if he couldn't work. Loves 'is job, does Rip."

On the way back to the car, he nudged me and opened the door of a shed. In the corner, in a nest of straw, a cat was sitting with her family of tiny kittens. He lifted two out, holding one in each of his roughened hands. "Look at them little fellers, aren't they lovely!" He held them against his cheeks and laughed.

As I started the engine, I felt I ought to say something encouraging. "Don't worry too much about Rip, Jack. These cases usually recover in time."

But Rip did not recover. After several months his leg was as useless as ever, and the muscles had wasted greatly. The nerve must have been irreparably damaged, and it was an unhappy thought that this attractive little animal was going to be three-legged for the rest of his life.

Jack was undismayed and maintained stoutly that Rip was still a good working dog.

The real blow fell one Sunday morning as Siegfried and I were arranging the rounds in the office. I answered the door bell and found Jack on the step with his dog in his arms.

"What's wrong?" I asked. "Is he worse?"

"No, Mr. Herriot." The farmer's voice was husky. "It's summat different. He's been knocked down."

We examined the dog on the surgery table. "Fracture of the tibia," Siegfried said. "But there's no sign of internal damage. Do you know exactly what happened?"

Jack shook his head. "Nay, Mr. Farnon. He ran onto the village street and a car caught 'im. He dragged 'imself back into t'yard."

"Dragged?" Siegfried was puzzled.

"Aye, the broken leg's on the same side as t'other thing."

My partner blew out his cheeks. "Ah, yes, the radial paralysis. I remember you told me about it, James." He looked at me across the table, and I knew he was thinking the same thing as I was. A fracture and a paralysis on the same side was a forbidding combination.

"Right, let's get on," Siegfried murmured.

We set the leg in plaster, and I held open the door of Jack's old car as he laid Rip on the back seat.

The farmer smiled out at me through the window. "I'm takin' the family to church this mornin', and I'll say a little prayer for Rip while I'm there."

I watched until he drove round the corner of the street, and when I turned I found Siegfried at my elbow.

"I just hope that job goes right," he said thoughtfully. "Jack would take it hard if it didn't." He turned and carelessly dusted his old brass plate on its new place on the wall. "He's a truly remarkable chap. He says he's going to say a prayer for his dog, and there's nobody better qualified. Remember what Coleridge said? 'He prayeth best who loveth best all things both great and small.' "

"Yes," I said. "That's Jack, all right."

The farmer brought his dog into the surgery six weeks later for the removal of the plaster.

"Taking a cast off is a much longer job than putting it on," I said as I worked away with my little saw.

Jack laughed. "Aye, ah can see that. It's hard stuff to get through."

I have never liked this job, and it seemed a long time before I splayed open the white roll with my fingers and eased it away from the hair of the leg.

I felt at the site of the fracture and my spirits plummeted. Hardly any healing had taken place. There should have been a healthy callus by now but I could feel the loose ends of the broken bones moving against each other, almost like a hinge. We were no further forward.

I could hear Siegfried pottering among the bottles in the dispensary, and I called to him.

He palpated the limb. "Damn! One of those! And just when we didn't want it." He looked at the farmer. "We'll have to try again, Jack, but I don't like it."

We applied a fresh plaster, and the farmer grinned confidently. "Just wanted a bit more time, I reckon. He'll be right next time."

But it was not to be. Siegfried and I worked together to strip off the second cast, but the situation was practically unchanged. There was little or no healing tissue around the fracture.

We didn't know what to say. Even at the present time, after the most sophisticated bone-pinning procedures, we still find these cases where the bones just will not unite. They are as frustrating now as they were that afternoon when Rip lay on the surgery table.

I broke the long silence. "It's just the same, I'm afraid, Jack."

"You mean it 'asn't joined up?"

"That's right."

The farmer rubbed a finger along his upper lip. "Then 'e won't be able to take any weight on that leg?"

"I don't see how he possibly can."

"Aye . . . aye . . . well, we'll just have to see how he goes on, then."

"But Jack," Siegfried said gently. "He can't go on. There's no way a dog can get around with two useless legs on the same side."

The silence set in again, and I could see the familiar curtain coming down over the farmer's face. He knew what was in our minds, and he wasn't going to have it. In fact, I knew what he was going to say next.

"Is he sufferin'?"

"No, he isn't," Siegfried replied. "There's no pain in the fracture now and the paralysis is painless anyway, but he won't be able to walk, don't you see?"

But Jack was already gathering his dog into his arms. "Well, we'll give him a chance, any road," he said and walked from the room.

Siegfried leaned against the table and looked at me, wide-eyed. "Well, what do you make of that, James?"

"Same as you," I replied gloomily. "Poor old Jack. He always gives everything a chance, but he's got no hope this time."

But I was wrong. Several weeks later I was called to the Scott farm to see a sick calf and the first thing I saw was Rip bringing the cows in for milking. He was darting to and fro around the rear of the herd, guiding them through the gate from the field, and I watched him in amazement.

He still could not bear any appreciable weight on either of his right limbs, yet he was running happily. Don't ask me how he was doing it because I'll never know, but somehow he was supporting his body with his two strong left legs and the paws of the stricken limbs merely brushing the turf. Maybe he had perfected some balancing feat like a one-wheel bicycle rider but, as I say, I just don't know. The great thing was that he was still the old friendly Rip, his tail swishing when he saw me, his mouth panting with pleasure.

Jack didn't say anything about "I told you so," and I wouldn't have cared because it thrilled me to see the little animal doing the job he loved.

"This calf, Mr. Herriot," Jack began, then he pointed excitedly at a pigeon perched on the byre roof. "By gaw, that little feller looks better. I've been watching 'im for months. He went down to skin and bone, but he's fillin' out now."

I smiled to myself. Even the pigeons were under Jack's eye.

He dragged himself back to more practical things. "Aye, now, this calf. Never seen one like it. Goin' round and round as if it was daft."

Depression flowed over me. I had been hoping for something straightforward this time. My recent contacts with Jack's animals could be described as abortive treatment and wrong prognosis, and I did want to pull something out of the bag. This didn't sound good.

It was a bonny little calf about a month old. Dark roan—the Shorthorn farmer's favourite colour—and it was lying on its straw bed looking fairly normal, except that its head was inclined slightly to one side. Jack touched the hairy rump with his toe, and the calf rose to its feet.

That was where the normality ended because the little creature blundered away to the right, as if drawn by a magnet, until it walked into the wall. It picked itself up and recommenced its helpless progress, always to the right. It managed to complete two full circuits of the pen until it collapsed against the door.

Ah, well, so that was it. I was relieved and worried at the same time because I knew what the trouble was, and I was pretty sure I could cure it . . . but not quite sure.

The temperature was 106°F.

"This is a thing called listeriosis, Jack," I said.

He looked at me blankly.

"Circling disease is the other name, and you can see why. It's a brain disease, and the animal can't help going round and round like that."

The farmer looked glum. "Brain again, just like them lambs? God 'elp us, there must be summat in the air about here. Are all me stock goin' to go off their heads?" He paused, bent over the calf and began to stroke it. "And there'll be nowt you can do for this, either, I suppose."

"I hope I can do something, Jack. This is a different thing altogether from the swayback lambs. It's an actual bug affecting the brain, and with a bit of luck I can put this calf right."

I felt like crossing my fingers. I was still not vastly experienced. I had seen only a few of these cases and in the prewar days they had been invariably fatal, but the causal organism was sensitive to antibiotics and the whole scene had changed. I had seen animals with listeriosis recover completely within a few days.

I shook up my bottle of penicillin-streptomycin suspension and injected 5 c.c.'s into the thigh. "I'll be back tomorrow," I said. "I hope to find the little thing improved by then."

Next day the temperature was down, but the symptoms had not abated. I repeated the injection and said I would call again.

I did call, again and again, because I was gripped by a kind of desperation, but after a week, though the temperature was normal and the appetite excellent, the calf was still circling.

"How d'you feel about t'job, then, Mr. Herriot?" the farmer asked.

Actually I felt like screaming and railing against fate. Was there a hoodoo on this place? Could I do nothing right?

I calmed down and took a deep breath. "I'm sorry, Jack, but we don't seem to be getting anywhere. The antibiotic has saved the calf's life, but there must be some brain damage. I can't see any hope of recovery now."

He didn't seem to have heard me. "It's a grand 'un, a heifer, too, and out of me best cow. She'll make a smashin' milker. Just look at the shape of 'er—and that grand colour. We've called her Bramble."

"Yes, but Jack . . ."

He patted me on the shoulder and led me out to the yard. "Well, thank ye, Mr. Herriot. Ah'm sure you've done all you can." Quite obviously he didn't want to pursue the matter further.

Before I left, I took a final glance over the door of the pen at that calf reeling in the straw. As I walked to the car, Rip gambolled at my feet, and the almost useless legs mocked me with further evidence of my veterinary skill. What kind of an animal doctor was I, anyway?

As I started the engine, I looked out through the open window and was about to speak when I saw the familiar blank look on Jack's face. He didn't want to hear any advice from me on what he should do with his calf. Clearly he had decided to give Bramble a chance.

It turned out that Jack's faith was rewarded and that my prognosis was wrong again, but I cannot blame myself because the sequence of events in Bramble's recovery is not contained in any textbook.

Over the next two years the brain symptoms gradually diminished. The improvement was so slow as to be almost imperceptible, but every time I was on Jack's farm I had a look into her pen and saw to my astonishment that the little animal was just a bit better. For many weeks she circled, then this subsided into an occasional staggering towards the right. This, in turn, faded over the months into an inclination of the head to one side, until one day I looked in and found that this, too, had disappeared and a fine, normal two-year-old heifer was strolling around unconcernedly in the straw. I didn't mind being wrong. I was delighted.

"Jack," I said. "How marvellous! I'd have bet anything that this was a hopeless case, and there she is, absolutely perfect."

The farmer gave me a slow smile with a hint of mischief in it. "Aye, ah'm right capped with her, Mr. Herriot, and she's goin' to be one of the best cows in the herd before she's finished. But . . ." He raised a finger and his smile broadened. "She's not perfect, tha knows."

"Not . . . what do you mean?"

"I mean there's just a little somethin'." He leaned towards me conspiratorially. "Keep watchin' her face."

I stared at the heifer, and the calm, bovine eyes looked back at me with mild interest. We inspected each other for a couple of minutes, then I turned to the farmer. "Well, I can't see a thing wrong with her."

"Hang on a bit," Jack said. "She doesn't allus do it."

"Do what?" I was mystified. "There's nothing at all . . . my God!"

The farmer laughed and thumped me on the back. "Did ye see it?"

I certainly had, and it was startling. Just for an instant Bramble's placid expression was transfigured by a faint twitch of the eyes and head to the right. There was something human about the gesture; in fact, I was reminded instantly of the film "vamps" of the twenties, when a girl would stand, hand on hip, and beckon seductively at her quarry. It was a come-hither look.

Jack was still laughing. "I reckon you've never seen owt like that afore, Mr. Herriot?"

"No, you're right. I haven't. What an extraordinary thing. How often does she do it?"

"Oh, every now and then. I suppose it'll go away in time like all t'other things?"

"I expect it will," I said. "But how very strange."

The farmer nodded. "Aye, there's summat right cheeky about it. I allus get the feelin' she's trying to ask me somethin'."

I laughed, too. "Yes, that's it, exactly. You'd think she was trying to communicate, but, of course, it's just the last trace of the condition she had. Anyway, the main thing is, she's a grand, bonny heifer."

"She is that," Jack said. "I'm glad we persevered with 'er." (It was nice of him to say "we.") "Ah've had 'er served, and she should be calvin' just right for Darrowby show."

"Well, that will be interesting. She's certainly a show animal."

And there was no doubt that Bramble had developed into a classical Dairy Shorthorn with all the delicacy and grace of that now-lost breed—the beautifully straight back, the neat tail-head and the makings of a fine udder. She was a picture.

She was even more of a picture a few months later as she stood in the centre of the show ring with the August sun glinting on her rich, dark coat. She had recently produced a calf, and her udder, tight and flat-based, with a small teat thrusting proudly from each corner, bulged between the back limbs.

She would take some beating, and it was a pleasant thought that the seemingly doomed little creature of two and a half years ago might be just about to win a championship trophy.

However, Bramble was in pretty hot company. The judge, Brigadier Rowan, had narrowed the field down to three after much cogitation, and the other two contestants, a red-and-white and a light roan, were beautiful animals. It would be a close thing.

Brigadier Rowan himself was a splendid sight. He was a distinguished soldier, a gentleman farmer and an unrivalled judge of dairy cattle in the district.

His dress and general bearing were fully in keeping with his position. That tall, lean figure would have been aristocratic and impressive enough without the beautifully cut check suit, yellow waistcoat, cravat and bowler hat. The fact that he was one of the few people I have ever seen wearing a monocle added the final touch.

The brigadier strolled up and down the little row of cattle, shoulders high, hands clasped behind his back, occasionally screwing the glass tighter into his eye as he bent to inspect a particular point. Clearly, he was having difficulty in deciding.

His normally pink face was bright red, not, I felt, from the sunshine, but from the long succession of brandies and sodas I had seen him consuming in the president's tent. He pursed his lips and approached Bramble, who stood patiently at the end of the row nearest to me with her head held by Jack Scott on a halter.

The brigadier leaned forward and peered into the animal's face as though to examine the eyes. Something happened then. I was standing behind Bramble and could not see her face, but my suspicion is that she gave the little twitch which had startled me. In any case, something undoubtedly pierced the brigadier's patrician calm. His eyebrows shot up and the monocle dropped to the end of its cord, where it dangled for a few seconds before he retrieved it, gave it a thorough polish and returned it to his eye.

He again studied Bramble fixedly for quite a long time, and even after he had moved away, he glanced back at her once or twice. I could read his mind. Had he really seen that, or was it the brandy?

As he came slowly back down the row, he had the look of a man who was definitely going to make up his mind this time, even though he was confronted by three superb animals. He finished up in front of Bramble, and as he gave her a final appraising stare, he flinched suddenly, and I had a strong conviction that she had done her trick again.

The brigadier kept a grip on himself this time, but though the monocle remained in position, the man was obviously shaken. It seemed, however, to remove all doubts from his mind. He immediately placed Bramble first, the red-and-white second and the light roan third.

The brigadier, having made his decision, strode straight as a cadet, albeit a red-faced one, to the edge of the ring where he was greeted by a beaming Jack.

"A bonny lass, 'ant she, Brigadier? Almost human, ye might say."

"Quite," said the brigadier, adjusting his monocle. "Actually, she reminded me of someone I used to know . . . briefly."

Chapter
28

"Disaster! Disaster! Disaster!"

The voice at the other end was so shrill and panic-stricken that I almost dropped the telephone. "Who . . . who is that?"

"It's Mrs. Derrick! Oh, such a disaster!"

"Yes, Mrs. Derrick, what on earth has happened?"

"It's my goat, Mr. Herriot! It's really terrible!"

The Derricks were a young couple who had recently come to live in one of the villages near Darrowby. They were in their early thirties, and Ronald Derrick was a businessman who commuted daily to Brawton. His wife was extremely attractive and a pleasant young woman in every way, but she was slightly scatterbrained, and I had felt misgivings in the first place when she told me she had bought a goat.

I gripped the receiver tightly. "Has the goat had an accident?"

"No, no, it's not the goat I'm worried about. It's the tomatoes!"

"Tomatoes?"

"Yes, the wretched thing has eaten all my husband's tomatoes. I left the greenhouse door open by mistake."

A chill swept through me. Ronald Derrick loved his tomatoes dearly and since I, too, found them fascinating things, I had been very interested when he had shown me his plants.

Like many people coming to live in a country district, he and his wife had been seized with a passion for the country things, like growing all sorts of vegetables in the big garden behind the house and keeping livestock. They had a few hens, ponies for their children and, of course, the goat. But with Ronald, the tomatoes were his great joy.

There was a little greenhouse in the garden, and on my last visit there he had shown me the twelve plants with justifiable pride. It was early July, and the young fruits were still green and small but obviously thriving.

"Magnificent trusses," I remembered saying. "You are going to have a wonderful crop." I could recall the smile of gratification on his face as his wife continued on the phone.

"He counts them every morning, Mr. Herriot. In fact, before he left for the office today, he told me there were two hundred and ninety-three. Do please come. I'm afraid that when he gets home he'll kill the goat *and* me!" There was a pause. "I think I can see him through the window. Oh, yes, my God, here he is now!"

There was a thud in my ear as she crashed the receiver down, and I found I was shaking slightly. What was I supposed to do? Act as peacemaker? Prevent a murder? Anyway, Ronald Derrick was a gentle, good-humoured man who would certainly not resort to violence. But, by heck, he was going to be annoyed—and maybe the goat would be ill after that feast. I dashed out to the car.

I was at the scene of the catastrophe within ten minutes. The Derricks' home was a gracious old manor house with an open drive at one side leading to the garden. I roared down there, leaped from my car and the whole sad spectacle lay before me.

Mrs. Derrick, still very attractive despite the tears which trickled down her cheeks, was standing on a strip of lawn, twisting a sodden handkerchief in her fingers.

"Darling," she was saying, "I just went in for a moment to get the watering can. I can't think why I forgot to close the door."

Her husband did not answer, and I could see that his was a bereavement too deep for words. He was leaning against the open doorway, gazing into the greenhouse. He was quite motionless, and plainly he had not moved since his arrival because he was like a business executive who had been frozen to the spot: dark-suited, bowler-hatted, briefcase dangling from one hand.

I stepped forward and looked over his shoulder, and the sight was even more bizarre than I had expected. The tastes and eating habits of goats are often unfathomable, but this one had, for some reason, consumed all the tomatoes and leaves and left the slender green stalks, naked and pathetic, still neatly tied to the canes that led up to the glass roof.

As a fellow tomato lover, I felt for him deeply, but there was nothing I could do. I patted him on the shoulder and murmured a few words of sympathy, but still he continued to stare at the row of stalks.

I could see the goat on its tether at the other end of the garden. That was another point—how had it got free to wreak this devastation? But I wasn't going to add more tension to the situation by bringing that up.

I went over and had a look at the animal. It was bright-eyed and cheerful and clearly didn't require my services in any way. In fact, as I watched it began to nibble at a cabbage with obvious relish. As I say, I was sad for the Derricks, but I could not but look with admiration at any creature whose appetite was not satisfied by the consumption of two hundred and ninety-three tomatoes.

A large part of the veterinary life seems to be made up of these little incidents. Trivial, perhaps, but rewarding. I recall a visit I made to test the herd of Rupe and Will Rowney. Rupe and Will just didn't get on. They were bachelor brothers who had run a dairy farm for many years together, but they didn't seem to be able to agree about anything.

Visits there could be embarrassing as the brothers argued continually and criticised each other's every move, but on this particular day I found they had forgotten to keep the cows in for me.

I stood to one side as they castigated each other.

"Ah told ye the postcard said today."

"Naw, ye didn't, ye said Tuesday. It was me as said today."

"Well, fetch the bloody card from t'house and let's 'ave another look at it."

"How can I? Ye burned it, ye daft bugger!"

I let the debate go on for a few minutes, then intervened tactfully.

"It's all right," I said. "There's no harm done. The cows are just there in the field. It shouldn't take long to get them in."

Rupe gave his brother a final glare and turned to me. "Nay, it won't take long, Mr. Herriot. The byre door's open. Ah'll soon call 'em in."

He inflated his lungs and began a series of shrill cries. "Come on, Spotty Nose, come on, Big Lugs, come on, Mucky Tail, come on, Fat Tits, come on, Fuzzy Top!"

Will, nettled at being upstaged, broke in with his own shout. "Come on, Long Legs! Come on, Slow Coach!"

Rupe froze him with a stare, then bent towards me. "Ye'll have to excuse me brother, Mr. Herriot," he said in a confidential whisper. "Ah've tried to tell 'im many a time, but he will call the cows them daft names."

Contrasts in people always intrigue me. I was called to see a bullock with a swollen foot. The owner was one of the new breed of young farmer who had been to agricultural college and was steeped in modern science. He was a nice lad, but like many of his kind, he gave me the uncomfortable feeling that he knew about as much as I did.

He showed me the animal.

"Bit of infection there," he said. "Bacteria must have gained entry through that abrasion. I should think he needs about twenty c.c.'s of long-acting procaine penicillin intramuscularly."

He was right, of course, and I duly injected the dose into the animal's rump.

It happened that my next call, just a mile along the road, was to a similar case, but this time the farmer was old Ted Buckle, one of the fast-disappearing old characters and a great favourite of mine.

"Now, then, Mr. Herriot," he said and led me into the fold yard. He pointed to the lame bullock standing in a corner. "There's a youth ower there wants a jab in t'arse."

Then there was Mr. Bogg whose tight-fistedness was a byword in a community where thrift was the norm. I had heard many tales of his parsimony, but I have a few experiences of my own that I cherish.

He owned a herd of good Ayrshire cows and ran a few turkeys and chickens on the side. He certainly would not be short of money.

His turkeys were frequently afflicted with blackhead, and he used to come to us for Stovarsol tablets which were the popular treatment at that time.

One afternoon he approached me in the surgery.

"Look," he said. "Ah keep comin' here for fifty or a hundred of them little tablets, and it's a flippin' nuisance. I'd rather buy a whole tinful—it 'ud save a lot of journeys."

"Yes, Mr. Bogg, you're right," I replied. "It would be a much better idea. I'll get you some now."

When I returned from the dispensary, I held up the tin. "This contains a thousand tablets, and as it happens, it's the only one we have in stock. It has been opened and a few have been taken out, but it is virtually a new tin."

"A few . . . taken out . . . ?" I could read the alarm in his eyes at the idea of paying for the full thousand when he was getting less than that.

"Oh, don't worry," I said. "There's maybe something like a dozen tablets short—no more."

My words clearly failed to reassure him, and as he left the surgery he looked gloomy and preoccupied.

[263]

He was back again that same evening. He rang the bell at about eight o'clock, and I faced him on the front doorstep.

"I've just come in to tell ye," he said. "I've been counting them tablets, and there's nine hundred and eighty-seven."

On another occasion I went to buy some eggs from Mr. Bogg. I got a dozen from him most weeks because his farm was on the outskirts of the town. When I returned home with this particular batch I found that there were only eleven eggs in the bag, so when I saw him a week later I mentioned the fact.

"Mr. Bogg," I said. "There were only eleven eggs in last week's lot."

"Aye, ah know," he replied, fixing me with a steady eye. "But one of 'em was a double-yolked 'un."

I have a dear memory, too, of the time—the only time—I did a farm round in shorts.

I had just got back from the family holiday in Scotland. The weather had been perfect, and after spending a fortnight in shirt and shorts, I rebelled at the idea of climbing into workaday clothes.

Looking from our bedroom window at the sun blazing from a clear sky, I made a sudden decision. I pulled on the shorts. And as I walked down the long garden to get my car, the air played round my legs, and I half-closed my eyes at the sensation of coolness and freedom. I was still on holiday, still striding the hills around Ullapool.

The conviction that I had done the right thing was strengthened when I got out at the first farm. The day was going to be really hot, and the whole green landscape shimmered in the morning haze. Yes, this was the right garb for country practice in the summer.

The place was a smallholding, and old Mrs. Meynell answered my knock. At first she did not reply to my cheerful greeting but stared in silent fascination at my exposed knees. After a few seconds I repeated my query.

"Is your husband in, Mrs. Meynell?"

"Nay . . . nay . . . " She still had difficulty in dragging her eyes away from my legs. "He's over t'field, mendin' a wall." At last she looked up at my face. "I'm sorry, Mr. Herriot, but when I peeped through the window, I thought it was a boy scout comin' to see us."

Slightly abashed, I opened the gate to the pasture and headed over the long stretch of green to where the farmer was resetting the stones on the wall.

He did not hear my approach, and I spoke to his back. "Good morning, Mr. Meynell, it's a lovely day."

The old man turned round, and his reaction was very like his wife's. He did not speak but directed a prolonged, unsmiling gaze at my knees until I began to feel uncomfortable.

At length, I broke the silence. "I believe you have a sick calf."

He nodded slowly, still staring downwards.

I cleared my throat. "Touch of scour, is it?"

"Aye . . . aye . . . that's right." There was no change in his attitude, and I felt we weren't getting anywhere.

"Well," I said. "Will we go and have a look at him?"

Without warning, the old man dropped into the sprint starting position, one knee on the turf, fingers outsplayed.

He looked up at me eagerly. "Come on, then, I'll race ye back to the house."

Chapter 29

Again I step forward in time from the postwar years. It was 1963, and John Crooks was visiting me once more. He lay back in his chair and laughed.

"You know, Jim, I often think about your Russian trip, and honestly, it doesn't sound as though you had a very comfortable time. Force nine gales, only just avoiding being thrown into jail, nearly savaged by a killer dog—not my idea of pleasure. In fact, I feel a bit guilty about sending you out there."

"Please don't feel like that, John," I said. "I loved it. Wouldn't have missed it for anything."

He sat up. "I've been thinking. You deserve a bit of luxury and relaxation after that, and I've got just the thing for you."

"What's that?"

"Well, I'll tell you." He leaned closer, his eyes eager. John's natural enthusiasm and eloquence had pushed him to the top in veterinary practice and like most people, I fell easily under his spell. "Last spring I had the most wonderful voyage to Istanbul with a cargo of Jersey cows. How would you like that?"

"Istanbul?" Immediately my mind was full of the mysterious East. Mosques, minarets, blue skies, tranquil seas, exotic perfumes, Scheherazade . . .

"Yes, Jim, and it was memorable. We sailed from Hull to

Jersey, picked up the cattle from there and came right round to Gibraltar. After that, it was just a beautiful Mediterranean cruise. The cows never ailed a thing, and all I did was eat lovely food, bask out on the deck and sleep in a super cabin. The sea hardly rippled, the sun shone all the time and I saw places I'd only dreamed about: the Greek Islands, the coast of Asia and, of course, Istanbul itself."

"Fascinating city, they say."

"It certainly is," John said. "And really, you have to see it for yourself. You can't describe it—it's magic."

"Did you have some spare time to look around?"

"Oh yes, the whole trip took seventeen days, and I had a full two days to explore. The cattle were unloaded as soon as we arrived, and after that my time was my own. The Export Company put me up in a five-star hotel, too—luxury room, gourmet food—I tell you, it was terrific. Talk about living like a sultan!"

"And you got paid for that?"

"Yes, and so will you."

"You really mean I can go?"

"Yes, Jim, of course you can." John smiled. "There's another load of Jerseys to go over there in August, and I'll book you in."

I rubbed my hands. "That's marvellous, but how about you? Don't you want another trip?"

"Oh, it would be very nice, but I can't leave the practice too often. It would have to be you or another of my friends."

It was the beginning of another little adventure. For the next few weeks as I drove on my rounds, the green hills and bracken-clad slopes that sped past my windows were intermingled with the heady scenes of my imaginings. New places have always intrigued me, and as I have said before, I have seafaring blood. I could smell the salty freshness of the wide ocean that had thrilled me on the voyage to Klaipeda; only this time it would be sunshine and a calm sea and one of the most exciting cities in the world at the end of it.

As John promised, I had a telephone call at the beginning of August from Mr. Costain, the representative of the Export Company.

"I'd like you to be here at two o'clock on Thursday, the eighth, at our offices," he said. "And then I'll take you out to Gatwick."

"Gatwick?"

"Yes, that's right. The plane takes off at around eight o'clock in the evening."

"Plane! I thought we were going by sea."

Mr. Costain laughed for quite a long time at this. "No, no, no —whatever gave you that idea?"

"John Crooks did."

"Ah, well, as it happened John did go by sea, and I suppose it was natural he would think the next trip would be the same. But you'll thoroughly enjoy the flight, and it means you get the whole thing over quickly. Less than four days."

"I see." I didn't want to get the whole thing over quickly. I had been looking forward to that leisurely seventeen days. But never mind, this could be fun, too.

"Right," I said. "I'll see you on the day."

The night before I left, I packed the same attaché case I had taken to Russia. Antibiotics, calcium, steroids, bandages and suture materials. I hoped I would not have to use anything in that case, particularly the humane killer lying in the corner.

August 8, 1963

On the train to London my enthusiasm grew steadily. It was a pity about the sea voyage, and I was sorry that it would not be worth keeping a daily diary on such a short trip. I would have to write it up later. But on the other hand, I liked flying, and it would be interesting to see the reaction of the animals. On the Klaipeda voyage I had learned a lot about the behaviour of animals aboard ship, and now I had the chance to observe the reaction of cows to being whisked into the air. I felt a faint twinge of alarm when

I remembered a story of how a veterinary surgeon had been in charge of some racehorses flying to America, and one of the animals had gone berserk and kicked a hole in the side of the aircraft. But I put away the disturbing image. Jersey cows would never do that.

Another happy thought was that I was able to take my camera and bring back a record of my adventure. That had been forbidden on the Russian trip.

Mr. Costain was pleasant and friendly. We took the train to Gatwick, and I had my first view of our aircraft standing a few hundred yards away out on the airfield. It looked very smart, its red, white and silver-grey paint glittering in the sunshine.

"Gosh, it's big!" I said.

Mr. Costain nodded. "Yes, it's a Globemaster, and to the best of my knowledge it is the biggest aircraft in the world at the present time."

I don't know whether he was right about this but it was easy to believe, because as we approached the Globemaster it seemed to get larger all the time. It also became less smart because on closer inspection the paint wasn't nearly as glossy and there was a faint air of delapidation about the whole mighty machine. The rubber was worn smooth and frayed in parts and, in fact, if you took a motor car out with tyres like that you would be fined and have your licence endorsed.

There were four propellor engines, and along one side the name *Heracles* sprawled in large red letters.

I climbed up the steps into the flight cabin, and here the impression of age and a long, hard life was stronger still. The black paintwork had been almost rubbed away from the bank of dials and levers in the cockpit, leaving the bare metal gleaming through, and the seats showed the outline of their contents bulging dangerously against their leather coverings. A curtain, when drawn aside, revealed a toilet of the most primitive type. This was, indeed, an elderly aeroplane.

I looked back wonderingly at the enormous empty belly stretching away to the tail and at that moment Mr. Costain poked his head in from the steps.

"Tremendous, isn't it?" he said. "It was used as a troop carrier and general transport during the war."

I nodded silently. That was quite a long time ago.

We walked back together to the airport terminal and had a cup of tea and a sandwich while keeping an eye open for the arrival of the cattle. I learned that we were taking forty pedigree cows and heifers, and as the time stretched round to half-past six, I wondered just how they were going to be loaded in time for an eight o'clock take-off.

At length two cattle wagons rumbled onto the airfield, and we hurried to meet them. I was pleased and relieved to find that two Jersey farmers were joining us on the flight, and I was introduced to them before the loading started. They were both dark-haired and spoke with a slow drawl, very different from my Yorkshire clients. Noel would be in his early thirties, smiling and with an ingenious air about him; Joe, probably ten years older, similarly amiable but, it seemed to me, a hard man at bottom. He was easy to like, but I couldn't imagine him suffering fools gladly.

It didn't take me long to realise that the two of them knew what they were doing. One of the Globemaster's crew, a little Dane called Karl, operated an electric hoist with tubular metal sides that descended from the underside of the aircraft, while Joe and Noel led the cattle up a ramp and jockeyed them into position until the hoist was full and they could be lifted up.

Above, in the cavernous interior, they arranged the animals in rows of six facing the front, with a metal tube clamped behind each row.

Those farmers were good stocksmen. There was no shouting, no brandishing of sticks, just a continual gentle nudging and pushing and soft words of encouragement. And, of course, they had the ideal subjects to handle. I have often said that I wished all cows were Jerseys, and I felt it again that day.

I do not think I have ever seen a more beautiful group of cattle —mostly heifers with a few young cows, and all of them fine-boned and graceful, with their lambent, kind eyes regarding us with mild interest as they took their places.

It was a steamy, hot London evening and as Joe and Noel toiled, the sweat streamed down their faces. But, like my Yorkshire farmers, hard work seemed to be something they took for granted. Sleeves rolled high on their sunburned arms, they kept at it without pausing.

More than half the animals had been loaded when the main members of the crew arrived. Captain Birch looked down at me from a gaunt six feet four as he shook hands, and the sombre face above the black, grey-flecked beard emanated authority. This was a man of formidable presence.

The co-pilot and navigator, Ed, and the engineer, Dave, were in their twenties and grinned cheerfully as they hoisted their bags into the flight cabin. The captain was English and dressed in a formal dark uniform, but these young men were American, and their clothing intrigued me. They wore white, loose-fitting jackets and trousers of a light-weight material which, with their peaked caps cocked at an angle, gave them a carefree appearance.

As I thought, there was no possibility of an eight o'clock take-off, and it was nearly eleven when the last heifer was loaded and clamped in safely. The forty cattle were quite a sight as they stood patiently in their rows, their feet deep in straw and an armful of hay in front of each of them. The long stretch of backs made a ripple of fawn gold under the interior lights of the aircraft. One snag was that the heat in the packed interior was almost overpowering, and I prayed that some ventilation would come into operation when we were airborne.

Mr. Costain prepared to leave. He had spent quite a long time in a financial negotiation, almost a wrangle with the captain, about the cost of the transportation, and I gathered that the captain either owned the aircraft personally or was a top director of the firm that did. They came to an agreement at last, and Mr. Costain shook my hand.

"Have a good trip, Mr. Herriot," he said. "You will be refuelling in Rome and reach Istanbul early tomorrow. I know you'll love that city. Goodbye."

The thought of this huge, heavily loaded aeroplane landing anywhere on those bald tyres gave me a moment of disquiet, but I put it out of my mind and sat down with Joe and Noel on one of the battered seats in the cabin.

We waited and waited for something to happen, but a seemingly interminable discussion was going on in the cockpit. The humans in the aircraft were quite clearly in two camps—the crew and the cattlemen—and the only attention we three got during this period was a piercing look from the captain and a stern admonition. "You'll look after these cattle, won't you? They are very valuable and they're my responsibility. You'll keep a constant eye on them, I hope."

"Of course," I replied. "That's what we're here for." I spoke confidently, but I had no idea how the animals would react when this monster began to roar its way into the sky. If they started to run amuck and break their legs there wasn't much I could do but use my humane killer, and I didn't think the captain would be overjoyed at that.

The two farmers and I talked in the dimly lit cabin during the long wait. They told me of their stock troubles and I described the veterinary life in Yorkshire, then, to our relief, around 1 A.M., the aircraft's engine began to cough into life. We actually started to taxi along to the end of the runway.

This was the moment I had been waiting for, and I turned in my seat and gazed over the forty sleek backs as the aircraft began to roll. The engines bellowed, the vast frame shook and juddered as the machine hurtled down the runway, then there was the wrench of lift-off and the sensation of climbing, climbing.

And all those cattle did was sway gently from side to side, their eyes looking at me, calm and untroubled. Some even nibbled at their hay as we rose into the night sky.

Thank heaven, flying seemed to be second nature to them, and I was relaxing happily when I noticed a commotion in the cabin. The huge undercarriage had not retracted fully and Karl, Dave and Ed were pulling with all their strength on a loop attached to it. After a few moments of concentrated effort, the wheels came up with a clunk, and the crewmen returned to their places. They did this calmly, as though it were a regular procedure. I wondered idly how many other things didn't work on this aeroplane.

I was grateful for one thing—my worries about the heat had been groundless because as we climbed, the atmosphere became steadily colder.

It had been a long day for Noel, Joe and me. We had left home early that morning and we dozed fitfully on the uncomfortable seats in the semi-darkness, glancing at our charges from time to time. After a few hours, I was jerked to wakefulness. We were coming in to land, descending quickly over the lights of an air-field. I watched the cattle again as we bumped and rattled along the runway, but they took it all with the same aplomb as before.

When we halted, I looked out at a brightly lit sign—Munchen.

"Refuelling," Karl muttered. Mr. Costain said it would be Rome, and it was Munich. The nagging little thought returned that nothing about this trip since John Crooks first drew the scenario had turned out as expected.

Anyway, we had landed safely on those awful tyres and we took off, too, without disaster, although once more Karl and Dave had to haul with all their might until the undercarriage thumped into position.

By 5 A.M., the two farmers and I were weary and desperate to stretch our cramped limbs. Finally Joe beckoned to us to follow him, and we groped our way down by the side of the animals right to the tail of the aircraft, where a deep pile of hay was lying. He stretched out and Noel and I followed suit.

Again, this was different from my friend John's bed in his cabin on the Mediterranean, but it was heaven. I closed my eyes and floated away. The captain had adjured us to do our duty carefully, but I couldn't keep my eyes open anymore. And though I was thousands of feet up somewhere in the dark skies above Yugoslavia, I might have been back in Darrowby, because the scents and the sounds were the same. The fragrance of hay, the sweet bovine smell and the soft grunting, coughing and champing of many cattle. These were familiar things and they lulled me into slumber within minutes.

Bright sunshine was streaming into the aircraft when I opened my eyes again. I looked at my watch—seven o'clock. The two farmers were still nestled motionless in the hay, and I got to my feet and looked with a touch of anxiety along the rows of cattle. I need not have worried; they were as contented as if they had been in their byres in Jersey. Some were lying in the straw; others stood chewing their cud. It was a peaceful scene.

It was not peaceful, however, in the flight cabin and cockpit. In fact, as I gazed beyond the animals to the front of the aircraft, I could see evidence of intense activity. The crew members were leaping around, staring at the starboard window and operating controls which I couldn't see.

I pushed my way past the metal standings to the cabin and had a look for myself.

The starboard inner engine had been switched off, and its four propellor blades hung motionless as oil gushed from its interior, spiralling into the flawless blue of the sky, flowing in black tendrils over the wing and spattering against the window. Nobody bothered to say good morning to me. There was no panic but there was definitely consternation.

As I looked, I saw that there was something more alarming than an oil leak. Flames were licking around the engine cowling, and a long tongue of fire crept back towards the wing. I scarcely had time to digest the meaning of all this when the flames disappeared, apparently extinguished by the crew's efforts.

There was a general relaxation in the cockpit, and some wan smiles were exchanged.

I heard a whisper in my ear. "Some bloody aeroplane, this, Jim boy." Joe had joined me at the window and was looking with disbelief at the still, scarred engine. Behind him, Noel was wide-eyed but silent.

On our three engines we flew on through the cloudless sky, and below, a turquoise sea sparkled. Soon we began to lose height, and I looked down on a great city with domes and minarets abounding. This was indeed some bloody aeroplane, but it had got us to Istanbul.

Chapter
30

Mr. Garrett's words about parents needing nerves of steel have come back to me many times over the years. One notable occasion was the annual recital given by Miss Livingstone's piano class.

Miss Livingstone was a soft-voiced, charming lady in her fifties who started many of the local children in piano lessons, and once a year she held a concert in the Methodist Hall for her pupils to show their paces. They ranged from six-year-olds to teenagers, and the room was packed with their proud parents. Jimmy was nine at the time and had been practising without much enthusiasm for the big day.

Everybody knows everybody else in a small town like Darrowby, and as the place filled up and the chairs scraped into position, there was much nodding and smiling as people recognised each other. I found myself on the outside chair of the centre aisle, with Helen on my right, and just across the few feet of space I saw Jeff Ward, old Willie Richardson's cowman, sitting very upright, hands on knees.

He was dressed in his Sunday best, and the dark serge was stretched tightly across his muscular frame. His red, strong-boned face shone with intensive scrubbing, and his normally wayward thatch of hair was plastered down with brilliantine.

"Hello, Jeff," I said. "One of your youngsters performing today?"

He turned and grinned. "Now then, Mr. Herriot. Aye, it's our Margaret. She's been comin' on right well at t'piano, and I just hope she does herself justice this afternoon."

"Of course she will, Jeff. Miss Livingstone is an excellent teacher. She'll do fine."

He nodded and turned to the front as the concert commenced. The first few performers who mounted the platform were very small boys in shorts and socks or tiny girls in frilly dresses, and their feet dangled far above the pedals as they sat at the keyboard.

Miss Livingstone hovered nearby to prompt them, but their little mistakes were greeted with indulgent smiles from the assembly, and the conclusion of each piece was greeted with thunderous applause.

I noticed, however, that as the children grew bigger and the pieces became more difficult, a certain tension began to build up in the hall. The errors weren't so funny now, and when little Jenny Newcombe, the fruiterer's daughter, halted a couple of times, then bowed her head as though she were about to cry, the silence in the room was absolute and charged with anxiety. I could feel it myself. My nails were digging into my palms and my teeth were tightly clenched. When Jenny successfully restarted and I relaxed with all the others, the realisation burst upon me that we were not just a roomful of parents watching our children perform; we were a band of brothers and sisters, suffering together.

When little Margaret Ward climbed the few steps to the platform, her father stiffened perceptibly in his seat. From the corner of my eyes I could see Jeff's big, work-roughened fingers clutching tightly at his knees.

Margaret went on very nicely till she came to a rather complicated chord which jarred on the company with harsh dissonance. She knew she had got the notes wrong and tried again . . . and again . . . and again, each time jerking her head with the effort.

"No, C and E, dear," murmured Miss Livingstone, and Margaret crashed her fingers down once more, violently and wrongly.

"My God, she's not going to make it," I breathed to myself,

aware suddenly that my pulse was racing and that every muscle in my body was rigid.

I glanced round at Jeff. It was impossible for anybody with his complexion to turn pale, but his face had assumed a hideously mottled appearance and his legs were twitching convulsively. He seemed to sense that my gaze was on him, because he turned tortured eyes towards me and gave me the ghastly semblance of a smile. Just beyond him, his wife was leaning forward. Her mouth hung slightly open and her lips trembled.

As Margaret fought for the right notes, a total silence and immobility settled on the packed hall. It seemed an eternity before the little girl got it right and galloped away over the rest of the piece, and though everybody relaxed in their seats and applauded with relief as much as approval, I had the feeling that the episode had taken its toll of all of us.

I certainly didn't feel so good and watched in a half-trance as a succession of children went up and did their thing without incident. Then it was Jimmy's turn.

There was no doubt that most of the performers and parents were suffering from nerves, but this couldn't be applied to my son. He almost whistled as he trotted up the steps, and there was a hint of swagger in his walk up to the piano. This, he clearly thought, was going to be a dawdle.

In marked contrast, I went into a sort of rigor as soon as he appeared. My palms broke out in an instant sweat, and I found I was breathing only with difficulty. I told myself that this was utterly ridiculous, but it was no good. It was how I felt.

Jimmy's piece was called "The Miller's Dance," a title burned on my brain till the day I die. It was a rollicking little melody which, of course, I knew down to the last semi-quaver, and Jimmy started off in great style, throwing his hands about and tossing his head like Artur Rubinstein in full flow.

Around the middle of "The Miller's Dance," there is a pause in the quick tempo where the music goes from a brisk ta-rum-tum-tiddle-iddle-om-pom-pom to a lingering taa-rum, taa-rum, before starting off again at top speed. It was a clever little ploy of the composer and gave a touch of variety to the whole thing.

Jimmy dashed up to this point with flailing arms till he slowed down at the familiar taa-rum, taa-rum, taa-rum. I waited for him to take off again, but nothing happened. He stopped and looked down fixedly at the keys for a few seconds, then he played the slow bit again and halted once more.

My heart gave a great thud. Come on, lad, you know the next part—I've heard you play it a hundred times. My voiceless plea was born of desperation, but Jimmy didn't seem troubled at all. He looked down with mild puzzlement and rubbed his chin a few times.

Miss Livingstone's gentle voice came over the quivering silence. "Perhaps you'd better start at the beginning again, Jimmy."

"Okay." My son's tone was perky as he plunged confidently into the melody again, and I closed my eyes as he approached the fateful bars. Ta-rum-tum-tiddle-iddle-om-pom-pom, taa-rum, taa-rum, taa-rum,—then nothing. This time he pursed his lips, put his hands on his knees and bent closely over the keyboard as though the strips of ivory were trying to hide something from him. He showed no sign of panic, only a faint curiosity.

In the almost palpable hush of that room, I was sure that the hammering of my heart must be audible. I could feel Helen's leg trembling against mine. I knew we couldn't take much more of this.

Miss Livingstone's voice was soft as a zephyr or I think I would have screamed. "Jimmy, dear, shall we try it once more from the beginning?"

"Yes, yes, right." Away he went again like a hurricane, all fire and fury. It was unbelievable that there could ever be a flaw in such virtuosity.

The whole room was in agony. By now the other parents had come to know "The Miller's Dance" almost as well as I did, and we waited together for the dread passage. Jimmy came up to it at breakneck speed. Ta-rum-tum-tiddle-iddle-om-pom-pom, then taa-rum, taa-rum, taa-rum . . . and silence.

Helen's knees were definitely knocking now, and I stole an anxious glance at her face. She was pale, but she didn't look ready to faint just yet.

As Jimmy sat motionless except for a thoughtful drumming of his fingers against the woodwork of the piano, I felt I was going to choke. I glared around me desperately, and I saw that Jeff Ward, across the aisle, was in a bad way. His face had gone all blotchy again, his jaw muscles stood out in taut ridges and a light sheen of perspiration covered his forehead.

Something had to break soon, and once more it was Miss Livingstone's voice which cut into the terrible atmosphere.

"All right, Jimmy, dear," she said. "Never mind. Perhaps you'd better go and sit down now."

My son rose from the stool and marched across the platform. He descended the steps and rejoined his fellow pupils in the first few rows.

I slumped back in my seat. Ah, well, that was it. The final indignity. The poor little lad had blown it. And though he didn't seem troubled, I was sure he must feel a sense of shame at being unable to get through his piece.

A wave of misery enveloped me, and though many of the other parents turned and directed sickly smiles of sympathy and friendship at Helen and me, it didn't help. I hardly heard the rest of the concert, which was a pity because as the bigger boys and girls began to perform, the musical standard rose to remarkable heights. Chopin nocturnes were followed by Mozart sonatas, and I had a dim impression of a tall lad rendering an impromptu by Schubert. It was a truly splendid show—by everybody but poor old Jimmy, the only one who hadn't managed to finish.

At the end, Miss Livingstone came to the front of the platform. "Well, thank you, ladies and gentlemen, for the kind reception you have given my pupils. I do hope you have enjoyed it as much as we have."

There was more clapping, and as the chairs started to push back, I rose to my feet, feeling slightly sick.

"Shall we go then, Helen?" I said, and my wife nodded back at me, her face a doleful mask.

But Miss Livingstone wasn't finished yet. "Just one thing more, ladies and gentlemen." She raised a hand. "There is a young man here who, I know, can do much better. I wouldn't be happy going home now without giving him another opportunity. Jimmy." She beckoned towards the second row. "Jimmy, I wonder . . . I wonder if you would like to have one more try."

As Helen and I exchanged horrified glances, there was an immediate response from the front. Our son's voice rang out, chirpy and confident. "Aye, aye, I'll have a go!"

I couldn't believe it. The martyrdom was surely not about to start all over again. But it was true. Everybody was sitting down, and a small, familiar figure was mounting the steps and striding to the piano.

From a great distance I heard Miss Livingstone again. "Jimmy will play 'The Miller's Dance.'" She didn't have to tell us—we all knew.

As though in the middle of a bad dream, I resumed my seat. A few seconds earlier, I had been conscious only of a great weariness, but now I was gripped by a fiercer tension than I had known all afternoon. As Jimmy poised his hands over the keys, a vibrant sense of strain lapped around the silent room.

The little lad started off as he always did, as though he hadn't a care in the world, and I began a series of long, shuddering breaths designed to carry me past the moment that was fast approaching. Because I knew he would stop again. And I knew just as surely that when he did, I would topple senseless to the floor.

I didn't dare look round at anybody. In fact, when he reached the crucial bars I closed my eyes tightly. But I could still hear the music—so very clearly. Ta-rum-tum-tiddle-iddle-om-pom-pom, taa-rum, taa-rum, taa-rum . . . There was a pause of unbearable length, then, tiddle-iddle-om-pom, tiddle-iddle-om-pom, Jimmy was blissfully on his way again.

He raced through the second half of the piece, but I kept my eyes closed as the relief flooded through me. I opened them only when he came to the finale, which I knew so well. Jimmy was making a real meal of it, head down, fingers thumping, and at the last crashing chord, he held up one hand in a flourish a foot above the keyboard before letting it fall by his side in the true manner of the concert pianist.

I doubt if the Methodist Hall has ever heard a noise like the great cheer which followed. The place erupted in a storm of clapping and shouting, and Jimmy was not the man to ignore such an accolade. All the other children had walked impassively from the stage at the end of their efforts, but not so my son.

To my astonishment, he strode from the stool to the front of the platform, placed one arm across his abdomen and the other behind his back, extended one foot and bowed to one side of the audience with the grace of an eighteenth-century courtier. He then reversed arms and pushed out the other foot before repeating his bow to the other side of the hall.

The cheering changed to a great roar of laughter which continued as he descended the steps, smiling demurely. Everybody was still giggling as we made our way out. In the doorway we bumped into Miss Mullion, who ran the little school our son attended. She was dabbing her eyes.

"Oh, dear," she said breathlessly. "You can always depend on Jimmy to provide the light relief."

I drove back to Skeldale House very slowly. I was still in a weak condition, and I felt it dangerous to exceed twenty-five miles an hour. The colour had returned to Helen's face, but there were lines of exhaustion round her mouth and eyes as she stared ahead through the windscreen.

Jimmy, in the back, was lying full-length along the seat, kicking his legs in the air and whistling some of the tunes that had been played that afternoon.

"Mum! Dad!" he exclaimed in the staccato manner so typical of him. "I like music."

I glanced at him in the driving mirror. "That's good, son, that's good. So do we."

Suddenly he rolled off the back seat and thrust his head between us. "Do you know why I like music so much?"

I shook my head.

"Because it's"—he groped rapturously for the phrase—"because it's so soothing."

Chapter
31

When Walt Barnett asked me to see his cat, I was surprised. He had employed other veterinary surgeons ever since Siegfried had mortally offended him by charging him ten pounds for castrating a horse, and that had been a long time ago. I was surprised, too, that a man like him should concern himself with the ailments of a cat.

A lot of people said Walt Barnett was the richest man in Darrowby—rolling in brass which he made from his many and diverse enterprises. He was mainly a scrap merchant, but he had a haulage business, too, and he was a dealer in second-hand cars, furniture, anything, in fact, that came his way. I knew he kept some livestock and horses around his big house outside the town, but there was money in these things, and money was the ruling passion of his life. There was no profit in cat keeping.

Another thing that puzzled me as I drove to his office was that owning a pet indicated some warmth of character, a vein of sentiment, however small. It just didn't fit into his nature.

I picked my way through the litter of the scrap yard to the wooden shed in the corner from which the empire was run. Walt Barnett was sitting behind a cheap desk and he was exactly as I remembered him, the massive body stretching the seams of the shiny, navy-blue suit, the cigarette dangling from his lips, even the brown trilby hat perched on the back of his head. Unchanged, too, was the beefy red face with its arrogant expression and hostile eyes.

"Over there," he said, glowering at me and poking a finger at a black and white cat sitting among the papers on the desk.

It was a typical greeting. I hadn't expected him to say, "Good morning," or anything like that, and he never smiled. I reached across the desk and tickled the animal's cheek, rewarded by a rich purring and an arching of the back against my hand. He was a big tom, long-haired and attractively marked, with a white breast and white paws, and though I have always had a predilection for tabbies, I took an immediate liking to this cat. He exuded friendliness.

"Nice cat," I said. "What's the trouble?"

"It's 'is leg. There's summat wrong with that 'un there. Must've cut 'isself."

I felt among the fluffy hair, and the little creature flinched as I reached a point halfway up the limb. I took out my scissors and clipped a clear area. I could see a transverse wound, quite deep, and discharging a thin, serous fluid. "Yes . . . this could be a cut. But there's something unusual about it. I can't see how he's done it. Does he go out in the yard much?"

The big man nodded. "Aye, wanders around a bit."

"Ah, well, he may have caught it on some sharp object. I'll give him a penicillin injection and leave you a tube of ointment to squeeze into the wound night and morning."

Some cats object strongly to hypodermics, and since their armoury includes claws as well as teeth, they can be difficult, but this one never moved. In fact, the purring increased in volume as I inserted the needle.

"He really is good-natured," I said. "What do you call him?"

"Fred." Walt Barnett looked at me expressionlessly. There didn't appear to be anything particularly apposite about the name, but the man's face discouraged further comment.

I produced the ointment from my bag and placed it on the desk. "Right, let me know if he doesn't improve."

[285]

I received no reply, neither acknowledgment nor goodbye, and I took my leave feeling the same prickle of resentment as when I had first encountered his boorishness.

But as I walked across the yard, I forgot my annoyance in my preoccupation with the case. There was something very peculiar about that wound. It didn't look like an accidental laceration. It was neat and deep, as though somebody had drawn a razor blade across the flesh. I listened as I had listened so often before to that little inner voice—the voice that said things were not as they seemed.

A touch on my arm brought me out of my musings. One of the men who had been working among the scrap was looking at me conspiratorially. "You've been in to see t'big boss?"

"Yes."

"Funny thing, t'awd bugger botherin' about a cat, eh?"

"I suppose so. How long has he had it?"

"Oh, about two years now. It was a stray. Ran into 'is office one day, and, knowin' him, I thought he'd 'ave booted it straight out, but 'e didn't. Adopted it, instead. Ah can't reckon it up. It sits there all day on 'is desk."

"He must like it," I said.

"Him? He doesn't like anythin' or anybody. He's a . . ."

A bellow from the office doorway cut him short.

"Hey, you! Get on with your bloody work!" Walt Barnett, huge and menacing, brandished a fist, and the man, after one terrified glance, scuttled away.

As I got into my car, the thought stayed with me that this was how Walt Barnett lived—surrounded by fear and hate. His ruthlessness was a byword in the town, and though no doubt it had made him rich, I didn't envy him.

I heard his voice on the phone two days later. "Get out 'ere sharpish and see that cat."

"Isn't the wound any better?"

"Naw, it's wuss, so don't be long."

Fred was in his usual place on the desk, and he purred as I went up and stroked him, but the leg was certainly more painful. It was disappointing, but what really baffled me was that the wound was bigger instead of smaller. It was still the same narrow slit in the skin, but it had undoubtedly lengthened. It was as though it was trying to creep its way round the leg.

I had brought some extra instruments with me, and I passed a metal probe gently into the depths of the cut. I could feel something down there, something which caught the end of the probe and sprang away. I followed with long forceps and gripped the unknown object before it could escape. When I brought it to the surface and saw the narrow brown strand, all became suddenly clear.

"He's got an elastic band round his leg," I said. I snipped the thing through, withdrew it and dropped it on the desk. "There it is. He'll be all right now."

Walt Barnett jerked himself upright in his chair. "Elastic band! Why the 'ell didn't you find it fust time?"

He had me there. Why the hell hadn't I? In those days my eyesight was perfect, but on that first visit all I had seen was a little break in the skin.

"I'm sorry, Mr. Barnett," I said. "The elastic was embedded in the flesh, out of sight." It was true, but I didn't feel proud.

He puffed rapidly at the ever-present cigarette. "And 'ow did it get there?"

"Somebody put it on his leg, without a doubt."

"Put it on . . . wot for?"

"Oh, people do that to cats. I've heard of cases like this but never actually seen one. There are some cruel folk around."

"One o' them fellers in the yard, ah'll wager."

"Not necessarily. Fred goes out in the street, doesn't he?"

"Oh, aye, often."

"Well, it could have been anybody."

There was a long silence as the big man sat scowling, his eyes half-closed. I wondered if he was going over the list of his enemies. That would take some time.

"Anyway," I said. "The leg will heal very quickly now. That's the main thing."

Walt Barnett reached across the desk and slowly rubbed the cat's side with a sausagelike forefinger. I had seen him do this several times during my previous visit. It was an odd, unsmiling gesture, but probably the nearest he could get to a caress.

On my way back to the surgery I slumped low in the car seat, hardly daring to think of what would have happened if I hadn't found that elastic. Arrest of circulation, gangrene, loss of the foot or even death. I broke into a sweat at the thought.

Walt Barnett was on the phone three weeks later, and I felt a twinge of apprehension at the sound of the familiar voice. Maybe I wasn't out of the wood yet.

"Is his leg still troubling him?" I asked.

"Naw, that's 'ealed up. There's summat matter with 'is head."

"His head?"

"Aye, keeps cockin' it from side to side. Come and see 'im."

This sounded to me like canker, and, in fact, when I saw the cat sitting on the desk twisting his head around uneasily, I was sure that was it, but the ears were clean and painless.

This amiable cat seemed to like being examined, and the purring rose to a crescendo as I made a close inspection of his teeth, mouth, eyes and nostrils. Nothing. Yet something up there was causing a lot of discomfort.

I began to work my way through the black hair, and suddenly the purring was interrupted by a sharp "miaow" as my fingers came upon a painful spot on his neck.

"Something here," I murmured. I took out my scissors and began to clip. And as the hair fell away and the skin showed through, a wave of disbelief swept through me. I was looking down at a neat little transverse slit, the identical twin of the one I had seen before.

My God, surely not on the neck. I went into the wound with probe and forceps, and within seconds I had brought the familiar brown band to the surface. A quick snip and I pulled it clear.

"More elastic," I said dully.

"Round 'is neck!"

"Afraid so. Somebody really meant business this time."

He drew his enormous forefinger along the furry flank, and the cat rubbed delightedly against him. "Who's doin' this?"

I shrugged. "No way of telling. The police are always on the lookout for cruelty, but they would have to catch a person actually in the act."

I knew he was wondering when the next attempt would come, and so was I, but there were no more elastic bands for Fred. The neck healed rapidly, and I didn't see the cat for nearly a year till one morning Helen met me as I was coming in from my round.

"Mr. Barnett's just been on the phone, Jim. Would you please go at once? He thinks his cat has been poisoned."

Another attack on this nice little animal, and after all this time. It didn't make sense, and my mind was a jumble as I hurried into Walt Barnett's office.

I found a vastly different Fred this time. The cat was not in his old place on the desk but was crouched on the floor among a litter of newspapers. He did not look up, but as I went over to him, he retched and vomited a yellow fluid onto the paper. More vomit lay around among pools of diarrhea which had the same yellowish hue.

Walt Barnett, overflowing the chair behind the desk, spoke past the dangling cigarette. "He's poisoned, isn't 'e? Somebody's given 'im summat."

"It's possible. . . . " I watched the cat move slowly to a saucer of milk and sit over it in the same crouching attitude. He did not drink but sat looking down with a curious immobility. There was a sad familiarity in the little animal's appearance. This could be something worse even than poison.

"Well, it is, isn't it?" the big man went on. "Somebody's tried to kill 'im again."

"I'm not sure." As I took the cat's temperature, there was none of the purring or outgoing friendliness I had known before. He was sunk in a profound lethargy.

The temperature was 105°F. I palpated the abdomen, feeling the doughy consistency of the bowels, the lack of muscular tone.

"Well, if it's not that, what is it?"

"It's feline enteritis. I'm nearly certain."

He looked at me blankly.

"Some people call it cat distemper," I said. "There's an outbreak in Darrowby just now. I've seen several cases lately, and Fred's symptoms are typical."

The big man heaved his bulk from behind the desk, went over to the cat and rubbed his forefinger along the unheeding back. "Well, if it's that, can you cure 'im?"

"I'll do my best, Mr. Barnett, but the mortality rate is very high."

"You mean, most of 'em die?"

"I'm afraid so."

"How can that be? I thought you fellers had all them wonderful new medicines now."

"Yes, but this is a virus, and viruses are resistant to antibiotics."

"Awright, then." Wheezing, he drew himself upright and returned to his chair. "What are you goin' to do?"

"I'm going to start right now," I said. I injected electrolytic fluid to combat the dehydration. I gave antibiotics against the secondary bacteria and finished with a sedative to control the vomiting. But I knew that everything I had done was merely supportive. I had never had much luck with feline enteritis.

I visited Fred each morning, and the very sight of him made me unhappy. He was either hunched over the saucer or he was curled up on the desk in a little basket. He had no interest in the world around him.

He never moved when I gave him his injections. It was like pushing a needle into a lifeless animal, and on the fourth morning I could see that he was sinking rapidly.

"I'll call in tomorrow," I said, and Walt Barnett nodded without speaking. He had shown no emotion throughout the cat's illness.

Next day, when I entered the office, I found the usual scene —the huge figure in his chair, brown trilby on the back of his head and cigarette hanging from his lips, the cat in the basket on the desk.

Fred was very still and as I approached, I saw with a dull feeling of inevitability that he was not breathing. I put my stethoscope over his heart for a few moments, then looked up.

"I'm afraid he's dead, Mr. Barnett."

The big man did not change expression. He reached slowly across and rubbed his forefinger against the dark fur in that familiar gesture. Then he put his elbows on the desk and covered his face with his hands.

I did not know what to say; I watched helplessly as his shoulders began to shake and tears welled between the thick fingers. He stayed like that for some time, then he spoke.

"He was my friend," he said.

I still could find no words, and the silence was heavy in the room until he suddenly pulled his hands from his face.

He glared at me defiantly. "Aye, ah know what you're thinkin'. This is that big, tough bugger, Walt Barnett, cryin' his eyes out over a cat. What a joke! I reckon you'll have a bloody good laugh later on."

Evidently he was sure that what he considered a display of weakness would lower my opinion of him, and yet he was so wrong. I have liked him better ever since.

Chapter
32

August 9, 1963

There was a general chattering and lightening of spirits when we landed safely and taxied to a halt. With everybody else, I climbed out and looked around. We were standing on a wide, concreted airfield. Nearby there was a hangar; away on the other side a long stretch of coarse grass ran down to the sea, and over everything the beautiful hot sunshine washed in a comforting flood. The airport buildings were about a quarter of a mile away and far beyond in the shimmering heat haze I could make out the high buildings of the city. It was just eight o'clock. We would unload the cattle, and then there would be most of the day to explore Istanbul. I felt a tinge of excitement at the prospect.

The two farmers were soon ready for action, jackets off, sleeves rolled up. Noel grinned at me as he flexed his muscles after the long night of inactivity. "Where are the wagons?" he asked.

It was a good question. Where indeed were they? They should have been awaiting our arrival, but I scanned the airfield in vain. Karl went over to the buildings to make enquiries but returned looking despondent.

"Nobody knows," he said. "We wait."

So we waited as the sun beat on the concrete and the sweat trickled inside our shirts. It was over an hour later when the wagons rolled up.

Just then, the captain's tall form hovered over me. "Mr. Herriot." The grave eyes looked down, and he ran a finger over his beard. Again I felt the impact of a masterful personality. "Mr. Herriot, there are a few things I must do. I have to see about getting that engine repaired and there is the hotel accommodation to arrange. I am leaving now and I rely on you to supervise things here."

"Okay," I replied. "Don't worry. I'll see that the animals are all right."

He nodded slowly. "Good, good." Then he swept the two farmers with his unsmiling gaze. "And that goes for you chaps, too. I don't want any of you to leave this spot until the last cow has been taken away. You do understand me?"

We mumbled our assent. I don't suppose many people would have tried to argue with Captain Birch. Anyway, the mention of the hotel had lit a cheerful spark in me as I remembered John Crooks's description of his five-star opulence. I am not attracted by continual luxury, but I do like a little bit now and again. Especially now. I was hot and sweaty and very hungry. The sandwiches at Gatwick were only a hazy memory, and the thought of a bath and a good meal was idyllic. I wanted the unloading to be as quick as possible.

The farmers seemed to have the same idea because they already had the first batch of heifers on the hoist. Little Karl pulled a lever, there was a long, high-pitched whine, but nothing happened. He operated the lever again with the same result.

"The hoist, she is jammed," he said and began to fiddle about with switches and other parts of the mechanism. Finally he dealt the shining metal a vicious kick. He shrugged his shoulders and looked at us. "Is no good. I have to get electrician."

He ambled off to the airport buildings, and the three of us were left looking at each other in some dismay. It was getting hotter by the minute.

It was half-past ten before he returned with a man in white overalls who appeared determined to take the hoist to pieces. He muttered and exclaimed in Turkish all the time, and I just hoped he knew his business because he was taking an age to find the cause of the trouble. Finally, after an hour and a half, the hoist answered to the pull on the lever and began to move. But we had lost a lot of time.

Meanwhile, it was reassuring to see a party of mechanics working on the damaged engine. I hoped even more fervently that they knew their stuff.

As Noel and Joe leaped into action and commenced the unloading, a party of Turkish vets arrived to inspect the animals. They were a most impressive group—handsome, olive-skinned men in smart light-weight suits, much more prosperous-looking than the average British vet. Only one of them spoke English, but he did so almost without accent.

"Beautiful creatures, Mr. Herriot," he murmured as the first cattle were ushered up the ramp into the wagons. The other vets, too, clucked their appreciation, and I felt personally proud that Britain could still lead the world in this field. So many countries had to turn to our green pastures to find livestock to improve their own strains.

The head man explained that they were all government vets from the Turkish Ministry of Agriculture, and their job was to examine the animals for health and to ensure that all the ear numbers were correct. We both laughed heartily at this because it seemed that in Turkey an ear number is as world-shakingly important and sacrosanct as in England.

The unloading was a painfully slow business. The electrician hadn't done a perfect job because the hoist kept stopping in mid-air for tense periods while Karl tugged at the lever and swore, but it always restarted and the work went on.

Fortunately, the animals' wagons were shaded by the hangar because the sun was truly fierce. Also, they had water and some hay, so they were comfortable.

The same could not be said of the farmers and myself. I was dirty, sweaty, unshaven and starving, and I was only popping up

[294]

and down from aircraft to ground, supervising things. How Joe and Noel felt, wrestling with the cattle, I could not imagine. And all the time Istanbul lay tantalisingly out of reach.

As the hours wore on and the sun blazed, there was no sign of the captain, but the two young Americans, Ed and Dave, wandered over frequently to inspect the repairs on the engine. Occasionally they stopped and chatted to me about their life and job, and I found them most likable men. They didn't seem to have a care in the world. They slouched around smilingly in their baggy suits, hands deep in their pockets. Those pockets, I was to find later, were filled with the currency of a dozen nations. Pesetas rubbed shoulders with drachmas, guilders, lira, dimes, kroner, shillings. They roamed the world in their old aircraft, free as birds, taking each day and new country as it came, and, though hardly more than boys, they must have seen almost everything. They have remained in my mind as true soldiers of fortune.

It was around four o'clock when the last heifer entered its wagon and the Turkish vets were completing their examination. Noel came up to me. His shirt was a wet rag clinging to his chest, and he wiped his streaming face with his forearm. "I tell you, Jim," he said. "Moi stomach thinks moi throat's cut."

"Mine too, Noel," I replied. "I'm ravenous. I've gone nearly round the clock since the sandwiches at Gatwick."

"Oi could murder a pint, too," Joe put in. "Can't remember when oi've had such a bloody thirst on."

It seemed that our troubles weren't over yet. The vets were taking their time over the inspection, but at any rate there did not seem to be any complaints. They were clearly satisfied with what they saw.

Unfortunately, this did not last. From our place under the Globemaster's wing where we were sheltering from the sun, we saw a sudden stillness fall on the group of men. They were looking in a cow's ear and consulting a sheaf of papers again and again and even from a distance I sensed the tension. There followed a consultation, and then a lot of waving of arms.

[295]

Finally the head vet shouted across, "Mr. Herriot, come here, please!"

With the farmers I walked over to the wagon.

"Mr. Herriot," the man went on, "we have found a wrong number." His dark complexion had paled, and his lips trembled. The expressions on the faces of the other men in the group were uniformly distraught.

I groaned inwardly. The unthinkable had happened.

One of the vets, upright and set-faced, waved me towards the offending cow with a dramatic gesture of his arm. I climbed into the wagon and looked in the ear. It was number fifteen. With the same theatrical flourish, the vet handed me the sheaf of papers. They contained the descriptions, ages and numbers of the animals, and, sure enough, no number fifteen.

I smiled weakly. I wasn't quite sure whether this was my responsibility or not. I had checked off all the numbers on our own sheet when we loaded at Gatwick, and I had thought they all tallied. Had I made some awful boob? It made it worse being so far from home.

I turned to Joe. "You brought the list from Jersey, didn't you?"

"Oi did," Joe replied with an edge of belligerence in his voice. "And it's correct. It's in moi bag."

"Slip over and get it, will you, Joe?" I said. "We'll see if we can sort this out."

The farmer strolled unhurriedly to the Globemaster, climbed inside and duly returned with the sheet.

Breathlessly I scanned the list. "There it is!" I said triumphantly. "Pedigree number, then number fifteen!" Relief flowed through me. We were saved.

The Turkish vet took Joe's list and retired for a further consultation. For a long time there was an incomprehensible chattering and much brandishing of arms, then apparently there was a unanimous decision. All the men nodded firmly, and some of them folded their arms. The head man stepped forward, taut-faced.

"Mr. Herriot, we have concluded that there is only one thing to do. You will understand that we have to follow our own list. There is no guarantee that this is the animal which we purchased originally, so with regret I have to tell you that you must take her back."

"Take her back!" This was a bombshell. "But that's impossible!" I cried. "This cow doesn't just come from England, she is from the Island of Jersey. I can't see any way of doing what you say."

"I am sorry," he said, "but nothing can change our decision. We cannot accept a wrong animal. How you do it is your concern, but you must take her back."

"But . . . but . . . "I quavered. "How do you know it's a wrong animal? The whole thing is probably a simple clerical error at your office."

He drew himself up to his full height. He was a well-fleshed six-footer, and he looked most impressive as he stared at me and held up his hand. "Mr. Herriot, I repeat, what I have said is irrevocable."

"I . . . I . . . well, you see . . . " I was beginning to gabble when I felt Joe's hand on my arm. He eased me gently to one side and stepped up in front of the head vet. He put his hands on his hips and pushed his craggy, sweat-streaked face close to the man's moustache. His steady eyes held the imperious stare of the Turk for several seconds before he spoke.

"Oi ain't takin' 'er baack, mate," he said in his slow drawl. "That's *moi* job, and oi ain't takin' 'er baack." The voice was soft, the words unhurried, but they held a wonderful note of finality, and the effect was dramatic. The big man's facade collapsed with startling suddenness. His whole face seemed to crumble, and he looked at Joe with an almost pathetic appeal. His mouth opened and I thought he was going to say something, but instead he turned slowly and rejoined his friends.

There was a murmured consultation, punctuated by shrugging

of shoulders and sorrowful glances in the farmer's direction, then the head man gave the signal for the wagons to move away. The battle was over.

"Bless you, Joe," I said. "I thought we'd had it that time."

We obeyed the captain's instructions and hung around till the cows had left the airfield. It pleased me to think they were heading for a good life. They were all going to top-class pedigree farms; in fact, they were animal VIP's.

I was also pleased when my Turkish colleagues came up and bade us goodbye in the most cordial manner. I had an uncomfortable feeling that the incident might have spoiled their day, but they were all smiles and appeared to have recovered magically.

I looked at my watch. Five o'clock. We had been out on that oven of an airfield for nine hours. It was actually seven o'clock Turkish time, so the precious day was fast slipping away. I felt at the stubble on my chin. The first thing was a shave and a wash.

With the farmers, I made my way over to the airport terminal, and in the men's room we stripped off, drank a lot of water and made our ablutions. I have a vivid memory of a little man who kept dabbing talc on my bare back all the time. I thought he was working for a tip, but all he wanted was one of my razor blades, which I gave him.

"That's better," Noel said as we came into the lounge. "If only we could get some grub. Oi'm famished."

I knew how he felt. My appetite now was wolfish, but surely food couldn't be far away.

This hope received a boost when we saw the towering form of Captain Birch striding towards us.

"I've been looking for you fellows," he said. "There are a few things I want to tell you. Come and sit down over here."

We arranged ourselves on padded chairs round a small table, and the sombre eyes looked us over for a few moments before he spoke.

"I don't know who is in charge of your party, but I'll address my remarks to you, Mr. Herriot."

"Right."

"Now, I'm sorry to tell you that all attempts to rectify the oil leak in the engine have failed."

"Oh."

"This means that we will have to fly the aircraft on three engines to our headquarters in Copenhagen for major repairs."

"I see."

"It also means that you chaps can't come with us."

"What!"

His expression softened. "I'm sorry to have to spring this on you, but the position is, frankly, that the aircraft is in an unsafe condition, and we are not allowed to carry passengers or any personnel but the crew."

"But . . . " I asked the obvious question. "How do we get home?"

"I've been thinking about that," the captain replied. "The obvious thing is to contact the Export Company in London by telephone—I have their number here—and I'm sure they will make arrangements for you to be flown to England."

"Well . . . thank you . . . I suppose that would be the thing to do." Another thought occurred to me. "You say the aircraft is unsafe?"

The majestic head nodded gravely. "That is so."

"In other words, you might never make Copenhagen."

"Quite. There is that possibility. Flying over the Alps under these circumstances is going to be a little tricky."

"But how about you? How about you and the crew?"

"Ah yes." He smiled, and suddenly he looked like a kind man. "It's good of you to ask, but this is our job. We have to go, don't you understand? It's our job."

I turned to the farmers. "Well, I suppose we'd better do as the captain says?"

They nodded silently. They looked shattered, and I felt the same. But I took the point about that strange aeroplane. If one engine had given up, how reliable were the other three?

"I'd better find a phone, then. Will I do it from here or from the hotel?"

The captain cleared his throat. "That's another thing I was going to mention. I haven't been able to find a hotel."

"Eh?"

"Afraid not," he said. "I've tried everywhere, but it's some kind of a public holiday here, and all the hotels are booked."

I had nothing to say to this. Everything was turning out great.

"But don't worry," he went on. "I am assured that if we go a few miles up the Bosporus, we'll find some little place which will put us up."

Some little place . . . The visions of five-starred splendour evaporated rapidly.

"Yes, of course."

The captain smiled again encouragingly. "I've got a minibus outside. We'll soon find somewhere."

Dave and Ed were already installed in the little vehicle, lounging comfortably in their silky suits.

"Hi," they said cheerfully. "Hi," said little Karl, grinning at us from the back seat. Such contretemps were no doubt part of their normal lives, and they were taking everything in their stride. I made a sudden resolve to do the same. Things were looking a bit sticky, but I was here in Istanbul and I was going to enjoy what little time I had.

I fished out my camera. I had taken some pictures of the flight and of the Globemaster during the unloading. Even if it was a fleeting thing, I would capture some memories of this city.

As the minibus shot through the streets, I snapped away like mad, and when I wasn't snapping, I was devouring the scene greedily. The knowledge that I was going to have only a short time in these surroundings made every new spectacle imprint itself on my mind.

As we sped through the teeming traffic on that gloriously sunny evening, exquisite mosques and minarets towered incongruously over modern tenements, then unexpectedly there would be a long stretch of waste ground with stubbly, scorched grass and garish billboards. Tremendous stone aqueducts, ancient and overgrown, appeared briefly in our windows and were gone before I could do more than catch them on my film. The massive ruins of the walls of old Constantinople, the crumbling fortresses on the shattered walls—I glimpsed them briefly, but even today among my photographs I can still look at the slightly blurred images beyond the smeared glass.

Among all these wonders eddied the Istanbul street scene—the vendors of coloured cordials, sweetmeats and peaches, the dark-skinned pedestrians in Kemal Ataturk's obligatory westernised clothes: the women in cotton dresses, the men in an outfit of shirt and slacks so unvarying that it looked like a uniform.

Soon we were running along the side of the Bosporus, surely one of the most beautiful and romantic waterways in the world —wide and blue, bounded by tree-lined hills where elegant houses and even palaces nestled. Families sunned themselves on chairs on the little beaches, while out on the water a great variety of craft lay at anchor. There were large modern ships, fishing smacks and some wonderful old wooden vessels.

I had fair opportunity to view the Bosporus because we kept stopping in our efforts to find accommodation. At last we were successful, and we climbed out of the minibus in front of a small building. It wasn't Claridges, nor was it a flea pit. It was an unpretentious little hotel up a side street.

The members of the staff were friendly and cheerful, but I had a strong impression that they couldn't care less whether we stayed there or not. I managed to communicate to the manager that I wanted to telephone London. Smilingly he assured me that I would have to go to the local post office for that and said there was a taxi nearby.

The taxi whirled me through the streets with the same reckless speed as our minibus driver. This is something I had noticed straightaway; all traffic seemed to proceed at about seventy miles an hour.

[301]

At the post office I explained my needs to a little fat lady, who nodded and smiled repeatedly. She knew enough English to assure me that all would be well.

She lifted a phone and made enquiries. Turning back to me, she beamed happily. "Long wait, maybe hour. You go back hotel, I send taxi."

When I got back to the hotel, all my colleagues had been installed in rooms. There seemed to be no reception desk, so I asked various members of the staff where I was to sleep. My queries were received with uncomprehending shrugs until I found the manager again. He seemed to take a certain amount of pleasure in telling me that there was no room for me, but my obvious dismay softened his heart, because he took me downstairs and showed me into a cell-like apartment in the basement where he left me. There was a single unmade bed with a rumpled pile of blankets on a chair in a corner. That was all, but I was thankful for it. The bathroom was a long, long way away.

But then all my senses were submerged by one thing—the smell of food. A rich, spicy aroma was beginning to pervade the little place, and I began to stumble towards its source. I suppose eating nothing for more than twenty-four hours is an unimportant detail to people who go on diets and visit health farms, but I have always believed in a regular hearty intake, and at that moment I was more ravenous than I have ever been in my life.

I found the dining room where the crew and the farmers were already at the table, and as I sat down with them, the glorious victuals began to arrive—great heaped-up plates of kebabs resting on beds of saffron rice and peppers, steaming bowls of mixed vegetables and an abundance of coarse Turkish bread. I love bread, and I bit into this stuff immediately. It was delicious, and Ed laughed as he saw my expression. "Good, isn't it?" he said. "It's got sunflower seeds in it."

Whether it had or it hadn't, it was some of the best bread I have ever tasted. But I couldn't wait to get at the serious eating, and I was poising my fork over the skewer laden with chunks of assorted meats when the taxi driver burst into the room.

"Mr. Herroot, come quick. Phone, phone!"

I could have wept. To have my food snatched from me before I had even started was too much. But this was important. I dropped my fork and hurried out. Once more I was swept at breakneck speed to the post office, where the fat lady, still all smiles, indicated the phone.

I tried a lot of, "Hello, hello," before I heard anything, and then it was a faint voice in the crackling distance. "Meester Harrioot, Meester Harrioot." I replied with a, "Yes, yes, Herriot speaking," but that was as far as I got. I don't want to bore anybody with a detailed account of my session with that phone. Sufficient to say that it lasted about three-quarters of an hour and was made up of long silences, hopeful clicks and crackles and every few minutes that tiny voice, "Meester Harrioot." My desperate outbursts were totally wasted.

Only once was there a shaft of light in the darkness, when a very English female voice said loudly as though from the same room, "Oh, God, I can't hear a thing!" That was evidently London, and I set up an almost tearful yammering in reply, but the silence came down again, and though I waited hopefully the voice never came back.

As I looked out at the gathering dusk in the street, the realisation grew on me that I was never going to get through.

I thanked the fat lady and left.

At the hotel I didn't know how much to pay the taxi driver, so I held out a handful of notes. A huge grin split his face as he selected a few, but before he could get them into his pocket a little man, apparently one of the staff, dashed down the steps and grabbed the money from him. He reduced the amount by about half which he handed back to me, then he shook his fist in the man's face and showered him with eloquent abuse before getting out of the car.

The driver's big grin never slipped, and he bade me good night with a courteous wave of the hand before leaving.

I thanked my benefactor, but as I passed into the hotel, my spirits were touching zero. I was stranded in Istanbul with no prospect of ever returning to hearth and home, my relaxing trip to the Orient had so far turned out to be a fairly steady-going fiasco, I was hungrier than I had ever been in my life and I had missed my supper.

On top of that, I wasn't looking forward to telling my two nice farmers that I had failed them. Not my fault, of course, but it had been left to me to organise something, and I was coming back empty-handed.

Joe and Noel were waiting for me in the dining room. I was touched that they were more concerned about my food than their immediate future.

Noel leaped to his feet. "We asked them to keep it warm for you, Jim," he cried and ran from the room.

Within minutes he was back with a tray with the entire meal, including the gorgeous bread.

They watched in silence as I devoured everything down to the last crumb, then they looked at me expectantly.

"I'm sorry, chaps," I said. "I had no joy there." I gave them details of my forty-five minutes in the post office.

When I had finished my story, they looked pretty glum. Joe stared down at his knees. "What the 'ell are we goin' to do, Jim?"

A few minutes ago I would have been compelled to say I had no idea, but maybe the food had stimulated my brain because suddenly everything became clear.

"I didn't bring much with me from home," I said. "But I did bring a cheque book. I'll go to the B.E.A. desk at the airport tomorrow and get three tickets to London. The Export Company will reimburse me later. It's obvious, isn't it? There was no need for all that phoning tonight."

The mood of our little company cheered magically, and we

were doing a bit of mutual backslapping when I saw the captain passing the doorway.

I ran out and told him about our plan.

"Yes," he said seriously. "That sounds like a good scheme." He paused and looked at his watch. "The only alternative would be to go to the British Consul, but it's after nine now—I don't suppose they'd be able to arrange anything at this time of night, and we're taking off at ten o'clock tomorrow morning. No, I think yours is the best idea."

When he had gone, we were gripped by a frothy elation.

"We got nothing to worry about, Jim, boy," said Joe. "So we might as well enjoy ourselves. Oi could still murder that pint, so · let's go out on the town and enjoy ourselves.

Joe's pint was our immediate goal, and there is no doubt we were three country cousins because searching for a pub in a Muslim city is a fruitless venture, but, full of enthusiasm, we piled into a taxi.

The night life of Istanbul seemed to be just getting into its stride. The streets were crowded, and the traffic had, if possible, speeded up after dark. Our taxi catapulted between other hurtling vehicles, the driver exchanging a running fire of shouted insults with his colleagues. I was relieved when he deposited us in what we hoped was the city centre.

Immediately, in the warm darkness, I was reminded that we were in the Orient. I could see nothing now of the romantic buildings and ruins, only the lighted shop windows, but the air was filled with mysterious scents, and over everything hung the heavy aroma of Turkish tobacco.

My other overriding impression was the noise: an unbroken, strident chorus of automobile horns of every conceivable pitch, punctuated by the screeching of brakes and the roar of engines.

In our search for a pub, we gazed into the windows of many interesting shops. Some were selling rugs and other souvenirs of the area, and I was intrigued by the large number of bakers who were turning out very sweet-looking cakes and confections and doing a brisk trade.

We stuck to one side of the street because it seemed like suicide to head into that boiling torrent of vehicles. There were, in fact, pedestrian crossings, but I noticed only one unfortunate little man trying to negotiate one. He was about halfway across when, to my horror, a car struck him and sent him flying high in a tangle of arms and legs. In Britain that motorist would have been heavily fined and received a dressing-down from the magistrates, but as I watched, a large, helmeted policeman loomed over the injured victim, who stood trembling in his inevitable shirt and slacks and rubbing his backside. The policeman shook his truncheon over the little man's head and bawled out a flood of vituperation, which was unintelligible to me except for one word which sounded very like "stupido" and vividly reflected his attitude in the matter. He never even looked at the driver of the car.

"Hey, look, Jim." Joe nudged me. "There's a lot of fellers goin' in there. How about it?"

Joe's quest for a pint was becoming an obsession, so I acquiesced and followed him through a doorway and up a long staircase. We came out on an open balcony which was really the flat roof of the shop beneath and, to the farmer's disgust, scores of shirt-sleeved men were sitting at tables, smoking and drinking coffee out of tiny cups.

We would have retreated then but a waiter was upon us, so we sat down and ordered the coffee. It was very thick and very sweet, and both Joe and Noel screwed up their faces, but I rather liked it. I also enjoyed just sitting there above the roar and smell of the city, taking in the atmosphere of the place. In my hurried visit to Istanbul this is one of my persisting memories and, rightly or wrongly, it appealed to me as a typical scene.

After the coffee we resumed our tour of the streets, with Joe becoming more depressed by the minute. Then he suddenly gave tongue. "Look in there, lads! That's a bit more like it!" He pointed through a window at a big, brightly lit room where a large number of men and women were sitting around, drinking from tall glasses. There wasn't a coffee cup in sight.

He did not hesitate but opened a swing door and bustled inside, with Noel and I following. We sat down at a vacant table, and Joe beckoned to a waiter.

"Drink! Drink!" he said, and when the man's face registered polite incomprehension, he made the unmistakable motion of raising a glass to his lips.

The waiter smiled immediately and brought a tray bearing three tumblers of bright-red liquid. I offered him money, but he shook his head, laughed and walked away.

"What the 'ell's this?" Joe grunted. He tried a sip and pulled a worse face than over the coffee. "It's bloody lemonade!" he spluttered.

I tried it myself. It wasn't lemonade. It was a bland, syrupy concoction, sickly sweet and obviously non-alcoholic. It was too sugary for me, but Noel, who, I suspected, wasn't much of a drinker, seemed to enjoy it.

"All right, this," he said, imbibing contentedly.

Joe looked at him in disgust. Like me, he could not tackle the stuff, whatever it was, and with an air of defeat he flopped back in his chair.

Within a few minutes, the same waiter came back with a dish of cakes and pastries and laid them before us. Again he refused any money and walked away, laughing and shaking his head.

Biting into one of the sticky cakes, I found it had the same characteristic as the coffee and the coloured drinks. It seemed to me that a sweet tooth would be a prerequisite for anybody living in Istanbul.

However, it was an interesting scene. The big room was crowded with beautifully dressed people—I noticed that most of the women wore white evening gowns—and they nibbled the cakes and drank from glasses like ours not only bright-red liquid but equally brilliant blue, green and yellow.

When I saw that several children were present, something

[307]

began to stir in the back of my mind. The children were playing among the tables, and some of the adults were moving from group to group as though they knew everybody.

"Hey, wait a minute," I said. "Do you know what I think?"

Joe gave me a sideways glance. "What?"

"I think this is a private party and we've gate-crashed it."

Both the farmers sat up suddenly as I went on. "Those kids down there and all the people seem to be friends. And remember that waiter who thought it was funny to be offered money?"

Just at that moment a handsome young couple appeared at the far end of the room, the man in a dark suit, the girl in a glittering, spangled bridal gown.

"My God!" I said. "It's a wedding reception!"

And it was, indeed. The newlyweds moved around among their guests, and when they reached us, I half expected to be thrown out, but, on the contrary, they seemed to regard our presence as a gracious courtesy visit. They bowed and shook hands with us and made us welcome with smiles and gestures. Before they moved on, the bride gave each of us a long silver thread. She did this with some ceremony, and I deduced that it was an honoured local custom, the thread having possibly been taken from her gown. In any case, I took it in this spirit, and I carried that thread in my wallet for many years thereafter until it gradually disintegrated.

We were still recovering from our surprise when two men in traditional Turkish dress appeared on a stage at the other end of the room. They were obviously entertainers and comedians to boot, because very soon the room was echoing with laughter. It was strange for the three of us sitting there to hear the totally unintelligible cross talk, followed by the roars of mirth, the little children jumping up and down and clapping their hands in delight.

They were versatile chaps, those two. When they had finished being funny, one of them produced a one-string fiddle and began

[308]

to play, while the other sang in that peculiar wail which is associated only with Eastern countries.

I had no way of telling whether it was a love song, a happy song or a sad song, but as I listened to that strange ululation going on and on, I felt very far from home.

It was about then that my eyelids began to droop. I remembered that I had had only two hours' sleep the night before and that rather a lot had happened in a short time. I was very tired, and when I turned to look at my farmer friends, I saw that Joe was nodding and Noel was slumbering peacefully, his chin on his chest.

I stood up and suggested that we ought to leave. They didn't need much persuading.

Back in the hotel, I descended to my basement room and made up the bed from the pile of blankets on the chair. I would have fallen asleep immediately but from somewhere quite close at hand came the same wailing which I had heard at the wedding reception. At first I thought I was dreaming but then I realised there was a party going on in one of the hotel rooms. It was a noisy party, too, with screams of laughter, outbursts of music, thumping of dancing feet. It went on and on, and it must have been the middle of the night before the din subsided and I fell into an exhausted sleep.

Chapter
33

I stood, head bowed, leaning on my great guillotine which stood chest high. It occurred to me that my pose was exactly that of the executioner resting against his axe as I had seen in old pictures of the beheading of Sir Walter Raleigh and other unfortunates.

However, I wasn't wearing a hood; I was standing in a deep-strawed fold yard, not on a scaffold; and I was waiting for a bullock to be dehorned, not for a hapless victim to lay his head upon the block.

In the fifties, bovine horns quite suddenly went out of fashion. To veterinary surgeons and most farmers their passing was unlamented. Horns were at best a nuisance, at worst extremely dangerous. They worked their way under vets' coats and pulled off the buttons and tore out pockets. They could whip round and bash the hand, arm or even the head of a man injecting the neck and, of course, in the case of a really wild cow or bull, they could be instruments of death.

Horns were a menace, too, to other bovines. Some cows and bullocks were natural bullies, and one animal could impose a reign of terror on its more timid neighbours, driving them away viciously from food troughs in open yards and inflicting savage wounds on any that resisted. The farmers in Yorkshire used to call these injuries "hipes," and they ranged from massive haematomata over the ribs to deep lacerations of the udder. It was strange how a boss cow would always go for the udder and the results were often ruinous. Since the passing of horns you never heard the word "hipe" now.

There were farmers, notably pedigree breeders, who attached great importance to well-set horns and pointed out that a neat, "cocky" little horn looked well in the show ring and that their highly bred animals would be disfigured, but their voices were lost in the tumult for abolition.

One down-to-earth dairyman said to me at the time, "You don't get much milk out of a bloody horn," and that seemed to be the general attitude.

From my own point of view, the only thing I missed was that convenient handle to get hold of a cow. For many years I had smacked one hand down on the horn, then pushed the fingers of the other hand into the nose, but after the dehorning revolution there was nothing to grasp. Most cows were expert at tucking their noses down on the ground or round the other side where you couldn't get at them, but that was a small thing.

So, by and large, the disappearance of these dangerous and largely useless appendages was a great blessing but, oh dear, there was one tremendous snag. The horns didn't just go away by themselves. They had to be removed by the vets, and that removal wrote a gory and ham-fisted chapter in veterinary history that still hangs like a dark cloud in my memory.

I suppose Siegfried and I reacted just like the other members of our profession. As the situation arose and we looked out on a countryside apparently dominated by a waving forest of horns, we wondered how we would start. Was it to be general or local anaesthesia? Did we saw them off or chop them off?

In the beginning the chop school appeared to hold sway, because there were many advertisements in the *Veterinary Record* for villainous-looking guillotines. We ordered one of these, but we both experienced a sense of shock when we unpacked it. As I said, it was nearly as tall as a small man and its weight was frightening.

Siegfried, groaning slightly, hefted the thing by its long wooden handles till the huge, sliding blades were at eye level, then he lowered it quickly and leaned against the wall.

He took a long, shuddering breath. "Hell, you need to be a trained athlete just to lift that bloody thing!" He paused in thought. "There's no doubt we'll need something like that for the big beasts, but surely we can find something else for the little stirks." He raised a finger. "James, I believe I know the very thing."

"You do?"

"Yes. I saw some nice light hedge-clippers in Albert Kenning's window yesterday. I bet they'd do the job. Tell you what—let's go round and try them."

When Siegfried had one of his ideas, he didn't mess about. Within seconds we were hurrying, almost at a trot, through the market place to the ironmonger's.

I followed close on Siegfried's heels as he burst into the shop.

"Albert!" he shouted. "Those hedge-clippers! Let's have a look at them!"

They certainly looked all right—round, gleaming, wooden shafts terminating in small, curved blades which crossed each other scissors-wise.

"Mm, yes," I said. "Do you think they'll be strong enough to cut through a little horn?"

"Only one way to find out." Siegfried brandished his new weapon. "Fetch me one of those canes, Albert!"

The little man turned towards a bundle of thick bamboos that were on sale for tying up flowers and shrubs. "These?"

"That's right. Look sharp."

Albert selected a cane and brought it over.

"Now, hold it out towards me," Siegfried said. "No, no, no, upright. That's fine, fine."

Starting at the top, he began to clip off inch lengths of the bamboo at lightning speed. The fragments flew in all directions, and Albert had to duck several times as they flew past his ears. But he was more anxious about his hand as the blades worked rapidly downwards. Apprehensively, he kept lowering his grasp until Siegfried made his final slash an inch above his thumb. Holding the tiny stump at arm's length, he looked wide-eyed at my colleague.

But Siegfried wasn't finished yet. He continued to chop away at the air, obviously enjoying his work. "Let's have another one, Albert!"

Wordlessly, the little man produced a second cane, half closed his eyes and held it as far away from his body as possible.

My colleague recommenced his onslaught with such vigour that the woody cylinders whizzed round the shop like machine-gun bullets. A customer entering by the door backed away and took cover behind a stack of milking buckets.

Albert had gone pale by the time Siegfried demolished the second cane, finishing once more just above the little man's thumb.

"Grand little machine, this, James." Siegfried hesitated, tried a few more practice snips, then turned to the ironmonger. "Just one more, Albert."

"Really, Mr. Farnon, don't ye think . . . "

"C'mon, c'mon, we've got work to do. Don't hang about!"

This time the little man's jaw dropped, and the cane wobbled uncontrollably in his grasp. Siegfried, obviously determined to make the most of this last test, put everything into his effort, and his movements were almost too rapid to follow. There was a brief fusillade of clippings, then Albert was left breathless, clutching his small remnant.

"Splendid!" Siegfried cried happily. "We'll take it. How much?"

"Twelve an' six," gasped the ironmonger.

"And the canes?"

"Oh, er . . . another shillin'."

My colleague delved in his pocket and pulled out a handful of notes, coins and small veterinary instruments. "There's a quid among that lot, Albert. Help yourself."

Tremblingly, the little man extracted the pound from Siegfried's palm, then crunched over the carpet of bamboo clippings to get change.

Siegfried crammed the money into his pocket without looking and tucked his new purchase under his arm. "Goodbye, Albert, and thank you," he said, and we left.

As I passed the shop window at a brisk pace, I could see the ironmonger following us wonderingly with his eyes.

The hedge-clippers did indeed perform nobly for us with the smaller bovines, but there were so many other complications. For a long time we used general anaesthesia by means of the chloroform muzzle, and when the animal collapsed unconscious, we whipped the horns off quickly. But we found to our dismay that the haemorrhage was massive and terrifying. Red jets fountained several feet in the air, spraying everything and everybody for yards around. In those days you could always tell when a vet had been out dehorning because his collar and face were spattered with blood.

An ingenious tourniquet was devised by laying a length of binder twine longways to the inside of each horn, then encircling both horns with another piece of twine. By knotting the first two tightly over the encircling one, the arteries were effectively compressed and haemorrhage was nil.

But then, often the chopping blades severed the twine and we were in trouble again.

As time passed, two advances emerged. The first was that by removing the horn by sawing and taking about half an inch of skin with it, there was virtually no bleeding. The second was that local anaesthesia was infinitely easier and more effective. It was quite simple to inject a few c.c.'s of local under the temporal ridge and into the branch of the fifth cranial nerve, which supplies the horn.

There was nothing to it, and it gave a perfect nerve block. The animal couldn't feel a thing.

I have seen cows chewing their cud while I sawed away, and this merciful improvement in our method signalled the end of all the old things. The horrible choppers and guillotines and tourniquets disappeared almost overnight.

Nowadays, of course, a horn is rarely seen anywhere because calves are painlessly disbudded early in life, using this same nerve block.

But, as I say, the whole period of adult dehorning left a scar on my memory, and it was during the guillotine period that Andrew Bruce came to visit me.

For several years after the war, people were still renewing contact with each other. The war brought the normal lives of so many to a full stop that the ensuing period was a time of taking stock, of looking around and wondering what had happened to one's friends.

Andrew and I had not met since our schooldays, and I hardly recognised the dark-suited, bowler-hatted figure on the doorstep. It turned out that he was doing very nicely in a bank in Glasgow and was on a business trip down south when he saw the sign to Darrowby and decided to pay me a call. A lot of my schoolmates seemed to have gone into banking, and since I have always had to use my fingers for counting, I regarded these men with a certain amount of awe.

"I don't know how you do it, Andy," I said after lunch. "I wouldn't last a couple of days in your job."

He shrugged and smiled. "Oh, it's meat and drink to me. I loved maths at school, if you remember."

"Oh yes." I shivered. "That's right. You used to get prizes for dreadful things like trigonometry."

We chatted for a few minutes over our coffee, then I stood up. "I'm afraid I've got to go," I said. "I have to be on a farm by two-fifteen."

"Okay, Jim. . . . " He hesitated for a moment. "Do you think I could come with you? I've never seen a country vet at work, and I could easily drive to Birmingham this evening."

I smiled. So many people wanted to accompany me on my rounds. There seemed to be some fascination in the veterinary life. "Of course you can, Andy. But I don't think you'll find it very entertaining. All I have is an afternoon's dehorning."

"Really? Sounds interesting. I'd love to come, if you don't mind."

I found a spare pair of Wellingtons for him, and we got into the car. As we drove away I noticed him looking around him: at the boxes of bottles and instruments on the back seat, at my clothes which contrasted so sharply with his own natty outfit. At that time I had discarded the breeches and leggings that were almost a vet's uniform when I qualified and now wore brown corduroy trousers with a sort of canvas jacket made for me by a German prisoner and which I had cherished for years.

The corduroys were frayed and stiffened with mud and muck, and the jacket, too, despite the protective clothing I always wore, bore ample evidence of my trade.

I could see Andy's nostrils wrinkling as he took in the rich bouquet of manure, dog hairs and assorted chemicals that was the normal atmosphere in my car, but after a few minutes he appeared to forget everything as he gazed out of the window.

It was a golden afternoon in October, and beyond the stone walls, the fell-sides, ablaze with their mantle of dead bracken, rose serenely into a deep, unbroken blue. We passed under a long canopy of tinted leaves thrown over us by the roadside trees, then followed a stretch of white-pebbled river before turning along a narrow track that led up the hillside.

Andrew was silent as we climbed into the stark, airy solitude that is the soul of the Dales, but as the track levelled out on the summit, he put a hand on my arm.

"Just stop a minute, Jim, will you?" he said.

I pulled up and wound down the window. For a few moments

he looked out over the miles of heathery moorland and the rounded summits of the great hills slumbering in the sunshine, then he spoke quietly as though to himself.

"So this is where you work?"

"Yes, this is it, Andy."

He took a long breath, then another, as if greedy for more.

"You know," he said. "I've heard a lot about air like wine, but this is the first time I've realised what it means."

I nodded. I always felt I could never get enough of that air, sharp and cool and tinged only with the grass scent that lingers in the high country.

"Well, you're a lucky beggar, Jim," Andrew said with a touch of weariness. "You spend your life driving around in country like this, and I'm stuck in a damned office."

"I thought you liked your job."

He ran a hand through his hair. "Oh yes, I suppose playing around with figures is what I'm best at but, oh hell, I have to do it all inside. In fact," he said, becoming a little worked up, "when I start to think about it, I live and have my being in a bloody centrally heated box with no windows and electric light blasting down all day, and I share what passes for air with a whole crowd of other people." He slumped back in his seat. "Makes me wish I hadn't come out with you."

"I'm sorry, Andy."

He laughed ruefully. "Oh, I didn't really mean that, but, honestly, this is idyllic."

At the end of the moor the land dipped into a lush valley where the herd of Mr. Dunning grazed and grew fat on the abundant grass around the farm buildings. The Dunnings were not dairymen, as was usual in the Dales, but raised beef cattle. And they did so on a large scale, with more than two hundred animals under their care.

I had been there for the last few afternoons, dehorning, and I was glad that this was my last visit because the bullocks on which I had been operating were massive three-year-old shorthorns, and

[317]

I had had a rough time. Nowadays, with the housewife's preference for smaller, leaner joints, most beef cattle are slaughtered at around eighteen months, and the kind of huge creatures I had to face at Mr. Dunning's are rarely seen any more.

As we drove into the farmyard, there were about twenty of them milling around in a collecting pen.

"We'll run 'em into the fold yard one at a time as usual," Mr. Dunning cried as he trotted towards me. He was a small, excitable man, bursting with energy, and his voice seldom fell below a piercing shout.

His sons, large young men with the classical Dales names of Thomas, James and William followed more slowly.

I introduced Andy, and he gazed with interest at the enormous boots, the work-worn clothes and the tangle of hair pushing from under the caps. The farmers, in turn, seemed similarly intrigued with my friend's pinstripes, gleaming white collar and tasteful tie.

Once the action commenced, Mr. Dunning launched into full cry, poking at the beasts' rumps with his stick and emitting shrill yelps of, "Haow, haow, cush-cush, get on there!"

Finally one of the bullocks trotted into the fold yard, and the brothers guided it into a loose box. I handed the chloroform muzzle in to them and leaned on my mighty guillotine, thinking how much easier life had become over the past few days.

At the start of this session I had applied every tourniquet myself, then buckled on the muzzle before putting the halter over the top. But farmers are very adaptable people and the brothers soon devised a better way.

On the second day, Thomas, the eldest, made a quiet suggestion. "We could put on them bands and the muzzle ourselves, Mr. Herriot, while you wait outside t'box."

I leaped happily at the idea. That rough binder twine had to be pulled very tight and my soft palms had been rubbed sore, but the horny fingers of the Dunning boys would be impervious to such a detail. Also, I would not be thrown around in the tying process.

As I leaned there, feeling again like an executioner, I bethought myself of my friend.

"Andy," I said, "I think it would be a good idea if you climbed up there." I pointed to one of a long row of square wooden feeding troughs known as "tumblers" which stretched down the middle of the straw-covered yard. Above them, running the full length of the tumblers, a hayrack dangled on chains.

He smiled indulgently. "Oh, I'll be all right here." He rested a shoulder against a post opposite the box and lit a cigarette. "I don't want to miss anything and, anyway, it sounds very interesting in there."

It did indeed sound interesting behind the wooden doors of the box. It always did. Gruff outbursts of "Ow!" "Stand still, ya bugger!" "Gerroff me foot!" blended with tremendous crashes as the big beast hurled itself against the timbers.

At length came the inevitable volley of yells. *"Right! 'e's comin' out!"*

I tensed myself as the doors were thrown wide and the great animal, festooned with binder twine and wearing the muzzle like a wartime gas mask, catapulted outwards, with two of the brothers hanging grimly to the halter.

As the bullock felt the straw around its knees, it paused for a moment in its headlong rush and looked around till the eyes, glaring above the rim of the muzzle, focussed on the elegant form of my friend leaning against the post. Then it put its head down and charged.

Andy, confronted by fourteen hundredweights of hairy beef hurtling towards him, did not linger. He vaulted onto the tumbler, grabbed the slats of the hayrack and swung himself to safety as the horns sent the tumbler crashing away beneath his feet. I recalled that he had been very good on the wall bars in the school gymnasium, and it was apparent that he had lost none of his agility.

Cradled in the fragrant clover, he looked down at me as the rack swung gently to and fro on its chains.

[319]

"I'd stay up there if I were you," I said.

Andy nodded. I could see he didn't need much persuading. He had lost a little colour, and his eyebrows were arched high on his forehead.

All three of the Dunning brothers were needed to bring the bullock to a halt, and they stood there, leaning back on the rope and breathing heavily as they waited for me to make the next move.

This was the tricky bit. I leaned the guillotine against a tumbler and slowly approached the beast. Opening the front of the muzzle, I trickled chloroform onto the sponge. At this moment I never knew what was going to happen. Some animals turned sleepy almost immediately, while others, on inhaling the strange vapour, seemed to resent my presence and took a sudden dive at me. And in the deep straw it was difficult to get out of the way.

I was relieved to see that this was one of the former type. His charge at Andy and his subsequent struggles had made him breathless, and as he gulped deeply at the anaesthetic, his eyes glazed and he began to sway. He took a few stumbling steps, toppled onto his side and slipped into unconsciousness.

Now I had to move fast. I struggled through the straw, grabbed the guillotine and dropped the cutting jaws over a horn. I seized the shafts and began to pull. With small animals a single swift clip did the job, but the horns of these big bullocks were extraordinarily wide at the base, and I had to haul away with all my strength for several panting seconds till the knives crunched together. I repeated the process with the other horn, and it was just as tough to remove.

"Right," I gasped. "Get the muzzle off him." I was sweating and I had done only one beast, with about nineteen to go.

The brothers leaped into action, unbuckling the muzzle and running to usher another bullock from the pen where their father was already screaming and flailing around him with his stick.

With the loss of a little more perspiration I did the second and third, but the fourth defeated me. The horns were so vast that I had to open the shafts wider and wider until they were almost in a straight line. I groaned and strained, but it was obvious I would never be able to close them. Thomas, who had the build of a heavyweight wrestler, came up behind me.

"Move in a bit closer, Mr. Herriot," he said.

I grasped the shafts halfway up their length, while Thomas seized the extreme ends in his great hands. Even with our united effort nothing happened for a few seconds, then the horn came off with a crack. But unfortunately I was the man in the middle, and as the shafts came together, they thudded with pitiless force against my ribs. It was the same with the other horn. Thomas had to help again, and my ribs took another hammering.

As the brothers trotted off for the next beast, I sank down on the straw and moaned softly, massaging my aching sides.

"Are you all right, Jim?" The voice came from above, and I looked up into Andy's anxious face. I had been vaguely aware of him all the time, rocking on his chains as he twisted around in the rack to see as much as possible.

I gave him a rueful smile. "Oh yes, Andy, I'm okay. Just a bit bruised."

"I don't doubt it. I wouldn't like that big bloke squeezing me in those choppers." My friend's head, protruding from the hay, was all I could see of him, but his eyes looked startled.

They looked still more startled when the next beast, at the first sniff of chloroform, launched himself forward and knocked me flat on my back. In fact, it was clear that little Mr. Dunning was upsetting the cattle with his constant shrieking and the poking with his stick.

Thomas thought so, too. "For God's sake, Dad," he said in his slow way. "Put that bloody stick away and shurrup." He spoke without anger because he was fond of his father, as indeed I was, because he was a nice little man at heart.

Mr. Dunning quieted down, but he could contain himself for only a brief spell. Very soon he was yelling again.

About halfway through, the dreaded accident happened. I chopped through the tourniquet on one of the horns.

"Quick! More twine!" I shouted, groping my way through the red fountains spurting high from the sleeping animal. I had to retie the tourniquet with the warm fluid spraying my face. There was no escape. As I pulled the last knot tight, I turned to Mr. Dunning.

"Could I have a bucket of warm water, some soap and a towel, please?" My eyes were almost closed, the lashes gummed with the fast-clotting blood.

The little man hurried to the house and was back soon with a steaming bucket into which I eagerly plunged my hands. A second later I was hopping round the fold yard, yelping with pain and shaking my scalded fingers.

"That bloody water's boiling hot!" I cried.

The brothers regarded me stolidly, but little Mr. Dunning was highly amused.

"Hee-hee, hee-hee, hee-hee." His high-pitched giggles went on and on. He hadn't seen anything so funny for a long time.

While he was recovering, William fetched some cold water and diluted the original sufficiently for me to give my hands and face a rough wash.

I went on with my work almost automatically and with increasing weariness. The driving of each bullock into the box, the bangings and oaths from behind the door, the final yell of *"He's comin' out!,"* then the straining and the chopping, and all the time in the back of my mind the question every veterinary surgeon of that era must have asked himself—"Why in heaven's name did I have to study five years at college just to do this?"

But at last I saw with relief that there was only one more to do. I had just about had enough. Thomas had done his nutcracker act on my ribs a few times more, and every muscle in my body seemed to be protesting. I watched thankfully as Mr. Dunning started to drive the beast into the yard.

This animal, however, was reacting differently to the little man's bawling and stick work. I remembered that the brothers had described the beast as being "bully-headed," and indeed there was a vibrant masculinity about this shape and expression which suggested that the bloodless castrators might not have done their work completely.

The shaggy head, instead of turning away from Mr. Dunning's importunities, kept pushing towards him. The little farmer poked at the nose with his stick but still it came on, and at that point Mr. Dunning evidently decided he would be better out of the way.

He walked off through the straw and the bullock walked after him. He broke into a trot and the bullock did the same. The trot became a stiff-legged gallop and the bullock followed suit.

At no time did the beast show any sign of charging the farmer, but Mr. Dunning didn't seem reassured. He kept on running and his face registered increasing alarm. His progress was impeded by the deep straw and it must have been like running in knee-high water but for all that, he cut out a very fair pace for a sixty-year-old.

Nobody interfered. Maybe we were all a bit irritated by his antics during the afternoon, but we stood back and laughed. I laughed so much that it hurt my bruised ribs as Mr. Dunning shot down one side of the row of tumblers, then up the other, with the big animal's nose a foot behind his neck. It might have been a Roman arena, with the mocking spectators and Andy away above rocking perilously in his cradle as he watched the chase.

It had to end sometime. After the second circuit Mr. Dunning's cap flew off, he made a few lunging strides, then fell flat on his face in the straw. The animal did nothing more than run over the top of him, then allowed itself to be caught as though the whole thing had been a tease.

The little farmer jumped to his feet, hurt only in his dignity, and glared at us as he retrieved his cap.

With the help of the brothers I dehorned the beast, and the afternoon's work was over.

We helped Andy down from the rack, and it took quite a while to brush the hayseeds from his smart serge. He watched impassively as I cleaned and dried my guillotine and with an effort heaved it into the boot. Then, with my own little brush, I washed the thick plastering of muck from my Wellingtons before putting on my shoes.

We got into the car and drove away into the darkening countryside. Andy lit another cigarette, and I could see him glancing at my sweaty, blood-flecked face and at my hand feeling the tenderness of my ribs under my jacket.

"Jim," he said at length. "It's funny how you can jump to conclusions. Maybe my own job isn't so bad after all."

Chapter
34

In the semi-darkness of the surgery passage I thought it was a hideous growth dangling from the side of the dog's face, but as he came closer, I saw that it was only a condensed milk can. Not that condensed milk cans are commonly found sprouting from dogs' cheeks, but I was relieved because I knew I was dealing with Brandy again.

I hoisted him onto the table. "Brandy, you've been at the dustbin again."

The big golden Labrador gave me an apologetic grin and did his best to lick my face. He couldn't manage it since his tongue was jammed inside the can, but he made up for it by a furious wagging of tail and rear end.

"Oh, Mr. Herriot, I am sorry to trouble you again." Mrs. Westby, his attractive young mistress, smiled ruefully. "He just won't keep out of that dustbin. Sometimes the children and I can get the cans off ourselves, but this one is stuck fast. His tongue is trapped under the lid."

"Yes . . . yes . . ." I eased my finger along the jagged edge of the metal. "It's a bit tricky, isn't it? We don't want to cut his mouth."

As I reached for a pair of forceps, I thought of the many other occasions when I had done something like this for Brandy. He was one of my patients, a huge, lolloping, slightly goofy animal, but this dustbin raiding was becoming an obsession.

He liked to fish out a can and lick out the tasty remnants, but his licking was carried out with such dedication that he burrowed deeper and deeper until he got stuck. Again and again he had been freed by his family or myself from fruit salad cans, corned beef cans, baked bean cans, soup cans. There didn't seem to be any kind of can he didn't like.

I gripped the edge of the lid with my forceps and gently bent it back along its length till I was able to lift it away from the tongue. An instant later, that tongue was slobbering all over my cheek as Brandy expressed his delight and thanks.

"Get back, you daft dog!" I said, laughing, as I held the panting face away from me.

"Yes, come down, Brandy." Mrs. Westby hauled him from the table and spoke sharply. "It's all very fine, making a fuss now, but you're becoming a nuisance with this business. It will have to stop."

The scolding had no effect on the lashing tail, and I saw that his mistress was smiling. You just couldn't help liking Brandy because he was a great ball of affection and tolerance, without an ounce of malice in him.

I had seen the Westby children—there were three girls and a boy—carrying him around by the legs, upside down, or pushing him in a pram, sometimes dressed in baby clothes. Those youngsters played all sorts of games with him, but he suffered them all with good humour. In fact, I am sure he enjoyed them.

Brandy had other idiosyncracies, apart from his fondness for dustbins.

I was attending the Westby cat at their home one afternoon when I noticed the dog acting strangely. Mrs. Westby was sitting, knitting in an armchair, while the oldest girl squatted on the hearth rug with me and held the cat's head.

It was when I was searching my pockets for my thermometer that I noticed Brandy slinking into the room. He wore a furtive

[326]

air as he moved across the carpet and sat down with studied carelessness in front of his mistress. After a few moments he began to work his rear end gradually up the front of the chair towards her knees. Absently, she took a hand away from her knitting and pushed him down, but he immediately restarted his backward ascent. It was an extraordinary mode of progression, his hips moving in a very slow rumba rhythm as he elevated them inch by inch, and all the time the golden face was blank and innocent, as though nothing at all were happening.

Fascinated, I stopped hunting for my thermometer and watched. Mrs. Westby was absorbed in an intricate part of her knitting and didn't seem to notice that Brandy's bottom was now firmly parked on her shapely knees which were clad in blue jeans. The dog paused, as though acknowledging that phase one had been successfully completed, then ever so gently he began to consolidate his position, pushing his way up the front of the chair with his fore limbs, till at one time he was almost standing on his head.

It was at that moment, just when one final backward heave would have seen the great dog ensconced on her lap, that Mrs. Westby finished the tricky bit of knitting and looked up.

"Oh, really, Brandy, you are silly!" She put a hand on his rump and sent him slithering disconsolately to the carpet, where he lay and looked at her with liquid eyes.

"What was all that about?" I asked.

Mrs. Westby laughed. "Oh, it's these old blue jeans. When Brandy first came here as a tiny puppy, I spent hours nursing him on my knee, and I used to wear the jeans a lot then. Ever since, even though he's a grown dog, the very sight of the things makes him try to get on my knee."

"But he doesn't just jump up?"

"Oh, no," she said. "He's tried it and got ticked off. He knows perfectly well I can't have a huge Labrador in my lap."

"So now it's the stealthy approach, eh?"

She giggled. "That's right. When I'm preoccupied—knitting

or reading—sometimes he manages to get nearly all the way up, and if he's been playing in the mud he makes an awful mess, and I have to go and change. That's when he really does receive a scolding."

A patient like Brandy added colour to my daily round. When I was walking my own dog, I often saw him playing in the fields by the river. One particularly hot day many of the dogs were taking to the water, either to chase sticks or just to cool off, but whereas they glided in and swam off sedately, Brandy's approach was quite unique.

I watched as he ran up to the river bank, expecting him to pause before entering. But, instead, he launched himself outwards, legs splayed in a sort of swallow dive, and hung for a moment in the air rather like a flying fox before splashing thunderously into the depths. To me it was the action of a completely happy extrovert.

On the following day in those same fields I witnessed something even more extraordinary. There is a little children's playground in one corner—a few swings, a roundabout and a slide. Brandy was disporting himself on the slide.

For this activity he had assumed an uncharacteristic gravity of expression and stood calmly in the queue of children. When his turn came he mounted the steps, slid down the metal slope, all dignity and importance, then took a staid walk round to rejoin the queue.

The little boys and girls who were his companions seemed to take him for granted, but I found it difficult to tear myself away. I could have watched him all day.

I often smiled to myself when I thought of Brandy's antics, but I didn't smile when Mrs. Westby brought him into the surgery a few months later. His bounding ebullience had disappeared, and he dragged himself along the passage to the consulting room.

As I lifted him onto the table, I noticed that he had lost a lot of weight.

"Now, what is the trouble, Mrs. Westby?" I asked.

She looked at me worriedly. "He's been off-colour for a few

days now, listless and coughing and not eating very well, but this morning he seems quite ill, and you can see he's starting to pant."

"Yes . . . yes . . . " As I inserted the thermometer I watched the rapid rise and fall of the rib cage and noted the gaping mouth and anxious eyes. "He does look very sorry for himself."

Temperature was 104. I took out my stethoscope and ausculated his lungs. I have heard of an old Scottish doctor describing a seriously ill patient's chest as sounding like a "kist o' whustles," and that just about described Brandy's. Rales, wheezes, squeaks and bubblings—they were all there against a background of laboured respiration.

I put the stethoscope back in my pocket. "He's got pneumonia."

"Oh, dear." Mrs. Westby reached out and touched the heaving chest. "That's bad, isn't it?"

"Yes, I'm afraid so."

"But . . . " She gave me an appealing glance. "I understand it isn't so fatal since the new drugs came out."

I hesitated. "Yes, that's quite right. In humans and most animals the sulpha drugs, and now penicillin, have changed the picture completely, but dogs are still very difficult to cure."

Thirty years later it is still the same. Even with all the armoury of antibiotics that followed penicillin—streptomycin, the tetracyclines, the synthetics and the new non-antibiotic drugs and steroids—I still hate to see pneumonia in a dog.

"But you don't think it's hopeless?" Mrs. Westby asked.

"No, no, not at all. I'm just warning you that so many dogs don't respond to treatment when they should. But Brandy is young and strong. He must stand a fair chance. I wonder what started this off, anyway."

"Oh, I think I know, Mr. Herriot. He had a swim in the river about a week ago. I try to keep him out of the water in this cold weather, but if he sees a stick floating, he just takes a dive into the middle. You've seen him—it's one of the funny little things he does."

"Yes, I know. And was he shivery afterwards?"

"He was. I walked him straight home, but it was such a freezing-cold day. I could feel him trembling as I dried him down."

I nodded. "That would be the cause, all right. Anyway, let's start his treatment. I'm going to give him this injection of penicillin, and I'll call at your house tomorrow to repeat it. He's not well enough to come to the surgery."

"Very well, Mr. Herriot. And is there anything else?"

"Yes, there is. I want you to make him what we call a pneumonia jacket. Cut two holes in an old blanket for his forelegs and stitch him into it along his back. You can use an old sweater if you like, but he must have his chest warmly covered. Only let him out in the garden for necessities."

I called and repeated the injection on the following day. There wasn't much change. I injected him for four more days, and the realisation came to me sadly that Brandy was like so many of the others—he wasn't responding. The temperature did drop a little, but he ate hardly anything and grew gradually thinner. I put him on sulphapyridine tablets, but they didn't seem to make any difference.

As the days passed and he continued to cough and pant and to sink deeper into a blank-eyed lethargy, I was forced more and more to a conclusion which, a few weeks ago, would have seemed impossible—that this happy, bounding animal was going to die.

But Brandy didn't die. He survived. You couldn't put it any higher than that. His temperature came down and his appetite improved, and he climbed onto a plateau of twilight existence where he seemed content to stay.

"He isn't Brandy anymore," Mrs. Westby said one morning a few weeks later when I called in. Her eyes filled with tears as she spoke.

I shook my head. "No, I'm afraid he isn't. Are you giving him the halibut liver oil?"

"Yes, every day. But nothing seems to do him any good. Why is he like this, Mr. Herriot?"

"Well, he has recovered from a really virulent pneumonia, but it's left him with a chronic pleurisy, adhesions and probably other kinds of lung damage. It looks as though he's just stuck there." She dabbed at her eyes. "It breaks my heart to see him like this. He's only five, but he's like an old, old dog. He was so full of life, too." She sniffed and blew her nose. "When I think of how I used to scold him for getting into the dustbins and muddying up my jeans. How I wish he would do some of his funny old tricks now."

I thrust my hands deep into my pockets. "Never does anything like that now, eh?"

"No, no, just hangs about the house. Doesn't even want to go for a walk."

As I watched, Brandy rose from his place in the corner and pottered slowly over to the fire. He stood there for a moment, gaunt and dead-eyed, and he seemed to notice me for the first time because the end of his tail gave a brief twitch before he coughed, groaned and flopped down on the hearth rug.

Mrs. Westby was right. He was like a very old dog.

"Do you think he'll always be like this?" she asked.

I shrugged. "We can only hope."

But as I got into my car and drove away, I really didn't have much hope. I had seen calves with lung damage after bad pneumonias. They recovered but were called "bad doers" because they remained thin and listless for the rest of their lives. Doctors, too, had plenty of "chesty" people on their books; they were, more or less, in the same predicament.

Weeks and then months went by, and the only time I saw the Labrador was when Mrs. Westby was walking him on his lead. I always had the impression that he was reluctant to move, and his mistress had to stroll along very slowly so that he could keep up with her. The sight of him saddened me when I thought of the lolloping Brandy of old, but I told myself that at least I had saved his life. I could do no more for him now, and I made a determined effort to push him out of my mind.

In fact, I tried to forget Brandy and managed to do so fairly well until one afternoon in February. On the previous night I felt I had been through the fire. I had treated a colicky horse until 4 A.M. and was crawling into bed, comforted by the knowledge that the animal was settled down and free from pain, when I was called to a calving. I had managed to produce a large live calf from a small heifer, but the effort had drained the last of my strength, and when I got home, it was too late to return to bed.

Ploughing through the morning round, I was so tired that I felt disembodied, and at lunch Helen watched me anxiously as my head nodded over my food.

There were a few dogs in the waiting room at two o'clock, and I dealt with them mechanically, peering through half-closed eyelids.

By the time I reached my last patient, I was almost asleep on my feet. In fact, I had the feeling that I wasn't there at all.

"Next, please," I mumbled as I pushed open the waiting-room door and stood back, expecting the usual sight of a dog being led out to the passage.

But this time there was a big difference. There was a man in the doorway all right, and he had a little poodle with him, but the thing that made my eyes snap wide open was that the dog was walking upright on his hind limbs.

I knew I was half-asleep, but surely I wasn't seeing things. I stared down at the dog, but the picture hadn't changed. The little creature strutted through the doorway, chest out, head up, as erect as a soldier.

"Follow me, please," I said hoarsely and set off over the tiles to the consulting room. Halfway along, I just had to turn round to check the evidence of my eyes, and it was just the same—the poodle, still on his hind legs, marching along unconcernedly at his master's side.

The man must have seen the bewilderment in my face because he burst suddenly into a roar of laughter.

"Don't worry, Mr. Herriot," he said. "This little dog was circus-trained before I got him as a pet. I like to show off his little tricks. This one really startles people."

"You can say that again," I said breathlessly. "It nearly gave me heart failure."

The poodle wasn't ill; he just wanted his nails clipped. I smiled as I hoisted him onto the table and began to ply the clippers.

"I suppose he won't want his hind claws doing," I said. "He'll have worn them down himself." I was glad to find I had recovered sufficiently to attempt a little joke.

However, by the time I had finished, the old lassitude had taken over again, and I felt ready to fall down as I showed man and dog to the front door.

I watched the little animal trotting away down the street— in the orthodox manner this time—and it came to me suddenly that it had been a long time since I had seen a dog doing something unusual and amusing. Like the things Brandy used to do.

A wave of gentle memories flowed through me as I leaned wearily against the doorpost and closed my eyes. When I opened them, I saw Brandy coming round the corner of the street with Mrs. Westby. His nose was entirely obscured by a large, red tomato-soup can, and he strained madly at the leash and whipped his tail when he saw me.

It was certainly a hallucination this time. I was looking into the past. I really ought to go to bed immediately. But I was still rooted to the doorpost when the Labrador bounded up the steps, made an attempt, aborted by the soup can, to lick my face and contented himself with cocking a convivial leg against the bottom step.

I stared into Mrs. Westby's radiant face. "What . . . what . . . ?"

With her sparkling eyes and wide smile, she looked more attractive than ever. "Look, Mr. Herriot, look! He's better, he's better!"

[333]

In an instant I was wide awake. "And I . . . I suppose you'll want me to get that can off him?"

"Oh, yes, yes, please!"

It took all my strength to lift him onto the table. He was heavier now than before his illness. I reached for the familiar forceps and began to turn the jagged edges of the can outwards from the nose and mouth. Tomato soup must have been one of his favourites because he was really deeply embedded, and it took some time before I was able to slide the can from his face.

I fought off his slobbering attack. "He's back in the dustbins, I see."

"Yes, he is, quite regularly. I've pulled several cans off him myself. And he goes sliding with the children, too." She smiled happily.

Thoughtfully I took my stethoscope from the pocket of my white coat and listened to his lungs. They were wonderfully clear. A slight roughness here and there, but the old cacophony had gone.

I leaned on the table and looked at the great dog with a mixture of thankfulness and incredulity. He was as before, boisterous and full of the joy of living. His tongue lolled in a happy grin, and the sun glinted through the surgery window on his sleek golden coat.

"But Mr. Herriot," Mrs. Westby's eyes were wide, "how on earth has this happened? How has he got better?"

"*Vis medicatrix naturae,*" I replied in tones of deep respect.

"I beg your pardon?"

"The healing power of nature. Something no veterinary surgeon can compete with when it decides to act."

"I see. And you can never tell when this is going to happen?"

"No."

For a few seconds we were silent as we stroked the dog's head and ears and flanks.

"Oh, by the way," I said, "has he shown any renewed interest

[334]

in the blue jeans?"

"Oh, my word, yes! They're in the washing machine at this very moment. Absolutely covered in mud. Isn't it marvellous!"

Chapter
35

August 10, 1963

My sleep in that Bosporus hotel seemed to last only a short time, because apparently within minutes I was roused by one of the hotel staff and looked up to see the sunshine flooding into my room from the street above.

I washed and shaved and hurried to the dining room. Noel and Joe had suffered from the noisy party and were looking heavy-eyed, but the captain and the rest of the crew had been sleeping at the back of the hotel and had heard practically nothing. This was a good thing, because they were the ones who had a tough day ahead of them.

After breakfast the minibus whisked us along the glittering Bosporus and through the city, where I had my second fleeting glimpse of its wonders. It was frustrating. I had hoped to explore the treasures of Istanbul at my leisure—the Blue Mosque, Saint Sophia and so many others, but maybe another day . . .

At the airport there was the bustle of early-morning departures with aircraft taking off and climbing into the sunny sky, but I found something ominous in the sight of our Globemaster stand-ing on its own, vast, shabby, with the scorch marks on its useless engine. Dave, Ed and Karl didn't seem to be worried as they went over to it, the little Dane whistling, the young Americans slouching, relaxed, hands as ever buried in the pockets of their white trousers.

I made straight for the B.E.A. desk, and it was a relief to see the fresh-faced Englishman in the familiar uniform.

"And what can I do for you, sir?" he asked, smiling.

I brandished my cheque book. "I want three tickets to London on the first flight, if possible."

"You want to pay by cheque?"

"Yes, please."

"I'm sorry, but we cannot accept personal cheques."

"What!"

"I'm afraid that is the rule, sir." He was still smiling.

"But . . . we're stuck here." I gave him a brief outline of our plight.

He shook his head sadly. "I do wish I could help, but I have to abide by the rules."

I kept at him for a few minutes longer, but it was no good. Then, when he wasn't looking, I tried one of the other B.E.A. officials further along, but I got the same answer.

My heart was beating fast as I returned to my friends who were waiting for me in the airport lounge. They were speaking to the captain. I was beginning to feel like an expert in the bringing of evil tidings, and I hardly knew what to say to them. In fact, they took the news surprisingly well, and if they thought I was a hopeless organiser they disguised their feelings.

We all looked at the captain.

"If I were you," he said, "I should go to the British Consul."

I turned to the farmers. "Have you ever had anything to do with consuls?"

They shook their heads dumbly.

"Neither have I. I don't know how they'd react in a situation like this. Would they be sure to fly us home?"

"Oh, yes." The captain gave me a faint, reassuring smile. "I'm pretty certain you'd have no trouble."

"Pretty certain, you say, but not absolutely?"

The big man stroked his beard. "Well, Mr. Herriot, like yourself, I have never had the need to approach them."

"When do you take off?"

"In about half an hour."

I had a nasty vision of the three of us trailing back into the city, being turned down by the Consul and coming back with hardly any money in our pockets to find the Globemaster gone.

"Look, Captain," I said. "The way I see it, your aircraft is our only link with home. If you got us to Copenhagen, would you be able to arrange a flight to London from there?"

He gave me a long, appraising stare. "Oh, of course. Copenhagen is our headquarters. But you would be very silly to take the chance."

"Well, I'm willing to take it. How about you chaps?"

The farmers both nodded immediately.

"Oi'm game," Joe said. "Oi want to get 'ome."

The captain looked down at him. "But you do realise there is a very real danger."

Joe grinned back. "Ah, you'll get us there, Caap'n. I ain't worried about that."

He was voicing my own thoughts. Captain Birch inspired confidence.

"All right, then, if you've made up your minds," the big man said. "But I'm afraid you'll have to sign a document which I must leave here in Istanbul. I'll go and draw it up now." He paused. "As I explained earlier, since the aircraft is in an unsafe condition you are, in effect, unauthorised personnel. Signing this document verifies that you are aware of this and that you relinquish all rights to compensation if the worst should happen." He swept us again with his serious gaze. "I must point out that if you lose your lives today, your dependents will receive nothing, no insurance, nothing."

I think we all gulped a bit at this, and there was a longish silence. For once it was Noel who broke it, and he echoed his friend. "You'll get us there, Caap'n."

The document was drawn up and we signed it, and with hindsight I know without any doubt that we behaved like complete idiots, because the danger was not imaginary. We could have been killed that day.

The captain's advice was right, of course. We should have gone to the British Consul. Over the years I have read frequently of football fans being flown home by the Consul after getting drunk and missing their charter planes, and when I think that we three were on legitimate business, it makes our decision all the more crazy. I, in particular, should have known better.

I suppose part of the reason was that we were not thinking straight. The three of us were tired out with lack of sleep and the series of niggling mishaps in strange surroundings. We were in the mood to clutch at straws.

In any case the thing was done now, and we walked over the hot concrete to the Globemaster. It seemed that a fair proportion of the population of Istanbul had heard about our aircraft and had turned out to spectate, because a large crowd of people watched us as we went. I had an uncomfortable feeling that they didn't expect us to get off the ground.

When we climbed into the aircraft, I saw that the interior had been swept clean and that a large door had been removed from one side of the fuselage to allow aeration after the cattle had gone.

Joe elected to sit up front in the flight cabin, while Noel and I strapped ourselves into two drop-down seats at the very back. We felt very insignificant sitting there in the tail, looking at the yawning emptiness in front of us.

We couldn't see what was happening, and it was a shock when the engines roared into life. With that big opening in the side the noise was intolerable, and we both instinctively pushed our fingers into our ears. Noel's face worked, and his mouth opened and closed soundlessly as he tried to talk to me. I knew we couldn't stand this for long, and I reached for my bag. I pulled out some cotton wool and stuffed it into the farmer's ears. I did the same for myself and there was no doubt it relieved the noise problem, but at the same time it gave me a strange, unreal feeling, as if I were in limbo.

From the jerkings and vibrations, I deduced that we were taxi-ing to the end of the runway prior to take-off. Then we stopped, and I knew we were in position.

The roar of the engines increased to a deep-throated bellow which penetrated the ear plugs and made my head spin. I looked at Noel, and he shaped his lips into, *"Taking off now?"* I nodded encouragingly. I don't know what his emotions were, but I felt utterly fatalistic about the whole thing. I am not brave but I have always felt like that about flying and though this was a very special case, my attitude was the same.

For a long time we sat there, listening to the roar and feeling the great aircraft shaking under and around us. This went on and on until I began to wonder if we had, in fact, left the ground. Noel's puzzled face and the spreading of his hands told me he was thinking the same thing. After another five minutes I decided we must be high in the air by now but I had to have a look to make sure. I unstrapped myself and crawled on hands and knees to the open side. I pushed my head out and looked down, and with a jolt of disappointment I saw the grey concrete of the runway a few feet below me.

I slithered back to my place and shook my head at Noel. What, I wondered, was going on? Could the captain not get up enough power, or was he just giving his three remaining engines a long test before making his attempt?

I think it must have been the latter, because suddenly we were under way. We couldn't see anything, but the surge forward was unmistakable. There were a tense few seconds as the vibration rose to a crescendo, then a calm that told us we were airborne. I felt the impact of the undercarriage thudding into place, and

[340]

I pictured Karl and his friends hauling it up over the last few inches. I leaned back in my seat. The first obstacle was behind us.

The feeling of relief seemed to affect Noel immediately because when I looked round he was sound asleep, slumped against the webbing strap. My natural curiosity was too much for me, and I returned to the gap in the fuselage to view the scene passing below.

I sat there, entranced, all day, the cotton-wool plugs dangling from my ears. It wasn't like flying in a modern jet where you can't see much else besides clouds. I watched an unfolding, ever-changing panorama of mountains and sea, islands, yellow beaches, arid plains, the tightly clustered houses of large cities and tiny villages. Occasionally I took pictures, leaning precariously against the strip of sacking that was the only thing between me and the dazzling blue water thousands of feet below.

In mid-afternoon I broke off to consume the contents of a white carton the captain had solemnly handed out to each of us in Istanbul. It contained a slab of unidentifiable meat, the inevitable sticky cake and, to my delight, some slices of that delicious bread and a wedge of cheese.

I also went up to the flight cabin for a few minutes to get some pictures of the stricken engine with its four propellor blades, dangling still and useless. It was a sad sight, but I was glad to see that the other three engines were buzzing away with heartening vigour.

When I returned to my post by the open side, the great rampart of the Alps was rising before us. This, I knew, was the crucial time. The Globemaster climbed higher, but when we reached the tumbled mass of peaks we still seemed to be very near to the summits. Beneath me I could see the loose boulders and scarred rock on the mountaintops quite plainly, but, like my friends, I had faith in that bearded man's ability to take us over, and he did.

It was growing dusk when we circled above Copenhagen, and

I had a glimpse of the little mermaid in the bay. Soon Joe was happy at last with a glass of real beer in his hand in the airport bar.

There isn't much more to tell. We had to wait till 2 A.M. for a flight to Heathrow, and I was sitting on a luggage barrow trying to read the Sunday *Times* at seven o'clock in the morning at King's Cross Station. I wasn't very successful, because the paper kept slipping from my fingers as my eyes closed involuntarily.

My last memory is of a friendly old gentleman in the compartment of the north-bound train trying to engage me in conversation, but to my shame I fell asleep in front of him and didn't wake up until York.

After I had slipped again into the routine of the practice, I looked back on my Istanbul trip as a memorable experience. A bit too concentrated, perhaps, and by no means the rest cure my friend John had pictured, but fascinating in its way. And, of course, I felt I had greatly exaggerated any possible danger on the flight home. From the comfort of my car as I drove round the familiar roads of the Yorkshire Dales, the whole thing had a touch of fantasy.

It all came back to me in stark truth when I heard, many months later, that, soon after the Istanbul flight, the Globemaster had plunged into the Mediterranean with the loss of all her crew. The news came to me indirectly, and I did my best to find out if it was true, but it was a long time afterwards and I had no success.

Ever since, I have thought often about those men: the captain, the two young Americans and Karl. During those few days I had come to admire them, and even now I still cling to the faint hope that that terrible news was wrong.

Chapter
36

What horrible little dogs!

It was a sentiment that rarely entered my mind because I could find something attractive in nearly all my canine patients.

I had to make an exception in the cases of Ruffles and Muffles Whithorn. Try as I might, I could find no lovable traits, only unpleasant ones—like their unvarying method of welcoming me into their home.

"Down! Down!" I yelped, as I always did. The two little animals—West Highland Whites—were standing on their hind limbs, clawing furiously at my trouser legs with their front paws, and I don't know whether I have unusually tender shins but the effect was agonising.

As I backed away on tiptoe like a ballet dancer going into reverse, the room resounded to Mr. and Mrs. Whithorn's delighted laughter. They found this unfailingly amusing.

"Aren't they little pets!" Mr. Whithorn gasped between paroxysms. "Don't they give you a lovely greeting, bless them!"

I wasn't so sure about that. Apart from excoriating my flesh through my grey flannels, the dogs were glaring up at me balefully, their mouths half-open, lips quivering, teeth chattering in a characteristic manner. It wasn't exactly a snarl, but it wasn't friendly, either.

"Come, my darlings." The man gathered the dogs into his arms and kissed them both fondly on the cheeks. He was still giggling. "You know, Mr. Herriot, isn't it priceless that they welcome you into our house so lovingly and then try to stop you from leaving?"

I didn't say anything but massaged my trousers in silence. The truth was that these animals invariably clawed me on my entry, then did their best to bite my ankles on the way out. In between, they molested me in whatever ways they could devise. The strange thing was that they were both old—Ruffles fourteen and Muffles twelve—and one might have experienced some mellowness in their characters, but it was not so.

"Well," I said, after reassuring myself that my wounds were superficial, "I understand Ruffles is lame."

"Yes." Mrs. Whithorn took the dog and placed him on the table where she had spread some newspapers. "It's his left front paw. Just started this morning. He's in agony, poor dear."

Gingerly I took hold of the foot, then whipped my hand away as the teeth snapped shut less than an inch from my fingers.

"Oh, my precious!" Mrs. Whithorn exclaimed. "It's so painful. Do be careful, Mr. Herriot, he's so nervous and I think you're hurting him."

I breathed deeply. This dog should have a tape muzzle applied right at the start, but I had previously caused shock and dismay in the Whithorns by suggesting such a thing, so I had to manage as best I could. Anyway, I wasn't a novice at the business. It would take a very smart biter to catch me.

I curled my forefinger round the leg and had another look, and I was able to see what I wanted in the fleeting instant before the next snap—a reddish swelling pouting from between the toes.

An interdigital cyst! How ridiculous that a vet should be making a house call for such a trivial ailment. But the Whithorns had always firmly refused to bring their dogs to the surgery. It frightened the darlings, they said.

I stood back from the table. "This is just a harmless cyst, but I agree that it is painful, so I'd advise you to bathe it in hot water until it bursts, and that will relieve the pain. Many dogs burst these things themselves by nibbling at them, but you can hasten the process."

I drew some antibiotic into a syringe. "Nobody knows exactly what causes an interdigital cyst. No specific causal organisms have been found, but I'll give him this shot in case of infection."

I achieved the injection by holding the little animal by the scruff of the neck; then Mrs. Whithorn lifted the other dog onto the table.

"You'd better give him a checkup while you're here," she said.

This usually happened, and I palpated the snarling bundle of white hair and went over him with stethoscope and thermometer. He had most of the afflictions that beset old dogs—arthritis, nephritis and other things, including a heart murmur difficult to hear among the bad-tempered rumblings echoing round his thorax.

My examination completed, I replenished his various medicaments and prepared to leave. This was when the exit phase of my visit started, and it was relished by Mr. and Mrs. Whithorn even more than the entry.

The ritual never changed. As their owners tittered gleefully the two little dogs stationed themselves in the doorway, effectively barring my way out. Their lips were drawn back from their teeth. They were the very picture of venom. To draw them away from their posts I feinted to the right, then made a rush for the door, but with my fingers on the handle I had to turn and fend off the hungry jaws snapping at my ankles, and as I skipped around on my heels, my previous dainty ballet steps were superseded by the coarser hoppings of a clog dance.

But I escaped. A final couple of quick pushes with my feet and I was out in the fresh air, crashing the door thankfully behind me.

I was regaining my breath when Doug Watson, the milkman, drew up in his blue van. He kept a few dairy cows on a smallholding on the edge of the town and augmented his income by operating a retail round among the citizens of Darrowby.

"Mornin', Mr. Herriot." He gestured towards the house. "You been in to see them dogs?"

"Yes."

"Proper little sods, aren't they?"

I laughed. "Not very sweet-tempered."

"By gaw, that's the truth. I've got to watch meself when I deliver t'milk. If that door happens to be open, they're straight out at me."

"I'll bet they are."

His eyes widened. "They go for me feet. Sometimes I feel a right bloody Charlie, jumpin' about like a daft thing in front of everybody."

I nodded. "I know exactly how you feel."

"You've got to keep movin' or you've 'ad it," he said. "Look 'ere." He pushed his leg out of the van and pointed to the heel of one of the Wellington boots he always wore on his rounds. I could see a neat puncture hole on either side. "One of 'em got me there, just t'other day. Went right through to me skin."

"Good heavens, which one did that?"

"Don't rightly know—what's their names, anyway?"

"Ruffles and Muffles," I replied.

"Bloody 'ell!" Doug looked at me wonderingly. His own dog was called Spot. He spent a few moments in thought, then raised a finger. "But ah'll tell tha summat, and maybe ye won't believe me. Them dogs used to be real nice little things."

"What!"

"I'm not jokin' nor jestin'. When they fust came here, they were as friendly as any dogs I've ever seen. It was afore your time, but it's true."

"Well, that's remarkable," I said. "I wonder what happened."

Doug shrugged his shoulders. "God knows, but each one of 'em turned nasty after a few months, and they've got wuss and wuss ever since."

Doug's words stayed with me until I got back to the surgery. I was puzzled. Westies, in my experience, were a particularly amiable breed. Siegfried was in the dispensary, writing directions on a bottle of colic mixture. I mentioned the situation to him.

"Yes," he said. "I've heard the same thing. I've been to the Whithorns' a couple of times, and I know why those dogs are so objectionable."

"Really? Why is it?"

"Their owners make them that way. They never correct them, and they slobber over them all the time."

"You could be right," I said. "I've always made a fuss of my own dogs, but all that kissing and cuddling is a bit sickening."

"Quite. Too much of that is bad for a dog. And another thing, those two animals are the bosses in that home. A dog likes to obey. It gives them security. Believe me, Ruffles and Muffles would be happy and good-tempered if they had been controlled right from the start."

"There's no doubt they rule the roost now."

"Absolutely," Siegfried said. "And really, they hate it. If only the Whithorns would take off the rose-tinted spectacles and treat them normally. But it's too late now, I'm afraid." He pocketed the colic mixture and left.

The months passed, I had a few more visits to the Whithorns' and went through the usual dancing routine; then, oddly, both the old dogs died within a few weeks of each other. And despite their tempestuous lives, they had peaceful ends. Ruffles was found dead in his basket one morning, and Muffles wandered down the garden for a sleep under the apple tree and never woke up.

That was merciful, anyway. They hadn't treated me very well, but I was glad they had been spared the things that upset me most in small-animal practice—the road accident, the lingering illness, the euthanasia.

It was like a chapter in my life closing, but shortly afterwards Mr. Whithorn rang me.

"Mr. Herriot," he said, "we have acquired another pair of

Westies, and I wonder if you would call and give them their distemper inoculations."

It was a delightful change to go into the room and be met by two tail-wagging puppies. They were twelve weeks old, and they looked up at me with benevolent eyes.

"They're beautiful," I said. "What have you called them?"

"Ruffles and Muffles," Mr. Whithorn replied.

"Same again, eh?"

"Yes, we wanted to keep the memory of our other darlings alive." He seized the puppies and showered kisses on them.

After the inoculations, it was a long time before I saw the little dogs again. They seemed to be singularly healthy. It must have been nearly a year later when I was called to the house to give them a checkup.

When I went into the sitting room, Ruffles and Muffles Mark Two were seated side by side on the sofa. There was an odd immobility in their attitude. As I approached they stared at me coldly, and as if responding to a signal they bared their teeth and growled softly but menacingly.

A chill ran through me. It couldn't be happening all over again. But as Mr. Whithorn lifted Ruffles onto the table and I took the auroscope from its box, I quickly realised that fate had made history repeat itself. The little animal stood there, regarding me with a bristling mistrust.

"Hold his head, will you, please?" I said. "I want to examine his ears first." I took the ear between finger and thumb and gently inserted the auroscope. I applied my eye to the instrument and was inspecting the external meatus when the dog exploded into action. I heard a vicious snarl, and as I jerked my head back, the draught of the crunching teeth fanned my face.

Mr. Whithorn leaned back and abandoned himself to mirth. "Oh, isn't he a little monkey! Ha-ha-ha, he just won't stand any nonsense." He rested his hands on the table for some time, shaking with merriment, then he wiped his eyes. "Dear, oh dear, what a character he is."

[348]

I stared at the man. The fact that he might easily have been confronted by a noseless veterinary surgeon did not seem to weigh with him. I looked, too, at his wife standing behind him. She was laughing just as merrily. What was the use of trying to instil reason into these people? They were utterly besotted. All I could do was get on with the job.

"Mr. Whithorn," I said tautly, "will you please hold him again, and this time take a tight grip with your hands on either side of his neck?"

He looked at me anxiously. "But I won't hurt the little pet?"

"No, no, of course not."

"All right." He placed his cheek against the dog's face and whispered lovingly, "Daddy promises to be gentle, my angel. Don't worry, sweetheart."

He grasped the loose skin of the neck as I directed, and I warily recommenced operations. Peering at the interior of the ear, listening to Mr. Whithorn's murmured endearments, I was tensed in readiness for another explosion. But when it came with a ferocious yap, I found I was in no danger because Ruffles had turned his attention elsewhere.

As I dropped the auroscope and jumped back, I saw that the dog had sunk his teeth into the ball of his master's thumb. And it wasn't an ordinary bite. He was hanging on, grinding deeply into the flesh.

Mr. Whithorn emitted a piercing yell of agony before shaking himself free.

"You rotten little bugger!" he screamed, dancing around the room, holding the stricken hand. He looked at the blood pouring from the two deep holes, then glared at Ruffles. *"Oh, you bloody little swine!"*

Siegfried's words came back to me as Mr. Whithorn recommenced bending and jumping like an Apache summoning rain, all the while looking in a new way at the dog. Maybe, I said silently to Siegfried, we have a start here.

Chapter
37

"Are ye all right, Mr. Herriot?"

Lionel Brough looked down at me solicitously as I crawled on hands and knees through the gap in the wire netting.

"Yes," I gasped. Lionel was very thin and he had slipped through the aperture like a snake, but I was having a little difficulty.

There were some unusual farms and smallholdings in our practice—converted railway wagons, henhouses and other artifices—but this one, I always thought, took the prize.

Lionel was one of a plentiful breed in those days, a roadman who kept livestock as a sideline and hobby. Some of them had four cows, others a few pigs, but Lionel had the lot.

He had housed his motley collection in a large hut by the side of his cottage. He appeared to have divided the hut into sections by using the first thing that came to hand. It was a labyrinth, a monumental piece of improvisation, with up-ended bed frames, sheets of plywood and corrugated iron, and stretches of wire netting separating the animals. There were no doors or passages anywhere.

I got to my feet, puffing slightly. "Where is this calf?"

"Not far to go now, Mr. Herriot." We passed his solitary cow, then little pigs nibbled at my heels as Lionel laboriously undid a series of knots tied with coarse string so that we could enter the next compartment.

Here, a couple of nanny goats regarded us impassively.

"Grand milkers, them two," the roadman grunted. "T'missus makes some smashin' cheese from 'em, and it's healthy milk, isn't it?"

"That's right, it is." At that time, when T.B. infection was still a constant threat, the milk from the comparatively immune goat was highly regarded. The far wall of their pen consisted of a mahogany dining table lying on its side, its legs projecting into the interior. I skirted it warily before climbing over. I had suffered some nasty blows from those castored knobs.

We were among the calves now, three of them, and it was easy to pick out my patient, a small black animal with a purulent discharge crusting his nostrils.

As I bent to take his temperature I had to push aside a couple of squawking hens, and a fat Muscovy duck waddled out of my way. These feathered creatures seemed to have the run of the place, jumping and fluttering from pen to pen and in and out of the building. From my position by the calf I could see an assortment of cats perched on window sills or on the tops of partitions. A sudden snarling from the end of the hut marked the beginning of a friendly fight among Lionel's three dogs. Beyond the doorway two sheep were visible, grazing contentedly in the field by the cottage.

I looked at the thermometer—103°, then I ausculated the chest with my stethoscope. "Just a touch of bronchitis, Lionel, but I'm glad you called me. He's quite rough in his lungs, and pneumonia could be just round the corner. As it is, a couple of injections will probably clear him up."

Lionel nodded in quiet satisfaction. He was a vague man, but kind, and all his animals were comfortable and well fed in their eccentric dwelling. Deep straw abounded, and the hayracks and troughs were well supplied.

I felt in my pockets. They were bulging with bottles and syringes. I had brought everything I might possibly need. On this establishment, it wasn't easy to slip back to the car as an afterthought.

After the injection I turned to the roadman. "I'll look in tomorrow morning. It's Sunday, so you won't be working, eh?"

"That's right. Thank ye, Mr. Herriot." He turned and began to lead me back through the obstacle course.

On the following day I found the calf greatly improved. "Temperature normal, Lionel," I said. "And he's on his feet now. That's a good sign."

The roadman nodded abstractedly, and I could see that his mind was elsewhere. "Aye, well, that's grand . . . ah'm right pleased." His eyes looked past me vacantly for a few moments, then he suddenly seemed to come back to the world.

"Mr. Herriot!" His voice took on an unaccustomed urgency. "There's summat I want to ask ye."

"Oh, yes?"

"Aye, I'll tell you what it is." He looked at me eagerly. "Ah fancy goin' in for pigs in a big way."

"You mean . . . keep a lot of pigs?"

"That's right. Just pigs and nowt else, and keep 'em in a proper place."

"But that would mean building a piggery."

He thumped a fist into his palm. "You've just said it. That's what I fancy. I've allus liked pigs, and I'd like to do the job proper. Ah could build the piggery out there in t'field."

I looked at him in surprise. "But Lionel, these things cost a lot. There's the question of . . ."

"Money? Oh, ah've got t'money. Remember, me awd uncle died a bit back? Lived with us for years. Well, 'e left me a little legacy. Not a fortune, tha knows, but I could branch out a bit now."

"Well, it's up to you, of course," I said. "But are you sure it's what you really want? You've always seemed to be happy with your bit of stock here, and you're not a youngster—you'll be fifty-odd, won't you?"

"Aye, I'm fifty-six, but they say you're never too old to have a go at something new."

I smiled. "Oh, I'm a strong believer in that. I'm all for it—providing you're happy doing it."

He looked very thoughtful and scratched his cheek a few times. I suppose, like most happy men, he didn't realise the fact. "Get bye, duck!" he grunted with a flash of irritation and nudged the Muscovy with his toe as it tried to march between his legs. Still deep in thought, he bent and lifted a hen's egg from the straw in the corner and put it in his pocket.

"Nay, ah've thought it over for a bit now, and me mind's made up. I've got to have a go."

"Okay, Lionel," I said. "Have at it, and the best of luck."

With a speed unusual in the Dales, the piggery took shape in the field. Rows of concrete pens with a covered yard appeared, and within a few weeks, sows and a boar were installed in the pens and a solid bunch of porkers grunted among the straw in the yard.

To me, this modern structure looked out of place, with the ancient dry-stone walls encircling its green setting and the smooth bulk of the fell rising to the stark moorland above, but I hoped it would bring Lionel the satisfaction he craved.

He still carried on with his road work. He had to get up earlier in the morning to feed and clean out his pigs, but he was a fit man and seemed to be enjoying it.

His vet bills went up, of course, but there was nothing serious, and everything I treated went on well—an occasional sow with mastitis, a farrowing, a few piglets with joint ill. He accepted these things without complaint because the old adage, "Where there's stock there's trouble," was as familiar to him as to anybody else.

The only thing that bothered me a little was that, whereas, before, he spent a lot of time just leaning on his various partitions looking at his animals and smoking his pipe, he now had no time for that. He was always bustling about, pushing wheelbarrows, filling up troughs, mucking out, and it seemed to me that all this was foreign to his nature.

He certainly wasn't as relaxed as he had been. He was happy enough, caring for his fine new charges, but there was a tautness in his expression, a slight anxiety that had not been there before.

There was anxiety in his voice, too, when he rang up one evening. "Just got back from work, Mr. Herriot, and there's some young pigs here I don't like t'look of."

"What symptoms are they showing, Lionel?"

"Well, they haven't been doin' right for a bit. Not thrivin' like the others. But they've been eatin' and not really off it, like, so I haven't bothered you."

"But how about now?"

There was a pause. "They look different now. They're kind o' crambly on their back legs, and they're scourin' a bit . . . and there's one dead. Ah'm a bit worried."

I was worried, too. Instantly and profoundly. It sounded horribly like swine fever. In my early days those two words were burned into my soul, and yet, to the modern young vet, they don't mean a thing.

For around twenty years I was literally haunted by swine fever. Whenever I did a postmortem on a dead pig, I feared I might come across the dreaded button ulcers and haemorrhages. And what I feared still more was that I might fail to spot the disease and be responsible for its spread.

It wasn't as bad as foot-and-mouth in that respect, but the same principles held good. If I didn't recognise the symptoms, pigs might go from that farm to a market and be sold to places scattered over many miles. And every pig would carry its own load of infection and would spread the incurable disease among its healthy neighbours. Then the Ministry of Agriculture would be called in, and they would painstakingly trace the thing right back to Herriot, the man who had made the original unforgivable blunder.

It was a recurring nightmare, because, unlike foot-and-mouth, the disease was a common one, waiting round the corner all the time. I often used to think I would be blissfully happy if only there were no such thing as swine fever. In fact, when I look back at all the worry it caused me and my contemporaries, I feel that the present-day veterinarians should leap happily from their beds each morning and dance around the room crying out, "Hurrah, hurrah, there's no swine fever now!"

At the farm, Lionel led me to a pen at the far end of the yard.

"They're in there," he said gloomily.

I leaned over the wall, and a wave of misery flowed through me. There were about a dozen young pigs in the pen—around sixteen weeks old—and they were nearly all showing the same symptoms.

They were thin and had a scruffy, unthrifty look, the backs of their ears were a dark purple-red, they staggered slightly as they walked and a thin diarrhea ran down the limp-hanging tails. I took a few temperatures. They were around 106.

It was classical—straight out of the book—but I didn't tell Lionel right away. In fact, I wasn't allowed to until I had gone through all the ritual.

"Where did you get this lot?" I asked.

"Haverton market. They were a right-good level bunch when they came, but by gaw they've gone down." He pushed at a little corpse with his Wellington. "And now ah've got this dead 'un."

"Yes . . . well, I'll have to open him up and look inside him, Lionel." My voice sounded weary. I was starting again on the agonising merry-go-round. "I'll get my knife from the car."

I came back with the postmortem knife, rolled the dead pig on its back and slit open the abdomen. How often had I done this with just the same feeling of taut apprehension?

The region of the ileo-caecal valve was the textbook site, and I aimed for it first. But as I cut into the intestine and scraped the mucosa with my knife, I found only haemorrhages and small necrotic spots, some dark red, others yellowish.

Sometimes you found the real thing further along in the colon,

[355]

and for a long time I snipped my way along the coils of bowel with my scissors without finding anything definite.

Here I was again. I was sure this was swine fever, but I couldn't say so to the farmer. The Ministry insisted that theirs was the right of diagnosis, and until they issued confirmation I could say nothing.

There were the usual petechial haemorrhages in kidney and bladder, but not one typical ulcer.

I sat back on my heels. "Lionel, I'm very sorry, but I'll have to report this as a suspected case of swine fever."

"Oh, 'ell, that's bad, isn't it?"

"Yes . . . yes, it is. But we can't be positive until the Ministry confirms it. I'm going to take samples and send them off to the laboratory in Surrey."

"And can't you do owt to cure them?"

"No, I'm afraid not. It's a virus, you see. There's no cure."

"And how about t'others? Does it spread?"

I cringed at having to answer, but there was no point in playing the thing down. "Yes, it spreads like anything. You'll have to take every precaution. Keep a tray of disinfectant outside this pen, and dip your boots if you have to go in. In fact, I would go in as little as possible. Feed and water them over the top, and always attend to the healthy pigs first."

"And how about if me other pigs get it? How many are goin' to die?"

Another horrible question. The books say the mortality rate is eighty to a hundred percent. In my experience it had been a hundred percent.

I took a long breath. "Lionel, they could all die."

The roadman looked slowly over the rows of new concrete pens with their sows and litters, and the pigs rooting happily among the straw in the yard. I felt I had to say something, however lame.

"Anyway, it might not be what I fear. I'll send these samples off to the lab and let you know what they say. In the meantime, get these powders into them, either in their food or by dosing."

I stowed the loops of bowel in my car boot, then went round the piggery making notes of the different grades of pigs. Because another little purgatory lay ahead of me—the filling up of the forms. I have a blind spot where forms are concerned, and the swine fever form was a horrendous pink thing about two feet long, with closely packed questions on each side about how many sows and boars and unweaned pigs and weaned pigs and fattening pigs, and heaven help you if you got any of the numbers wrong.

That evening at Skeldale House I wrestled with this pink thing for a long time, then turned to the real horror—the packing of the sample of bowel. The Ministry provided a special little outfit for this purpose. At first sight it looked just like a flat square of corrugated cardboard, some pieces of grease-proof paper, several lengths of hairy string and a sheet of brown paper. However, on closer examination you found that the cardboard folded into a small square box. The instructions were very explicit. You didn't just bung a piece of bowel into the box; you had to lay a three-feet portion lengthwise on the grease-proof paper, then fold the ends of the paper inwards and tie the whole thing up in one of the pieces of string.

However, there was a catch here, because among the swine fever kit were two stridently printed red and black cards saying, "Pathological Specimen. Urgent." With spaces for the address of the infected premises and all kinds of things. These cards had holes in each end, and the string containing the bowel had to be threaded through these holes before the box was closed. The other card went on the outside.

I painstakingly went through the ritual, and as I finally fumbled the string through the holes in the outside card and tied the box in the brown paper, I fell back exhausted because this sort of thing took more out of me than calving cows.

It was then, just as I was staring with glazed eyes at the envelopes containing the form for Head Office and the one for

Divisional Office, the cardboard creation packed at last, that I saw the other card lying on the table. I had forgotten to include it with the contents.

"Damn and blast it to hell!" I yelled. "I always do that! I bloody well always do that!"

Helen must have thought I might have had some kind of seizure because she hurried through to the dispensary where I was working.

"Are you all right?" she asked anxiously.

I hung my head and nodded weakly. "Yes, sorry. It's just this damned swine fever."

"Well, all right, Jim." She looked at me doubtfully. "But try to keep your voice down. You'll wake the children."

In grim silence I dismantled the box, threaded in the card and reconstructed the outfit once more. I had done this so often, and, oh, how I hated it. I thought bitterly that if ever I wanted something to kill a quiet evening, I had only to do an S.F. report.

I took the thing to the station and sent it off, and in an attempt to ease my mind I turned to one of my veterinary bibles, Udall's *Practice of Veterinary Medicine.* Even among those hallowed pages I found little comfort. The great man's pronouncements only reconfirmed my suspicions. He was an American and he called it hog cholera, but everything he described reminded me of what I had seen on Lionel's place. He talked about injection of serum to protect the healthy pigs, but I had tried that, and it just didn't work. It would be more expense for Lionel, with nothing to show for it.

Within a few days I got the result. The Ministry was unable to confirm the presence of swine fever on these premises. On that day I also heard from the roadman.

"Them pigs is worse. Your powders have done no good, and I 'ave another dead 'un."

Again the dash out to the piggery and the postmortem examination, and this time, as I slit the intestine along its length, I really thought I had found something definite. Surely those ulcers were slightly raised and concentric. The Ministry must confirm it this time, and then, at least, we would know where we were.

I had another evening of form filling and another struggle with the cardboard box and the papers, but as I sent off the samples, I was very hopeful that my doubts would be resolved.

When the word came back that the Ministry was once more unable to confirm the disease, I could have cried.

I appealed to Siegfried. "What the hell are they playing at? Can you tell me how they ever do diagnose S.F. from these samples at the lab?"

"Oh, yes." My partner looked at me gravely. "They take the length of bowel from the paper and throw it against the ceiling. If it sticks there it's a positive, if it falls off it's negative."

I gave a hollow laugh. "I've heard that one before, and sometimes I feel like believing it."

"But don't be too hard on the Ministry boys," Siegfried said. "Remember, they have to be dead sure before they confirm, and they'd look damn silly if they were wrong. Lots of things can look like S.F. You find necrotic ulcers in worm infestations, for instance. It's not easy."

I groaned. "Oh, I know, I know. I'm not blaming them, really. It's just that poor old Lionel Brough is sitting on the edge of a precipice, and I can't do anything to help him."

"Yes, James, it's a hell of a situation. I've been there and I know."

Two days later Lionel rang to say he had another dead pig. This time I found more typical ulcers, and though I still had no idea what the Ministry would say, I knew exactly what I had to do. My brain seemed to have worked it out during the night hours because my decision was crystal clear.

"Lionel," I said, "you've got to slaughter every healthy pig on the place."

His eyes widened. "But there's hardly any of 'em ready for killin' yet. And there's in-pig sows and all sorts."

"Yes, I know, but if the disease had been confirmed, I would have advised you to get rid of them all. You are under restrictions, as you know, and you can't send any pigs to the market, but I can give you a licence for all the healthy pigs to go to the bacon factory."

"Aye, but . . ."

"I can understand how you feel, Lionel. It's tragic, but if once the disease gets among your other pigs, I won't be able to give you a licence then, and you'll just have to watch them die. This way I can save you about a couple of thousand pounds."

"But the bacon pigs . . . the porkers . . . ah'd get a lot more in two months from now."

"Yes, but you'd get something for them now and nothing if they get swine fever. And apart from the money, wouldn't you rather have your pigs humanely slaughtered than see them waste away like this sick lot?"

My words brought home to me the fundamental sadness of a country vet's work—that so many of our patients are ultimately destined for the butcher's hook, and no matter how attractive farm animals may be, all our activities have a commercial foundation.

"Well, ah don't know. It's a big thing." He looked again over the new piggery and the animals he had tended so carefully, then he turned and gave me a level stare. "And what if it isn't swine fever?"

He had me there. Under those steady eyes I could only give him an honest answer. "If it isn't, Lionel, I'll be costing you thousands instead of saving you thousands."

"Aye . . . aye . . . I see that. But you think it is?"

"As I told you before, I am not allowed to make an official diagnosis, but in my own mind I'm bloody sure it is."

He nodded quickly. "Right, Mr. Herriot. Start makin' out your licences. I've got a bit o' faith in you."

A "bit o' faith" was a tremendous compliment from a plain Yorkshireman, and I hoped fervently that it was not misplaced. I got out my blue forms and started to write.

It wasn't long before the new piggery was an empty, silent place. There remained only the pen of affected animals, and they died off rapidly. With all its terrors I was sure that swine fever was not a painful disease, and the one gleam of light in the little tragedy was that the diseased pigs quietly faded away and the others had a humane end. There was no real suffering.

Towards the end of the episode I heard from the Ministry that they had confirmed the disease. I showed the letter to Lionel, and he put his spectacles on and read it through carefully.

"You were right, then," he said. "So it were a good job we did what we did." He folded the paper and handed it back to me. "I got a nice bit from the factory for them pigs we sent in, and if we'd hung on I'd have got nowt. Ah'm grateful to ye."

So that was what I got from that simple roadman after he had seen his dream collapse and melt away—no moaning, no complaints, only gratitude.

Different people reacted in different ways when they were ravaged by this terrible thing, but thank heaven it is all in the past now. A Crystal Violet vaccine was introduced and this helped to control the disease, but finally the Ministry started a compulsory slaughter policy, as in foot-and-mouth, and that was the end of swine fever. It must be nearly thirty years since I had to witness these disasters and wrestle with the forms and boxes and grease-proof papers, but the memory still lingers.

In the meantime, I wondered what Lionel would do with his new buildings. When the last pig had gone, he meticulously cleaned out and disinfected the place, but he didn't say anything about his intentions. When the place had stood empty for four months, I concluded that he had had enough of large-scale farming, but I was wrong.

One evening when I had finished seeing a few dogs and cats, I found him sitting in a corner of the waiting room.

"Mr. Herriot," he said without preamble, "I want to start again."

"You mean, with pigs?"

"Aye, ah want to fill that place up again. Can't bear seein' it standin' empty."

I looked at him thoughtfully. "Are you absolutely sure? You took a nasty knock last time. I thought it might have put you off."

"Nay, nay—ah still have this feelin'. I want to be in pigs. There's just one thing, and that's what I've come to ask ye. Could there be any of them germs left from t'last do?"

It was the sort of question I don't like being asked. In theory, the infection should have died out on that place long ago, but I had heard some funny things about the swine fever virus surviving for long periods. But four months . . . the place had to be safe by now.

Anyway, it's not much help when a vet says he doesn't know. This man wanted an answer.

"I'm sure it would be safe to bring more pigs on now—if you've quite made up your mind."

"Right, right, ah'll get started again." He turned and left me as though he couldn't begin quickly enough.

And, indeed, it wasn't long before the piggery echoed once more to the grunts, snorts and squeals of a new colony. And it wasn't long, either, before trouble struck.

Lionel's voice on the phone was more agitated than I had ever heard it. "I've just got back from me work, and me pigs are in a 'ell of a state. Laid out all over t'place."

My heart gave one mighty wallop against my ribs. "What do you mean . . . laid out?"

"Well, it's like they were takin' fits."

"Fits!"

"Aye, they're on their sides, kickin' and slaverin', and when they get up they stagger around and fall down again."

"I'll be right out." The receiver rattled on its rest as I replaced it. I felt suddenly drained. I had advised this poor man that it was safe to restock, and there was no doubt swine fever could display nervous symptoms. I rushed for Udall and whipped through the pages. Yes, by God, there it was. "Motor irritation may be noted in the beginning in the form of circling, muscular twitchings and even convulsions."

I didn't see a thing as I threw my car at full speed along the narrow road. I never even noticed the trees speeding past the windows or the green fell rising beyond. I had only a horrid mental picture of what was waiting for me at the other end.

And it was worse than I expected. Much worse. The yard was littered with pigs of all sizes, from young stores to big pregnant sows. Some of them were reeling and toppling in the straw, but most were on their sides, foaming at the mouth, trembling and pedalling frantically with their feet at the empty air. Udall had talked about convulsions, and, dear God, I had never seen worse convulsions than these.

Pale-faced and wordless, Lionel led me round the pens. Suckling sows lay twitching as their litters fought at their udders for milk. The boar paced around his area like a blind thing, bumping into the walls, then sitting down, doglike, in a stupor. There was hardly a normal animal on the place.

The roadman turned to me with an attempt at a smile. "Well, we can't licence off the healthy 'uns this time. There aren't any."

I shook my head dumbly. I was utterly bewildered. I found my voice at last. "When did this start?"

"They were all right as ninepence this mornin', t'whole lot of 'em. Bawlin' for their grub like they allus do. Then when I came 'ome, they were like this."

"But dammit, Lionel," I said almost in a shout, "it's too sudden! It doesn't make sense!"

He nodded. "Aye, that's what t'plumber said when 'e saw them. Got a bit of a shock, did t'feller."

"Plumber?"

"Aye, the missus noticed at dinnertime that t'pigs had no water. She sent for Fred Buller, and 'e came out this afternoon. Said there was a blockage in the pipes somewhere. He's put it right now."

"Then they've been without water most of the day?"

[363]

"Ah reckon so. They must 'ave."

Oh, glory be, now I knew. I was still full of apprehension, but the weight of guilt was suddenly lifted from me. Whatever happened now, it wasn't my fault.

"So that's it!" I gasped.

Lionel looked at me questioningly. "What d'ye mean? The water? That 'ud only make 'em a bit thirsty."

"They're not thirsty, they've got salt poisoning."

"Salt poisoning? But they haven't 'ad no salt."

"Yes, they have. There's salt in nearly all pig meal." My mind was racing. What was the first thing to do? I grabbed his arm and hustled him into the yard. "Come on, let's get some of these pigs onto their feet."

"But they've allus had the same meal. What's happened today?" He looked mystified as we trotted through the straw.

I selected a big sow that was lying quiet between convulsions and started to push at her shoulder. "They've been without water. That's what happened. And that causes a higher concentration of salt in the brain. Gives them fits. Push, Lionel, push! We've got to get her over to that trough. There's plenty of water in there now."

I could see he thought I was raving but he helped me to raise the sow to her feet, and we supported her on either side as she tottered up to the long metal trough that bounded one side of the yard. She took a few gulps at the water, then collapsed.

Lionel took a few panting breaths. "She hasn't had much."

"No, and that's a good thing. Too much makes them worse. Let's try this other pig. She's lying very still."

"Makes 'em worse?" He began to help me to lift. "How the 'ell's that?"

"Never mind," I puffed. "It just does." I couldn't very well tell him that I didn't know myself, that I had never seen salt poisoning before and that I was only going by the book.

He groaned as we pushed the second pig towards the trough.

"God 'elp us. This is a bloody funny carry-on. I've never seen owt like this."

Neither have I, I thought. And I only hoped all those things I was taught at college were true.

We spent a busy hour, assisting the stricken animals to the water or carefully dosing them when they were unable to move. We did this by pushing a Wellington boot with the toe cut off into the mouths and pouring the water down the leg of the boot. A pig would certainly crunch the neck off a glass bottle.

The animals with the most powerful convulsions I injected with a sedative to control the spasms.

When we had finished, I looked round the piggery. All the animals had got some water into them and were lying within easy reach of the troughs. As I watched, several of them got up, took a few swallows, then lay down. That was just what I wanted.

"Well," I said wearily, "we can't do anymore."

He shrugged. "Right, come in and 'ave a cup o' tea."

As I followed him to the house, I could tell by the droop of his shoulders that he had lost hope. He had a defeated look, and I couldn't blame him. My words and actions must have seemed crazy to him. They did even to me.

When the bedside phone rang at seven o'clock in the morning, I reached for it with half-closed eyes, expecting the usual calving or milk fever, but it was Lionel.

"I'm just off to me work, Mr. Herriot, but I thowt you'd like to know about them pigs first."

I snapped wide awake. "Yes, I would. How are they?"

"They're awright."

"How do you mean, all right? Are they all alive?"

"Aye, every one."

"Are they ill in any way?"

"Nay, nay, every one of 'em shoutin' for their breakfast just like they were yesterday mornin'."

I fell back on the pillow, still grasping the phone, and my sigh

[365]

of relief must have been audible at the other end because Lionel chuckled.

"Aye, that's how ah feel, too, Mr. Herriot. By gaw, it's a miracle. I thought ye'd gone round the bend yesterday with all that salt talk, but you were right, lad. Talk about savin' ma bacon —ye really did it, didn't ye?"

I laughed. "I suppose I did. In more ways than one."

Over my forty years in practice, I have seen only about half a dozen cases of salt poisoning or water deprivation or whatever you like to call it. I don't suppose it is all that common. But the one at Lionel's stays in my mind as the most exciting and the happiest.

I thought this unexpected triumph would settle the roadman down for good as a pig keeper, but I was wrong again. It was several weeks before I was on his place, and just as I was leaving, a young man rode up on a bicycle.

Lionel introduced him. "This is Billy Fothergill, Mr. Herriot." I shook hands with a smiling lad of about twenty-two.

"Billy's takin' over ma place next month."

"What?"

"It's right. Ah've sold 'im the pigs, and he's goin' to rent the building's from me. In fact, he's doin' all t'work now."

"Well, I'm surprised, Lionel," I said. "I thought you were doing what you wanted to do."

He looked at me quizzically. "So did I, for a bit. But ah'll tell ye, that salt job really gave me a shock. I thowt I was ruined, and that's a nasty feelin' at my time of life. Billy's been pigman for Sir Thomas Rowe for three years, and he's just got married. Feels like branchin' out for 'imself, like."

I looked at the young man. He wasn't tall, but the bullet head, muscular shoulders and slightly bowed legs gave the impression of great power. He looked as though he could run through a brick wall.

"Ah know it's for t'best," Lionel went on. "That piggery was all right, but it was allus just a bit on top o' me. Sort of a worry, like. I reckon Billy'll manage the job better than me."

[366]

I looked again at Billy's stubby features, at the brown skin, the unclouded eyes and the confident grin.

"Oh yes," I said. "He'll manage all right."

As the roadman walked back towards my car with me, I tapped his elbow. "But Lionel, aren't you going to miss your livestock? It was your great hobby, wasn't it?"

"By gaw, you're right. It was and it still is. Ah couldn't do without some stock to look after. I've filled up t'awd hut again. Come and have a look."

We walked over to the hut and opened the door, and it was like turning back the clock—a cow, three calves, two goats, two pigs and some assorted poultry, all sectioned off with outlandish partitions. I could see the bed frames and wire netting with loops of binder twine hanging from every corner. The only difference was that he had moved the dining table to a position immediately inside the door, and a grand-piano lid stood proudly by the side of the cow.

He pointed out the various animals and gave me a brief history of each, and as he spoke there was a contentment in his face that had been absent for some time.

"Only two pigs, eh, Lionel?" I said.

He nodded slowly. "Aye, it's enough."

I left him there and went over to the car, and as I opened the door I looked back across the field. From this angle I could shut out the garish new piggery so that I saw only the stone cottage with its sheltering trees and the old hut nearby. The roadman was leaning against the upended dining table, and as he gazed in at his mixed charges, the smoke from his pipe rose high against the back-cloth of the hills. The whole picture looked just right, and I smiled to myself.

That was Lionel's kind of farming.

Chapter
38

It was a Sunday morning in June, and I was washing my hands in the sink in Matt Clarke's kitchen. The sun was bright, with a brisk wind scouring the fell-sides, so that through the window I could see every cleft and gully lying sharp and clear on the green flanks as the cloud shadows drove across them.

I glanced back beyond the stone flags at the white head of Grandma Clarke bent over her knitting. The radio on the dresser was tuned to the morning service and, as I watched, the old lady looked up from her work and listened intently to some words of the sermon for a few moments before starting her needles clicking again.

In that brief time I had a profound impression of serenity and unquestioning faith that has remained with me to this day. It is a strange thing, but over the years whenever I have heard discussions and arguments on religion, on the varying beliefs and doctrines, on the sincerity or otherwise of some pious individuals, there still rises before me the seamed old face and calm eyes of Grandma Clarke. She knew and was secure. Goodness seemed to flow from her.

She was in her late eighties and always dressed in black with a little black neckband. She had come through the hard times of farming and could look back on a long life of toil, in the fields as well as in the home.

As I reached for the towel, the farmer led Rosie into the kitchen.

"Mr. Clarke's been showing me some baby chicks, Daddy," she said.

Grandma looked up again. "Is that your little lass, Mr. Herriot?"

"Yes, Mrs. Clarke," I replied. "This is Rosie."

"Aye, of course. I've seen her before, many a time." The old lady put down her knitting and rose stiffly from her chair. She shuffled over to a cupboard, brought out a gaily coloured tin and extracted a bar of chocolate.

"How old are ye now, Rosie?" she asked as she presented the chocolate.

"Thank you, I'm six," my daughter replied.

Grandma looked down at the smiling face, at the sturdy, tanned legs in their blue shorts and sandals. "Well, you're a grand little lass." For a moment she rested her work-roughened hand against the little girl's cheek, then she returned to her chair. They didn't make much of a fuss, those old Yorkshire folk, but to me the gesture was like a benediction.

The old lady picked up her knitting again. "And how's that lad o' yours? How's Jimmy?"

"Oh, he's fine thank you. Ten years old now. He's out with some of his pals this morning."

"Ten, eh? Ten and six . . . ten and six . . ." For a few seconds her thoughts seemed far away as she plied her needles, then she looked at me again. "Maybe ye don't know it, Mr. Herriot, but this is the best time of your life."

"Do you think so?"

"Aye, there's no doubt about it. When your children are young and growin' up around ye—that's when it's best. It's the same for everybody, only a lot o' folk don't know it and a lot find out when it's too late. It doesn't last long, you know."

"I believe I've always realised that, Mrs. Clarke, without thinking about it very much."

"Reckon you have, young man." She gave me a sideways smile. "You allus seem to have one or t'other of your bairns with you on your calls."

As I drove away from the farm, the old lady's words stayed in my mind. They are still in my mind, all these years later, when Helen and I are soon about to celebrate our Ruby Wedding of forty years of marriage. Life has been good to us and is still good to us. We are lucky—we have had so many good times—but I think we both agree that Grandma Clarke was right about the very best time of all.

When I got back to Skeldale House that summer morning, I found Siegfried replenishing the store of drugs in his car boot. His children, Alan and Janet, were helping him. Like me, he usually took his family around with him.

He banged down the lid of the boot. "Right, that's that for another few days." He glanced at me and smiled. "There are no more calls at the moment, James; let's have a walk down the back."

With the children running ahead of us, we went through the passage and out into the long garden behind the house. Here the sunshine was imprisoned between the high old walls, with the wind banished to the upper air and ruffling the top leaves of the apple trees.

When we reached the big lawn, Siegfried flopped on the turf and rested on his elbow. I sat down by his side.

My partner pulled a piece of grass and chewed it contemplatively.

"Pity about the acacia," he murmured.

I looked at him in surprise. It was many years since the beautiful tree, which had once soared from the middle of the lawn, had blown down in a gale.

"Yes, it is," I said. "It was magnificent." I paused for a moment. "Remember, I fell asleep against it the first day I came here to apply for a job? We first met right on this spot."

Siegfried laughed. "I do remember." He looked around him at the mellow brick and stone copings of the walls, at the rockery and rose bed, the children playing in the old henhouse at the far end. "My word, James, when you think about it, we've come through a few things together since then. A lot of water, as they say, has flown under the bridge."

We were both silent for a while, and my thoughts went back over the struggles and the laughter of those years. Almost unconsciously I lay back on the grass and closed my eyes, feeling the sun warm on my face, hearing the hum of the bees among the flowers, the croaking of the rooks in the great elms that overhung the yard.

My colleague's voice seemed to come from afar. "Hey, you're not going to do the same trick again, are you? Going to sleep in front of me?"

I sat up, blinking. "Gosh, I'm sorry, Siegfried, I nearly did. I was out at a farrowing at five o'clock this morning and it's just catching up with me."

"Ah, well," he said, smiling. "You won't need your book tonight."

I laughed. "No, I won't. Not tonight."

Neither Siegfried nor I suffered from insomnia, but on the rare occasions when sleep would not come we had recourse to our particular books. Mine was *The Brothers Karamazov*, a great novel, but to me, soporific in its names. Even at the beginning I felt those names lulling me. "Alexey Fyodorovich Karamazov was the third son of Fyodor Pavlovich Karamazov." Then, by the time I had encountered Grigory Kutuzov, Yefim Petrovich Polenov, Stepanida Bedryagina and a few others, I was floating away.

With Siegfried, it was a book on the physiology of the eye which he kept by his bedside. There was one passage that never failed to start him nodding. He showed it to me once: "The first ciliary muscle is inserted into the ciliary body and by its contraction pulls the ciliary body forward and so slackens the tension on the suspensory ligament, while the second ciliary muscle is a circular muscle embedded in the ciliary body and by its contraction drags the ciliary body towards the crystalline lens." He had never managed to get much further than that.

"No," I said, rubbing my eyes. "I won't need any encouragement tonight." I rolled onto my side. "By the way, I was at Matt Clarke's this morning." I told him what Grandma had said.

Siegfried selected a fresh piece of grass and resumed his chewing.

"Well, she's a wise old lady and she's seen it all. If she's right we'll have no regrets in the future, because we have both enjoyed our children and been with them from the beginning."

I was beginning to feel sleepy again when my partner startled me by sitting up abruptly.

"Do you know, James," he said, "I'm convinced that the same thing applies to our job. We're going through the best time there, too."

"Do you think so?"

"Sure of it. Look at all the new advances since the war—drugs and procedures we never dreamed of. We can look after our animals in a way that would have been impossible a few years ago, and the farmers realise this. You've seen them crowding into the surgery on market day to ask advice—they've gained a new respect for the profession and they know it pays to call in the vet now."

"That's true," I said. "We're certainly busier than we've ever been, with the Ministry work going full blast, too."

"Yes, everything is buzzing. In fact, James, I'd like to bet that these present years are the high noon of country practice."

I thought for a moment. "You could be right. But if we are on the top now, does it mean that our lives will decline later?"

"No, no, of course not. They'll be different, that's all. I sometimes think we've only touched the fringe of so many other things, like small-animal work." Siegfried brandished his gnawed piece of grass at me and his eyes shone with the enthusiasm that always uplifted me.

"I tell you, this, James. There are great days ahead!"